INSTRUMENTATION AND SENSORS
FOR ENGINEERING
MEASUREMENTS AND PROCESS
CONTROL

Arun Shukla
University of Rhode Island

James W. Dally
**University of Maryland
at College Park**

College House Enterprises, LLC
Knoxville, Tennessee

The manuscript was prepared with 11 point Times New Roman font. Publishing and Printing Inc., located in Knoxville, TN printed and bound this textbook.

College House Enterprises, LLC.
5713 Glen Cove Drive
Knoxville, TN 37919, U. S. A.
Visit our web site at http://www.collegehousebooks.com

ISBN 978-1-935673-06-4

Dedicated to my wife Vinita
for her understanding and whole-hearted support of my (Arun's) work
and to my children Anish, Anita and Kush.

This book is for Anne
who has shared Jim's dreams for many years
and
for Lisa, William (Bill) and Michelle who are breaking new ground.

Arun Shukla obtained a Bachelor of Technology degree from the Indian Institute of Technology (IIT), Kanpur and his Master of Science and Doctorate degrees from the University of Maryland, all in Mechanical Engineering. He joined the University of Rhode Island in 1981 as a faculty member and currently serves as the Simon Ostrach Professor in the Department of Mechanical, Industrial and Systems Engineering. He has also served as the Clark. B Millikan Visiting Professor at the California Institute of Technology, Visiting Professors at the Indian Institute of Technology and Texas A&M Universities and as Design Engineer at Voltas Limited.

He is a Fellow of the Society for Experimental Mechanics, American Academy of Mechanics and American Society for Mechanical Engineers. He was elected to the European Academy of Sciences and Arts in 2011. He has received the Frocht, Lazan, Taylor and Tatnall Awards and Murray Medal from the Society for Experimental Mechanics. At the University of Rhode Island, he is a recipient of the Simon Ostrach First Endowed Professorship Award, the Vincent and Estelle Murphy Faculty Excellence Award, Distinguished Engineering Professor Award, the University's Scholarly Excellence Award, the Albert E Carlotti Faculty Excellence Award and the University's Outstanding Research Achievement Award. He received the Distinguished Alumnus Award from IIT, Kanpur in 2009.

In 2003, he served as the President of the Society for Experimental Mechanics. He has served as the Technical Editor of the journal "Experimental Mechanics". He has also served the National Research Council, on the United States National Committee on Theoretical and Applied Mechanics. Along with his many graduate students and post docs, Professor Shukla has published more than 300 papers in refereed journals and proceedings. He has also co-authored and edited 5 books, and has delivered numerous plenary and keynote lectures.

James W. Dally obtained a Bachelor of Science and a Master of Science degree, both in Mechanical Engineering from the Carnegie Institute of Technology. He obtained a Doctoral degree in mechanics from the Illinois Institute of Technology. He has taught at Cornell University, Illinois Institute of Technology, the U. S. Air Force Academy and served as Dean of Engineering at the University of Rhode Island. He is currently a Glenn L. Martin Institute Professor of Engineering (Emeritus) at the University of Maryland, College Park.

Dr. Dally has also held positions at the Mesta Machine Co., IIT Research Institute and IBM. He is a Fellow of the American Society for Mechanical Engineers, Society for Experimental Mechanics, and the American Academy of Mechanics. He was appointed as an honorary member of the Society for Experimental Mechanics in 1983 and elected to the National Academy of Engineering in 1984. Professor Dally was selected by his peers to receive the Senior Faculty Outstanding Teaching Award in the College of Engineering and the Distinguish Scholar Teacher Award from the University. He was also a member of the University of Maryland team receiving the 1996 Outstanding Educator Award sponsored by the Boeing Co. He received the Daniel C. Drucker Medal from the American Society for Mechanical Engineers in 2012 for developing innovative teaching materials and textbooks for undergraduate and graduate education.

Professor Dally has co-authored several other books: *Experimental Stress Analysis, Experimental Solid Mechanics, Photoelastic Coatings, Instrumentation for Engineering Measurements, Packaging of Electronic Systems, Mechanical Design of Electronic Systems, Production Engineering and Manufacturing, Mechanics I: Statics++, Mechanics II: Mechanics of Materials + and Introduction to Engineering Design, Books 1, 2, 3, 4, 5, 6, 7, 8 and 9.* He has authored or coauthored about 200 scientific papers and holds five patents.

PREFACE

This textbook represents a major revision of the second edition of **Instrumentation for Engineering Measurements**, which was published by Wiley in 1993. Over the past two decades many developments of sensors and instruments have occurred that impact methods for making engineering measurements and controlling processes. We have reviewed these developments and have updated the content in Instrumentation for Engineering Measurements. The coverage of obsolete techniques and instruments was deleted and descriptions of newer sensors and measurement methods were added. Also the material was reorganized to reduce redundancy and to focus the reader's attention on more important topics. The resulting book is shorter and more of its contents can be covered in a course lasting a single semester or quarter.

The first four chapters provide the foundation for understanding circuits, analog and digital signals, measurement systems and instruments for measuring voltage. Chapter 1 is an introduction to applications of measurement systems, where engineering measurements and process control are described. The details of process control and engineering analysis are presented. Finally experimental error and the factors that cause it are given in considerable detail. Chapter 2 provides methods for analysis of circuits. It includes a brief review of electrical and electronic principles important in understanding the operation of instrument systems. Of particular importance is the introduction of the frequency response function which is of vital importance in making dynamic measurements. Chapter 3 covers digital recording systems and contains detailed descriptions of the analog-to-digital and digital-to-analog conversion processes. This chapter also covers the characteristics of both static and dynamic voltage measuring instruments. Chapter 4 gives a detailed description of potentiometer and Wheatstone bridge circuits, which condition sensor output. Also included is a treatment of several types of amplifiers and filter circuits.

Chapters 5 through 10 deal with methods for measuring many different mechanical quantities. Chapter 5 describes sensors for measuring displacement and velocity of an object when a fixed reference for mounting the sensor is available. Optical methods including interferometers and digital image correlation have been added to this coverage. Chapter 6 provides an extensive treatment on the measurement of strain. It includes signal condition circuits, recording instruments, calibration methods, lead wire effects, electrical noise and the effect of temperature. Methods of converting strain to stress for different types of stress states are covered. Finally mechanical and optical strain sensors have been introduced.

Chapter 7 covers methods used to measure force, torque and pressure. The emphasis is on the sensors (transducers) employed. Methods for designing transducers are introduced. Finally the important topic of the response of transducers is developed for both a ramp and sinusoidal forcing functions. Chapter 8 deals with measuring temperatures that range from cryogenic to plasmas. Sensors such as the RDT, IC, thermistor and thermocouples and recording instruments are described. For very high temperatures the pyrometers used for both point and full field measurements are treated. Chapter 9 deals with measurements of fluids flowing in space, in open and closed channels. Pitot tubes, anemometers and turbine flow meters are described. For flow in closed systems the venturi and orifice meters are covered. Weirs are treated for measuring flow in open channels. A brief coverage for measuring flow in compressible fluid is given.

Chapter 10 deals with the most difficult topic covered in this textbook as it addresses measurements that cannot be made relative to a fixed reference. To manage this constraint, a seismic transducer model is introduced. This model is represented as a second order differential equation. Analysis of the seismic model indicates that it can be designed to accommodate different sensors with outputs that give the force, pressure, displacement, velocity or acceleration. Two types of sensors are employed with the seismic transducers—piezoelectric and more recently piezoresistive.

Chapters 11 and 12 are different because they do not deal directly with measurements. Instead Chapter 11 provides a brief coverage of those topics in Statistics that are commonly employed in analyzing data and in reporting the results from experimental studies. Chapter 12, which is entirely new, deals with a systematic approach to preparing technical and laboratory reports. Engineers are required to write reports to management, their peers and others outside their firms. This chapter outlines an approach for preparing well received documentation of design developments and of experimental measurements.

Material included in this textbook provides an in depth coverage of the sensors and instrumentation used in making engineering measurements without introducing significant errors. For a first course, which is usually taught in the 3rd year after the students have completed an introductory course on circuits, we recommend a lecture/laboratory sequence covering Chapters 1-8, and 12. For a second course for undergraduates, we recommend a lecture/project sequence with material from Chapters 9-12 used as required to properly cover the instrumentation principles used in executing the projects. In spite of the costs for modern laboratory instruments and faculty time, laboratory exposure with hands-on experience is essential for a thorough understanding of the topic.

We have also employed this text at the graduate level. Since graduate students are more experienced with a better background in mathematics, it is possible to cover most of the content in a typical 14 week semester. The emphasis on applications (Chapters 5-10) will depend upon the interests of the instructor and of the class.

Exercises are included for each chapter and solutions for a few exercises are also included at the end of each chapter. We recognize the value of and, therefore, encourage the student to use spread sheets, MATHCAD or other software in performing many of these exercises. The use of these codes eliminates the tedium and permits the student to explore solution space rather than grinding out a single answer. We hope that students and instructors alike will find the presentation clear and informative and that many of the mysteries of the laboratory and of instrument systems will be clarified.

We thank Mr. Nicholas J. Heeder for his help in preparingof this manuscript.

Arun Shukla
University of Rhode Island

James W. Dally
University of Maryland at College Park
August 2012

CONTENTS

CHAPTER 4 SIGNAL CONDITIONING CIRCUITS

CHAPTER 5 DISPLACEMENT AND VELOCITY MEASUREMENTS — FIXED REFERENCE

CHAPTER 6. MEASURING STRAIN

CHAPTER 7. MEASURING FORCE, TORQUE AND PRESSURE

CHAPTER 8. TEMPERATURE MEASUREMENTS

CHAPTER 9. FLUID FLOW MEASUREMENTS

CHAPTER 10. ACCELERATION MEASUREMENTS, SEISMIC AND PIEZO SENSORS

CHAPTER 11. STATISTICAL METHODS

CHAPTER 12. REPORT WRITING

Appendix A. Temperature Resistance Data for Thermistors and Thermoelectric Voltages for Thermocouples

Appendix B. Tables of Properties of Some Common Liquids and Gases

LIST OF SYMBOLS

a Acceleration
a_x, a_y, a_z Cartesian components of acceleration
A Area
B Magnetic flux density
c Velocity of light in a vacuum
c_p Specific heat at constant pressure
c_v Specific heat at constant volume
C Capacitance
C Calibration Constant
C Count
C_D Discharge coefficient
C Viscous damping constant
C_C Contraction coefficient
C_D Drag coefficient
C_{eq} Equivalent capacitance
C_f Feedback capacitance
C_p Pitot tube coefficient
C_t Transducer capacitance
C_v Coefficient of variation
C_V Coefficient of velocity
d Damping ratio
d Damping coefficient
d Deviation
d Displacement
d_x Mean deviation
d* Full-scale displacement
DR Deviation ratio
e Junction potential per unit temperature
E Modulus of elasticity
E Potential gradient
E_λ Radiation power
E Electric field strength
E Error
E_a Accumulated error for a system
E_A Amplifier error
E_M Multimeter error
E_R Resolution error
E_{Sc} Signal-conditioner circuit error
E_t Transducer error
f Focal length
f Cyclic frequency
f_c Cutoff frequency
f_D Doppler-shift frequency
f_n Natural frequency
f_r Resonant frequency
f_s Sampling frequency
f* Nyquist frequency
f_{sh} Self-heating factor
g Gravitational constant
G Conductance
G Gain
G Shear modulus of elasticity
G_c Gain for a common mode voltage
G_d Gain for a difference voltage
h Convective heat-transfer coefficient
h Planck's constant
I Current
I_i Input current
I_i* Full-scale input current
I_o Output current
I_s Source current
I Current density
I intensity of light
I Moment of inertia
J Polar moment of inertia
k Adiabatic exponent
k Boltzmann's constant
k Spring constant or stiffness
K Dielectric constant
K_t Transverse sensitivity factor
L Inductance
L Loss factor
m Mass
M Magnification
M Mach number
M Moment
M_x, M_y, M_z Cartesian components of M
N Number of charge carriers
N Safety factor
N_{dB} Number of decibels
p Pressure
p Probability
p_d Dynamic pressure
p_d' Measured dynamic pressure
P Power
P_D Power density
P_g Power dissipated by a strain gage
p_s Stagnation pressure
P_T Power dissipated by a transducer
q Charge
Q Volume flow rate
Q_i Input quantity
Q_0 Output quantity
r Frequency ratio
r Resistance ratio
R Range
R Reliability
R Resistance
R Resolution
R Universal gas constant
R_A Amplifier resistance
R_e Equivalent resistance
R_f Feedback resistance
R_g Gage resistance
R_L Leadwire resistance
R_L Load resistance

CHAPTER 1

APPLICATIONS OF MEASUREMENT SYSTEMS

1.1 INTRODUCTION

The primary objective of this book is to introduce a number of measurement systems in a manner sufficiently complete that the reader will be able to make accurate and meaningful measurements of electrical, mechanical and thermal quantities. The electrical quantities include voltage, current, resistance, inductance and capacitance. The mechanical quantities include strain, force, pressure, moment, torque, displacement, velocity, acceleration, flow velocity, mass flow rate, volume flow rate, frequency and time. The thermal quantities include temperature, heat flux, specific heat and thermal conductivity.

Applications of measurement systems are:

1. Automatic process control to provide on-line real-time measurements pertaining to a process. These measurements are used as feedback signals in closed-loop control systems to continuously control, for example, a manufacturing process, a testing machine or smart structures within a narrow control band.
2. Monitoring processes to provide on-line real-time measurements pertaining to a process that allows an operator to make adjustments and thereby control the process within control limits.
3. Engineering analysis where measurements are used to insure the safety, reliability, efficiency and performance of machine components, structures and vehicles.
4. Machinery diagnostics where measurements provide insight for preventive maintenance of reciprocating and rotating equipment.
5. Monitoring human body functions to diagnose the status of an individual's heath.

This listing is not intended to be complete, but to indicate the scope of the applications that are dependent on accurate measurements of a wide range of electrical, mechanical, thermal and biological quantities.

Most readers have a conceptual understanding of these quantities through exposure in previous engineering or physics courses, such as circuit theory, electronics, statics, dynamics, mechanics of materials, thermodynamics, heat transfer, etc. The reader's experience in actually measuring these quantities by conducting experiments, however, is usually more limited. An objective of this textbook is to introduce methods commonly employed to make such measurements. Through this exposure to measurement methods, it is believed that the reader will improve his or her understanding of many of the concepts that have been introduced previously in their more analytically oriented courses. Other objectives include: an introduction to the essential elements of measurement systems; providing the background needed for the reader to design effective experiments; using effective measurement methods that yield solutions to practical engineering problems.

Emphasis in the text will be directed toward electronic instrumentation systems because these systems provide measurements that more accurately and more completely characterize the structural design or manufacturing process being evaluated. Also, electronic measurement systems provide output signals that can be used directly for analog control of processes or digitized for automatic data reduction. The use of computers with suitable software for acquisition and processing the data will also be emphasized.

1.2 MEASUREMENT SYSTEMS

A complete electronic measurement system usually contains at least six of the eight subsystems presented in Fig. 1.1. The **transducer** is an analog device that converts a change in a mechanical or thermal quantity being measured into a change of an electrical quantity. For example, a strain gage (sensor and transducer) bonded to a component converts a change in strain $\Delta\varepsilon$ in that component to a change in electrical resistance ΔR in the gage. The change in resistance ΔR is then converted to a change in voltage ΔV by using a signal conditioning circuit (Wheatstone bridge). The output voltage from the signal conditioning circuit is measured accurately with a digital voltmeter. Because this output voltage is proportional to the strain, the strain sensed by the gage can be determined when the measurement system is properly calibrated.

Power supplies provide the energy to drive the transducer and other devices in the measurement system. For instance, a differential transformer, which is a transducer used to measure displacement, requires an ac voltage supply to create a fluctuating magnetic field that excites two sensing coils. Power supplies, such as constant dc voltage sources, constant dc current sources, and ac voltage sources, are selected to satisfy the requirements of the transducer and other devices employed in the system.

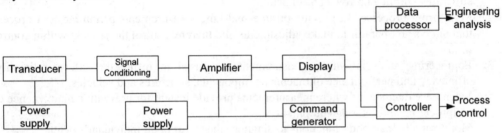

Fig. 1.1 Block diagram showing components of an electronic measurement system for either engineering analysis or process control.

Signal conditioners are electronic circuits that convert, compensate, or manipulate the output from the transducer into a more usable electrical quantity. The Wheatstone bridge, used with a strain sensor-transducer, converts the change in gage resistance ΔR to a change in voltage ΔV. Filters, compensators, modulators, demodulators, integrators and differentiators are other examples of signal conditioning circuits in common usage in electronic instrument systems.

Amplifiers are required in the system when the voltage output from the transducer-signal conditioner combination is small (signals of a millivolt or less are common). Amplifiers with gains of 10 to 1,000 are used to increase these signals to levels (1 to 10 V) that are compatible with the voltage-measuring devices used in the system.

Displays are devices that are used to show measurements in a form that can be read and interpreted. The display is often a digital instrument such as a voltmeter. The voltage from the amplifier is an analog signal that is the input to the voltmeter. Digital voltmeters accept an analog input, converting this signal to a digital code that is then displayed on a numerical array or stored on magnetic or optical media.

Data processors are used with measurement systems that incorporate analog to digital converters (ADC) and provide an output signal representing the measurement in a digital code. The data processors are usually microcomputers, which accept the digital input and then perform computations in accordance with programmed instructions. The output from the processor is displayed in graphical form or in tabular format on a monitor to illustrate the salient results from an experimental study in nearly real-time.

Command generators are devices that provide control voltage that represents variations (usually with respect to time) of an important parameter in a given process. As an example, the time-temperature profile for an oven must be controlled in curing plastics. The command generator provides a voltage signal that varies with time in exact proportion to the temperature-time profile required in the curing oven. This signal is then amplified and used to drive the circuit providing power to the heating elements in the oven.

Process controllers are used to monitor and adjust any quantity that must be maintained at a specified value to produce a material or product in a controlled process. The signal from the measurement system is compared to a command signal, which reflects the required value of the quantity in the process. Comparison of the command signal and the measurement signal forms the difference to give an error signal. This error signal is then used to automatically adjust the process.

1.3 PROCESS CONTROL

Electronic measurement systems are used in two types of process control: open-loop (monitoring control) and closed-loop (automatic control). **Open-loop control**, involving a process that is being monitored with several transducers, is illustrated in Fig. 1.2. Data from the transducers are displayed continuously on an instrument panel containing charts, meters and digital displays. An operator observes the measurements displayed and makes the necessary adjustments to the process input parameters to maintain control of the process. The operator serves to close the loop in this type of process control. The accuracy and reliability of the data displayed on the instrument panel are extremely important as they provide the basis for the operator's decisions in adjusting the quantities controlling the process. The operation of ships is often performed with open-loop control. An operator on the bridge or in the engine room monitors measurements of ship speed, engine RPM, engine temperature, oil pressure, fuel consumption, etc., and manually makes the adjustments to the engine controls needed to maintain the required speed of the ship and the efficient functioning of its engine.

A second type of process control, known as automatic or **closed-loop control**, is illustrated in Fig. 1.3. In the closed-loop control system, the operator is not required except for system maintenance. Instead, the signals from the electronic measurement system are compared to command signals that represent voltage-time relationships for the important quantities associated with the process. The first controller measures the difference between the command signal and the transducer signal and develops an error or feedback signal. The feedback signal is then transmitted to a second controller where it is amplified and used to drive devices (heaters, motors, valves, solenoids, etc.) that act to adjust the process to minimize the error signal.

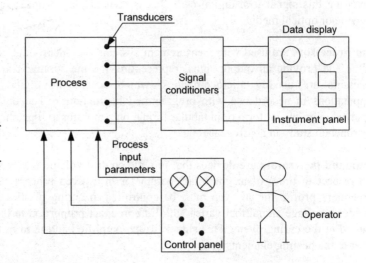

Fig. 1.2 Schematic diagram of open-loop process control that requires an operator to monitor and adjust process parameters.

As an example of closed-loop control, consider a screw-actuated positioning mechanism that moves an engine block through a battery of drilling and tapping machines. The desired position of the engine block along a track, together with the time required at each position, are used by the command generator to establish a voltage-time trace that represents the required position of the block at any time. The actual position of the engine block is measured with a displacement transducer. The difference between the command signal and the measured displacement signal is used by the first controller to generate a feedback signal that is proportional to the adjustment needed to correct the position. The feedback signal is amplified and used to drive a current amplifier in the second controller. The current from this amplifier drives a servo controlled motor which turns a positioning screw. The screw drive moves the engine block and zeros the feedback signal so that the block is correctly positioned for the subsequent machining operation.

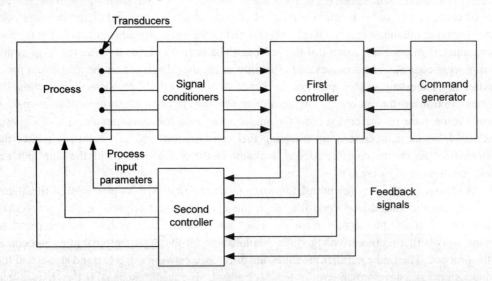

Fig. 1.3 Block diagram of closed-loop process control that does not require operator intervention.

1.3.1 Process Control Devices

Control of a manufacturing process requires frequent adjustment of the parameters involved in the process. Devices used in closed-loop control are similar in many respects to those used in open-loop control. For example, fluid flow is controlled with a valve that is opened or closed manually by an operator in an open-loop control system. A similar valve is automatically adjusted with a servo motor in closed-loop control. A number of control devices are introduced below to indicate the various hardware used in adjusting the controlling parameters involved in a process.

A. DC Motors

Motors are, with few exceptions, rotating machines that employ axial conductors which move in a magnetic field in a cylindrical gap between two iron cores. The magnetic field is produced by stationary coils that are wound around pole pieces incorporated into the stator as shown in Fig. 1.4.

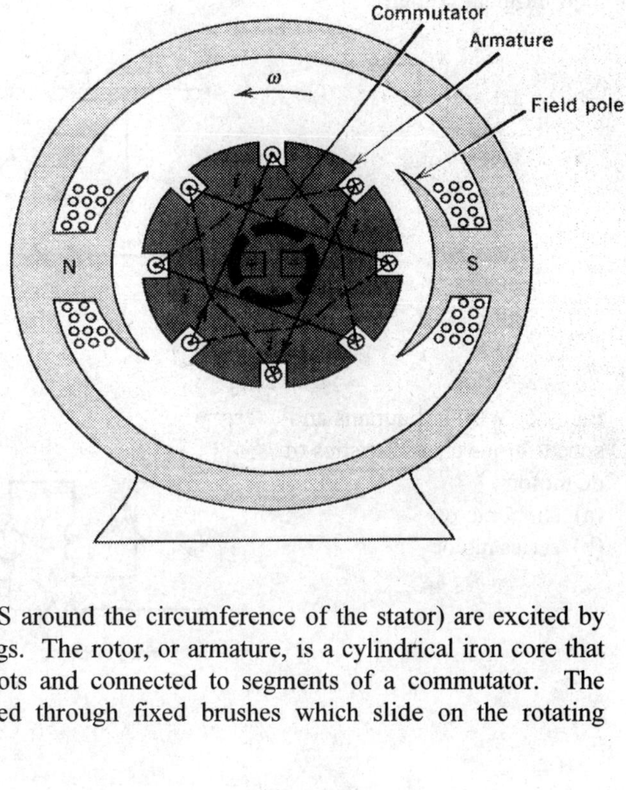

Fig. 1.4 Configuration of armature, field poles and commutator in a dc motor.

In practice, the poles (alternating N and S around the circumference of the stator) are excited by direct current flowing in the field windings. The rotor, or armature, is a cylindrical iron core that carries axial conductors embedded in slots and connected to segments of a commutator. The current to the armature coils is provided through fixed brushes which slide on the rotating commutator.

The speed-torque relations for all dc motors are given by:

$$V = E_{mf} + IR_A = K\phi\omega + IR_A \qquad (1.1)$$

$$T = K\phi I \qquad (1.2)$$

where V is the terminal voltage; E_{mf} is the emf produced by the rotating armature; ϕ is the magnetic flux per pole (in Weber); I is the armature current; R_A is the resistance of the armature winding and other resistances; K is a constant for a specific motor and T is the torque produced by the motor.

If both mechanical and electrical losses are ignored, the electrical power input to the motor equals the mechanical power output. DC motors are classified as shunt, series or compound according to the field coil connections. Wiring diagrams and speed-torque characteristics of shunt and series motors are shown in Fig. 1.5. Compound motors (shunt and series fields connected so that their emfs add) have operating characteristics that are intermediate between those of series and shunt motors as indicated in Fig. 1.6.

In control systems, dc motors are used to operate valves for controlling flow, to rotate a screw drive, to adjust dampers, etc. In these applications, control of the speed and torque delivered by the motor is important. DC motors can be controlled in many different ways. From Fig. 1.6, it is evident that the torque T developed by these three types of dc motors can be adjusted by varying the current. With a series motor, a variable resistor is used in series with the field coils to adjust its speed. With a shunt motor, the variable resistance is placed in series with the armature coils to adjust its speed. In all three types of motors, the speed and torque can be controlled by adjusting their terminal voltage.

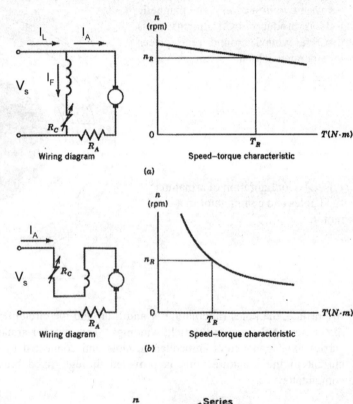

Fig. 1.5 Wiring diagrams and speed-torque characteristics of dc motors.
(a) shunt motor
(b) series motor

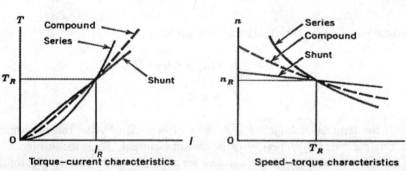

Fig. 1.6 Operating characteristics of dc motors.

B. Stepping Motors

Stepping motors differ in several ways from the dc motors described previously. As shown in Fig. 1.7, the stator incorporates a large number of small field poles deployed around its circumference. Moreover, each pole piece is fabricated with several teeth (5 in this example). The armature is constructed with one or two rows of teeth uniformly spaced around its periphery, as shown in Fig. 1.7c. Fabrication of the armature core from permanent magnet materials eliminates the need for the armature coils, the commutator and the brushes.

   The stepping motor is driven by a train of pulses delivered to the windings of the field coils. The pulse characteristics (rise time, duration, decay time and amplitude) are matched to the inertia of the motor so that the armature rotates one step for each pulse. Angular position control is accomplished with stepping motors simply by counting the number of input pulses applied to each set of field coils. The speed of a stepping motor is controlled by adjusting the rate of these pulses.

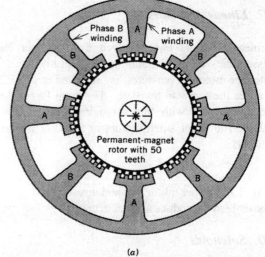

(a)

Fig. 1.7 Construction details of a stepping motor.
(a) stator.
(b) field coil windings.
(c) permanent magnet armature.

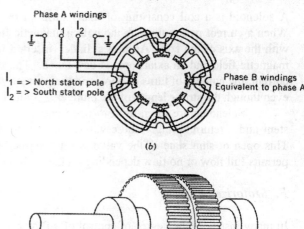

(b)

(c)

A typical permanent-magnet stepping motor with a 50 tooth pitch and a four-pole single phase stator produces $50 \times 4 = 200$ steps per revolution. This construction provides for a rotation of 1.8 degrees per step or per pulse. When a second row of teeth is used in constructing the armature (see Fig. 1.7c) that row is displaced by 1/2 pitch with respect to the first row, the resolution of the stepping motor is improved to 0.9 degrees per step.

The precision of a stepping motor is excellent if its torque capacity is not exceeded. Regardless of the number of steps (N), the position of the armature will be 1.8 N degrees with an error of less the 3% of 1 step or 3.24 minutes. The speed and torque capabilities depend upon the size and construction of the motors. Large motors with stacked rotors produce torques up to 14 N-m. Small single-rotor motors can operate at very low torques at speeds to 15,000 pulses per second (4,500 rpm).

C. Linear Actuators

Linear actuators have evolved from stepper motors and are used for precise positioning of assemblies during machining or assembly operations. A typical linear actuator consisting of a stepper-motor-driven-screw is presented in Fig 1.8. The stepper motor rotates a nut, which in turn causes the screw to translate. The axial forces developed depend on the torque capabilities of the stepper motor with forces ranging from a low of about 100 N for small motors to 5,000 N for larger motors.

Fig. 1.8 Stepper motor, nut and threaded rod assembled to produce a linear actuator.

D. Solenoids

A solenoid is a coil consisting of many turns of magnet wire wound around a cylindrical core. When a current passes through the coil, a magnetic field develops with the N and S poles aligned with the axis of the coil. An iron cylinder, inserted into the core of the solenoid, responds to the magnetic field and an axial force is developed. The force on the solenoid plunger depends on the current, the number of turns of wire, and the geometry of the coil. Significant forces are developed even though the stroke length of the plunger is limited.

Solenoids are often used to open and close valves by coupling the plunger to the valve stem and a return spring. These valves control the flow of liquids in many different processes. This open or shut state of the valve is often termed bang-bang control, because the valve either permits full flow or no flow depending on the position of the solenoid plunger.

E. Motorized Valves

In many instances the degree of control of a flow by a solenoid operated valve is not adequate. In these cases, motorized valves are employed where a dc motor acting through a screw mechanism moves the valve stem to open or close the valve. With this arrangement, the valve opening is adjustable and the flow rate is accurately controlled. Closed-loop control is achieved when the flow rate is measured and compared to the specified flow rate. The difference in these two rates produces an error signal with polarity. This error signal is transmitted to the appropriate controller to adjust the dc motor, modifying the flow rate until it is within acceptable limits. The acceptable limits constitute control bands above and below the specified flow rate.

Motorized valves are effective in controlling flow in quasi-static processes where the rate of change in the flow rate is small. In these cases, the relatively slow valve adjustments are acceptable. However, in some applications flow control by motorized valves is not sufficient to accommodate rapidly changing requirements. In these applications, servo control valves with much higher frequency response are employed.

F. Servo Control Valves

Servo-control-valves are electro-magnetic devices used to control flow. They differ from motorized valves, because they can respond quickly to a change in command signals. Indeed, frequency response for smaller valves is usually in the range from 20 to 40 Hz. Construction details of a typical servo-valve are shown in Fig. 1.9. The valve contains two interacting subsystems. The first subsystem consists of two electro-magnetic coils, which are located at the top of the valve. Control signals from a current amplifier energize the coils to produce a force which translates the coil insert. The coil insert moves the drive arm between the control nozzles in proportion to the coil current. This motion unbalances the four-arm hydraulic bridge circuit formed by the two fixed control orifices and the two control nozzles in the hydraulic subsystem.

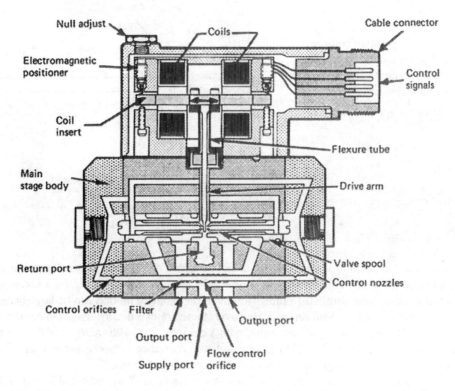

Fig. 1.9 Cutaway view showing the operating principles of a servo control valve.

The hydraulic unbalance results in fluid flow to one end of the valve spool, and the subsequent movement of the spool to a position where one of the output ports is uncovered. The hydraulic amplification incorporated into the subsystem permits a large valve spool to be moved with very small electromagnetic forces applied to the drive arm. This reduced force permits the servo valve to be driven by small control currents that usually range from 10 to 50 mA.

G. Positioning Devices

Rotational position is easily accomplished by using a dc motor with feedback control or with a stepping motor (either with or without feedback control). Linear positioning, on the other hand, requires additional mechanical subsystems to produce linear movement. The simplest method used for precision control of linear motion is to attach a servo motor or a stepper motor to a drive screw as illustrated in Fig. 1.10a.

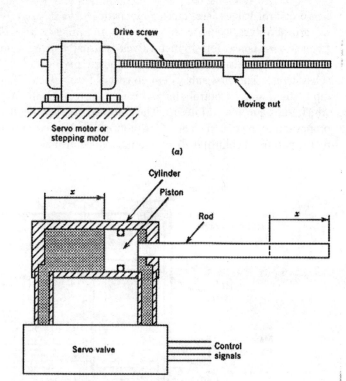

Fig. 1.10 Linear position control.
(a) with a motor and drive screw.
(b) with a servo-controlled hydraulic cylinder.

The precision in the position x which can be achieved with a drive screw is excellent. For example, if a stepping motor is positioned with limits of ± 3.24 minutes, the drive nut on a screw with a 1 mm pitch is positioned to within 0.15 µm. Moreover, the range of motion can be large because it is not difficult to produce long lead screws. However, there are two disadvantages in employing lead screws for positioning. First, they are slow, with velocities $\dot{x}$ of 100 mm/s near the upper limit. Second, when the direction of motion is changed, the clearance between the nut and the screw produces backlash and the precision of positioning cannot be maintained.

For higher speed positioning, a hydraulic cylinder is used, as indicated in Fig. 1.10b. In this approach, the position x of the end of the piston rod is controlled by the servo valve which adjusts the flow to one side of the piston or the other. The velocity $\dot{x}$ of the rod depends on the flow rate of the servo valve and the area A of the piston. For small bore cylinders equipped with high flow rate valves, rod velocities of 10 m/s can be achieved. The forces developed by hydraulic actuators are a function of the hydraulic pressure (usually 3,000 to 5,000 psi) and the area A of the piston. The forces are large even with the relatively large pressure drop that occurs across the servo valve, when it is operating at high frequencies.

H. Resistance Heaters

When it is necessary to increase the temperature of a body or a mass of fluid in controlling a process, resistance heaters are often employed. The power P dissipated by these resistive elements is given by:

$$P = I^2R = \frac{V^2}{R} \tag{1.3}$$

where I is the current, R is the resistance of the heater element and V is the applied voltage.

For liquids, immersion heaters that incorporate the resistive element in a protective sheathing are deployed in the flow field. For solid objects in an oven, the resistances may be coils of high-resistance heat-resistant wire, glow bars (rods of SiC) or quartz lamps. Glow bars or quartz lamps provide a very high temperature (in excess of 1,000 °C). Heat is transferred to the body by infrared radiation. In all cases, control is achieved by using a feedback signal with a current amplifier to adjust the power level until the temperature of the body is within the error bands of the command temperature.

I. Gas Heaters

For processes that require large quantities of liquids or the control of large ovens or furnaces, natural gas or propane burners are often employed. In the case of liquids, a tank is used to contain the fluid. The combustion products from the burning of natural gas or propane are carried in tubes that traverse the containment tank. Heat is transferred through the tubes to the surrounding fluid. In some instances, agitators are employed to stir the fluids to achieve a more uniform temperature distribution and to avoid separation of various fluids in the mix. Control of the temperature is achieved by adjusting the flow rate of the natural gas or propane. In some cases, the control is on or off (bang-bang control) but in more advanced systems the flow rate is adjusted using motorized valves that control the amount of gas flowing through the burner.

For large ovens or furnaces used to heat solids, the control is achieved in a similar manner. The temperature of the furnace is measured and this signal is used in a feedback loop to adjust the flow rate of the gas flowing to the burner. Uniform temperature in the chamber of the furnace is achieved by using fans to circulate the hot air.

1.4 ENGINEERING ANALYSIS

Engineering analyses are conducted to evaluate new or modified designs of machine components, structures, electronic systems, or vehicles to ensure safe, efficient and reliable performance when the prototype or final product is placed in operation. Two approaches are followed in performing the engineering analysis:

1. Theoretical modeling
2. Experimental investigation.

When a **theoretical approach** is used, an analytical model of the component is formulated and assumptions are made pertaining to the operating conditions, the loads applied, the properties of the material and the mode of failure. Equations are then written that describe the behavior of the analytical model. These equations are solved by using either exact mathematical methods or, more frequently, with numerical computation using finite element codes. The results of a theoretical analysis provide the designer with an indication of the adequacy of the design and an estimate of the probable performance of the vehicle, device or structure in service.

Uncertainties often exist pertaining to the validity of results from either the analytical model or the numerical procedures. Does the model accurately reflect all aspects of the prototype design? Do the assumed operating conditions properly cover the full range of loadings imposed on the structure? Are the boundary conditions properly represented in the model? Have the variations in material properties been adequately assessed? Have errors been introduced in the analysis through use of the numerical procedures?

With an experimental approach, a prototype or a scale model of the component is fabricated and a test program is conducted to evaluate the performance of the component in actual service by making direct measurements of the important quantities that control the adequacy of the design. This approach eliminates two serious uncertainties in the theoretical approach. An analytical model is not required and the assumptions regarding operating conditions and material properties are not necessary. However, the experimental approach also has serious shortcomings. In comparison to the theoretical approach, it is expensive and time consuming. Also, uncertainties arise due to inevitable experimental error in the measurements. Finally, there is always a question whether the transducers were placed at the correct locations to record the quantities that actually affect the adequacy of the design.

The preferred approach is a combination of theoretical and experimental methods. The theoretical analysis is conducted to ensure a thorough understanding of the problem. The significance of the results of the theoretical analysis should be completely evaluated and any shortcomings of the analysis are clearly identified. An experimental investigation is then designed to verify the analytical model, to check the validity of assumptions pertaining to operating conditions and material properties, and to insure the accuracy of the numerical procedures.

The results of the theoretical analysis are extremely important in the design of an experimental program. The locations and orientations of the transducers can be specified more accurately and the number of measurements required are reduced appreciably. It is also possible to reduce the number of tests required to cover the full spectrum of operating conditions, when results from a verified theoretical model are available.

The results from an experimental investigation are intended to verify the analytical model and to check the validity of the assumptions and numerical procedures. If significant differences exist, the analytical model must be modified and new results developed for comparison with the experimental findings. After the theoretical approach is verified and confidence in the analysis is established, it is possible to optimize the weight, strength and cost of the component or structure while insuring a safe and reliable operating life.

A combined theoretical and experimental approach to engineering analysis provides the most cost-effective method to ensure safe, efficient and reliable performance of new or modified designs of mechanical, structural or electronic systems.

1.5 EXPERIMENTAL ERROR

Error is the difference between the true value and the measured value of a quantity such as displacement, pressure, temperature, etc. Most measurement systems are designed to limit the error to a value that is acceptable in terms of the accuracies required in an engineering analysis or in the control of a process. Errors result from the following causes:

1. Accumulation of acceptable error in each element of the measurement system.
2. Improper functioning of any element in the system.

3. Effect of the transducer on the component or the process.
4. Dual sensitivity of the transducer.
5. Other less obvious sources of error.

Each of these causes is described in terms of the general characteristics of the elements in the instrumentation system.

1.5.1 Accumulation of Acceptable Error

All elements of an instrumentation system have accuracy limits that are specified by the manufacturer. For instance, a multimeter may have an accuracy specified as ± 0.1% of the full-scale reading. The multimeter is expected to operate within these limits if it is used with care, properly maintained and periodically calibrated. Because of accuracy limits, this multimeter will introduce error in a measurement when it is placed in an instrumentation system. However, this error is known, provided the multimeter is operating within specifications.

The specified accuracy limits should be clearly understood, because an instrument accurate to within ± 0.1% can introduce larger errors than these limits seem to imply. Consider the input-output curve shown in Fig. 1.11 that characterizes a multimeter. The deviation d is defined as the product of the accuracy and the full-scale value of the response of the multimeter. Lines drawn parallel to the true response of the multimeter, but displaced by ± d, form the upper and lower accuracy bounds defining the actual response of the instrument. The area between these two bounds gives the region where the multimeter (or any other instrument) is operating within the manufacturer's specifications. If an instrument is operated at one-half scale, the deviation d remains constant; however, the true value of the measurement is reduced by a factor of 2. Thus, the error, which is defined as the deviation divided by the true value, is doubled. This example indicates that errors of ± 0.2% would be within specifications if this multimeter is operated at half scale. Operation of instruments at less than full scale is sometimes convenient; however, any reduction in scale should be carefully considered, because the error increases rapidly as the percent of scale used is reduced. Instruments should not normally be used at less than 1/3 to 1/2 of full scale without confirming that the magnification of errors involved in the measurement does not invalidate the objective of the experiment.

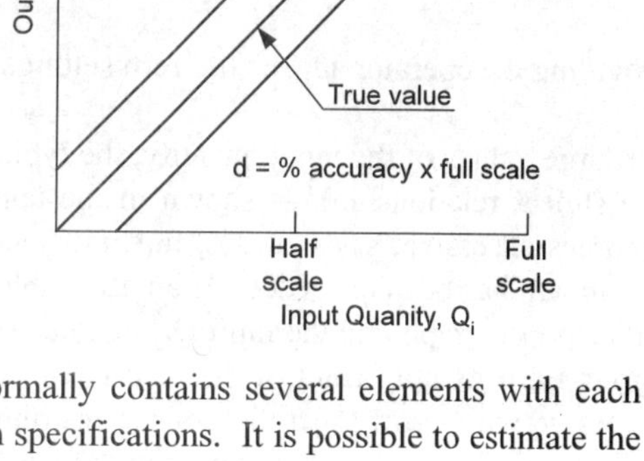

Fig. 1.11 Accuracy bounds for an instrument operating within specifications.

Error accumulates because a measurement system normally contains several elements with each element introducing error even when it operates within specifications. It is possible to estimate the accumulated error E_a for the complete system as:

$$E_a = \sqrt{E_T^2 + E_{SC}^2 + E_A^2 + E_M^2} \qquad (1.5)$$

where the errors are random; E_T is the transducer error; E_{SC} is the signal conditioner error; E_A is the amplifier error and E_M is the multimeter error.

It is evident from Eq. (1.5) that small but acceptable errors for each element in an instrument system can accumulate and become unacceptably large for critical measurements when high accuracy is required.

1.5.2 Improper Functioning of Instruments

If any element in the measurement system is not properly maintained or adjusted prior to use, calibration, zero offset, or range errors can occur. Before discussing these errors, consider the typical response curve for an instrument shown in Fig. 1.12. Here the **output quantity Q_0** is measured as the **input quantity Q_i** is varied. A significant portion of the response curve is represented by a straight line that is fit to the data using a least-squares method, which implies that the instrument response is linear. The slope of the straight line is the calibration constant or **sensitivity S** of the instrument. Thus,

$$S = \frac{\Delta Q_0}{\Delta Q_i} \qquad (1.6)$$

For an oscilloscope, the sensitivity S is given in units of trace displacement per volt. For a piezoelectric pressure gage, the sensitivity S is given as the voltage or charge output per unit of pressure.

If the response line does not pass through the origin, the deviation measured at the intercept with the ordinate is called the **zero offset Z_0**. It is evident from Fig. 1.12 that:

$$Q_0 = SQ_i + Z_0 \qquad (1.7)$$

Most instruments have a capability for adjusting the zero offset so it can be set equal to zero. The relationship for the output quantity Q_0 then reduces to:

$$Q_0 = SQ_i \qquad (1.8)$$

Providing the operator adjusts the zero setting.

For large values of the input quantity, the typical response curve frequently deviates from a straight line (linear relationship), as shown in the upper right portion of Fig. 1.12. When this deviation becomes excessive, say 1 or 2%, Eqs. (1.7) and (1.8) are no longer valid because the range of the instrument has been exceeded. If an allowable deviation is specified, a range line can be drawn on the response graph and the limit Q_i^R can be established (see Fig. 1.12). The value Q_i^R **defines the upper limit of operation** of the instrument. The **lower limit of operation Q_i^L** is determined by excessive scale error (operation of the instrument at less than full scale). The difference between the upper and lower limit of operation defines the **span s** of the instrument. Thus,

$$s = Q_i^R - Q_i^L \qquad (1.9)$$

Errors in the measurement of Q_0 will occur if the instrument is not properly calibrated and zeroed. Errors will also occur if the input Q_i is greater than the range of the instrument Q_i^R or less than the scale limit Q_i^L. Illustrations of calibration, zero-offset and range errors are shown in Fig. 1.13.

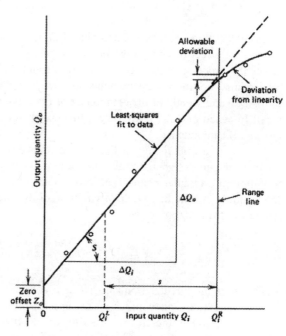

Fig. 1.12 Input-output response curves for a typical instrument.

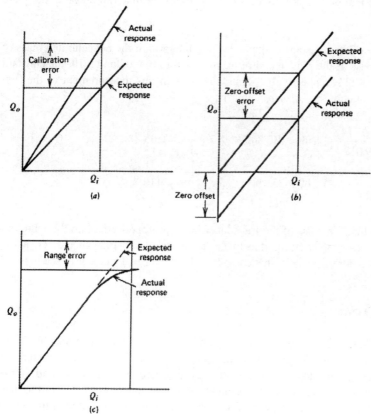

Fig. 1.13 Different types of errors. (a) calibration; (b) zero offset; (c) range

1.5.3 Effect of the Transducer on the Process

A transducer must be selected and placed in the process or on the test article in such a manner that it does not affect or change the process or the response of the test article. If the transducer does affect the process, serious errors can result and the measurements may be meaningless or even misleading. For most measurements, the size and weight of the transducer should be small relative to the size and weight of the component or process. In addition, the transducer should require very small forces to operate, draw very little energy from the process or affect the article or process in any significant manner.

To illustrate the errors that can occur as a result of the presence of the transducer, consider an experiment designed to measure the frequency associated with the fundamental mode of vibration of a circular plate of uniform thickness h with clamped edges. The equation governing the frequency of the first mode of vibration of this plate with an additional concentrated mass at the center of the plate is given by:

$$\omega = \frac{\lambda^2}{a^2\sqrt{\rho/D}} \qquad (1.10)$$

where ω is the circular frequency; λ is a constant that depends on the ratio of the concentrated mass to the plate mass; a is the radius of the plate; ρ is the mass density per unit area of the plate; D is the flexural rigidity of the plate. $D = Eh^3/12(1 - v^2)$; E is the modulus of elasticity of the plate material; v is Poisson's ratio of the plate material and h is the plate thickness.

For this experiment, the value of the constant λ^2 depends upon the ratio of the concentrated mass of the accelerometer m_a to the mass of the plate m_p. For m_a/m_p equal to 0, 0.05 and 0.10, the constant λ^2 equals 10.214, 9.012, and 8.111, respectively. Thus, the error in this measurement of the first natural frequency, due to the mass of the accelerometer, is:

$$\left(\frac{10.214}{9.012} - 1\right)100 = 13.3\% \qquad \text{for} \quad \frac{m_a}{m_p} = 0.05$$

$$\left(\frac{10.214}{8.111} - 1\right)100 = 25.9\% \qquad \text{for} \quad \frac{m_a}{m_p} = 0.10$$

It is clear from this example that the mass of the transducer has a profound effect on the vibratory process and that significant errors may occur due to the presence of the transducer. To avoid excessive errors, the mass of the transducer in this case should not exceed 1 percent of the mass of the plate.

1.5.4   Dual Sensitivity Errors

Transducers are usually designed to measure a single quantity such as force or strain; however, they usually exhibit some sensitivity to one or more other quantities such as temperature or acceleration. If a transducer is employed to measure, say pressure, in a process and if the temperature also changes during the period when the measurement is made, error due to the dual sensitivity of the transducer will occur. The effect of the dual sensitivity is illustrated in the input-output response graph of Fig. 1.14. As shown in this figure, two errors arise due to dual sensitivity when both quantities that affect the transducer are changing simultaneously during the time period of the measurement. First, a zero shift occurs due to the change in the secondary quantity. Second, a change in the sensitivity of the transducer occurs. These errors, illustrated in Fig. 1.14, can be significant in poorly designed transducers.

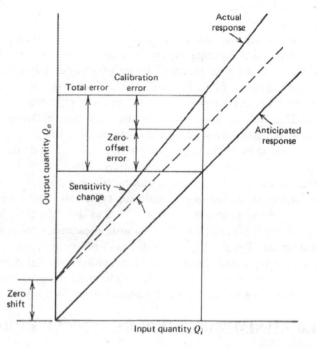

Fig. 1.14 Change in response of an instrument due to dual sensitivity.

In some experiments, the secondary quantity changes as a function of time. In these cases, the zero offset and sensitivity also vary as a function of time. The changing zero offset is referred to as zero drift and the varying sensitivity is termed sensitivity drift. It is very difficult to make accurate measurements under these conditions, because continuous changes in the zero and calibration constant of the transducer preclude any possibility of making a correction for the influence of the secondary quantity. A much better approach is to carefully select a transducer with a secondary sensitivity that is negligible. Also, the remaining elements of the measurement system should be housed, if possible, in a temperature-controlled environment.

While the emphasis of this discussion has centered on the influence of dual sensitivity of a transducer, it should be recognized that all elements in the measurement system exhibit dual sensitivity. This dual sensitivity of the other elements becomes particularly important if the study is of long duration (several days or weeks). Time then becomes an important secondary parameter and the stability characteristics of the signal conditioner, power supply, amplifiers, and multimeter affect the accuracy of the measurements. Because zero drift occurs in most instruments, particularly amplifiers, provision must be made in any long-duration experiment to periodically check and re-zero to correct for the zero shift due to drift.

1.5.5 Other Sources of Error

Other important sources of error include lead-wire effects, electronic noise and operator (human) error. The effects of lead wires, used to connect the transducer to the instrumentation system, can be significant if the transducer contains resistive sensing elements. Lead wires, which are long and small in diameter, exhibit a resistance that is significant relative to the transducer resistance. The added resistance of the lead wires changes the sensitivity or calibration constant of the transducer.

The lead wires also produce erroneous signals due to temperature-induced resistance changes in the wires. When long lead wires are placed in the arms of a Wheatstone bridge that is being used for strain measurements, the accuracy of the measurements are often compromised.

Electronic noise usually results from spurious signals that are picked up by the lead wires. When lead wires are positioned in close proximity to electrical devices, such as motors or lights, the fluctuating magnetic fields in the vicinity of the devices generate small voltages in the adjacent lead wires that superimpose on the measurement signal. Because the transducer output signal is often small, the error produced by lead-wire noise can be significant. The noise picked up by the lead wires can be minimized with proper shielding, which isolates the lead wires from the effects of the fluctuating magnetic fields. In certain measurements, where the measurement signal is very small, noise from a properly shielded lead-wire installation may still be objectionable. In these cases, notched filters that block passage of a narrow band of frequencies can be employed to eliminate most of the noise, because it usually exhibits the 60 Hz power-line frequency. Another approach is to incorporate a miniaturized version of an amplifier in the body of the transducer and amplify the signal before it is transmitted over the lead wires. When the noise from the leads is superimposed on the amplified signal, it is usually negligible.

Another source of error is due to the operator. The operator must properly record the sensitivity S of each element in the instrumentation system and he or she must accurately zero each instrument. Finally, the output that is displayed on a multimeter must be read and often recorded. Fortunately, digital displays which provide numerical display are easy to read and the output is recorded on a hard drive or a CD to eliminate the possibility of an operator recording error. The count error on a digital display is analogous to the trace width error on an oscilloscope.

1.6 MINIMIZING EXPERIMENTAL ERROR

In the preceding section, many sources of experimental error were identified to acquaint the reader with an understanding of some of the difficulties commonly encountered in conducting relatively simple experiments. Measurement systems, designed to yield accuracies of 0.1 or even 1%, are often unrealistic when the cost of the system and the time required to make the measurements are considered. Accuracies of 2 to 5% can usually be achieved at reasonable cost; however, procedures must be followed that minimize error at each step of the experiment. A single mistake can easily degrade the system beyond acceptable limits of error. In the worst case, the mistake will compromise the system so extensively that the measurements are meaningless or worse— misleading. Accepted procedures for minimizing error in a measurement system are:

1. Carefully select the transducer with close attention to its size, weight and energy requirements to ensure that it does not affect the process or the behavior of the test item.
2. Check the accuracy of each element in the measurement system, and determine the "accepted" error that can be accumulated.
3. Examine the process and the environment in which the measurement system must operate. Close attention to temperature variations and the time required for the measurement is important. Estimate the errors that will be produced due to dual sensitivity of each element in the measurement system due to temperature and time variations during the experiment.
4. Connect the system together with properly shielded and terminated lead wires, using wiring procedures that minimize lead-wire errors. Estimate errors that may be introduced by the lead wires.
5. Check the system for electronic noise. If necessary, reroute the lead wires, add shielding where required and insert suitable filters to eliminate most of the electronic noise.

6. Perform a system calibration by measuring the variable to be determined in a known process. This procedure, illustrated in Fig. 1.15, gives a single calibration constant for the entire measurement system and eliminates error accumulation due to small errors in measuring the calibration constants for the individual components.
7. Estimate the total error in the system due to all known sources.

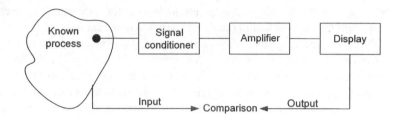

Fig. 1.15 Measurement system calibration.

This systematic method to minimize error does not insure a perfect measurement, because some error is always inherent in any experimental determination of unknown quantities. However, it does provide an organized approach for reducing error and to estimating the error involved at each step in the process.

1.7 USEFUL DEFINITIONS FOR INSTRUMENT PERFORMANCE

The quality of an instrument's readings is often described by the following terms. They are related to the expected errors of the instrument.

Accuracy: The difference between the measured and true values is defined as accuracy. Typically, a manufacturer will specify a **maximum** error as the accuracy.

Precision: The difference between the instrument's reported values during repeated measurements of the same quantity is defined as precision. Typically, this value is determined by statistical analysis of repeated measurements.

Resolution: The smallest increment of change in the measured value that can be readout by the instrument.

Sensitivity: As defined earlier, sensitivity is the change of an instrument or transducer's output per unit change in the measured quantity. A **more sensitive** instrument's reading changes significantly in response to **smaller** changes in the measured quantity. Typically, an instrument with higher sensitivity will also have finer resolution, better precision and higher accuracy.

1.8 SUMMARY

An electronic measurement system usually contains a transducer, a power supply, a signal conditioner, an amplifier, an analog-to-digital converter and a display device. Sometimes these components are integrated into a single package. Such a system is used to experimentally determine unknown quantities, such as force, pressure, displacement, temperature, etc. The output signals from an instrumentation system are used for engineering analyses of machine components, vehicles and structures, and for process monitoring using either open-loop process control or closed-loop automatic control.

Measurement systems are widely used to monitor or to control processes. Open-loop control requires an operator to adjust valves, rheostats, switches or other control devices to maintain the process between the control limits. Closed-loop control usually eliminates the operator. The output signal from an instrument system is compared with a command signal and the difference (known as the error signal) is used to adjust the process. The error signal is amplified in a process controller and used to drive process-control devices such as motors, solenoids, servo-valves, resistance heaters, etc. Adjustments to the process are made to reduce the error signal and to maintain the process within relatively narrow control limits.

Engineering analyses are conducted to evaluate new or modified designs of machine components, structures, electronic systems, vehicles, etc. to ensure safe, efficient and reliable performance of some prototype. A combined theoretical and experimental approach to engineering analysis provides the most thorough and most cost-effective design procedure.

Error will always occur in an experimental measurement of an unknown quantity. The error that accumulates may be due to many causes, such as summation of accepted error, improper functioning of an instrument, transducer interaction with the process, or dual sensitivity of the transducer. Measurement systems that yield accuracies of 0.1 to 1 percent are often too costly for many applications. Accuracies of 2 to 5 percent are more realistic and can be achieved if careful procedures are employed in the design and installation of the measurement system. It is imperative that meticulous attention to detail be observed so that errors are kept within acceptable bounds.

REFERENCES

1. Beckwith, T. G., R. D. Marangoni and J. H. Lienhard V: Mechanical Measurements, 6th ed., Prentice Hall, Englewood Cliffs, NJ, 2007.
2. Shukla, A, Dally, J. W. and W. F. Riley: Experimental Solid Mechanics, College House Ent. Knoxville, TN 2010.
3. Doebelin, E. O.: Measurement Systems Application and Design, 5th Edition, Tata McGraw-Hill, New York, 2004.
4. Holman, J. P.: Experimental Methods for Engineers, 8th ed., McGraw-Hill, 2011.
5. R. H. Dieck, Measurement Uncertainty Models, Proc. 42nd Int. Instrumentation Symposium, San Diego, CA, May 1996.
6. Dyer, S. A. Survey of Instrumentation and Measurement, John Wiley & Sons, New York, 2001.
7. Klaassen, K. B. and S Gee, Electronic Measurement and Instrumentation, Cambridge University Press, New York, 1996.
8. Wheeler, A. J., A. R. Ganji, Introduction to Engineering Experimentation, Prentice Hall, Englewood Cliffs, NJ, 2009.
9. Figliola, R. S., D. E. Beasley, Theory and Design for Mechanical Measurements, 5th Edition, John Wiley & Sons, New York, 2011.

EXERCISES

1.1 Why have electronic measurement systems largely replaced mechanical measurement systems?

1.2 (a) List the subsystems (instruments) usually contained in a complete electronic measurement system. (b) Describe the function of each of these subsystems.

1.3 Discuss three different types of applications for electronic measurement systems.

1.4 Write a one page description of the "engineering analysis" that is to be read and understood by an accountant.

1.5 Describe the preferred approach in performing an engineering analysis.

1.6 List the two common types of process control and describe the characteristic features of each type.

1.7 Prepare a block diagram illustrating the generic instruments in a typical closed-loop control system.

1.8 Describe the differences in performance characteristics of series- and shunt-type dc motors.

1.9 Write a short engineering brief describing the mechanical features incorporated in a stepping motor.

1.10 Compare the operating characteristics of stepping motors and dc motors used in control applications.

1.11 Describe the flow control devices used in automatic control of processes. List the advantages and disadvantages of each device.

1.12 A drive screw in a linear positioning device has a pitch of 1 thread/mm. If the screw is driven with a stepping motor with a 75 tooth pitch and a four-pole single phase stator, determine the movement per pulse of the positioning mechanism.

1.13 Discuss the advantages and disadvantages of lead-screw positioning devices.

1.14 Determine the maximum velocity of the piston rod in a 2 in. diameter hydraulic cylinder if the oil flow is through a servo valve with a maximum capacity of 10 gallon/min.

1.15 For the cylinder described in Exercise 1.14, determine the maximum force exerted by the piston rod if the hydraulic pump provides oil at 3,000 psi and the pressure drop across the servo valve is 400 psi.

1.16 Describe three types of resistance heaters and discuss their relative merits for different applications.

1.17 List several sources of error that must be considered in the design of an instrumentation system.

1.18 A multimeter is specified accurate to ± 1% of full scale and full scale is set at 100 mV. Determine the deviation that can be anticipated. Compute the probable percent error when the instrument is used at 3/4, 1/2, 1/4, and 1/8 scale. State the conclusion that can be drawn from the results of your computation.

1.19 An instrumentation system includes a transducer, power supply, signal conditioner, amplifier, and recorder. What error E will accumulate if the accuracies of the individual elements are:

	Case 1	Case 2	Case 3	Case 4
Transducer	0.05	0.01	0.01	0.02
Power supply	0.02	0.01	0.01	0.02
Signal conditioner	0.02	0.02	0.01	0.05
Amplifier	0.02	0.02	0.01	0.02
Display	0.02	0.03	0.01	0.02

1.20 Define range and span of an instrument.

1.21 Determine the error produced by a zero offset Z_0 if it is not taken into account in determining the output quantity Q_0.

1.22 Determine the error produced if an instrument sensitivity is S_1 instead of the anticipated sensitivity S.

1.23 Determine the error produced if an instrument sensitivity is S_1 instead of the anticipated sensitivity S and if a zero offset Z_0 is not taken into account in determining the output quantity Q_0.

1.24 Give an example of a transducer that produces error because of its influence on the quantity being measured.

1.25 Give an example of an instrument with dual sensitivity and explain how it may produce unanticipated error in a measurement.

1.26 (a) Explain why it is often difficult to accurately measure quantities over long periods of time. (b) What procedures are employed to improve the accuracy if the measurement must be made over a long period of time (weeks or months).

1.27 An amplifier in an instrumentation system exhibits a zero drift of ½% of full scale per hour. Determine the error if the measurement of Q_0 is taken 8 hours after the initial zero was established and if the amplifier is operated at one-half of full scale.

1.28 A pressure transducer exhibits a temperature sensitivity of 0.05 μV per degree Celsius and a pressure sensitivity of 5 μV per MPa. If the temperature changes 30 °C during a measurement of a pressure of 150 MPa, determine the error due to the dual sensitivity of the transducer.

1.29 The sensitivity of an electrical resistance strain gage is defined as:

$$S = \frac{\Delta R/R}{\varepsilon}$$

where ΔR is the resistance change of the gage due to an applied strain ε and R is the resistance of the gage. If the sensitivity S = 2.0 for a gage with a resistance of 350 Ω, compute the sensitivity if the gage is connected to the instrument system with lead wires having a total resistance of 3 Ω.

1.30 Determine the apparent strain indicated by the strain gage lead-wire system described in Exercise 1.29 if the lead wires are subjected to a temperature change of 12 °C after the initial zero is established for the system. Note that the lead wires change resistance with temperature according to:

$$\Delta R = R\gamma\Delta T$$

where γ is the temperature coefficient of resistance (0.0039 °C for copper).

1.31 Describe other common sources of error in electronic instrumentation systems.

1.32 Place a weight limit on a transducer used to determine the natural frequency of a clamped circular plate fabricated from aluminum and having a diameter of 250 mm and a thickness of 0.7 mm.

1.33 Describe calibration procedures for: (a) a power supply; (b) an amplifier; (c) a pressure transducer; (d) a voltmeter (e) a Wheatstone bridge.

1.34 Describe a calibration procedure to check the entire instrumentation system if the quantity being measured is: (a) strain; (b) displacement (c) pressure; (d) acceleration.

1.35 Describe two methods for reducing noise in an electronic measurement system?

EXERCISE SOLUTIONS

Exercise 1.5

The preferred approach in performing an engineering analysis employs a combination of theoretical and experimental methods. The theoretical analysis is conducted to ensure a thorough understanding of the product and its performance. The significance of the results of the theoretical analysis should be completely evaluated and any shortcomings of the analysis should be clearly identified. An experiment is then designed to verify the analytical model to insure the adequacy of the numerical methods used in generating the analytical results.

Exercise 1.9

Stepping motors differ from traditional dc motors. The differences are:

1. The stator incorporates a large number of small field poles deployed around the circumference.

2. Each pole piece is made with several teeth.

3. The armature resembles a gear with teeth uniformly spaced about the periphery.

4. The armature core is fabricated with permanent magnets that eliminate the need for armature coils.

5. The motor is driven by a train of pulses delivered to the field coils.

6. The pulse characteristics are matched to the motor inertia to give a rotation of one step (one tooth) for each pulse.

Exercise 1.14

$$A = \pi d^2/4 = \pi(4)^2/4 = 4\pi \text{ in.}^2$$

$$V = AL = 4\pi L \text{ in.}^3$$

$$\frac{dV}{dt} = A \frac{dL}{dt} \text{ in.}^3/\text{min}$$

$$v = \frac{dL}{dt} = \frac{dV/dt}{A} = \frac{10(231)}{4\pi} = 183.8 \text{ in./min.}$$

Exercise 1.21

From Eq. (1.7): $\qquad Q_o = SQ_i + Z_0 = SQ_{ia}$

where $\qquad\qquad\qquad Q_i$ = true input

$\qquad\qquad\qquad\qquad Q_{ia}$ = apparent input

$$\%\delta = \frac{Q_{ia} - Q_i}{Q_i}(100) = \frac{Q_o/S - (Q_o - Z_0)/S}{(Q_o - Z_0)/S}(100) = \frac{Z_0}{Q_o - Z_0}(100)$$

Exercise 1.27

$\qquad\qquad$ Let A = Full scale output of the amplifier

$\qquad\qquad$ Drift = 0.005(A)(6) = 0.03A

$\qquad\quad Q_{oA}$ = 0.50A + 0.03A = 0.53A

$\qquad\quad Q_{oT}$ = 0.50A

$$\%\delta = \frac{Q_{oA} - Q_{oT}}{Q_{oT}}(100) = \frac{0.53A - 0.50A}{0.50A}(100)$$

$$= 0.060(100) = 6.0 \ \%$$

Exercise 1.30

$$\Delta R = R \ \gamma \ \Delta T = 4(0.0039)(20) = 0.312 \ \Omega$$

$$\varepsilon_{apparent} = \frac{\Delta R/R}{S} = \frac{0.312/354}{1.977} = 0.000446 = 446 \ \mu m/m$$

Exercise 1.32

For aluminum: $\qquad\qquad \rho = 2800 \ kg/m^3$

$\qquad\qquad\qquad m_p = \rho V = 2800(\pi/4)(0.200)^2(0.0007)$

$\qquad\qquad\qquad\qquad = 0.06158 \ kg = 61.58 \ grams$

For m_a = 0.05m_p = 0.05(61.58) = 3.08 grams: $\qquad\qquad \delta$ = 13.3%

For m_a = 0.10m_p = 0.10(61.58) = 6.16 grams: $\qquad\qquad \delta$ = 25.9%

CHAPTER 2

CIRCUIT THEORY

2.1 INTRODUCTION AND DEFINITIONS

In the design and application of measurement systems, we utilize a number of analog circuits. While it is not necessary to design complex electrical circuits to utilize measurement systems, it is important to understand the basic laws that govern the behavior of both ac and dc circuits. It is also important to analyze signals to establish the effect of the instruments on the quantity being measured.

We begin the analysis of circuits by defining the SI system of units, where the meter is the unit of length, the kilogram the unit of mass and the second the unit of time. Other units of importance are absolute temperature in degrees Kelvin, relative temperature in degrees Celsius and electric current in amperes. Quantities, which will be used throughout this text together with their standard symbol, units and abbreviations, are defined in Table 2.1.

Table 2.1
Electrical quantities important in instrument systems

Quantity	Symbol	Unit	Abbreviation	Alternative unit
Force	F	newton	N	kg-m/s
Energy	W	joule	J	N-m
Power	P	watt	W	J/s
Charge	q	coulomb	C	A-s
Current	I	ampere	A	C/s
Voltage	V	volt	V	W/A
Electric field strength	$\mathcal{E}$	volt/meter	V/m	N/C
Magnetic flux density	$\mathcal{B}$	tesla	T	Wb/m^2
Magnetic flux	ϕ	weber	Wb	T-m^2

Brief definitions of each of these quantities are given below:

Force: A force of one N causes a mass of one kg to accelerate at one m/s^2.

Energy: An object weighing one N gains one J of potential energy when it is elevated one m. Alternatively, a mass of 2 kg moving with a velocity of one m/s possesses one J of kinetic energy.

Power: Power represents the time-rate at which energy is transformed. The transformation of one J of energy in one s represents an average power of one W. Instantaneous power is given by:

$$P = \frac{dW}{dt} \tag{2.1}$$

Charge: An electric charge is the integral of the current (I) with respect to time (t).

$$q = \int_0^t Idt \qquad (2.2)$$

A charge of one coulomb (C) is transferred in one second (s) by a current of one ampere (A).

Current: A current is the net rate of flow of positive charges.

$$I = \frac{dq}{dt} \qquad (2.3)$$

A current of one ampere (A) involves the transfer of a charge at the rate of one coulomb/second (C/s).

Voltage: A charge of one coulomb (C) receives or delivers an energy of one joule (J) in moving through a potential of one volt (V). In general:

$$V = \frac{dW}{dq} \qquad (2.4)$$

Electric Field: The electric field strength $\overline{\mathcal{E}}$ is defined by the magnitude and direction of a force $\overline{F}$ on a unit positive charge in the electric field.

$$\overline{F} = q\overline{\mathcal{E}} \qquad (2.5)$$

It is easy to show that electric field strength $\mathcal{E}$ is equal and opposite of the voltage gradient.

$$\mathcal{E} = -\frac{dV}{dl} \qquad (2.6)$$

Magnetic Flux Density: A magnetic field develops in the region around a moving charge carrier or a current. The intensity of this magnetic effect is determined by:

$$\overline{F} = q\overline{u} \times \overline{\mathcal{B}} \qquad (2.7)$$

where $\overline{u}$ is the velocity of the charge q, $\overline{\mathcal{B}}$ is the magnetic flux density and $\times$ is the symbol representing the vector cross product. A force of one newton (N) is developed by a charge of one coulomb (C) moving with a velocity of one m/s normal to a magnetic field with a flux density $\overline{\mathcal{B}} =$ one tesla (T).

Magnetic Flux: Magnetic flux ϕ is obtained by integrating the magnetic flux density over area $\overline{A}$.

$$\phi = \int \overline{\mathcal{B}} \bullet d\overline{A} \qquad (2.8)$$

where the symbol $\bullet$ represents the vector dot product.

The power P and the energy W transmitted in a circuit in terms of current I and voltage V are obtained as follows. From Eqs. (2.1), (2.3) and (2.4) we note that:

$$P = \frac{dW}{dt} = \frac{dW}{dq}\frac{dq}{dt}$$

$$V = \frac{dW}{dq} \quad \text{and} \quad I = \frac{dq}{dt}$$

Therefore:

$$P = V\,I \tag{2.9}$$

$$W = \int P\,dt = \int VI\,dt \tag{2.10}$$

2.2 PASSIVE AND ACTIVE COMPONENTS

Analog and digital circuits are developed using several different components (devices) that affect the behavior of the current flow and the voltage at different locations in a circuit. We will introduce four passive devices and give the laws which govern their effect on the behavior of a simple circuit. We will also introduce two active devices and describe their functions and their applications in measurement and control systems.

2.2.1 Passive Components—Resistors, Capacitors, Inductors and Diodes

A. Resistance

The symbol for resistance is illustrated in Fig. 2.1a, where the resistor R is shown inserted in a circuit. Ohm's law, named after the German physicist Georg Ohm, defines the relation between the voltage drop across the resistor and the current flow.

$$V = I\,R \tag{2.11}$$

When V is expressed in volts, V; I in amperes, A; R is given in ohms, Ω.

The conductance G of a component is the reciprocal of the resistance. Thus,

$$G = \frac{I}{R} \tag{2.12}$$

where G is expressed in terms of units known as siemens S.

B. Capacitance

The symbol for capacitance is illustrated in Fig. 2.1b, where the capacitor C is shown inserted in a simple circuit. Physically, the capacitor consists of two electrodes separated by a thin layer of dielectric material that serves as an insulator. When a voltage is applied, a positive voltage develops on the upper plate and a negative voltage develops on the lower plate. A capacitor stores the charge q according to:

$$q = CV \tag{2.13}$$

The energy stored W is determined from Eqs. (2.13) and (2.4) as:

$$\boldsymbol{W} = \int_0^V CV\, dV = \frac{1}{2}CV^2 \tag{2.14}$$

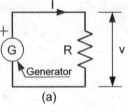

(a)

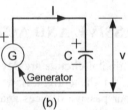

(b)

Fig. 2.1 Circuits with passive elements.
  (a) Resistor
  (b) Capacitor
  (c) Inductor

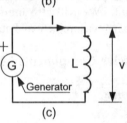

(c)

When the voltage V is constant, the charge on the capacitor is maintained but no current flows. However, when the voltage changes with time, current flows through the dielectric according to:

$$I = C\frac{dV}{dt} \tag{2.15}$$

In Eqs. (2.13) to (2.15), the capacitance is expressed in farads, F (in honor of Michael Faraday).

C. Inductance

The symbol for inductance is illustrated in Fig. 2.1c, where the inductor L is shown inserted in a simple circuit. Physically, the inductor is a multi-turn coil usually constructed with small diameter copper wire. The coil has a very small resistance to steady-state current flow; however, when the current varies with time, a voltage drop develops across the coil, which is given by:

$$V = L\frac{dI}{dt} \tag{2.16}$$

where the inductance L is expressed in henrys, H (in honor of Joseph Henry).

The energy stored in the inductor is determined from Eqs. (2.10) and (2.16) as:

$$\boldsymbol{W} = \int_0^I LI\, dI = \frac{1}{2}LI^2 \tag{2.17}$$

D. *Diodes*

The diode is another important circuit element that is fabricated by combining a p-type semiconductor material with an n-type semiconductor. Diodes act in some respects like a current switch or a check valve. A diode allows current to flow freely in one direction, but it does not permit current to flow in the opposite direction (called reverse-biased). Current can flow from the p-region to the n-region, but not vice-versa. A diode is the electrical equivalent of a check valve in a pipe carrying fluid. The symbol for a diode is shown in Fig. 2.2. The direction of the arrow indicates the direction in which the diode allows current to flow.

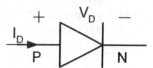

Fig. 2.2 Circuit symbol for a diode.

A diode exhibits a voltage drop (V_D) across its terminals when it transmits a current. This voltage drop depends on the diode specification and the amount of current, but it is usually between ½ and 4 V. Diodes exhibit a small reverse current when V_D is negative, but below the breakdown threshold. Normally this current is less than a few micro amps, and has little effect on most circuits. There is also a limit on the amount of current flow through the diode (I_D), because the voltage drop results in the diode dissipating power in the form of heat. Excess current flow causes the diode to overheat and fail.

Diodes also have a limit on the maximum negative voltage that can be applied. If V_D becomes more negative than this maximum, current will begin to flow in the opposite direction destroying the diode. This condition is called voltage breakdown. However, there are special diodes that are constructed to survive breakdown. The most common diode of this type is the Zener diode, which exploits this property to regulate voltages.

2.2.2 Active Devices—Transistors and Gates

Transistors and gates, which are more advanced components, are fabricated from semiconductors. They are employed together with passive devices in analog and digital circuits. Transistors and gates are classified as active, because they require power to perform their functions.

A. *Transistors*

Transistors are semiconductor devices that can be used either as amplifiers or as high-speed electronic switches. Unlike the previous two-terminal components that we have discussed, transistors have three terminals. One of these terminals is used to control current flow between the other two terminals. Bipolar-Junction Transistors (BJTs) use current in the control terminal (called the base) while Field-Effect Transistors (FETs) use a potential (voltage) difference between the control terminal (called the gate) and one of the other terminals to control the current flow.

The most widely used amplifier is the bipolar junction transistor illustrated in Fig. 2.3. The devices are planar and therefore can be fabricated using lithographic methods in P and N doped silicon. The devices are often extremely small because they are fabricated with feature sizes as small as 16 to 32 nm.

Transistors are three-terminal devices with the base represented by B, the collector by C, and the emitter by E. The theory of operation of a bipolar transistor is beyond the scope of this book; however, a transistor can act as a current amplifier because relatively small base currents I_B produce large collector currents I_C. For example, when a NPN transistor is connected in a common emitter configuration with voltage sources and a resistive load R_L, as shown in Fig. 2.4, the transistor acts to amplify the input current I_i. The input current I_i causes a variation in the base current I_B that in turn produces a variation in the collector current I_C along the load line as shown in Fig. 2.4b.

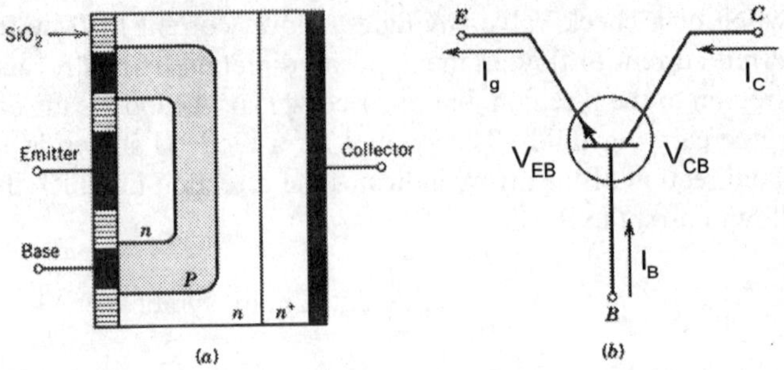

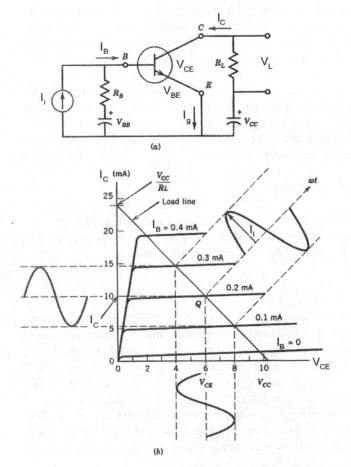

Fig. 2.3 A NPN bipolar transistor.
  (a) Planar structure in silicon.
  (b) Circuit symbol.

Fig. 2.4 A basic NPN transistor current amplifier.
  (a) Circuit diagram.
  (b) Operating characteristics.

The time-varying part of the collector current represents the amplified output current that is drawn from the source V_{CC} and flows through the load resistance R_L. The gain G is given by:

$$G = \frac{I_0}{I_i} \qquad (2.18)$$

where I_0 is the sinusoidal component of I_C.

The gain G depends on the base and collector characteristics of the transistor and V_{CC} and R_L. Signal gains for a single transistor vary from 10 to 100.

Transistors are also employed as very-high-speed electronic switches that are either open or closed depending upon the voltage applied to the base. When operated as a switch, the transistor is connected in the simple circuit shown in Fig. 2.5a. Because both P/N junctions are reversed biased, practically no collector current flows and the transistor is operated in the cutoff region of Fig. 2.5b at point 1, when the input voltage (current) to the base is zero. At point 1, the collector current is small (5 μA) with an applied voltage $V_{CC} = 5$ V. This condition corresponds to a cut off resistance of 1 MΩ and the switch, whose contacts are the collector and emitter terminals, is open.

When a positive voltage is applied at the input, the base current increases and the transistor's state moves along the load line of Fig. 2.5b to point 2. At this point, the transistor is operating in a saturated condition and the voltage drop V_{CC} across the transistor is small. The collector current is about 30 mA at a saturation voltage of 0.3 V, which yields a switch resistance of about 10Ω. In this state, the transistor is considered as a closed switch.

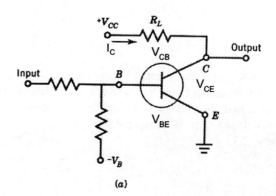

(a)

Fig. 2.5 Transistor in a switching application.
   (a) Switching circuit.
   (b) Operating regions.

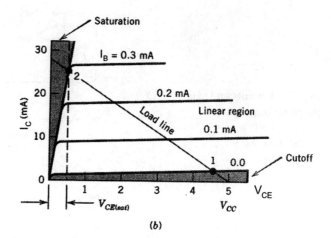

(b)

B. Gates

In processing digital signals, information is expressed in a digital code and is transmitted through logic operations to transform and manipulate this information. The **logic gate** is a device that controls the flow of information in a logic network. While there are many different gates that perform specialized logic operations, all of these more complex gates are made from three different elementary gates, namely the **AND**, **OR**, and **NOT** gates.

The **AND** gate may be represented by the circuit shown in Fig. 2.6a where two switches A and B are placed in series in the line from the source to the load. The voltage V_s is applied to the load only if switch A and switch B are both closed. The four possibilities for the **AND** gate are listed in a truth table shown in Table 2.2. Note the number (0) is used to represent a false statement and the number (1) to represent a true statement. With regard to the voltage applied to the load, the number (1) indicates that it is true that V_s is applied to the load.

Table 2.2
Truth table for the AND gate A • B = T

Switches or Inputs		Output
A	B	T
0	0	0
0	1	0
1	0	0
1	1	1

The **OR** gate is represented by the circuit shown in Fig. 2.6b where two switches, A and B, are placed in parallel in the line between the voltage source and the load. When A is closed **OR** when B is closed, the voltage is applied to the load (T = 1). The truth table for an **OR** gate with two in parallel switches is presented in Table 2.3.

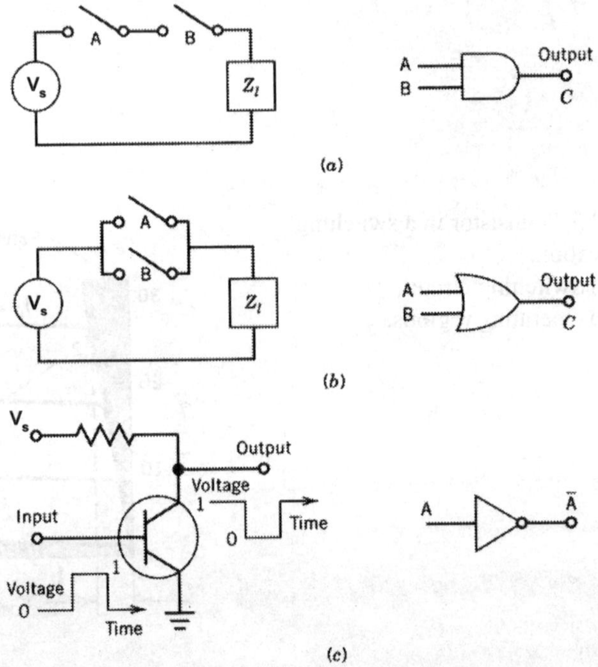

Fig. 2.6 Circuits and symbols for the three basic gates.
    (a) AND gate.
    (b) OR gate.
    (c) NOT gate

Table 2.3
Truth table for the OR gate A + B = T

Switches or Inputs		Output
A	B	T
0	0	0
0	1	1
1	0	1
1	1	1

The **NOT** gate, which is illustrated in Fig. 2.6c, is an inverter. In this figure, the mechanical switch has been replaced by a transistor that is turned on (closed) by a positive input voltage. If the input signal to the transistor is say (0), the transistor acts as an open switch, no current flows and the output voltage is V_s or (1). When the input signal goes to (1), the transistor conducts, acting like a closed switch, and the output is grounded, giving the low state or (0). It is clear from this description that when the input is high (A), the output is low ($\overline{A}$) and changing the input to low ($\overline{A}$) results in an output that is high (A).

These basic gates are arranged in circuits to perform digital functions. A digital system is composed of many of these digital functions and may contain several millions of the basic gates. The number of chips used to build the logic circuits depends on the scale of integration used to fabricate the circuits. With ULSI (ultra-large-scale-integration), it is possible to place features on silicon chips with dimensions of 32 nm, thus permitting the manufacture of extremely large digital systems with a limited number of chips. Another development, known as a system-on-a-chip (SOC) or a lab-on-a-chip (LOC), is an integrated circuit in which all the components required for a system are included on a single chip. The design of a SOC is complex and expensive, and fabricating different components on a single piece of silicon often compromises the efficiency of some components. However, these disadvantages are offset by lower manufacturing and assembly costs and by greatly reduced power consumption.

2.3 KIRCHHOFF'S CIRCUIT LAWS

Over two centuries ago Gustav Kirchhoff developed two circuit laws that provide the foundations for network theory. The first is the **current law**, illustrated in Fig. 2.7a, which states that **the algebraic sum of the currents flowing into a junction point at any instant is zero.**

$$\sum I = 0 \qquad\qquad (2.19)$$

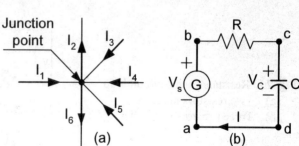

Fig. 2.7 Circuit models for Kirchhoff's laws.
  (a)   Kirchhoff's current law
  (b)   Kirchhoff's voltage law

The arrows representing the currents in Fig. 2.7 specify both magnitude and sign. Current flow into the junction is considered positive while flow away from the junction is considered negative.

The second circuit law due to Kirchhoff is the **voltage law**, which states that **the algebraic sum of the voltages around a circuit loop at any instant of time is zero.**

$$\sum V = 0 \qquad\qquad (2.20)$$

To show the application of Eq. (2.20) refer to the circuit loop presented in Fig. 2.7b and write the voltage change across each of the four legs of the loop as

$$\sum V = V_{ba} + V_{cb} + V_{dc} + V_{ad} = 0 \qquad\qquad (a)$$

where V_{ba} indicates the voltage at point b measured with respect to point a.

If V_{ba} is positive, point **b** is at a higher potential than point **a**. Begin summing the voltage changes at point **a**, and proceed clockwise around the loop and write an expression for the voltage drops at any instant of time.

$$\sum V = V_s - V_R - V_C + 0 = 0 \qquad\qquad (b)$$

or

$$V_s = V_R + V_C \qquad\qquad (c)$$

In this case, V_s represents the voltage source while V_R and V_C represent voltage drops in the direction of current flow.

2.4 DC CIRCUITS

In dc circuits, the current flow is constant with respect to time. This fact simplifies the circuit analysis because the voltage drop across an inductor is zero ($dI/dt = 0$) and the current flow through a capacitor is zero ($dV/dt = 0$). The resistor is the only component that produces a voltage drop in accordance with Ohm's law.

Consider first resistors R_1 and R_2 arranged in series in a dc circuit, as shown in Fig. 2.8a. Kirchhoff's voltage law, given by Eq. (2.19), and Ohm's law, given by Eq. (2.11), yields:

$$V_s = V_{d1} + V_{d2} = IR_1 + IR_2 = IR_e \qquad\qquad (2.21)$$

where $R_e = R_1 + R_2$ is the equivalent closed loop resistance as illustrated in Fig. 2.8a.

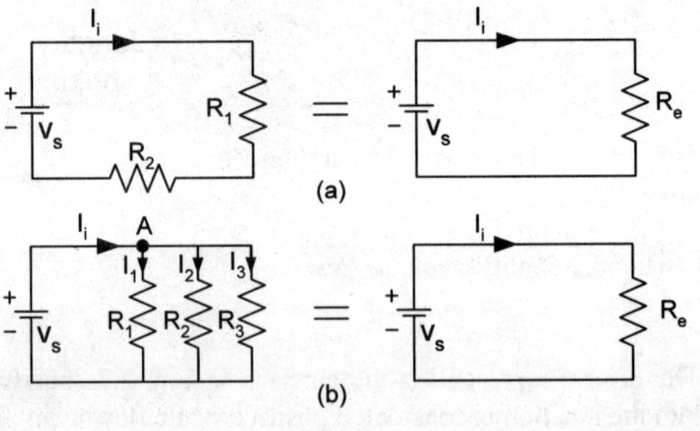

Fig. 2.8 Resistances in a circuit loop.
   (a)   Two resistors in series.
   (b)   Three resistors in parallel.

Next, consider the parallel circuit illustrated in Fig. 2.8b and apply Kirchhoff's current law, Eq. (2.19), to point A to obtain:

$$I_i = I_1 + I_2 + I_3 \tag{a}$$

Substituting Eq. (2.11) into Eq. (a) gives:

$$\frac{V_s}{R_e} = \frac{V_d}{R_1} + \frac{V_d}{R_2} + \frac{V_d}{R_3} \tag{b}$$

Because $V_s = V_d$, the equivalent resistance for a group of three parallel resistors is given by:

$$\frac{1}{R_e} = \frac{1}{R_1} + \frac{1}{R_2} + \frac{1}{R_3} \tag{2.22}$$

2.5 PERIODIC FUNCTIONS

When the current or voltage varies with time in a circuit, the signal is represented by some type of a wave form. There are many different types of wave forms which are considered to be either periodic or transient. Periodic signals are repetitive and can be represented by sinusoidal functions or by a series of sinusoidal components by means of Fourier analysis. Transient signals are one shot events that do not repeat. They are more difficult to analyze and a discussion of transient signals is deferred to a later chapter.

We will consider a special type of periodic function namely the sinusoid [sin (nωt) or cos (nωt), where n is an integer]. Sinusoidal functions are very important in describing the dynamic response of instrument systems, where the ratio of the input to the output voltage is a function of frequency. Also, sinusoid functions are used extensively in Fourier analysis of other periodic signals with more complex wave forms.

To illustrate two sinusoidal functions, consider a point rotating about a circle centered at point 0 in the x-y plane as shown in Fig. 2.9. The line OR rotates with a constant magnitude A_0 in a counterclockwise direction with an angular velocity ω. Hence, the projection of the line OR onto the x axis gives the position of point P as:

$$x = A_0 \cos \omega t \tag{2.23}$$

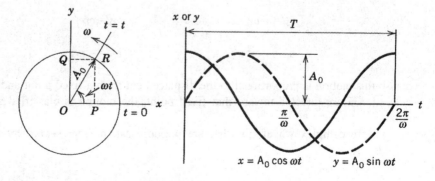

Fig. 2.9 Sinusoidal functions: $x = A_0 \cos \omega t$ and $y = A_0 \sin \omega t$.

The projection of the line OR onto the y axis gives the position of point Q as:

$$y = A_0 \sin \omega t \tag{2.24}$$

The sinusoidal function is repetitive, as indicated in Fig. 2.9, with the values of x and y repeated every period (T). The angular frequency ω (radian/s), the period T (s), and the cyclic frequency f (Hz) are related by the expression:

$$\omega = \frac{2\pi}{T} = 2\pi f \tag{2.25}$$

From Eq. (2.25) it is evident that:

$$f = \frac{1}{T} \tag{2.26}$$

The velocities v_P and v_Q of points P and Q, illustrated in Fig. 2.9, are given by:

$$v_P = \dot{x} = \frac{d}{dt}(A_0 \cos \omega t) = -A_0 \omega \sin \omega t = A_0 \omega \cos \omega t\left(\omega t + \frac{\pi}{2}\right)$$

$$\tag{2.27}$$

$$v_Q = \dot{y} = \frac{d}{dt}(A_0 \sin \omega t) = A_0 \omega \cos \omega t = A_0 \omega \sin \omega t\left(\omega t + \frac{\pi}{2}\right)$$

where the dot above a variable represents differentiation with respect to time. One dot represents the first derivative and two dots the second derivative.

The accelerations of points P and Q are given by:

$$a_P = \ddot{x} = -A_0 \omega^2 \cos \omega t = A_0 \omega^2 \cos \omega t(\omega t + \pi)$$

$$\tag{2.28}$$

$$a_Q = \ddot{y} = -A_0 \omega^2 \sin \omega t = A_0 \omega^2 \sin \omega t(\omega t + \pi)$$

Equations (2.27) and (2.28) show that the **magnitude** of the velocities and accelerations of points P and Q can be obtained by multiplying A_0 by ω and ω^2 respectively. Note that there is a phase difference and the velocities and accelerations lead the displacements (positions) by $\pi/2$ and π, respectively. From Eqs. (2.23), (2.24), (2.27) and (2.28), the **maximum** values of the velocities and accelerations can be written as:

$$v_P = -\omega y \qquad\qquad v_Q = \omega x$$

$$\tag{2.29}$$

$$a_P = -\omega^2 x \qquad\qquad a_Q = -\omega^2 y$$

Because this motion is proportional to the displacement from a fixed point and the velocity $\bar{v}$ and acceleration $\bar{a}$ are directed toward that fixed point, the motion is classified as simple harmonic motion.

More complex waveforms that are periodic can be represented by a Fourier series of sinusoids. Thus,

$$x = A_0 + \sum_{n=1}^{\infty} A_n \cos n\omega t + \sum_{n=1}^{\infty} B_n \sin n\omega t \qquad (2.30)$$

where A_0, A_n, and B_n are the harmonic amplitudes and ω is the fundamental frequency. If a sufficient number of terms are employed in the Fourier series representation, the periodic motions x, $\dot{x}$, or $\ddot{x}$ can be accurately described with a sum of simple harmonic motions of frequencies that are multiples of the fundamental frequency (i.e., 2ω, 3ω, ..., $n\omega$).

A second method of analysis of signals uses phasors in the complex plane, where the phasor projected on the real and imaginary axes exhibits real and imaginary parts of the signal. Consider a phasor A, shown in Fig. 2.10, which is expressed in exponential form as:

$$A = A_0 e^{j\omega t} \qquad (2.31)$$

where $j = \sqrt{-1}$. Recall the identity that:

$$e^{j\omega t} = \cos \omega t + j \sin \omega t \qquad (2.32)$$

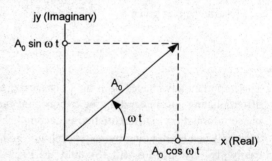

Fig. 2.10 Representation of the phasor $A = A_0 e^{j\omega t}$ on a complex plane.

Then Eq. (2.31) can be written as:

$$A = A_0 \cos \omega t + j A_0 \sin \omega t \qquad (2.33)$$

Note that the first term in Eq. (2.33) is real and the second term is imaginary. A graph of the complex plane, shown in Fig. 2.10, illustrates the phasor, the real and imaginary terms and the angle (ωt) that is taken as positive counterclockwise. Comparison of Figs. (2.9) and (2.10) clearly indicates that the phasor represents the rotating line OR providing an example of simple harmonic motion (or signal). Differentiation of the phasor A to obtain dA/dt gives:

$$\dot{A} = j\omega A_0 e^{j\omega t} \qquad (2.34)$$

Note from Eq. (2.32) that $j = e^{j\pi/2}$ and $j^2 = -1 = e^{j\pi}$. Substituting the first of these equalities in Eq. (2.34) yields:

$$\dot{A} = \omega A_0 e^{j(\omega t + \pi/2)} = \omega A_0 \cos\left(\omega t + \frac{\pi}{2}\right) + j\omega A_0 \sin\left(\omega t + \frac{\pi}{2}\right) \qquad (2.35)$$

Comparison of Eq. (2.35) with Eq. (2.27) shows that the real part of A corresponds to the velocity v_P and the imaginary part represents the velocity v_Q. Differentiating Eq. (2.34) to obtain $\ddot{A}$ gives:

$$\ddot{A} = -\omega^2 A_0 e^{j\omega t} \tag{2.36}$$

By using Eq. (2.32) with Eq. (2.36), it is evident that:

$$\ddot{A} = \omega^2 A_0 e^{j(\omega t + \pi)} = \omega^2 A_0 \cos(\omega t + \pi) + j\omega^2 A_0 \sin(\omega t + \pi) \tag{2.37}$$

A comparison of Eq. (2.37) with Eq. (2.28) indicates that the real part of A corresponds to a_P and the imaginary part represents a_Q. The phase angle for $\dot{A}$ is $\phi = \pi/2$ and for $\ddot{A}$ it is $\phi = \pi$, with both angles measured relative to the reference phasor. These phase angles are leading as shown in the complex plane in Fig. 2.11. Note, that leading phase angles are positive (counterclockwise) and lagging phase angles are negative (clockwise) with respect to the reference plane.

The amplitude A_0 of the phasor is:

$$A_0 = \sqrt{(\mathrm{Re})^2 + (\mathrm{Im})^2} \tag{2.38}$$

where Re is the amplitude of the real part and Im is the amplitude of the imaginary part of A.

Its phase angle ϕ is given by:

$$\phi = \tan^{-1} \frac{(\mathrm{Im})}{(\mathrm{Re})} \tag{2.39}$$

The important advantages of using a phasor representation of sinusoidal motion include the ease of differentiating and integrating the exponential function and the availability of both magnitude and phase information. Differentiation is accomplished simply by multiplying by $j\omega$ and integration is accomplished by dividing by $j\omega$. Amplitude and phase angles for A, $\dot{A}$ and $\ddot{A}$ can be determined easily by using Eqs. (2.38) and (2.39). Because of these advantages, the exponential notation is used throughout the remainder of this book.

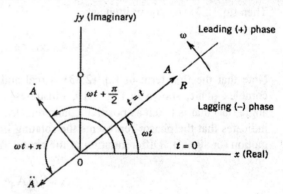

Fig. 2.11 Phase angles for $\dot{A}$ and $\ddot{A}$ relative to A, showing the velocity and acceleration leading the displacement by $\pi/2$ and π respectively.

2.6 AC CIRCUITS

The three fundamental electrical components used to describe the behavior of ac circuits are inductance L, resistance R and capacitance C. These three components are illustrated individually in Fig. 2.12, where they are connected to a sinusoidal input voltage V_s. The technique to determine the voltage drop V_d across, each of these components was described in Section 2.2. To determine the influence of each component in a circuit with an ac supply current let's represent the current by:

$$I = I_0 e^{j\omega t} \tag{2.40}$$

This expression can be substituted into Eqs. (2.11), (2.13), and (2.16) to give:

$$V_d = jLI_0e^{j\omega t} = jL\omega I = Z_L I \qquad \text{for the inductor}$$

$$V_d = RI_0e^{j\omega t} = RI = Z_R I \qquad \text{for the resistor} \qquad (2.41)$$

$$V_d = \left(\frac{I_0}{j\omega C}\right)e^{j\omega t} = \frac{I}{j\omega C} = Z_C I \qquad \text{for the capacitor}$$

where Z_L, Z_R and Z_C are the impedances for the basic components.

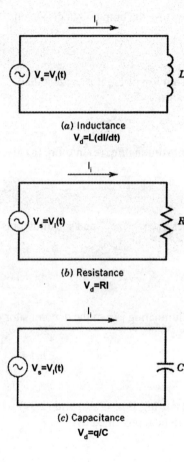

(a) Inductance
$V_d = L(dI/dt)$

(b) Resistance
$V_d = RI$

Fig. 2.12 Elementary circuits illustrating voltage drop across the three passive elements L, R and C.

(c) Capacitance
$V_d = q/C$

From Eq. (2.41) it is evident that:

$$Z_L = j\omega L$$

$$Z_R = R$$

$$(2.42)$$

$$Z_C = \frac{1}{j\omega C} = -\frac{j}{\omega C}$$

From Eq. (2.42) it is clear that the inductance voltage leads the resistance voltage and current with a phase angle of $\pi/2$.

To illustrate the use of the impedance relations and show introductory methods of ac circuit analysis, consider the circuit shown in Fig. 2.13. Applying Kirchhoff's law given in Eq. (2.20), together with Eqs. (2.13) and (2.16) gives:

$$V_s = V_i(t) = IR + \frac{q}{C} \tag{a}$$

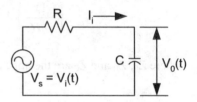

Fig. 2.13 A RC circuit with an output voltage $V_0(t)$ representing the voltage across a capacitor.

Because the output voltage $V_0 = q/C$, Eq. (a) can be reduced to:

$$V_s(t) = IR + V_0(t) \tag{b}$$

From Eq. (2.13) it is evident that:

$$I = C\frac{dV_0(t)}{dt} = C\dot{V}_0(t) \tag{c}$$

Substituting Eq. (c) into Eq. (b) gives a first order differential equation:

$$RC\dot{V}_0(t) + V_0(t) = V_i(t) = V_i e^{j\omega t} \tag{2.43}$$

Let $V_0(t) = V_0 e^{j\omega t}$ and substitute this relation into Eq. (2.43) to obtain:

$$V_0(t) = \frac{1}{1 + j\omega RC} V_i e^{j\omega t} \tag{2.44}$$

Eliminating j from the denominator of Eq. (2.44) gives:

$$V_0(t) = \frac{1 - j\omega RC}{1 + (\omega RC)^2} V_i e^{j\omega t} \tag{d}$$

By using Eqs. (2.38) and (2.39) with Eq. (d), the output voltage across the capacitor in Fig. 2.13 can be represented by:

$$V_0(t) = \frac{V_i e^{j(\omega t - \phi)}}{\sqrt{1 + (\omega RC)^2}} = V_0 e^{j(\omega t - \phi)} \tag{2.45}$$

where

$$V_0 = \frac{V_i}{\sqrt{1 + (\omega RC)^2}}$$

and the phase angle ϕ is:

$$\phi = \tan^{-1} \omega RC$$

Inspection of Eqs. (2.45) shows that the amplitude V_0 and the phase ϕ of the output voltage are functions containing the term (ωRC).

A second method of analysis for the circuit shown in Fig. 2.13 utilizes the impedances defined in Eq. (2.42). With this approach, the input and output voltages are written as sinusoids with $e^{j\omega t}$ notation. The voltage drop across a given element is taken as ($Z\,I$). For example, the output voltage $V_0(t)$ across the capacitor in Fig. 2.13 is given by Eq. (2.41) as:

$$V_0(t) = Z_C\,I \qquad\qquad (e)$$

But:

$$I = \frac{V_i e^{j\omega t}}{Z_R + Z_C} \qquad\qquad (f)$$

Then substituting Eq. (g) into Eq. (f) yields:

$$V_0(t) = \frac{Z_C}{Z_R + Z_C}\,V_i e^{j\omega t} \qquad\qquad (g)$$

Next use Eq. (2.42) with Eq. (h) to obtain:

$$V_0(t) = \frac{1}{1 + j\omega RC}\,V_i e^{j\omega t} \qquad\qquad (2.46)$$

Comparison of Eq. (2.46) with Eq. (2.44) shows that the results are identical and that both methods can be used to determine the dynamic performance of ac circuits; however, the approach using impedances is easier and requires less time.

2.6.1 Impedance

In ac circuits, the impedance Z is related to a complex function that depends on the frequency of the signal. To show the impedance in the most general way, consider the circuit shown in Fig. 2.14, which is driven by a sinusoidal voltage $V_s(t)$. If the voltage drops across the components are summed and equated to the supply voltage, then:

$$V_i = \left[R + j\left(\omega L - \frac{1}{\omega C}\right)\right]I_i \qquad\qquad (2.47)$$

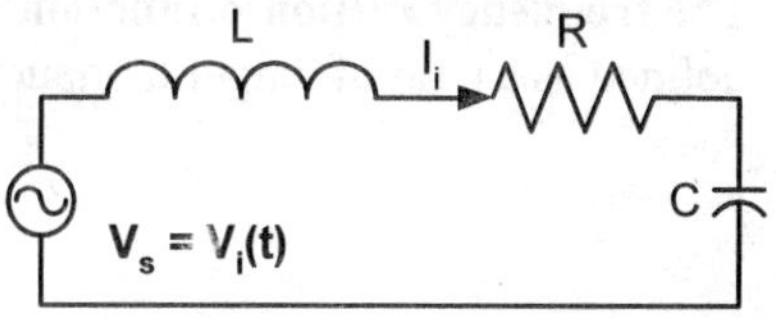

Fig. 2.14 An ac circuit containing three passive components L, R and C.

Examination of Eq. (2.47) shows that a complex function with real and imaginary parts is involved in the relation between V_i and I_i. If this complex function is divided into real and imaginary parts as illustrated in Fig. 2.15, a more useful expression for V_i in terms of I_i is obtained.

$$V_i = ZI_i \tag{2.48}$$

where Z is the total impedance of the circuit, which is given by:

$$Z = \left[R^2 + \left(\omega L - \frac{1}{\omega C} \right)^2 \right]^{1/2} \tag{2.49}$$

Equations (2.48) and (2.49) define the amplitude of the voltage and the current, but the phase of the voltage relative to the current remains to be determined. Reference to Fig. 2.15 and Eq. (2.39) and (2.47) shows the phase angle ϕ as:

$$\phi = \tan^{-1} \left(\frac{\omega L - 1/\omega C}{R} \right) \tag{2.50}$$

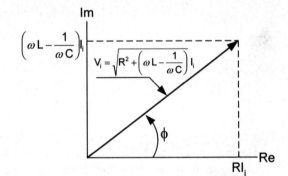

Fig. 2.15 Representing impedance components on the complex plane.

When the phase angle $\phi > 0$, as shown in Fig. 2.15, the voltage leads the current and the complete expression for $V_s(t)$ is:

$$V_s(t) = \left[R^2 + j \left(\omega L - \frac{1}{\omega C} \right)^2 \right]^{1/2} I_i e^{j(\omega t + \phi)} \tag{2.51}$$

Of particular importance is the effect of the frequency ω on both the impedance Z and the phase angle ϕ. The effect of frequency on the circuit impedance is discussed in Section 2.7.

2.7 FREQUENCY RESPONSE FUNCTION

The **frequency response function** $H(\omega)$, often termed the FRF, for a circuit or for an instrument is defined as a ratio of output to input voltages over some specified frequency range. Thus:

$$H(\omega) = \frac{V_0(\omega)}{V_i(\omega)} \tag{2.52}$$

where $V_0(\omega)$ and $V_i(\omega)$ are the frequency spectra of the output and the input voltages. The frequency response function for the circuit of Fig. 2.13 can be written from Eq. (2.44) as:

$$H(\omega) = \frac{1}{1 + j\omega RC} = \frac{e^{-j\phi}}{\sqrt{1 + (\omega RC)^2}} \tag{2.53}$$

where Eqs. (2.38) and (2.39) were used in the derivation of Eq. (2.53).

From Eq. (2.53) it is clear that the magnitude of the FRF is given by:

$$|H(\omega)| = \frac{1}{\sqrt{1 + (\omega RC)^2}} \tag{2.54}$$

and the phase ϕ is given by:

$$\phi = -\tan^{-1} \omega RC \tag{2.55}$$

It is evident from Eq. (2.54) that the frequency response function $H(\omega)$ gives the ratio for the amplitude of the output voltage to the input voltage and Eq. (2.55) gives the phase shift ϕ of the output voltage relative to the input voltage. A negative phase angle indicates that the output signal lags behind the input signal.

The frequency response function is often expressed as a relative number in terms of decibels N_{dB}. The number of decibels is defined as:

$$N_{dB} = 10 \log_{10} \left(\frac{P}{P_r} \right) \tag{2.56}$$

where P is the measured power and P_r is a reference power.

The decibel can also be expressed in terms of a voltage ratio by substituting $P = V^2/R$ into Eq. (2.56) to obtain:

$$N_{dB} = 20 \log_{10} \left(\frac{V}{V_r} \right) \tag{2.57}$$

When describing the dynamic behavior of a measurement system in N_{dB}, it is essential to specify the reference quantity P_r or V_r.

The magnitude and phase of $H(\omega)$ are represented graphically on a Bode diagram where $|H(\omega)|$ and ϕ are shown individually as functions of ωRC. The magnitude $|H(\omega)|$ is represented in terms of decibels on a Bode diagram and the ωRC parameter is shown on a $\log_{10}$ scale. To illustrate the construction of a Bode diagram, rewrite Eq. (2.54) in terms of dB by using Eq. (2.57) to obtain:

$$dB = 20\log\left[\left(1 + (\omega RC)^2\right)^{-1/2} \right] = -10\log\left[1 + (\omega RC)^2\right] \tag{2.58}$$

The phase ϕ is given directly by Eq. (2.55).

The Bode diagram corresponding to Eqs. (2.58) and (2.55) is shown in Fig. 2.16a. The magnitude of H(ω) is down 3 dB when ωRC = 1, and when ωRC >> 1, the magnitude decays linearly at 20 dB/decade. This example illustrates that the Bode diagrams provide a visual representation of a wide dynamic range of circuit or instrument characteristics. Thus, Bode diagrams are useful in determining the behavior of instruments in application to dynamic measurements.

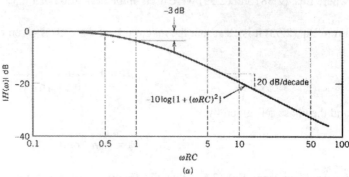

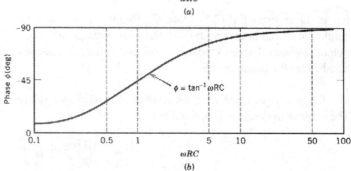

Fig. 2.16 (a) Bode diagram. (b) phase diagram for the RC circuit defined in Fig. 2.13.

2.8 SUMMARY

In the design and application of an instrumentation system, a number of analog and digital circuits are employed. An understanding of the basic laws that govern the behavior of these circuits is required to make effective use of measurement systems. In this chapter, brief definitions are provided for all the electrical quantities encountered in this textbook together with a listing of their standard symbols, units and abbreviations. Fundamental relations between these electrical quantities are summarized in Table 2.4.

Four basic components (resistors, capacitors, inductors and diodes) affect the behavior of the current flow and voltage in all electrical circuits. Ohm's law defines the voltage drop across a resistor and the current flow. A capacitor stores electrical charge. When a constant voltage is applied to a capacitor, the charge is maintained and no current flows. When the voltage changes with respect to time, current flows through the capacitor. An inductor exhibits a small resistance to a steady state flow of current. When the current varies with respect to time, however, a significant voltage drop develops across an inductor. A diode acts as a selective switch. It offers no resistance to current flow if a positive voltage is applied and an infinite resistance to current flow if the voltage is reversed.

Transistors and gates are active components that are employed with the basic passive components in most analog and digital circuits. Transistors are used as amplifiers or as high speed switches. Signal gains for an amplifier with a single transistor can range from 10 to 100. Gates are used in logic networks to control the flow of information. Circuits designed to perform specialized operations may contain large numbers of AND, OR and NOT basic gates on a single silicon chip.

Kirchhoff's two laws, the voltage and the current law, provide the foundations for circuit analysis. Analysis procedures were presented for both dc and ac circuits. In dc circuits, where the current flow is constant, the resistor is the only component producing a voltage drop. In ac circuits, the voltage varies with respect to time; therefore, the voltage drops across resistors, capacitors and inductors. Impedance in an ac circuit was defined and the magnitude and phase of the voltage drops with respect to the current flow was determined.

Signal analysis is an important part of any experimental investigation. Periodic signals are repetitive; transient signals are one-shot events that do not repeat. Sinusoidal functions, which are a special type of periodic functions, are very important in describing the dynamic response of instrument systems where the ratio of the input voltage to the output voltage is a function of frequency. Also, the sinusoid is used extensively in the Fourier analysis of other periodic functions with more complex waveforms.

A second method of analysis of signals uses phasors in the complex plane. The advantage of using phasor representation of sinusoidal signals includes the ease of differentiating and integrating and the presence of both magnitude and phase information. Differentiation is accomplished simply by multiplying by $j\omega$; integration is accomplished by dividing by $j\omega$.

The frequency response function $H(\omega)$ for a circuit or for an instrument gives the amplitude ratio of the input voltage to the output voltage and the phase shift of the input voltage relative to the output voltage . The frequency response function is often expressed as a relative number in terms of decibels N_{dB}. Bode diagrams provide a visual representation of a wide dynamic range of circuit or instrument characteristics. Thus, they are useful in determining the behavior of instruments in application to dynamic measurements.

Table 2.4
Summary of basic relations

Element	Unit	Symbol	Characteristics
Resistance (Conductance)	ohm (siemens)	$\xrightarrow{i}$ R $+\overset{}{\underset{v}{\wedge}}$ (G)	$V = R\,I$ $(I = GV)$
Inductance	henry	$\xrightarrow{i}$ L $+\ v$	$V = L\dfrac{dI}{dt}$ $I = \dfrac{1}{L}\int_0^t V dt + I_0$
Capacitance	farad	$\xrightarrow{i}$ C $+\ v$	$I = C\dfrac{dV}{dt}$ $V = \dfrac{1}{C}\int_0^t I dt + V_0$
Short circuit		$\xrightarrow{i}$	$V = 0$ for any I
Open circuit		$\circ\ \overset{+}{v}\ \circ$	$I = 0$ for any V
Voltage source	volt	$\underset{+\ v_s}{\bigcirc}$	$V = V_s$ for any I
Current source	ampere	$\underset{i_s}{\bigcirc}$	$I = I_s$ for any V

REFERENCES

1. Jackson, H., Temple, D., and Brian Kelly: Introduction to Electrical Circuits, Oxford Canada, 2008.
2. Nilsson, J. W., and S. Riedel, Electrical Circuits, 9th Edition, Prentice Hall, Upper Saddle River, 2011.
3. Alexander, C. K., and M. N. O. Sadiku, Fundamentals of Electric Circuits, McGraw Hill, New York, 2007.
4. Irwin, J. D., and R. M. Nelms, Basic Engineering Circuit Analysis, 10th Edition, Wiley, New York, 2011.
5. Dorf, R. C. and J. A. Svobada, Introduction to Electric Circuits, 8th Edition, Wiley, New York, 2010.
6. Bird, J., Electrical Circuit Theory and Technology, 3rd Edition, Elsevier Science and Technology, Oxford, U. K., 2007.

EXERCISES

2.1   List the symbol, units, and abbreviations for:
      (a) Force, charge and electric field strength
      (b) Energy, current and magnetic flux density
      (c) Power, voltage and magnetic flux

2.2   For a resistance $R = R_0$ placed across a voltage supply V, determine the power dissipated as V is increased from 0 to 500 volts. Prepare a graph showing these results if:
      (a) $R_0 = 50,000 \; \Omega$
      (b) $R_0 = 100,000 \; \Omega$
      (c) $R_0 = 250,000 \; \Omega$
      (d) $R_0 = 500,000 \; \Omega$

2.3   A voltage V_0 is switched across a capacitor C at time t = 0. Derive an equation that describes the current flow with time during charging of the capacitor if the voltage source has an internal resistance R.

2.4   Using the results of Exercise 2.3, prepare a graph showing I(t) if:
      (a) $V_0 = 10$ V   and $C = 10 \; \mu F$
      (b) $V_0 = 5$ V   and $C = 200 \; \mu F$
      (c) $V_0 = 100$ V   and $C = 1$ F
      (d) $V_0 = 3$ V   and $C = 1,500$ pF
    and the source resistance is $10 \; \Omega$.

2.5   Determine the charge and energy stored by the capacitor in each case listed in Exercise 2.4.

2.6   An ac voltage described by the expression $V = a \sin 2\pi ft$ is switched across an inductor L at t = 0. Derive an expression for the current flow with time through the inductor.

2.7   Using the results of Exercise 2.6, (a) prepare a graph showing V(t) on the abscissa and I(t) on the ordinate. Let:
      (1) f = 60 Hz, L = 10 mH, a = 10 V
      (2) f = 1 MHz, L = 10 μH, a = 5 V
    (b) What is the shape of the curve you have plotted?
    (c) Is the shape stationary with respect to time?

2.8   Determine the energy stored in the inductor for the two cases given in Exercise 2.7.

2.9 In your own words, describe Kirchhoff's first law. Also, indicate why it is an important principle in circuit analysis.

2.10 Repeat Exercise 2.9 for Kirchhoff's second law.

2.11 Sketch the symbol for a diode. Explain what is implied by positive bias voltage and negative bias voltage.

2.12 A voltage $V_i = 10 \sin (120\pi t)$ is applied to a diode as shown in Fig. E2.12. Prepare a graph showing $V_2(t)$.

Fig. E2.12 $v_1(t)$ ———▷|——— $v_2(t)$

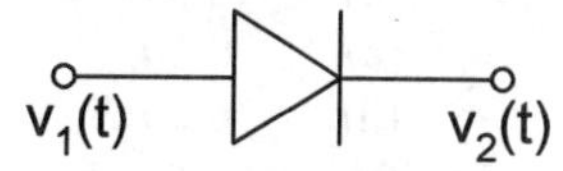

2.13 What are the two primary applications for transistors?

2.14 Using the characteristic curves for a transducer given in Fig. 2.5b, determine the maximum and minimum values of the collector current I_C if $I_i = (0.2 - 0.1 \sin \omega t)(10^{-3})$. Note: $V_{CC} = 10$ V and $R_L = 400\ \Omega$.

2.15 Sketch the circuit for an electronic switch that employs a bipolar transistor. Use your own words to describe its operation.

2.16 For a transistor employed as a switch, as illustrated in Fig. 2.5, determine the current flow through the switch when it is open and when it is closed. Compare these values to a mechanical switch. Are these differences important, and if so when?

2.17 Sketch the symbol and write a truth table for the **AND** gate and the **OR** gate.

2.18 Sketch the circuit using transistors as switches for the following basic gates.

      (a) **AND**   (b) **OR**   (c) **NOT**

2.19 With reference to Fig. 2.8, verify the relations for R_e given in Eqs. (2.21) an (2.22).

2.20 For a displacement given by $x = A_0 \cos \omega t$, show that the velocity $\dot{x}$ and the acceleration $\ddot{x}$ exhibit a phase difference with respect to the displacement of $\pi/2$ and π, respectively.

2.21 A quantity $Q = A_0 e^{j(\omega t - \phi)}$. (a) Find $\dot{Q}$ and $\ddot{Q}$. (b) What is the effect of the phase angle ϕ on these unknowns.

2.22 A phasor has a real part $Re = R$ and an imaginary part $Im = \omega L - 1/(\omega C)$. Find the amplitude of the phasor and its phase angle.

2.23 For the circuit shown in Fig. 2.13, (a) verify Eq. (2.45), (b) prepare a graph showing the amplitude of V_0/V_i as a function of ωRC, (c) what happens to the impedance Z_c as ω becomes very large?

2.24 For the circuit shown in Fig. E2.24, (a) derive an expression for $V_0(t)$. (b) Define the amplitude and the phase angle in this expression.

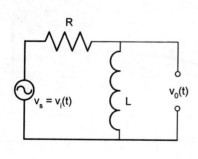

Fig. E2.24

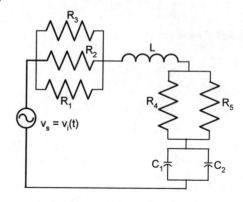

Fig. E2.25

2.25 For the circuit shown in Fig. E2.25, determine (a) the impedance and (b) the phase angle between the current and the voltage.

2.26 For the circuit shown in Fig. 2.14, prepare a graph of $Z(\omega)$ if L, C, and R have the following values.

	L (µH)	C (µF)	R (Ω)
(a)	0.01	0.50	10,000
(b)	0.05	0.20	1,000
(c)	0.10	0.10	500
(d)	0.20	0.20	200
(e)	0.50	0.50	100

2.27 Determine the magnitude $|H(\omega)|$ and the phase angle ϕ of the frequency response function for the circuit shown in Fig. 2.13 with the values of R and C listed in Exercise 2.26.

2.28 Determine the decibel equivalents for the following ratios of P/P_r and V/V_r.

	P/P_r	V/V_r
(a)	1,000	15
(b)	2.0	0.001
(c)	0.003	3,000

2.29 Construct a Bode diagram, in terms of decibels, for Eq. (2.54). Describe the results shown in this diagram.

2.30 Construct a phase diagram for the RC circuit shown in Fig. 2.13.

2.31 Construct a Bode diagram, in terms of decibels, for the RL circuit of Exercise 2.24.

2.32 Construct a phase diagram for the RL circuit of Exercise 2.24.

EXERCISE SOLUTIONS

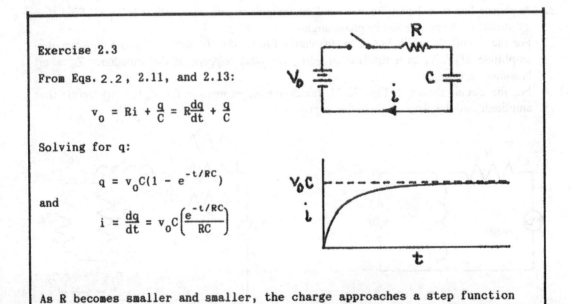

Exercise 2.3

From Eqs. 2.2, 2.11, and 2.13:

$$v_0 = Ri + \frac{q}{C} = R\frac{dq}{dt} + \frac{q}{C}$$

Solving for q:

$$q = v_0 C(1 - e^{-t/RC})$$

and

$$i = \frac{dq}{dt} = v_0 C\left(\frac{e^{-t/RC}}{RC}\right)$$

As R becomes smaller and smaller, the charge approaches a step function and the current approaches a Dirac delta function.

Exercise 2.8

From Eq. 2.17: $$w = \frac{1}{2} L i^2$$

(1) For f = 60 Hz, L = 10 mH, and a = 10 V:

$$w = \frac{1}{2}(10)(10^{-3})(2.65)^2 = 0.0351 \text{ J}$$

(2) For f = 1 MHz, L = 10 μH, and a = 5 V:

$$w = \frac{1}{2}(10)(10^{-6})[(79.6)(10^{-3})]^2 = 31.7(10^{-9}) \text{ J}$$

Exercise 2.14

For V_{CC} = 10 V and R_L = 400 Ω:

$$V_{CC}/R_L = 10/400 = 0.025 = 25 \text{ mA}$$

Draw a load line on Fig. 2.5b by using $V_{CC}/R_L = 25$ mA and V_{CC} = 10 V.

From this load line for $i_i = [0.2 - 0.1 \sin(\omega t)](10^{-3})$ A:

$$i_c(\text{max}) = 15 \text{ mA} \quad \text{and} \quad i_c(\text{min}) = 5 \text{ mA}$$

Exercise 2.19

For resistors in series: $$v_s = iR_1 + iR_2 = i(R_1 + R_2) = iR_e$$

Therefore, $$R_e = R_1 + R_2$$

For resistors in parallel: $$i = i_1 + i_2 + i_3 = \frac{v_s}{R_1} + \frac{v_s}{R_2} + \frac{v_s}{R_3} = \frac{v_s}{R_e}$$

Therefore, $$\frac{1}{R_e} = \frac{1}{R_1} + \frac{1}{R_2} + \frac{1}{R_3}$$

Exercise 2.21

(a) $$Q = A_0 e^{j(\omega t - \phi)} \qquad \dot{Q} = j\omega A_0 e^{j(\omega t - \phi)} \qquad \ddot{Q} = \omega^2 A_0 e^{j(\omega t - \phi)}$$

(b) The phase angle ϕ affects each quantity by the same amount. All three are shifted ϕ radians with respect to a reference phasor $A_0 e^{j\omega t}$.

Exercise 2.23

(a) From Eqs. 2.13, 2.15, and 2.19:

$$v_s(t) = Ri + \frac{q}{C} \qquad v_o = \frac{q}{C} \qquad i = \dot{q} = C\dot{v}_o$$

Thus: $\qquad RC\dot{v}_o + v_o = v_s(t) = v_i e^{j\omega t}$

Assume: $\qquad v_o(t) = v_o e^{j\omega t} \qquad \dot{v}_o(t) = j\omega v_o e^{j\omega t}$

Then: $\qquad (jRC\omega + 1)v_o e^{j\omega t} = v_i e^{j\omega t}$

$$\frac{v_o}{v_i} = \left[\frac{1}{1 + jRC\omega}\right] = \frac{1}{\sqrt{1 + (RC\omega)^2}} e^{-j\phi}$$

$$\tan\phi = RC\omega$$

(b)

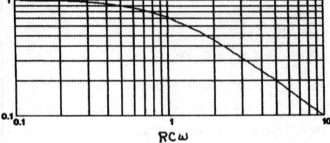

(c) $\qquad\qquad\qquad Z_C = \dfrac{1}{jC\omega}$

Thus, Z_C becomes very small for large values of ω.

Exercise 2.29

From Eq. 2.54:

$$|H(\omega)| = \frac{1}{\sqrt{1 + (\omega RC)^2}}$$

From Eq. 2.58:

$$N_{dB} = -10 \log [1 + (\omega RC)^2]$$

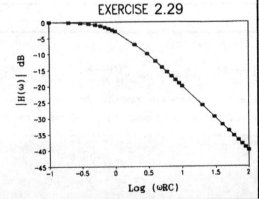

CHAPTER 3

MEASUREMENT SYSTEMS

3.1 INTRODUCTION

During the past fifty years, significant progress has been made in developing digital instrumentation. The combination of analog transducers with digital processing, accomplished through analog to digital conversion has placed new dimensions on both engineering analysis and process control. The digital processing of analog data provides many advantages, including more rapid measurements, simplicity, and improved accuracy and reduced costs. Equally important has been the integration of the personal computer into instrument systems. Circuit cards, which plug into slots on PCs, are commercially available that combine signal conditioning circuits, analog to digital conversion and storage of data into memory. Software such as LabVIEW enables the operator to access the data to perform either an engineering analysis or to control a process.

Measurements of physical quantities such as force, torque, strain, acceleration, etc. involve analog signals that vary as continuous functions of time. An analog instrument system, illustrated in Fig. 3.1, is used to acquire an analog signal V_0, which is proportional to the quantity that is being monitored. The analog system interfaces with a digital system through an analog to digital (A/D) interface. The key element, which represents the interface between the analog acquisition system and the digital processing system, is an analog to digital converter (ADC). This ADC takes the voltage V_0 from the acquisition system and converts it to an equivalent digital code. Once digitized, the signal (i.e. a digital code) can be displayed, processed, stored or transmitted. The arrangement of the combined analog and digital system, shown in Fig. 3.1, depends on the purpose of the system. A simple system involving the direct display of a single quantity will incorporate a transducer, a power supply, a number of integrated circuits (chips) and a numerical display[1]. A more involved digital system will include a computer for real-time processing, disk drives for storage of raw and processed data, a monitor for display, a printer for hard copy and data transmission lines to off-site facilities.

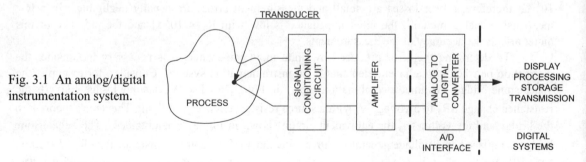

Fig. 3.1 An analog/digital instrumentation system.

In the design of an instrumentation system, it is important that each component be selected so that the output displayed is accurate, easily interpreted and rapidly processed. The general characteristics of these components must be understood before they can be employed in an instrumentation system.

---

[1] These simple systems are often housed in a small hand-held package that is powered with batteries that enable it to be used either in the laboratory or the field.

3.2 GENERAL CHARACTERISTICS OF A MEASUREMENT SYSTEM

The general characteristics that describe the behavior of a measurement system are input impedance, sensitivity, range, zero drift and frequency response. Each of these characteristics is described in the following subsections.

A. Input Impedance

Input impedance Z controls the energy required by the system in order to measure an input quantity. Consider a simple dc voltmeter used to measure a source voltage V. The power loss P through the meter is given by:

$$P = \frac{V^2}{Z_m} \tag{3.1}$$

where Z_m is the input impedance of the voltmeter. In most instances, the input impedance can be modeled by a resistance and a capacitance in parallel so that:

$$Z_m = \frac{Z_C Z_R}{Z_C + Z_R} = \frac{R_m}{1 + j\omega R_m C} \tag{3.2a}$$

From Eq. (3.2a) and Eq. (2.38) the magnitude of Z_m can be written as:

$$|Z_m| = \frac{R_m}{\sqrt{1 + j(\omega R_m C)^2}} \tag{3.2b}$$

For dc and quasi-static measurements of voltage, the signal frequency $\omega \Rightarrow 0$ and the input impedance $Z_m \Rightarrow R_m$, where R_m is the resistance of the meter.

It is evident from Eq. (3.1) that an ideal voltmeter should have an input impedance $Z_m = R_m \Rightarrow \infty$ to reduce the power loss and the measurement error to zero. In most modern digital meters, $R_m = 10^6$ to 10^8 Ω; therefore, power losses are small and measurement errors are usually negligible. In a few inexpensive analog meters[2], the input impedance is low with $R_m < 10^4$ Ω and the presence of this meter affects the accuracy of the measurements.

To determine the error produced by finite input impedance, it is necessary to consider the interaction between two adjacent elements in an instrumentation system. Consider, for example, the Wheatstone bridge—voltmeter combination shown in Fig. 3.2a. The Wheatstone bridge converts the resistance change ΔR_1 to a voltage V_i with a source resistance R_s. By applying Thevenin's theorem to the bridge and the voltmeter, the equivalent circuit shown in Fig. 3.2b is obtained. The Wheatstone bridge is replaced by a voltage generator with a potential V_i and a source resistance $R_s = R_1$. A current I flows in the loop and the voltmeter resistance R_m acts as a load on the source in series with R_s. The voltage displayed by the voltmeter is the drop across the resistor R_m. Thus, from Eq. (2.11) we can write:

---

[2] The cost of digital multimeters today is so low there is little reason to use analog multimeters or voltmeters where load effects may become an issue.

$$V_m = IR_m \qquad \text{(a)}$$

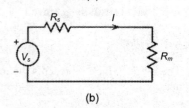

(a)

Fig. 3.2 (a) Combination of a Wheatstone bridge and voltage recorder.

(b) Equivalent circuit by Thevenin's theorem.

(b)

From Eq. (2.21), it is evident that:

$$I = \frac{V_i}{R_s + R_m} \qquad \text{(b)}$$

Substituting Eq. (a) into Eq. (b) gives:

$$V_m = \frac{V_i}{1 + (R_s / R_m)} \qquad (3.3)$$

Inspection of Eq. (3.3) shows that the meter indication V_m will be less than the source potential V_i. The error $\mathcal{E}$ is given by:

$$\mathcal{E} = \frac{V_i - V_m}{V_i} = \frac{R_s / R_m}{1 + (R_s / R_m)} \qquad (3.4)$$

Equation (3.4) shows that if $R_s / R_m < 0.01$ then the load error is less than 1%. Following the rule that the input impedance should be 100 times the source impedance, limits load error to less than 1%.

B. Sensitivity

The sensitivity S of an analog voltmeter is given by Eq. (1.6) as:

$$S = \frac{d}{V_i} \qquad (3.5)$$

where d is the smallest increment indicated on the scale of an analog instrument.

The sensitivity of a digital voltmeter is the smallest increment of voltage that can be detected and is determined by multiplying the lowest full-scale range by voltmeter's resolution. A four-digit DVM, with a count of 10,000 operating on its lowest full-scale range of 100-mV, has a sensitivity of $(1/10,000) \times 100$ mV = 0.01 mV.

From Eq. (3.5) it is clear that the voltage V_i is determined by measuring d and dividing by S. Because division is more difficult than multiplication, most manufacturers of recording instruments define a voltage sensitivity S_R as:

$$V_i = d\, S_R \tag{3.6}$$

where $S_R = 1/S$ is expressed in terms of volts per division of displacement.

High sensitivity S or low reciprocal sensitivity S_R is often achieved by incorporating high gain amplifiers in the instrument. The gain of the amplifier is varied to provide the instrument with several different sensitivities to accommodate a wide range of input voltages. With digital instruments, high sensitivity is usually achieved by employing analog to digital converters with higher bit counts.

C. Range

The range, which represents the maximum voltage that can be measured, is determined from Eq. (3.5) as:

$$V^* = \frac{d^*}{S} = d^* S_R \tag{3.7}$$

where V^* for an analog instrument is the maximum voltage or range and d^* is the maximum possible reading on its display. For a digital multimeter V^* is the maximum readout (count).

The form of Eq. (3.7) shows the trade-off that must be made between range and sensitivity. When the sensitivity S is high, the range V^* will be low; and conversely, if the range is high, the sensitivity will be low. A voltage amplifier with a variable gain extends the applicability of an analog instrument by matching appropriate sensitivity with the input voltage thereby extending its useful range. Digital instruments also employ amplifiers to improve their sensitivity; however both the range and sensitivity are determined by the capability (the count) obtained with the analog to digital converter. In many digital instruments the count of the analog to digital converter is increased to obtain improved sensitivity rather than increasing the gain of the instrument's amplifier.

D. Zero Drift

Most recording instruments have provisions for adjusting the zero offset so that the trace is at zero when the input voltage is zero. However, the position of the zero on the display may change with time, due to instabilities in one or more of the circuits in the measurement system. Zero drift is often due to circuit instabilities in the amplifier that occur due to temperature fluctuations, variations in line voltage and time.

Zero drift is specified for most recording instruments and can be minimized by using a regulated line voltage, by turning instruments on for a suitable time period before recording (warm up), and by controlling the temperature of the room in which the instrument is housed. If measurements are to be made over a long period of time, provisions should be made to periodically check and adjust the zero position, to account for the drift.

E. Frequency Response (Bandwidth)

If the voltage being recorded is dynamic, the measurement instrument should reproduce the transient input without amplitude or phase distortion. The ability of an instrument to respond to transient signals is determined by its frequency response (sometimes called bandwidth), which is based on the instrument's steady-state response to a sinusoidal input expressed as:

$$V_i = A_i \, e^{j\omega t} \qquad (3.8)$$

The output V_0 of the recorder is written as:

$$V_0 = A_0 \, e^{j(\omega t + \phi)} \qquad (3.9)$$

The frequency response function $H(\omega)$ for an instrument is given by Eqs. (2.54) and (2.55), which show that the amplitude ratio A_0/A_i and the phase angle ϕ both change as a function of the input signal's frequency ω. Curves, such as those presented in Fig. 3.3 for A_0/A_i and ϕ versus ω, define the frequency response of a recording system.

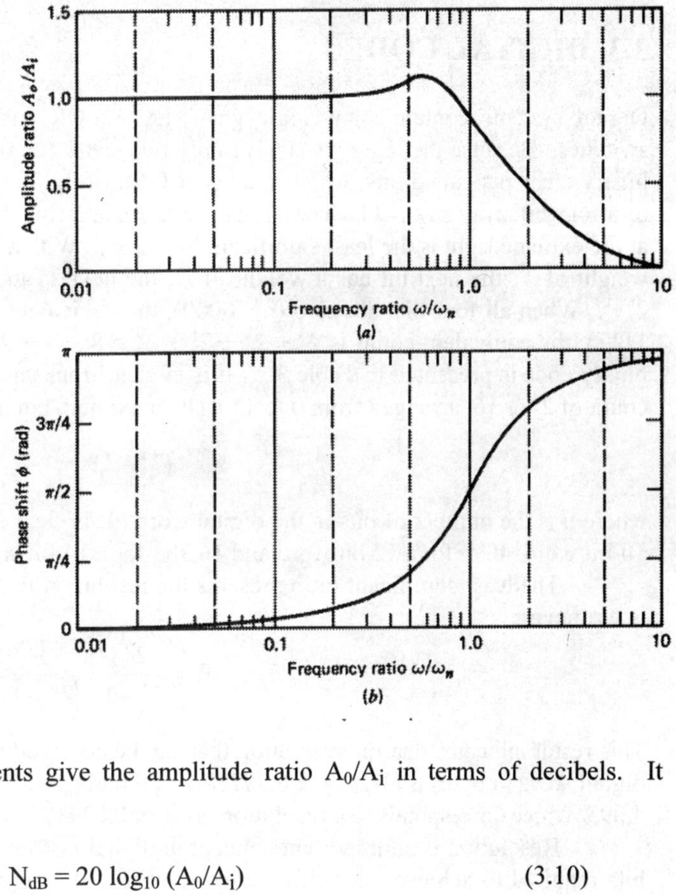

Fig. 3.3 Response of a voltage measuring instrument to harmonic excitation.
  (a) Amplitude as a function of frequency.
  (b) Phase shift as a function of frequency.

Frequently, specifications for instruments give the amplitude ratio A_0/A_i in terms of decibels. It should be noted from Eq. (2.57) that:

$$N_{dB} = 20 \, \log_{10} (A_0/A_i) \qquad (3.10)$$

where N_{dB} is the number of decibels and A_0 and A_i represent voltages.

Results from Eq. (3.10), shown in Table 3.1, indicate that significant errors result in recording dynamic signals even for relatively small values of N_{dB}. For instance, an instrument specification, which indicates that the frequency response is within ±3 dB over a specified frequency range, implies an error of +41.1% (1.413) for +3 dB and −29.2% (0.708) for −3 dB. Limits of ± 0.4 dB should be maintained to reduce measurement error to less than ±5 %.

Table 3.1

Conversion of Voltage Ratio A_0/A_i to N_{dB}

A_0/A_i	N_{dB}	A_0/A_i	N_{dB}
1	0	1	0
1.01	0.086	0.99	−0.087
1.02	0.172	0.98	−0.175
1.05	0.424	0.95	−0.446
1.10	0.827	0.90	−0.915
1.20	1.583	0.80	−1.938
1.50	3.522	0.707	−3.012
2.00	6.020	0.500	−6.021

3.3 DIGITAL CODES

Digital systems contain many logic gates, (AND, OR and NOT gates), which act like on or off switches. Because the logic gates have only two states (on or off), digital words consist of a string of binary elements called bits, which are either 0 for off or 1 for on. Consider a digital word consisting of a four-bit array say 1011. The "1" at the extreme left is the most significant bit (MSB) and the "1" at the extreme right is the least significant bit (LSB). With a binary code, the least significant bit has a weight of 2^0, the next bit has a weight of 2^1, the next 2^2 and the most significant bit m has a weight 2^{m-1}. When all four bits are zero (i.e. 0000), the equivalent count is 0. When all four bits are 1 (i.e. 1111), the equivalent count is $2^3 + 2^2 + 2^1 + 2^0 = 8 + 4 + 2 + 1 = 15$. A complete listing of a 4-bit binary code is presented in Table 3.2. It is evident from this listing that a 4-bit binary word permits a count of 2^4 or 16, arranged from 0 to 15. The maximum count C is:

$$C = (2^n - 1) \tag{3.11}$$

where n is the number of bits in the digital word. It is clear that C = 255 for an 8-bit word, 1023 for a 10-bit word, 4095 for a 12 bit word and 16,383 for a 14-bit word.

The least significant bit represents the resolution R of a digital count containing n bits, which is written as:

$$R = \frac{2^0}{2^n - 1} = \frac{1}{2^n - 1} = \frac{1}{C} \tag{3.12}$$

This result indicates that the resolution that can be achieved with logic gates arranged to yield an 8-bit digital word (a byte) is (1/255) or 0.392% of full scale. A 12-bit word provides a resolution of 1 part in 4,095, which corresponds to a resolution error of 0.024%.

Resolution is an important concept in digital instrumentation because it defines the number of bits required to achieve a specified error limit in a measurement or for the conversion of an analog voltage into a digital count representing that voltage. Values for C, R and resolution error ε_R as a function of the number of binary bits n are presented in Table 3.3. Clearly an 8-bit digital word that provides resolution to within ± 1 count of its full-scale count of 255 will limit the resolution error to 0.39%.

Table 3.2
Equivalent count for a 4-bit binary code.

MSB[a]	Bit 2	Bit 3	LSB[a]	MSB		Bit 2		Bit 3		LSB		Count
0	0	0	0	0	+	0	+	0	+	0	=	0
0	0	0	1	0	+	0	+	0	+	2^0	=	1
0	0	1	0	0	+	0	+	2^1	+	0	=	2
0	0	1	1	0	+	0	+	2^1	+	2^0	=	3
0	1	0	0	0	+	2^2	+	0	+	0	=	4
0	1	0	1	0	+	2^2	+	0	+	2^0	=	5
0	1	1	0	0	+	2^2	+	2^1	+	0	=	6
0	1	1	1	0	+	2^2	+	2^1	+	2^0	=	7
1	0	0	0	2^3	+	0	+	0	+	0	=	8
1	0	0	1	2^3	+	0	+	0	+	2^0	=	9
1	0	1	0	2^3	+	0	+	2^1	+	0	=	10
1	0	1	1	2^3	+	0	+	2^1	+	2^0	=	11
1	1	0	0	2^3	+	2^2	+	0	+	0	=	12
1	1	0	1	2^3	+	2^2	+	0	+	2^0	=	13
1	1	1	0	2^3	+	2^2	+	2^1	+	0	=	14
1	1	1	1	2^3	+	2^2	+	2^1	+	2^0	=	15

[a] Where MSB and LSB are the most and least significant bits, respectively.

Table 3.3
Count C, Resolution R and Error $\mathcal{E}_R$ as a function of the number of binary bits n.

n	C	R(ppm)[a]	$\mathcal{E}_R$ (%)
4	15	66,666	6.6666
5	31	32,258	3.2258
6	63	1,5873	1.5873
7	127	7,874	0.7874
8	255	3,922	0.3922
9	511	1,957	0.1957
10	1,023	978	0.0978
11	2,047	489	0.0489
12	4,095	244	0.0244
13	8,191	122	0.0122
14	16,383	61	0.0061
15	32,767	31	0.0031
16	65,535	15	0.0015

[a] ppm is parts per million.

3.4 CONVERSION PROCESSES

The analog—digital interface, illustrated in Fig. 3.1, shows an analog to digital converter (ADC) that transforms the analog voltage into a digital count. The ADC is a one-way device converting only from an analog signal to a digital code. To convert from a digital code to an analog voltage requires a digital to analog converter (DAC), which is also a one-way device. Because the DAC and ADC are the key functional elements in analog/digital instrument systems, they are described in detail in Sections 3.5 and 3.6, respectively.

First, consider a 4-bit DAC where the input is a digital code ranging from 0000 to 1111 as listed in Table 3.2. The digital input (the independent variable) is plotted along the abscissa of Fig. 3.4 and the analog voltage output from the DAC, ranging from 0 to 15/16 of full scale, is shown along the ordinate. While the full-scale value of 16 is not available as a digital input, it represents the reference quantity to which the analog voltage is normalized. For example, let 10 V be the full scale voltage (FSV), then the digital code 1000 will give, under ideal conditions, an analog voltage of $(8/16)(10) = 5$ V.

Next consider an ADC with the analog voltage being the independent variable shown in Fig. 3.5. Because all analog voltages between zero and full scale can exist, they must be quantized by dividing the complete range of voltage into sub ranges. If FSV is the full-scale analog voltage input, the quantization increment is equal to FSV × LSB where the LSB = 2^{-n}. For a 4-bit ADC, FSV × LSB = (1/16) FSV or 0.0625 FSV. All of the analog voltages within a given quantization increment are represented by the same digital code. The illustration in Fig. 3.5 shows that the digital code corresponds to the midpoint in each increment. The quantizing process, which replaces a linear analog function with a stair case digital representation, results in a quantization uncertainty of ± ½ LSB. The quantization error is shown at the top of Fig. 3.5 with the saw tooth pattern. The average value of the quantization error is zero; however, if it is assumed that it is equally probable that V/FSV takes any value within the quantization increment, it can be shown that the standard deviation σ of a number of measurements is given by:

$$\sigma = \frac{1}{2\sqrt{3}} \text{LSB} = \frac{2^{-(n+1)}}{\sqrt{3}} \tag{3.13}$$

Clearly this statistic indicates that the effective resolution of the ADC is much better than the usually specified resolution given by Eq. (3.12).

Fig. 3.4 Relation between digital count and analog voltage for a digital to analog converter (DAC).

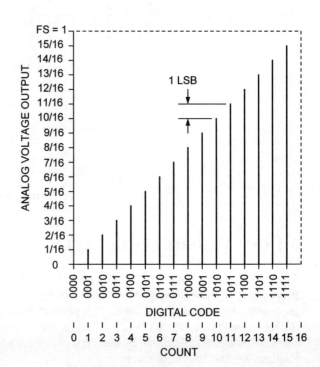

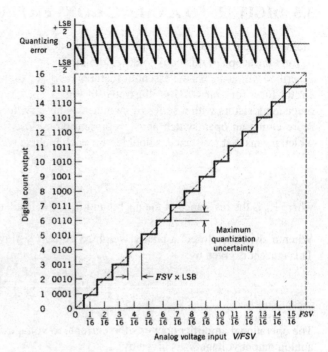

Fig. 3.5 Relation between analog voltage input digital counter-code output for four bit analog-to-digital converter (ADC).

Converters of either type (DAC or ADC) are not ideal and errors due to offset, gain and scale factor can occur. These three types of conversion errors are illustrated graphically in Fig. 3.6 for both the DAC and ADC.

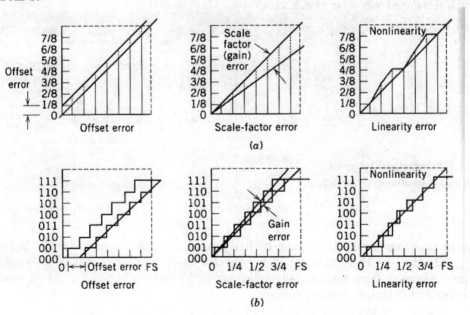

Fig. 3.6 Typical sources of error in (a) digital-to-analog converters and (b) analog-to-digital converters.

3.5 DIGITAL TO ANALOG CONVERTERS (DACs)

Many different circuits are employed in the design of digital to analog converters (DACs). It is beyond the scope of this book to cover the more sophisticated circuits; instead, a simple circuit will be described which shows the essential features involved in the digital to analog conversion process. The circuit for a four-bit DAC is illustrated in Fig. 3.7. A reference voltage V_R is connected to a set of precision resistors with a series of switches. These switches are gates in a digital logic circuit with 0 representing an open switch and 1 representing a closed switch. The resistors are binary weighted, which means that resistance is doubled for each higher switch or bit so that:

$$R_n = 2^n R_f \tag{a}$$

where R_n is the resistance of the n_{th} bit and R_f is the feedback resistance on the operational amplifier.

When a switch is closed, a binary weighted current I_n flows through resistor R_n to the summing bus. This current is given by:

$$I_n = \frac{V_R}{R_n} = \frac{V_R}{2^n R_f} \tag{3.14}$$

The operational amplifier converts the currents to voltages and provides a low-impedance output. The analog output voltage V_0 is given by:

$$V_0 = -R_f \sum_{n=1}^{k} I_n \tag{3.15}$$

where I_n is summed only if the switch n is closed.

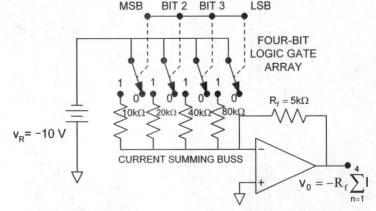

Fig. 3.7 Schematic diagram of a 4-bit digital-to-analog converter.

Consider as an example the digital code 1011 (equivalent to 11) for the circuit shown in Fig. 3.7 with $R_f = 5$ kΩ and $V_s = -10$ V. From Eq. (3.14) it is clear that $I_1 = -1$ mA, $I_2 = 0$, $I_3 = -\frac{1}{4}$ mA and $I_4 = -1/8$ mA. Summing these currents and multiplying by R_f gives $V_0 = 6.875$ V, which is the same as (11/16) of the full-scale (reference) voltage.

Commercial DACs are more complex than the schematic shown in Fig. 3.7 because they contain more bits (8, 12, 14 and 16 are common) and have several regulated voltages, integrating circuits for switching and on-chip registers. The large number of bits is serviced with a system of parallel conductors called an input bus. The voltage on each conductor in the bus is either high or low and activates each of the switches (gates) to provide the digital code as input to the device. The analog voltage output V_0 is constant with respect to time as long as the digital code is held at the same value on the input.

In many digital systems there are several functions occurring together and proper sequencing of these different functions is mandatory, if a common bus is used in the data distribution system. In these applications, the DAC is preceded by a register as indicated in Fig. 3.8. The register is a memory device where the input data may be stored and held. With a common data bus, which serves several digital devices, only select signals are converted by the DAC. The other signals are ignored as they are intended for different devices. Sorting the signals from the bus is accomplished with a strobe that is activated when the DAC has been addressed and given a signal to write. The strobe signal enables the register to read the data on the bus during the active period of this signal and the new data, a digital code, replaces the old data in an update. The register is then latched and the updated data is held in memory. This new digital data is then converted to an analog voltage in the DAC and the analog voltage is held constant until the strobe signal initiates the next update.

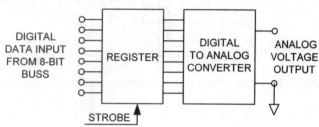

Fig. 3.8 A digital-to-analog converter with a register to control data flow.

3.6 ANALOG TO DIGITAL CONVERTERS (ADCs)

Conversion of analog signals to digital code is extremely important in any instrument system involving digital processing of analog signals from signal conditioning circuits. Of the systems available for analog to digital conversion, three of the most common will be described: the successive-approximation method, the integration method and the flash-conversion method.

3.6.1 Successive Approximation Method

The method of successive approximation is illustrated in Fig. 3.9 where a bias voltage V_b is shown as a close approximation to an unknown analog voltage V_u, which is given by:

$$V_b = V_u + \frac{1}{2^{n+1}} FSV \tag{3.16}$$

The term $\left(\dfrac{1}{2^{n+1}}\right)FSV$ in Eq. (3.16) is added to the unknown voltage to place the DAC output in the center of a quantization increment. In the case, illustrated in Fig. 3.9, a 4-bit DAC is employed to convert a fixed analog voltage $V_u = (10/16)FSV$. The bias voltage is given by Eq. (3.16) as:

$$V_b = \left(\frac{10}{16} + \frac{1}{2^5}\right)FSV = \frac{21}{32}FSV \tag{a}$$

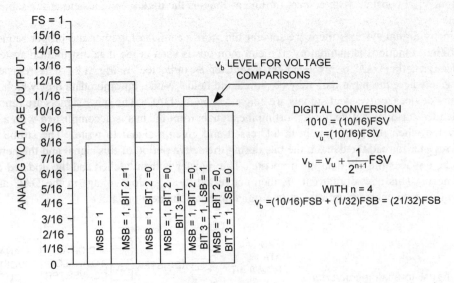

Fig. 3.9 Voltage changes in a successive approximation conversion of an analog signal to a digital code.

The bias voltage V_b is compared to a sequence of precise voltages generated by an input controlled DAC. The digital input to the DAC is successively adjusted until the known output V_0 from the DAC compares closely with V_u.

At the start of the conversion process, the input to the DAC is set at 1000 (i.e. the most significant bit is on and all other bits are off). The analog voltage $V_0 = (8/16)FSV$ and a voltage comparison shows $V_0 < V_b$. By turning bits on and off and making voltage comparisons after each change, the output voltage V_0 approaches the bias voltage as shown in Fig. 3.9. It should be noted that this method of successive approximations is analogous to weighing an unknown mass on a balance by using a set of n binary weights.

The input of the DAC, in this case 1010, is transferred to the output register of the ADC. In this simple example, the conversion process was exact because the unknown voltage V_u was selected at a 4-bit binary value $(10/16)FSV$. In general, an uncertainty in the conversion will occur when the unknown voltage differs from a binary value. To determine the uncertainty with an ADC involving n approximations consider:

$$V_0 = V_b - \frac{1}{2^n} FSV \tag{3.17}$$

Substituting Eq. (3.16) into Eq. (3.17) gives:

$$V_0 = V_u - \frac{1}{2^{n+1}} FSV \tag{3.18}$$

The relative difference Δ between V_u and V_0 referred to the full-scale voltage is given by:

$$\Delta = \frac{V_u - V_0}{FSV} = \frac{1}{2^{n+1}} \tag{3.19}$$

where n is the number of bits used in the approximation.

Equation (3.19) shows that analog to digital conversion results in a maximum uncertainty that is equivalent to (1/2)LSB. The quantization error, shown in Fig. 3.5, varies between $\pm$ (1/2)LSB and is bounded by the maximum uncertainty.

In this example, the analog input voltage did not change during the conversion process. In fact, accurate conversion cannot be accomplished when the input voltage changes with time. To avoid problems associated with fluctuating voltages during the conversion period, the ADC utilizes an input device that samples and holds the signal constant for the time required for conversion. When the conversion is complete, the 8-, 12- or 16-bit digital code is transferred to a register and the conversion process is repeated. Conversion rates depend on the number of bits, design of the circuit and the speed of the transistors used in switching. A moderate-cost, 12-bit ADC typically requires 5 μs or less to convert an analog signal. For a single channel application, a 5 μs conversion time gives a data acquisition rate of 200,000 S/s.

3.6.2 Integration Method

Analog to digital conversion by integration is based on counting clock pulses. A typical circuit for a dual slope ADC is shown in Fig. 3.10a. At the start of a conversion, the unknown input voltage V_u is applied together with a reference voltage V_R to a summing amplifier that gives an output voltage:

$$V_a = -\tfrac{1}{2}\,(V_u + V_R) \qquad\qquad\text{(a)}$$

This voltage is imposed on an integrator that integrates V_a with respect to time to obtain:

$$V_i = \frac{(V_u + V_R)t^*}{2RC} \qquad\qquad (3.20)$$

where t* is a fixed time of integration, as shown in Fig. 3.10a.

Upon completion of the integration at time t*, a switch on the input of the integrator is activated, which disconnects the summing amplifier and connects the reference voltage V_R to the integrator, as shown in Fig. 3.10b. The output voltage of the integrator then decreases with a slope of:

$$\frac{\Delta V_i}{\Delta t} = -\frac{V_R}{RC} \qquad\qquad (3.21)$$

A comparator monitors the output voltage V_i and issues a signal to the control logic when V_i goes to zero. This zero crossing occurs when:

$$\frac{(V_u + V_R)t^*}{2RC} = \frac{V_R \Delta t}{RC} \qquad\qquad\text{(b)}$$

Reducing Eq. (b) yields:

$$\frac{\Delta t}{t^*} = \frac{1}{2}\left(\frac{V_u}{V_R} + 1\right) \qquad\qquad (3.22)$$

It is clear from Eq. (3.22) that $\Delta t/t^*$, a proportional count of clock pulses, is related to V_u/V_R. If a counter is started by a switch on the integrator, the counter will give a binary number representing the unknown voltage V_u.

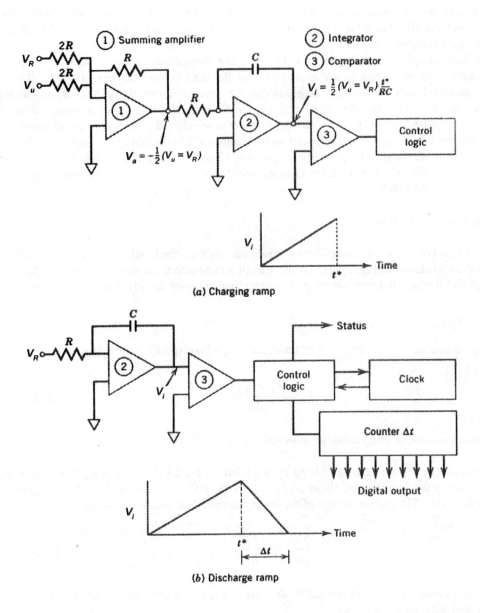

Fig. 3.10 Schematic circuit diagrams for an analog to digital converter using dual slope integration.

The integration method for analog to digital conversion has several advantages. It is extremely accurate as its output is independent of R, C and the clock frequency because these quantities affect both the up and down ramps in the same way. The influence of noise on the unknown signal is markedly attenuated because the electrical noise, which occurs at high frequency, is averaged toward zero during the integration period t*. The primary disadvantage of the integration method is the speed of conversion which is less than ½ t* conversions per second. In order to attenuate the effect of 60 Hz noise, t* must be greater than 16.67 ms; therefore, the speed of conversion must be less than 30 samples/s. This conversion rate is too slow for large high-performance data-acquisition systems, but it is satisfactory for digital voltmeters and slower lower cost recording systems.

The conversion speed of the ADC determines the frequency of the unknown analog signal that can be measured. To determine this frequency, let the input signal to an ADC be a sinusoid with a frequency f given by:

$$V_u = \frac{V_u^*}{2} \sin 2\pi ft \tag{3.23}$$

where the amplitude $V_u^*/2 = (FSV)/2$. The maximum rate of change of this input is obtained by differentiating Eq. (3.23) and letting $\cos 2\pi ft = 1$ to obtain:

$$\left(\frac{dV_u}{dt}\right)_{max} = \pi f V_u^* \tag{3.24}$$

The term $(dV_u/dt)_{max}$ is called the slew rate of the signal. If the ADC is to convert the signal into a digital code of n bits to within 1 LSB, then the change in input voltage ΔV must be limited to $\Delta V < (LSB \times FSV)$ during the conversion time T. It is clear from Eq. (3.24) that:

$$\Delta V_{max} = \pi f V_u^* \, T < (LBS \times FSV) \tag{3.25}$$

Solving Eq. (3.25) for the frequency limit f gives:

$$f < \frac{LSB \times FSV}{V_u^*}\left(\frac{1}{\pi T}\right) \tag{c}$$

Because $FSV = V_u^*$, Eq. (c) reduces to:

$$f < \frac{2^{-n}}{\pi T} \tag{3.26}$$

If the signal is unipolar, n is the number of bits. However, if the signal is bipolar, an additional bit is necessary to provide the sign of the output. For this reason, a unipolar signal can be sampled with twice the frequency of a bipolar signal. For example, a 10-bit ADC converting at 20 readings/s can monitor a unipolar signal with a frequency $f < 0.0062$ Hz. This signal with $V_u^* = 10$ V corresponds to a maximum slew rate of 0.195 V/s in an ADC with FSV = 10V.

3.6.3 Parallel or Flash Conversion Method

Parallel or flash analog to digital conversion is the fastest method for designing ADCs. The flash converter, illustrated in Fig. 3.11, employs $(2^n - 1)$ voltage comparators arranged in parallel. Each comparator is connected to the unknown voltage V_u. The reference voltage is applied to a binary resistance ladder so that the reference voltage applied to a given comparator is 1 LSB higher than the reference voltage applied to the lower adjacent comparator.

When an analog signal is presented to the comparator bank, all the comparators with $V_R^* < V_u$ will go high and those with $V_R^* > V_u$ will stay low. Because they are latching type comparators, they hold high or low until they are downloaded to a system of digital logic gates that convert the parallel comparator word into a binary coded word.

The illustration shown in Fig. 3.11 is deceptively simple because an 8-bit parallel ADC contains $2^8 - 1$ = 255 latching comparators and resistances and about 1,000 logic gates to convert the output to binary code. Also, the accuracy is improved by placing a sample-and-hold amplifier before the ADC so that the input voltage does not change over the period required to operate the comparators.

Parallel comparators have improved in performance at reduced cost in the past decade with the availability of very-large-scale integrated circuits that accommodate all of the components on a single chip of silicon. Flash type ADCs are employed on very-high-speed digital systems such as digital oscilloscopes and wave form recorders. Conversions in these applications are made at 4 to 8 GS/s, which give sampling times of 0.125 to 0.25 ns.

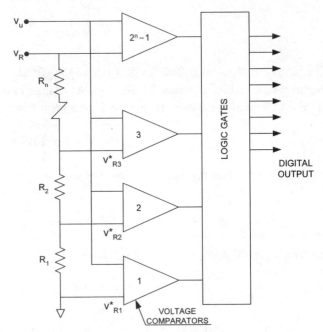

Fig. 3.11 Schematic diagram for a flash analog-to-digital converter.

3.7 DIGITAL VOLTMETERS

Digital voltmeters (DVM) offer many advantages over analog-type meters, such as speed in reading, increased accuracy, better resolution and the capability of automatic operation. Digital voltmeters display the measurement with easy to read numerals, as shown in Fig. 3.12, rather than a pointer deflection on a continuous scale as with analog meters. Digital multimeters measure current, resistance and ac and dc voltages. Some DVMs may also be used with a multiplexer and a printer or a hard drive to provide a simple but reliable automatic data-logging system.

Fig. 3.12 A 5-½ digital multimeter. Courtesy of Keithley Instruments, Inc.

The number of full digits in the display determines the range of a DVM. For example, a four-digit DVM can record a count to 9999. If the full scale of the DVM is set at 1 V, the count of 9999 provided by the four digits would register a reading of 0.9999 V. Some DVMs are equipped with partial digits to extend the range. The partial digit can only display a limited range of numbers. While zero and one are common for the 1/2 or most significant digit, some newer models are capable of displaying partial digits of 2, 3 or 4. The partial digit extends the resolution of the DVM. For example, consider use of a four-digit DVM for measuring 10.123 V. Because only four digits are available, the meter set on the 10-V scale would read 10.12 V. The last digit (3) would be truncated and lost. If a 4-½ digit DVM is used for the same measurement, the extra partial digit permits 100% over-ranging and a maximum count of 19999. The display of the 4-½ digit meter would show 5 numbers (10.123).

Over-ranging may be expressed as a percentage of full scale. For instance, a four-digit DVM with 100% over-range displays a maximum reading of 19999. Similarly, with a 200% over-range, the maximum display is 29999. In some instances, the over-range capability of the DVM is expressed in terms of the specified range. The four-digit DVM with 100% over-range, which has a maximum display of 19999, could be specified with full-scale ranges of 2, 20, 200 V, etc. and an over-range specification is not necessary.

Resolution of a DVM is determined by the maximum count that is displayed. For example, a 4-digit DVM with a maximum count of 10,000 has a resolution of 1 part in 10,000 or 100 parts per million (ppm). The sensitivity of a DVM is the smallest increment of voltage that can be detected and is determined by multiplying the lowest full-scale range by the resolution. Therefore, a four-digit DVM with a 100-mV lowest full-scale range has a sensitivity of $(1/10,000) \times 100$ mV = 0.01 mV = 10 µV.

Accuracy of a DVM is usually expressed as ± x percent of the reading ± N digits. A typical value for a 5-½ digit instrument operating on a 2 V range is x = 0.0011% and N = ± 2. Accuracy will depend strongly on calibration and instrument stability. A modern DVM utilizes electronic calibration where calibration constants are stored in non-volatile memory and calibration is accomplished without internal adjustments. Improved stability, which reduces fluctuations in the last digit, is the key to enhanced accuracy. Hermetically sealed resistance networks in the circuits have greatly improved stability in more modern designs.

The input to the multimeter may be an ac voltage, a dc voltage, a current or a resistance; however, in all cases, the input is immediately converted to a dc voltage. The signal is then amplified with variable-gain amplifiers. Their gain is automatically adjusted by control logic so that the voltage applied to the analog to digital converter (ADC) is within specifications avoiding an overload condition.

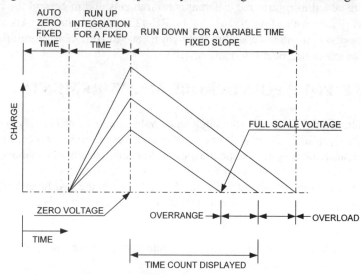

Fig. 3.13 Dual slope integration technique used in most DVMs.

The ADC changes the dc voltage input to a proportional clock count by using the dual-slope integration technique illustrated in Fig. 3.13. There are three different operations in the dual-slope integration technique for A/D conversion. First, during auto zero, the potential at the integrator output is zeroed for a fixed time, say 100 ms. Second, the dc input is integrated with respect to time for a fixed period, say 100 ms. The output of the integrator is a linear ramp with respect to time as shown in Fig. 3.13. At the end of the run-up, the dc input voltage is disconnected from the integrator and the third operation, run-down, is initiated. Run-down time may vary from zero to, say 200 ms, and will depend on the charge developed on the integrating capacitor during run-up. Since the discharge rate is fixed during run-down, the larger the charge on the integrating capacitor, the longer the discharge time. Because both run-up and run-down produce slopes on the voltage-time trace, this conversion method from voltage to time is called dual-slope integration. A counter is started at the beginning of a run-down and operates until the output voltage from the integrator crosses zero. The accumulated time is proportional to the dc voltage applied to the integrator. This time count is then displayed as the voltage. Polarity, range and function information that are provided by the controller are also displayed.

The characteristics of a digital voltmeter may be altered by changing the number of digits, the time interval for integrator run up and the frequency of the clock. A professional hand held multimeter with 3-½ digits and a maximum count of 1999 is designed with five different ranges: ± 200.0 mV, ± 2.000 V, ± 20.00 V, ± 200.0 V and ± 1500 V. The highest sensitivity is 100 μV on the 200-mV range. Accuracy is ± 0.5% of the reading plus one digit. The clock frequency is 200 kHz and the integration time is 100 ms. The reading rate is usually about 2.5 readings per second, depending on the input.

System DVMs are more complex than the hand held or small bench type DVMs because the former are provided with a microprocessor and local memory to facilitate interfacing with other components of an automated data-processing system. A typical data processing system incorporating a system type DVM includes a scanner or multiplexer for switching input voltages into the DVM for analog to digital conversion and a bus which is compatible with a personal computer (PC). The memory in the PC (RAM or disk) is used to store the data that is acquired. Reduction, manipulation and analysis of the data are performed according to programmed instructions and results are often presented in easily understood graphical form on a PC monitor or the output from a printer.

System multimeters are higher performance devices than bench or hand held multimeters. The number of digits is usually increased to 6-½ or 8-½, which increases the count and improves the resolution to 1 or 0.01 ppm, respectively. Clock frequencies are increased and advanced conversion techniques[3] are employed to give a reading rate of 100,000+ readings per second. Microprocessors are added to control the different measurements and to control the interface. System multimeters are available with either IEEE-488 or RS-422 bus structures. Also, the internal microprocessor has modest computing capability that permits one to add, subtract, multiply and divide as well as store and compare numerical information.

3.8 FOUR POINT PROBE MEASUREMENTS

The four-point probe technique can implemented to effectively measure the resistance of materials demonstrating either very low resistance or very high resistance. For such measurements, a two-point measurement system is not sufficient and requires a more elaborate method to achieve an accurate measurement. Typically, a four point probe measurement consists of sourcing current to the two outer probes while measuring the voltage drop between the two inner probes. In general, the use of the four probes eliminates measurement errors due to the probe resistance, the spreading resistance under each

---

[3] The advanced conversion techniques alleviate the constraint that the integration time $t^* \geq 16.17$ ms for integrating voltmeters.

probe, and the contact resistance present between each probe and surface. Fig. 3.14 (a), (b) and (c) represents a two-point measurement technique, four-point measurement technique, and an actual four-point probe specimen respectively. There are several advantages for using a four-point measurement rather than a two-point measurement.

(a)

(b)

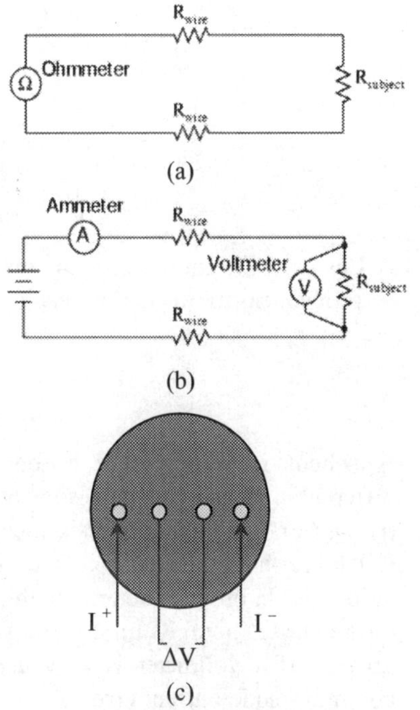

Fig. 3.14 (a) Two-point probe measurement.
     (b) Four-point probe measurement.
     (c) Actual four-point probe specimen

(c)

For measuring the resistance of materials with very low resistance, such as milli- or micro-ohm range, the two-point method is not sufficient due to the presence of the lead wire resistance. This lead wire resistance can be substantial when very long wires are present and/or the components to be measured have very low resistance. In such a case, the use of both an ammeter and a voltmeter provides the necessary means to effectively measure $R_{subject}$ by the use of Ohms law. Assuming the voltage drop across the subject was measured from a distance, one may postulate that the presence of long resistive wires will introduce a stray resistance back into the measuring circuit. However, since the voltmeter's wires carry very small currents, the resulting voltmeter indication contains negligible error due to the presence of the wires connected from the voltmeter to the specimen during four-point measurements.

Obtaining an accurate electrical measurement of materials having very high resistance is more complex and requires instrumentation with special capabilities and proper measurement techniques. These additional requirements include sourcing current with high output impedance, the ability to measure differential voltages, and providing perfect isolation between the voltmeter and current source to earth ground.

The output impedance of the current source should be significantly greater than the impedance of the material being tested to ensure stable current sourcing. If the output impedance is too low, the current source does not have the capacity to output the necessary current through the material. It should also be noted that a contact resistance at each probe is present which could be substantial depending on the material being measured and should be accounted for when determining if the output impedance of the current source is sufficient.

To measure the voltage drop between the two inner probes, a multi-meter or measuring device must have an input impedance much greater than the impedance of the material being measured. All digital multi-meters, along with some analog meters, have fixed input impedance (typically 1 or 10 $M\Omega$) which creates a measurement limitation. High-end multi-meters can provide an input impedance >10 $G\Omega$ making measurements of higher resistance materials possible.

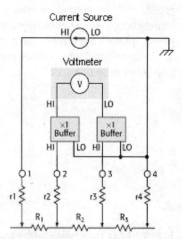

Fig. 3.15 Circuit representing making differential four-point probe measurement (Courtesy of Keithley Instruments, Inc)

A schematic representing a four-point collinear probe measurement setup capable of making differential measurements is shown in Fig. 3.15. The circuit includes a contact resistance at each probe (r_1, r_2, r_3, r_4), the material resistance between each set of probes (R_1, R_2, R_3), the finite resistance from LO to earth ground of both the current source and the voltmeter, and the input resistance of the voltmeter. In order to determine the material resistance R_2, the current must flow from the HI terminal of the current source, through the sample and then to the LO terminal of the current source and earth ground. If a voltmeter is only used to measure the voltage drop across the two inner probes, a common-mode current error occurs as a result of the imperfect isolation between the LO terminals of the voltmeter and current source to earth ground. The current will flow from the LO terminal of the current source through the sample and to the voltmeter's LO terminal, then back to ground. The resulting voltage drop across r_3 will cause erroneous results when the voltmeter measures the voltage drop between the probes 2 and 3. As the sample resistance increases, the errors due to the common-mode current become more significant. Hence, it becomes increasingly necessary to obtain a differential voltage measurement. To eliminate this common-mode problem, unity-gain buffers with very high input impedance or electrometers may be implemented so that little common-mode current will flow through r_3, and the value of R_2 can be calculated easily.

Further details on proper grounding procedures as well as additional information regarding the measurement of low and high resistance materials can be found in [10].

3.9 DATA-LOGGING SYSTEMS

A data-logging system consists of a scanner or multiplexer, a suitable digital voltmeter and a computer to store and analyze the data recorded. Such a system can be employed to record the output from a large number of transducers (hundreds) at a sampling rate, which depends on the capability of the DVM and the resolution required. Conversion rates for a modern DVM, which utilizes a multi-slope analog-to-digital converter, is shown in Table 3.4.

Because the DVMs are relatively fast, a system controller is needed to direct the scanner to each new channel, to control the integration time for the DVM and to transfer the output from the DVM to the memory in a computer. The system controller is a microprocessor that uses two separate busses; one for data transfer and the other for memory addressing as illustrated in Fig. 3.16. The firmware, which directs the operation of the controller, is stored in read-only memories (ROMs) and a random-access memory (RAM). The system operating programs are permanently stored in the ROMs, which are programmed during manufacture of the instrument. The input by the operator, individual channel parameters and other program routines is entered through a keyboard and stored in RAM.

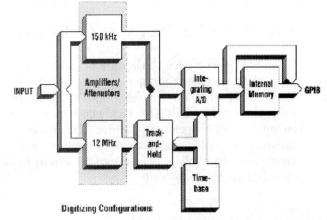

Fig. 3.16 Buss and component configuration for a DVM used in a multi-channel data logging system.

Table 3.4
Characteristics of a System Type DVM
Agilent Model 3458A

Number of Digits	Readings per second	Resolution (ppm)
4 – ½	1×10^5	33.3
5 – ½	5×10^4	3.33
6 – ½	6×10^3	0.333
7 – ½	60	0.033
8 – ½	6	0.003

*The number of digits, ranging from 4-½ to 8-½, is selectable with the Model 3458A.

The scanner contains a bank of switches (usually three poles) that serve to switch two leads and the shield from the input cable to the integrating digital voltmeter. In most cases, high-speed solid-state switching devices are employed. The system controller directs the scanner operation. The modes of operation available include single-channel recording, single scan of all channels, continuous scan and periodic scan. In the single-channel mode, a preselected channel is continuously monitored at the reading rate of the system. In this mode, the scanner makes a single sequential sweep through a preselected group of channels. The continuous-scan mode is identical to the single-scan mode, except that the system automatically resets and recycles on completion of the previous scan. The periodic scan is simply a single scan that is initiated at preselected time intervals such as 1, 5, 15, 30 or 60 min. The scanner also provides a signal for the visual display of the channel number and a code signal to the controller to identify the transducer being monitored.

The transducer signal is switched through the scanner[4] to a high-quality integrating digital voltmeter that serves as the ADC. The speed of operation depends primarily on the capabilities of the DVM and the resolution required. As is evident in Table 3.4, high reading rates are possible even with a 5-½ digit ADC that provides a resolution of 3.33 PPM.

The output from a data logger is displayed with a digital panel meter that indicates the voltage output, its polarity and the channel number. The output of most data logging systems is recorded on either local disk memories associated with a PC or workstation or a remote disk memory associated with a central computing center. Some of the more expensive system DVMs contain on board

---

[4] In some systems the DVM is incorporated in the scanner to provide an integrated system.

memory to facilitate data storage. One of the principal advantages of a data-logging system is the capability for processing the data in essentially real time with an on-line computer.

3.10 PC BASED DATA-ACQUISITION SYSTEMS

Relatively low cost circuit boards are available that contain many of the elements found in higher cost, more elaborate data-acquisition systems. Some data-acquisition boards (DAQs), such as the one shown in Fig. 3.17, are designed to interface with one or more sensors such as strain gages, resistance temperature detectors (RTDs), thermocouples, thermistors, etc. The sensor support contained on these circuit cards includes sensor excitation, linearization, cold reference compensation and conversion of the voltage output from the sensors to an output in engineering units.

Fig. 3.17 Data acquisition system on a pluggable circuit card.
Courtesy of National Instruments

The evolution from multiple component data acquisition systems to PC based data acquisition systems has occurred because of increased speed and reliability of PCs, their higher capacity hard drives and markedly reduced cost. The integration of data acquisition with the PC also affords the opportunity to process and analyze the data more effectively in less time and with less effort. Significant software developments, to enable the control of the signals on the circuit card and to interface with the PC, have also reduced the difficulty in employing these systems.

DAQs typically contain three sections. The first section acquires the analog signals, performs the signal conditioning for the compatible sensors, multiplexes to the appropriate sensor and then amplifies the signal with a programmable gain. The multiplexing (scanning) is performed at very high speed by employing solid state switching devices. The amplifiers are high quality with extremely rapid settling times (usually less than 5 µs) that are consistent with the high sampling rates at which the systems operate.

The second section on the DAQ performs A/D conversion. A typical card utilizes[5] either a 12-bit or 16-bit ADC with sampling rates varying from 100 kS/s to 10 MS/s. The digital output from the ADC is transferred to a custom designed register that serves an interface to the buss contained in the host PC. The output from this register is transferred to the PC's buss upon receiving a command from the master controller.

The third section incorporates a microcomputer with on-board memory that is used in processing data by performing tasks such as linearization, reference junction compensation and engineering unit conversion. The microprocessor also provides the logic to scan the sensors, adjust the amplifier gain and transfer the data to the standard bus registers. The standard bus interface incorporates drivers and receivers to facilitate communication with the PC host computer. This section also contains a number of high-resolution counters that are used to control the timing of the signal acquisition and the subsequent processing of the signal through the scanners, amplifier and

---

[5] See for example the numerous DAQs offered by National Instruments on their website www.ni.com.

DAC. Finally, both analog and digital trigger circuits are contained in the controller to enable the operator to initiate and terminate the data acquisition process.

An advantage of utilizing DAQs for measurements is their capability to minimize error due to temperature changes. All recording instruments tend to drift with changes in temperature and this drift produces error. High quality DAQs are designed with premium components that are relatively stable over a wide range of temperature. They also incorporate compensating components that tend to cancel temperature induced voltage and calibration changes. Well-designed DAQs have proper placed shielding and appropriately placed ground planes in the circuit card to minimize electrical noise generation in the data acquisition system. High quality DAQs are equipped with the highest-grade ADCs. These ADCs incorporate circuits that enable self-calibration thus eliminating linear errors.

The card is programmed from the PC host computer and the digitized data is transferred from the card to the memory of the PC using the standard bus in the host computer. Note that an external bus structure is not required for data transmission when the entire data-acquisition system is contained within the PC. At this point all further processing and preparation of graphics is performed on the host computer using commercially available software.

The software employed in acquiring and analyzing data is equally important in the design of an effective measurement system. Typically data acquisition software includes drivers and application codes. Drivers are a set of commands unique to the sensors or actuators involved in the measurement or in the control of a process. The interface to the sensors or actuators is compatible with the driver commands. The software also enables the operator to display and analyze the data in essentially real time. A popular software program used in measurements and process control is LabVIEW (Laboratory Virtual Instrument Engineering Workbench) which is described later in Chapter 14.

3.11 SYSTEMS FOR MEASURING RAPIDLY VARYING SIGNALS

Measuring transient phenomena, where the signal from the transducer is a rapid changing function of time, is the most difficult and most expensive measurement involved in experimental work. Frequency response or bandwidth is the dominant characteristic required of the recording instrument in dynamic measurements and usually accuracy and economy are sacrificed in order to improve the response capabilities. Two different recorders are used in modern instrument systems to record transient voltages: digital acquisition systems (DAQs), described in previous sections and the oscilloscope.

The DAQ's sampling rate controls the integrity of the record of the transient signal as will be described later in Section 3.11 when aliasing is discussed. Sampling rates for DAQs vary from about 100 kS/s to 10 MS/s, which enable them to be used to capture many of the transient signals associated with mechanical phenomena.

Oscilloscopes operate with a higher frequency response (bandwidth) than DAQs because they use higher performance electronic components. There are several different types of oscilloscopes including: analog, digital storage (DSO), and digital sampling[6]. Digital oscilloscopes can display any transient signal within its range of operation with clarity and stability. As with DAQs, the bandwidth of the digital oscilloscope is limited by its sampling rate, although these sampling rates are usually one or two orders of magnitude higher[7] than those found in a typical DAQ.

---

[6] Digital sampling oscilloscopes that are used to capture extremely high frequency repetitive signal will not be described in this textbook. The bandwidth of a typical sampling oscilloscope is about 50 GHz, which is well above the frequency of interest to most engineers making mechanical measurements.

[7] LeCroy currently offers an oscilloscope with a 45GHz band-width and a sampling rate of 120 GS/s.

3.11.1 Digital Storage Oscilloscopes

A digital storage oscilloscope (DSO) is identical to an analog oscilloscope except for:

1. The manipulation of the input signal prior to display on a cathode-ray tube.
2. The permanent-storage capabilities of the instrument.
3. The signal-processing capabilities of its microprocessor.

A block diagram showing the essential elements in a DSO is presented in Fig. 3.18. It is clear from this figure that the input signal is amplified and then converted to digital form in an ADC. A clock in the controller determines the sampling rate for the ADC. Next in this serial arrangement is a DEMUX that divides the data stream for subsequent processing. The digital values, called sample points are stored in an acquisition memory. Usually many data points represent a waveform. The number of data points used to establish a waveform is called the record length. A trigger system similar to that found in an analog oscilloscope initiates the sampling process.

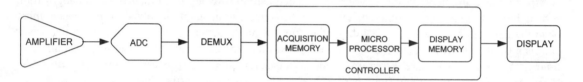

Fig. 3.18 Serial processing employed in a digital storage oscilloscope.

The signal path in a DSO passes through a microprocessor that processes the digital data, coordinates display activities and manages the front panel controls. The signal then is stored in the display memory before being displayed. From the display memory the digital signal is transferred to a DAC, where it is reconverted to an analog voltage for display on the CRT. A photograph of a modern digital oscilloscope is shown in Fig. 3.19.

Because the data are stored, in addition to being displayed, operation of the digital oscilloscope differs from operation of an analog oscilloscope. The display on the CRT of the digital oscilloscope is a series of points produced by the electron beam at locations controlled by the data in storage. The data collected during the sweep of the oscilloscope is in memory and can be recalled and analyzed either within the digital oscilloscope or by downloading to a host computer.

Several features establish the capabilities of a digital storage oscilloscope. First, the sampling rate and the bandwidth are important in recording transient signals. The sampling rate also determines the time interval between data points. For example, a digital oscilloscope with a 1.0 GS/s rate can sample, hold, convert and store a data point in 1.0 ns.

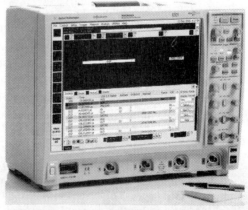

Fig. 3.19 A modern digital oscilloscope
    Courtesy of Agilent Technologies.

Second, the size of the memory is important because its size controls the record length that can be recorded. The record length is the number of data points (samples) that can be stored in the DSO's memory. Because of memory limitations, an oscilloscope can store only a specified number of samples; consequently, the waveform duration t_d is inversely proportional to the oscilloscope's sampling rate as given below:

$$t_d = RL/SR \qquad\qquad (3.27)$$

where RL is the record length and SR is the sampling rate.

The number of data points needed to adequately analyze a waveform depends on the application. If the waveform is a stable sinusoidal, a hundred data points are usually sufficient. However, if the analysis pertains to a complex data stream, several thousand data points may be required to adequately record the event. The waveform duration t_d that can be covered with a DSO is dependent on the choice of sampling rates and the duration can vary widely (500,000/1 is common).

A final feature of importance is whether the A/D conversion method is designed to measure single-shot events or repetitive signals. Repetitive signals are easier to measure as sampling can be repeated on the second and subsequent waveforms to give instruments with apparent sampling rates that are an order of magnitude higher than the real sampling rates. The delayed sequential sampling technique that is used to increase the number of data points (samples) that define a repetitive waveform is illustrated in Fig. 3.20. For pulse measurements, the signal occurs once and only once and repetitive measurements cannot be used to increase the sampling rate.

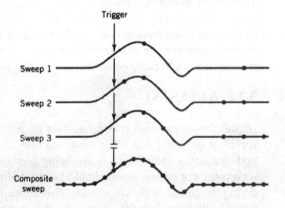

Figure 3.20 By varying the time between the trigger and the ADC, different data points can be recorder on each repetition (sweep).

In operation, A/D conversion takes place continuously at a prescribed sampling rate with the words going to storage until the data acquisition memory (DAM) is full. The address for each data word stored in the DAM is proportional to the time when the data were taken. After a sweep, when the DAM is full, the data is discarded, unless a trigger signal is received during the sweep, and the conversion process continues. If a trigger signal occurs during the sweep, the data in the DAM is transferred to the display memory. This data is then processed and displayed as a voltage-time trace on the CRT.

The fact that the input signal has been stored offers many advantages for data display and data processing. The data are displayed on the CRT in a repetitive manner so that traces from even one-shot transient events appear stationary. The trace can also be manipulated by expanding either the horizontal or vertical scales or both. This expansion feature permits a small region of the record to be enlarged and examined in detail. Readout of the data from the trace is also much easier and more accurate with digital oscilloscopes. A pair of marker lines called cursors (one vertical and the other horizontal) can be positioned anywhere on the screen. An operator positions the vertical line on the trace at a time when a reading of the voltage is required. The horizontal marker (or cross hair) automatically positions itself on the trace. The coordinates of the marker's intersection with the trace, are displayed on the monitor.

Modern digital oscilloscopes are usually equipped with a microprocessor that provides different on-board signal analysis features that often include:

1. Pulse characterization—rise time, fall time, base line and top line width, overshoot, period, frequency, rms, mean, standard deviation, duty cycle, etc.
2. Frequency analysis—power, phase and magnitude spectrum.
3. Spectrum analysis—100 to 50,000 point fast Fourier transforms (FFT).
4. Math package—add, subtract, multiply, integrate and differentiate.
5. Smoothing —1, 3, 5, 7 or 9 point averaging.
6. Counter—average frequency and event crossings.
7. Display Control—x zoom, x position, y gain, and y offset.
8. Plotting Display in either dots or vectors.
9. Mass storage to hard disk, CDs or nonvolatile memory.

If additional processing is required, the data can be downloaded to a host computer for final data analysis.

Early models of DSOs were introduced in 1972. Initially, their performance was limited due to the low-bandwidth capability; however, marked improvements in ADCs, microprocessors and high-speed, high-capacity memory chips have greatly enhanced speed of conversion, improved resolution and expanded the amount of data, which can be stored. With these improvements, the DSO is superior in every respect to an analog oscilloscope. Digital methods of recording have in most cases replaced analog methods because costs are competitive and performance is superior.

3.12 ALIASING

Digital data-acquisition systems contain an ADC that converts an analog signal to a digital signal at a specified sampling rate. This sampling rate is extremely important in dynamic measurements where high-frequency analog signals are being processed. For a well-defined representation of a dynamic waveform, the analog signal should be determined with digital measurements taken 10 or more times during the period of the waveform. This concept of using 10 measurements (samples) to define a sine wave is illustrated in Fig. 3.21. As the number of measurements decreases, the definition of the waveform and its characteristics degrade and the digital representation can be misleading. When the sampling frequency f_s is:

$$f_s \leq 2f \tag{3.28}$$

the waveform with frequency f takes on a false identity.

Nyquist sampling theory (beyond the scope of this textbook) is the basis for Eq. (3.28). The minimum sampling frequency is $f_s = 2f^*$ and the maximum conversion time is $T_s^* = 1/(2f^*)$ where f^* is called the Nyquist frequency and T_s^* is the Nyquist interval. If the frequency of the analog signal $f \geq f_s/2$, the sampling process is inadequate and the output from the ADC gives a false low-frequency waveform, called an alias, which differs from the true analog signal. To illustrate aliasing, consider a sinusoidal analog signal with a frequency f_1 given by:

$$V_1(t) = \cos(2\pi f_1 t) \tag{3.29}$$

The times at which the signal is sampled is given by:

$$t = nT_s = n/f_s \qquad n = 0, 1, 2, \ldots \qquad (3.30)$$

if the ADC has a sampling frequency f_s.

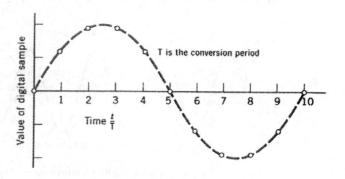

Fig. 3.21 Digital representation of a sinusoidal waveform that illustrates the definition achieved with ten sampling points.

Substituting Eq. (3.30) into Eq. (3.29) gives the sampled voltages as:

$$V_1(nT_s) = \cos\left(\frac{2\pi n f_1}{f_s}\right) \qquad (3.31)$$

Next, consider a second sinusoidal signal with a frequency f_2 which is greater than a cutoff frequency f_c so that:

$$f_2 = 2mf_c \pm f_1 \qquad m = 1, 2, \ldots \qquad (3.32)$$

If the ADC used with both signals is the same, then $V_2(nT_s)$ is obtained by interchanging f_2 for f_1 in Eq. (3.29) to give:

$$V_2(nT_s) = \cos\left(\frac{2\pi n(2mf_c \pm f_1)}{f_s}\right) \qquad (3.33)$$

Let the cutoff frequency be given by:

$$f_c = f_s/2 \qquad (3.34)$$

as indicated by sampling theory. Substituting Eq. (3.34) into Eq. (3.33) gives:

$$V_2(nT_s) = \cos\left(2\pi n m \pm \frac{2\pi n f_1}{f_s}\right) = \cos\left(\frac{2\pi n f_1}{f_s}\right) \qquad (3.35)$$

Comparing Eqs. (3.35) and (3.31) shows that V_1 and V_2 are identical at each sampling time (nT_s) and it is impossible to distinguish the signal amplitudes between the two frequencies f_1 and f_2. For example, if $f_c = 200$ Hz, then $f_s = 400$ Hz and an alias signal with a frequency $f_1 = 50$ Hz occurs whenever the input signal has frequencies f_2 of 350, 450, 750, 850, etc. The relation showing the alias frequency is obtained by substituting Eq. (3.34) into Eq. (3.32) to obtain:

$$\pm f_1 = f_2 - mf_s \qquad \text{if} \qquad f_2 \geq f_s/2 \qquad m = 1, 2, \ldots \qquad (3.36)$$

where f_1 is the frequency of the alias signal and f_2 is the frequency of the input signal.

The results of Eq. (3.36) are illustrated in Fig. 3.22 for the example when $f_s = (3/2)f_2$. Note that the recorded digital signal exhibits the alias frequency $f_1 = f_2/2$.

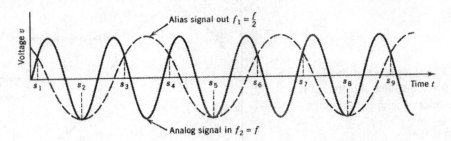

Fig. 3.22 Effect of aliasing when a sinusoid is sampled at a frequency $f_s = (3/2) f_2$.

Aliasing can be avoided if the sampling frequency exceeds twice the maximum frequency in the analog signal.

$$f_s = 2f_c > 2f_2 \tag{3.37}$$

This relation is essentially the same as Eq. (3.34), which defines the cutoff frequency in terms of the sampling frequency. If the maximum frequency in the analog signal does not exceed the cutoff frequency, the identity of Eqs. (3.31) and (3.35) cannot be established and aliasing will not occur.

3.12.1 Anti-aliasing Filters

Commercial instruments avoid the aliasing problem by using anti-aliasing analog filters to reduce the high frequency components in the analog signals. These filters have a frequency response function that exhibits a relatively sharp signal attenuation beginning at $f = 0.4\ f_s$, as shown in Fig. 3.23. The analog signal is attenuated 40 dB at the Nyquist frequency $f_s^* = f_s/2$. Because 40 dB is equivalent to a signal transmission of only 1%, the filter reduces the signal component that produces aliasing to an insignificant amount.

Unfortunately, anti-aliasing filters severely distort transient signals with high-frequency components. The possibility of distortion on the one hand and the need to prevent aliasing of the signal on the other implies that care must be exercised when selecting the sampling rate of the ADC for a specific high frequency measurement.

Fig. 3.23 Frequency response
function for an ideal analog anti-
aliasing filter for an ADC with a
sampling rate of f_s.

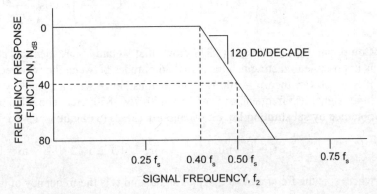

3.13 SUMMARY

A voltage recording instrument, the final component in a measuring system, is used to convert a voltage representing the unknown quantity Q_1 into a display for visual readout or into a digital code that is suitable for automatic data processing. The instruments, in use today, range from simple digital multimeters to complex digital oscilloscopes. While all five of the general characteristics of a recording instrument (input impedance, sensitivity, range, zero drift, and frequency response) are important, the single characteristic that often dominates selection of a recorder is frequency response.

Static measurements, where frequency response is not important and the unknown is represented by a single number that is independent of time, can be made quickly and accurately with relatively inexpensive multimeters. When the event being studied begins to vary with time, the recording instrument necessary for the measurement becomes more complex, less accurate and more expensive. The major difficulty experienced in measuring unknown parameters associated with time-dependent phenomena is the need to record and display the data with respect to time without distorting the signal.

Digital systems that employ analog to digital converters (ADCs) or digital to analog converters (DACs) are widely used in instrument systems for engineering analysis and for process control. The principal advantage of digital systems is the ability to store data and to process that data by using low cost commercially available storage devices, computers, controllers and effective application software.

Analog to digital conversion is the key element in systems utilized for data acquisition and for digital instruments such as digital voltmeters, data acquisition systems and digital oscilloscopes. Features such as sampling rate, resolution, accuracy and cost are used to compare ADCs. For high resolution and low cost, ADCs usually employ the integration method for conversion; however, the sampling rate is relatively low. For very high sampling rates, the flash method of conversion is used with more limited resolution and significantly higher cost. The method of successive approximation is used in ADCs with moderate sampling rates, good resolution and intermediate cost.

Digital to analog conversion is also employed in process control. After digital processing of data according to programmed instructions, the system automatically determines if the process must be modified to bring it under control. For example, assume the process being controlled is a curing oven and the temperature is to be increased. The digital signal for a specified temperature increase is converted to an analog signal using a DAC. This signal is then amplified and used to activate a temperature controller that increases the current flowing through its heating elements.

Finally, developments in digital devices are continuing at a rapid rate as the technology used in manufacturing integrated circuits permits further reductions in device size. Continued improvements will lead to higher sampling rates, more bits, higher resolution and lower costs for digital hardware. Software written for measurement and control is currently improving each year, particularly with PC-based data-acquisition systems.

REFERENCES

1. Floyd, Thomas L.: <u>Digital Fundamentals</u>, 8th ed., Prentice-Hall, Englewood Cliffs, NJ, 2003.
2. Tocci, L. and F. Ambrosio: <u>Microprocessors and Microcomputers: Hardware and Software</u>, 6th Ed, Prentice-Hall, Englewood Cliffs, NJ, 2003.
3. Hoeschele, D. F.: <u>Analog-to-Digital/Digital-to-Analog Conversion Techniques</u>, 2nd Ed., Wiley, New York, NY, 1994.

4. Kaplan, D. M. and C. G. White: Hands-On Electronics, Cambridge University Press, New York, 2003.
5. Dally, J. W., Riley W. F. and K. G. McConnell: Instrumentation for Engineering Measurements, Wiley, New York, 1993.
6. Maini, A. K., Digital Electronics: Principles, Devices and Applications, John Wiley, New York, 2007.
7. Figliola, R. S. and D. E. Beasley, Theory and Design for Mechanical Measurements, 5th Ed., Wiley, New York, 2010.
8. Bouwens, A., Digital Instrumentation, McGraw-Hill Education, New York, 2004.
9. Witte, R. A., Electronic Test Instruments: Analog and Digital Measurements, Prentice Hall, Englewood Cliffs, NJ, 2002.
10. Keithley Instruments, Inc. Measuring the Resistivity and Determining the Conductivity Type of Semiconductor Materials Using a Four-point Collinear Probe and the Model 6221 DC and AC Current Source. Ser. 2615, 2005.

EXERCISES

3.1 List the general characteristics of a recording instrument.

3.2 Prepare a graph showing power loss P through a voltmeter as a function of the voltage V. Let V range from 0 to 100 volts. Let the input impedance Z_m equal:
 (a) $10^3 \, \Omega$ (b) $10^4 \, \Omega$ (c) $10^5 \, \Omega$ (d) $10^6 \, \Omega$ (e) $10^7 \, \Omega$

3.3 The input impedance of a meter is modeled by a resistance $R_m = 10^6 \, \Omega$ in parallel with a capacitance $C = 100$ pF. Prepare a graph showing the magnitude of the impedance Z_m as a function of ωRC.

3.4 Determine the error involved in using the meter described in Exercise 3.3 to measure an ac voltage of 5 V if the output impedance of the source is $R_s = 10 \, \Omega$ and if ω is:
 (a) 10^2 rad/s (b) 10^4 rad/s (c) 10^6 rad/s

3.5 What limit must be placed on the resistance ratio R_s/R_m if the acceptable voltmeter load error is:
 (a) 0.5% (b) 1% (c) 2% (d) 5%

3.6 Determine the reciprocal sensitivity S_R and the input voltage V_i if the deflection exhibited by a recording instrument and its sensitivity is specified as:

	d (div)	S (div/V)	S_R (V/div)	V_i (V)
(a)	2.5	0.2		
(b)	6.1	0.5		
(c)	3.7	2.0		
(d)	7.6	0.1		

3.7 The instrument described in Exercise 3.6 has eight divisions in the vertical direction on the face of its display. For the sensitivities given in Exercise 3.6, determine its ranges. Is it possible to increase both sensitivity and range simultaneously?

3.8 Describe in your own words the relationship between sensitivity and range of an instrument.

3.9 An amplifier, which is being used in an instrumentation system to measure a voltage of 12 mV over a period of 15 days, exhibits a drift of 0.05 mV/h. Determine the error that may result from zero drift if the instrument is not re-zeroed.

3.10 Specifications for a recorder indicate that its output is down 1.5 dB at 1.0 kHz. Determine the error if the recorder is used to measure a signal with a frequency of 1.0 kHz.

3.11 Tests with a recorder at frequencies of 10, 20, 40, 60, 80 and 100 Hz provided the following output-to-input ratios C_0/C_i : 1.01, 1.03, 1.05, 1.00, 0.93 and 0.80. Determine the amplitude ratio in terms of decibels at each frequency.

3.12 Find the amplitude ratio A_0/A_i for a recorder if N_{dB} is given by:
(a) – 5.0 (b) +2.50 (c) –0.25 (d) + 0.70

3.13 What limits on N_{dB} must be maintained to reduce recorder error to less than:
(a) 5% (b) 2.0% (c) 1.0% (d) 0.50%

3.14 Prepare a block diagram showing a combined analog-digital instrumentation system to measure pressure for an application involving:
(a) engineering analysis (b) process control

3.15 Prepare a table showing the maximum count C as a function of the number of bits n. Let n equal from 1 to 32.

3.16 Add a column showing the resolution R to the table in Exercise 3.15.

3.17 Add a column showing the resolution error in percent to the table in Exercise 3.15.

3.18 What is the resolution error that can be expected, if you select an instrument with 8-bit logic circuits?

3.19 Write an engineering brief describing an A/D converter (ADC).

3.20 Write an engineering brief describing a D/A converter (DAC).

3.21 Describe the difference between resolution error and quantizing error. Which is the most important?

3.22 Prepare a graph showing the standard deviation of a number of measurements of V/FSV as n increases from 6 to 16.

3.23 Prepare a graph showing C versus V/FSV that demonstrates offset error.
(a) for a D/A converter (b) for an A/D converter.

3.24 Prepare a graph showing C versus V/FSV that demonstrates scale factor error.
(a) for a D/A converter (b) for an A/D converter.

3.25 Prepare a graph showing C versus V/FSV that demonstrates linearity error
(a) for a D/A converter (b) for an A/D converter.

3.26 For the 4-bit DAC shown in Fig. 3.7, determine the output voltage V_0 for the following digital codes.
(a) 1101 (b) 1010 (c) 0110 (d) 0101 (e) 1001 (f) 1110

3.27 Describe in a brief paragraph a register and indicate some of its uses in a digital system.

3.28 What is a strobe signal and how is it used in a D/A converter? Why is it necessary?

3.29 What are the three common systems used in designing A/D converters? List the advantages and disadvantages of each system.

3.30 Prepare an illustration, similar to Fig. 3.9, that demonstrates A to D conversion by the method of successive approximations if the fixed analog input voltage V_u is:
(a) (1/8) FSV (b) (7/16) FSV (c) (3/4) FSV (d) (13/16) FSV.

3.31 Explain why the conversions of Exercise 3.30 were all exact.

3.32 Because A to D conversions requires some time for switching and comparing, how do we avoid errors due to voltage fluctuations during the conversion period?

3.33 Using Fig. 3.9 as a guide, describe the operation of a successive approximation A/D converter. Indicate the purpose of each block element and each input or output signal.

3.34 Begin with Eq. (3.20) and verify Eq. (3.22).

3.35 Using Fig. 3.10 as a guide, describe the operation of a dual slope integrating A/D converter. Indicate the purpose of each block element, component and each input or output signal.

3.36 Verify Eq. (3.26) beginning with Eq. (3.23).

3.37 For a 12-bit unipolar dual slope integrating A/D converter capable of 10 S/s, determine the frequency limit.

3.38 If the A/D converter of Exercise 3.37 were bipolar determine the frequency limit.

3.39 Determine the slew rate of the A/D converter in Exercise 3.37 if the FSV is:
        (a) 1 V   (b) 2 V   (c) 5 V   (d) 10 V

3.40 Using Fig. 3.11 as a guide, describe the operation of a flash type A/D converter.

3.41 Describe instruments that employ the flash type A/D converter. What is the sampling rate employed in these instruments? How are the sampling rate, bandwidth and sampling times related?

3.42 Why is a plug-in data acquisition board so cost effective?

3.43 A five-digit DVM is capable of what maximum count if it has:
        (a) zero over ranging   (b) 100% over ranging   (c) 200% over ranging

3.44 You are to measure a voltage V_i with a 5-½ digit DVM capable of 100 % over ranging. If the meter is specified with an accuracy of $\pm$ 0.002% and $\pm$ 2 counts, determine the maximum and minimum readings anticipated if v_i is:
        (a) 1.80000 V   (b) 2.50000 V   (c) 9.99996 V

3.45 Determine the error in each of the three cases of Exercise 3.44.

3.46 The purchasing department of a state agency asks you to write a specification so that they can procure bids for a system multimeter. Prepare this specification.

3.47 Explain the use of ROM and RAM memory incorporated into a data logging system.

3.48 Describe the scanner employed in a data logging system.

3.49 Prepare a graph showing observation time in a digital oscilloscope as a function of sampling rate. Use memory size in words as a parameter and let the sampling rate vary from 10 S/s to 10^7 S/s. Let the memory size be 1,000, 2,000, 5,000, 10,000 and 20,000 words.

3.50 In measuring periodic signals, it is possible to increase the apparent sampling rate of a digital oscilloscope. Explain how this is accomplished.

3.51 Explain how data preceding the trigger time can be recovered on a digital oscilloscope.

3.52 Describe the common on-board signal analysis features found on digital oscilloscopes equipped with a microprocessor.

3.53 Verify Eq. (3.37).

3.54 Prepare a graph, similar to the one shown in Fig. 3.22, showing the analog and the alias signals if:

	f_c (Hz)	f_c (Hz)	f_c (Hz)
(a)	200	400	850
(b)	300	600	1,500
(c)	1,000	2,000	5,000
(d)	5,000	10,000	30,000

3.55 What are the characteristics of an anti-aliasing filter?

3.56 List the advantages and disadvantages of using an anti-aliasing filter.

EXERCISE SOLUTIONS

Exercise 3.5

From Eq. (3.4):

$$\varepsilon = \frac{R_s/R_m}{1 + (R_s/R_m)}$$

Solving for R_s/R_m:

(a) For $\varepsilon = 0.5\%$:

$$\frac{R_s}{R_m} = \frac{\varepsilon}{1 - \varepsilon} = \frac{0.005}{1 - 0.005} = 0.00503$$

(b) For $\varepsilon = 1.0\%$:

$$\frac{R_s}{R_m} = \frac{\varepsilon}{1 - \varepsilon} = \frac{0.01}{1 - 0.01} = 0.0101$$

(c) For $\varepsilon = 2.0\%$:

$$\frac{R_s}{R_m} = \frac{\varepsilon}{1 - \varepsilon} = \frac{0.02}{1 - 0.02} = 0.0204$$

(d) For $\varepsilon = 5.0\%$:

$$\frac{R_s}{R_m} = \frac{\varepsilon}{1 - \varepsilon} = \frac{0.05}{1 - 0.05} = 0.0526$$

Exercise 3.12

From Eq. (3.10):

(a) $N_{dB} = 20 \, Log_{10} \, (A_o/A_i) = -5.0$

$Log_{10} \, (A_o/A_i) = \frac{-5.0}{20} = -0.250$

$A_o/A_i = 10^{-0.250} = 0.562$

(c) $N_{dB} = 20 \, Log_{10} \, (A_o/A_i) = -0.25$

$Log_{10} \, (A_o/A_i) = \frac{-0.25}{20} = -0.0125$

$A_o/A_i = 10^{-0.0125} = 0.972$

(b) $N_{dB} = 20 \, Log_{10} \, (A_o/A_i) = 2.5$

$Log_{10} \, (A_o/A_i) = \frac{+2.5}{20} = +0.125$

$A_o/A_i = 10^{+0.125} = 1.334$

(d) $N_{dB} = 20 \, Log_{10} \, (A_o/A_i) = +0.70$

$Log_{10} \, (A_o/A_i) = \frac{+0.70}{20} = +0.035$

$A_o/A_i = 10^{+0.035} = 1.084$

Exercise 3.17

$$\varepsilon_R \, (\%) = 100 \, R$$

N	C	R	ε_R (%)
1	1	1	100
4	15	$6.667(10^{-2})$	6.667
8	255	$3.922(10^{-3})$	$3.922(10^{-1})$
12	4095	$2.442(10^{-4})$	$2.442(10^{-2})$
16	65,535	$1.526(10^{-5})$	$1.526(10^{-3})$
20	1,048,575	$9.537(10^{-7})$	$9.537(10^{-5})$
24	16,777,215	$5.960(10^{-8})$	$5.960(10^{-6})$
28	268,435,455	$3.725(10^{-9})$	$3.725(10^{-7})$
32	4,294,967,295	$2.328(10^{-10})$	$2.328(10^{-8})$

Exercise 3.26

From Eq.

$$v_o = -R_f \sum_{n=1}^{4} (R_f/R_i)$$

For the 4-bit DAC

$$v_o = 10 \left[\frac{5}{10} + \frac{5}{20} + \frac{5}{40} + \frac{5}{80}\right] = 10 \left[\frac{1}{2} + \frac{1}{4} + \frac{1}{8} + \frac{1}{16}\right]$$

(a) $1101 \rightarrow 10 \left[\frac{1}{2} + \frac{1}{4} + 0 + \frac{1}{16}\right] = 8.125$ volts

(b) $1010 \rightarrow 10 \left[\frac{1}{2} + 0 + \frac{1}{8} + 0\right] = 6.250$ volts

(c) $0110 \rightarrow 10 \left[0 + \frac{1}{4} + \frac{1}{8} + 0\right] = 3.750$ volts

(d) $0101 \rightarrow 10 \left[0 + \frac{1}{4} + 0 + \frac{1}{16}\right] = 3.125$

(e) $1001 \rightarrow 10 \left[\frac{1}{2} + 0 + 0 + \frac{1}{16}\right] = 5.625$

(f) $1110 \rightarrow 10 \left[\frac{1}{2} + \frac{1}{4} + \frac{1}{8} + 0\right] = 8.75$ volts

---

Exercise 3.34

From Eq. 3.20

$$v_i = \frac{(v_u + v_R)t^*}{2RC}$$

From Eq. 3.21

$$\Delta v_i = -v_R \frac{\Delta t}{RC}$$

At the zero crossing:

$$v_o = v_i + \Delta v_i = v_i - v_R \frac{\Delta t}{RC} = 0$$

Thus,

$$\frac{v_u + v_R}{2RC} t^* = v_R \frac{\Delta t}{RC}$$

From which,

$$\frac{\Delta t}{t^*} = \frac{1}{2}\left(\frac{v_u}{v_R} + 1\right)$$

Exercise 3.37

For a 12-bit unipolar converter (n = 12) capable of 20 readings per second,

$$T = \frac{1}{20} = 0.05 \text{ s}$$

From Eq. 3.26

$$f < \frac{2^{-n}}{\pi T} < \frac{2^{-12}}{\pi(0.05)} = 0.001554 \text{ Hz}$$

Exercise 3.44

For a 5 1/2 digit DVM with 100 % overranging maximum count is 199,999.

For a specified accuracy of ±0.002 % ± 2 counts:

(a) $1.80000 \pm (0.000036 + 0.00002) \rightarrow$ 1.80006
                                                   1.79994

(b) $2.50000 \pm (0.000050 + 0.0002) \rightarrow$ 2.5003
                                                   2.4997

(c) $9.99996 \pm (0.000199 + 0.0002) \rightarrow$ 10.0004
                                                   9.9995

Exercise 3.48

A scanner, also known as a multiplexer, is a programmable switch. It is used as the interface between large numbers of transducers and the data-logging or data-acquisition system. Upon command, the scanner switches from one signal to another at a rate consistent with the capabilities of the data- logging or data-acquisition system.

Exercise 3.49

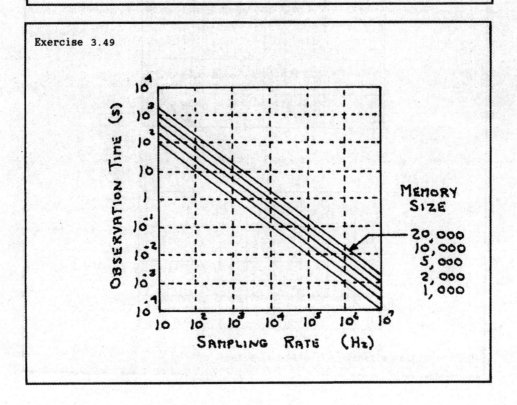

Exercise 3.52

Modern digital oscilloscopes are usually equipped with a microprocessor that provides several on-board, signal-analysis features. These features often include the following:

1. Pulse characterization - rise time, fall time, base-line and top-line width, overshoot, period, frequency, rms, standard deviation, and duty cycle.

2. Frequency analysis - power, phase, and magnitude spectrum.

3. Spectrum analysis - 100 to 50,000 point fast Fourier transforms.

4. Math package - add, subtract, multiply, integrate, and differentiate.

5. Smoothing - 1, 3, 5, 7, or 9 point.

6. Counter - average frequency and event crossings.

7. Display control - x zoom, x position, y gain, y offset.

8. Plotting display.

9. Mass storage to floppy disk, hard disk, or nonvolatile memory

Exercise 3.54 (a) and (b)

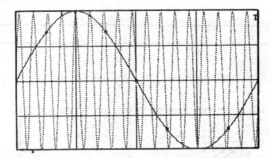

(a) —— alias signal, ···· original signal

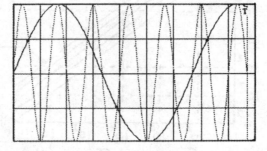

(b) —— alias signal, ···· original signal

CHAPTER 4

SIGNAL CONDITIONING CIRCUITS

4.1 INTRODUCTION

An instrumentation system contains many elements that are used either to supply power to the transducer or to condition its output signal so that it can be displayed by a voltage-measuring instrument. Signal conditioning circuits and power supplies are common to instrumentation systems designed to measure acceleration, displacement, flow, force, strain, etc. For this reason, some power supplies and signal conditioning circuits will be described independent of its application in a particular measuring system.

Because a very large number of signal conditioning circuits are available today, a complete coverage of the subject is beyond the scope of this text. However, the general characteristics of those circuits that are frequently encountered in engineering measurements are reviewed in detail.

4.2 POWER SUPPLIES

With few exceptions, transducers are supplied with the energy needed for their operation using either a constant-voltage or a constant-current power supply.

4.2.1 Battery Power Supplies

The simplest and least expensive constant-voltage power supply is a battery that can provide a reasonably constant voltage with large current flow for short periods of time. The difficulty experienced with batteries is that their voltage decays with time under load and they must be replaced or recharged periodically.

Using a simple regulating circuit incorporating a Zener diode, as shown in Fig. 4.1a, eliminates the problem of voltage decay from a battery supply. The Zener diode is operated in reverse bias and only leakage current flows until V_i exceeds the breakdown voltage V_z. When V_i exceeds V_z in reversed bias, the Zener diode breaks down and high currents flow, as indicated in Fig. 4.1b. A resistor is used to limit the current flow and to protect the Zener diode. As long as V_i exceeds V_z, the output voltage V_0 equals the breakdown voltage V_z, and the breakdown voltage controls the output and not the condition of the battery. The breakdown voltage for commonly available Zener diodes can vary widely from 1.2 volts to 200 volts. Good voltage regulation can be achieved by using the circuit of Fig 4.1.

Different types of batteries are used to power instruments depending upon their power requirements. For large power requirements, the lead-calcium rechargeable (LCR) battery is used. These batteries are available in many different sizes and with voltages ranging from 4 to 12 V. The discharge rate is quite high at 20 A/hr and capacity in A-hr is a function of size. At 12 V, these batteries exhibit a capacity of about 16 V-A-h/lb. Storage life is temperature dependent and will exceed 6 months at normal room temperature. They can be recharged about 1,000 times, if the discharge is limited to 50% of the capacity. Because this type of battery is completely sealed, it can be used in any position and treated as a dry cell.

Nickel-cadmium batteries are also used when recharging is an important requirement. These nickel-cadmium cells are much smaller than the lead-calcium cells and exhibit lower capacities.

Individual cell voltage is 1.2 V and capacities range from 100 to 4,000 mA-h depending on size. One of the better nickel-cadmium cells with an AA size has a capacity of 800 mA-h. At 1.2 V, these batteries exhibit a capacity of 23 V-A-h/lb. The discharge characteristics of a Ni-Cd battery are superior to ordinary dry cells and they can be recharged about 500 times before replacement is required.

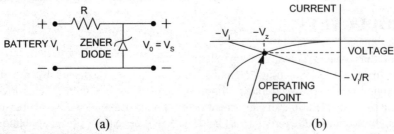

(a)   (b)

Fig. 4.1 (a) Voltage regulation with a Zener diode operating in reverse bias.

(b) Voltage-current characteristics of a Zener diode showing the breakdown at $V_Z = V_0$.

Lithium batteries have been developed during the past two decades with a number of different cell chemistries. The lithium thionyl chloride ($LiSOCl_2$) composition offers the highest energy density of any primary battery with up to 710 W-h/Kg and the highest operating voltage 3.6V. The capacity depends on the size of the battery with size—a AA size battery has a capacity of 2.10 A-h. The lithium batteries exhibit outstanding performance characteristics with high individual cell voltages, very low decay of voltage under load, extremely long shelf life and high energy density. The performance of a lithium thionyl chloride battery indicates continuous operation with negligible voltage decay for 5 to 15 years depending on load resistance. The capacity is 320 V-A-h/lb which is 20 times better than the Ni-Cd or the LCR battery. Indeed, with proper load resistances to limit current flow, the life is so long that recharging is not required.

In some low cost instruments where the current requirements are low and replacement is convenient, more conventional alkaline and carbon/zinc dry cells are used. Because these cells cannot be recharged, they are replaced when the supply voltage drops below specified values.

Properly regulated battery supplies, which can be recharged, are often superior to much more expensive and complex power supplies that convert an ac line voltage to a dc output voltage, because ripple and noise is eliminated. Also, the portability offered by a battery supply is mandatory when making field measurements where ac power is not available.

4.2.2 Line Voltage Supplies

The use of general-purpose power supplies that convert an ac line voltage (either 110 V or 220 V) to a lower dc output voltage (often variable) is quite common. A typical example of a high-performance dc power supply, which is capable of delivering nearly constant voltage or constant current, is shown in Fig. 4.2. The power supply uses a rectifier to convert the ac line voltage to a dc output voltage and a filter to reduce the ripple resulting from the rectification. The ripple and regulation are further improved by incorporating a transistor series regulator between the filter and the output. Performance characteristics of this unit that is capable of providing 0 to 15 V dc and 0 to 3 A are described to illustrate the important features of a power supply.

The load effect for a typical power supply, which is the voltage drop from an initial setting as the current is increased from zero to the maximum rated value, is 0.005% or 2mV, whichever is greater when the unit is operated as a constant-voltage source. When operated as a constant-current source, the current increases 0.2% or 5mA as the voltage is increased from zero to its maximum rated value. The source effect, which is the change in output for a change in line voltage, is 0.005% or 2mV for the voltage and 0.1% or 2 mA for the current. The ripple and noise, which is a small ac signal superimposed on the dc output, is typically about 0.25 mV rms.

The temperature coefficient, which is the change in output voltage or current per °C following a warm-up period, is 0.015% per °C. The output impedance of the power supply can be represented by a resistor and an inductor in series. The output impedance is usually low for voltage supplies because typical values for R and L are 2 mΩ and 1 mH, respectively.

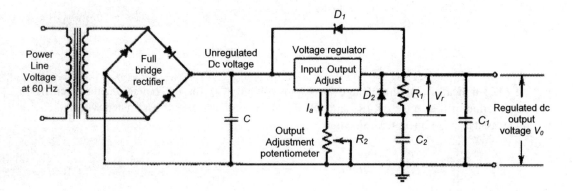

Fig. 4.2 The components in a regulated dc power supply with adjustable output voltage.

4.3 POTENTIOMETER CIRCUIT

4.3.1 Constant Voltage Supply

The potentiometer circuit, employed with resistance-type transducers to convert the transducer output ΔR/R to a voltage signal ΔV, is shown in Fig. 4.3. With fixed-value resistors in the circuit, the open-circuit output voltage V_0 can be expressed as:

$$V_0 = \frac{R_1}{R_1 + R_2} V_s = \frac{1}{1+r} V_s \qquad (4.1)$$

where V_s is the input voltage and $r = R_2/R_1$ is the resistance ratio.

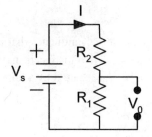

Fig. 4.3 A constant voltage potentiometer circuit.

If resistors R_1 and R_2 are varied by ΔR_1 and ΔR_2, the change ΔV_0 in the output voltage can be determined from Eq. (4.1) as:

$$V_0 + \Delta V_0 = \frac{R_1 + \Delta R_1}{R_1 + \Delta R_1 + R_2 + \Delta R_2} V_s \qquad (a)$$

Solving for ΔV_0 gives:

$$\Delta V_0 = \left(\frac{R_1 + \Delta R_1}{R_1 + \Delta R_1 + R_2 + \Delta R_2} - \frac{R_1}{R_1 + R_2} \right) V_s \qquad \text{(b)}$$

Equation (b) can be reduced and expressed in a more useful form by introducing the resistance ratio r. Thus:

$$\Delta V_0 = \frac{\dfrac{r}{(1+r)^2} \left(\dfrac{\Delta R_1}{R_1} - \dfrac{\Delta R_2}{R_2} \right)}{1 + \dfrac{1}{1+r} \left(\dfrac{\Delta R_1}{R_1} + r \dfrac{\Delta R_2}{R_2} \right)} V_s \qquad (4.2)$$

Equation (4.2) indicates that the change in output voltage ΔV_0 for the potentiometer circuit is a nonlinear function of the inputs $\Delta R_1/R_1$ and $\Delta R_2/R_2$. The nonlinear effects associated with the circuit can be expressed as a nonlinear term η, where:

$$\eta = 1 - \frac{1}{1 + \dfrac{1}{1+r} \left(\dfrac{\Delta R_1}{R_1} + r \dfrac{\Delta R_2}{R_2} \right)} \qquad (4.3)$$

Equation (4.2) then becomes:

$$\Delta V_0 = \frac{r}{(1+r)^2} \left(\frac{\Delta R_1}{R_1} - \frac{\Delta R_2}{R_2} \right)(1 - \eta) V_s \qquad (4.4)$$

Linearity within 1% can be obtained if $\Delta R_1/R_1 < 0.1$ and if $r = 9$ and $\Delta R_2 = 0$. The range of the potentiometer circuit is defined as the maximum $\Delta R_1/R_1$ that can be recorded without exceeding some specified value of the nonlinear term (usually 1 or 2%). In the special case with $r = 9$ and $\Delta R_2 = 0$, the range is $(\Delta R_1/R_1)_{max} = 0.101$ for linearity within 1% and $(\Delta R_1/R_1)_{max} = 0.204$ for linearity within 2%.

The sensitivity S_c of the potentiometer circuit is defined for a case where $\Delta R_2 = 0$ as:

$$S_c = \frac{\Delta V_0}{\Delta R_1 / R_1} = \frac{r}{(1+r)^2} V_s \qquad (4.5)$$

Equation (4.5) indicates that increasing the input voltage V_s can increase the sensitivity without limit; however, all transducers have power-dissipation limitations that constrain the input voltage. The power P_T dissipated by a transducer in a potentiometer circuit is given by the expression:

$$P_T = \frac{V_T^2}{R_T} \qquad (4.6)$$

where V_T is the voltage across the transducer and R_T is the transducer resistance.

From Eq. (4.1) it is clear that:

$$V_T = \frac{V_s}{1+r} \tag{4.7}$$

The upper limit of the voltage that can be applied to the potentiometer circuit is obtained from Eqs. (4.6) and (4.7) as:

$$(V_s)_{max} = (1+r)\sqrt{p_T R_T} \tag{4.8}$$

A realistic expression for the sensitivity of the constant-voltage potentiometer circuit S_{cv} is obtained by substituting Eq. (4.8) into Eq. (4.5). Thus:

$$S_{cv} = \frac{r}{1+r}\sqrt{p_T R_T} \qquad \text{with} \qquad \Delta R_2 = 0 \tag{4.9}$$

It is clear from Eq. (4.9) that maximum sensitivity is achieved with large r, with a high-resistance transducer, and with a transducer capable of dissipating a large amount of power. In practice, sensitivity is usually limited by supply voltage requirements. For r greater than about 5, the higher voltages required cannot be justified by the small additional gains in sensitivity.

The preceding equations for the potentiometer circuit have been based on the assumption that the input impedance of the voltage recording instrument is infinite (open-circuit voltage) and that no power is required to measure the output signal from the signal conditioning circuit. In practice, recording instruments have a finite resistance and a small amount of power is drawn from the signal conditioning circuit. The load error will be small provided that the recorder impedance $R_M > 100\ R_S$.

4.3.2 Constant Current Supply

The potentiometer circuit described in above, which was driven with a constant-voltage power supply, exhibits a nonlinear output voltage ΔV_0 when the input $\Delta R/R$ becomes large. In many applications, this nonlinear behavior limits the usefulness of the circuit and means are sought to extend its linear range of operation.

Many advances in solid-state electronics have continuously improved constant-current power supplies providing them with sufficient regulation for use in instrumentation systems. A constant-current power supply automatically adjusts its output voltage to compensate for a changing resistive load in order to maintain the current at a constant value.

A potentiometer circuit with a constant-current power supply is shown schematically in Fig. 4.4a. The open-circuit output voltage V_0 (measured with a high-impedance recording instrument so that loading errors are negligible) is:

$$V_0 = IR_1 \tag{4.10}$$

When the resistances R_1 and R_2 are changed by the amounts ΔR_1 and ΔR_2, the output voltage becomes:

$$V_0 + \Delta V_0 = I(R_1 + \Delta R_1) \tag{a}$$

From Eq. (4.10) and Eq. (a):

$$\Delta V_0 = I\Delta R_1 = IR_1 \frac{\Delta R_1}{R_1} \tag{4.11}$$

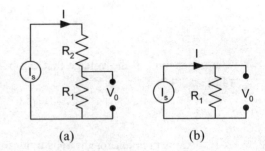

Fig. 4.4 Constant current potentiometer circuits.
(a) Two-resistor circuit. (b) Single-resistor circuit.

Equation (4.11) indicates that neither R_2 nor ΔR_2 influences the voltage output of the constant-current potentiometer circuit; therefore, it is possible to eliminate R_2 and use the simple circuit shown in Fig. 4.4b. It should also be observed that the change in output voltage ΔV_0 is a linear function of the input $\Delta R_1/R_1$, regardless of the magnitude of ΔR_1. This linear behavior extends the usefulness of the potentiometer circuit for many applications.

The circuit sensitivity S_{cc} for the constant-current potentiometer circuit is:

$$S_{cc} = \frac{\Delta V_0}{\Delta R_1/R_1} = IR_1 \tag{4.12}$$

If the constant-current source is adjustable with the current I increased to attain the maximum power capability of the transducer, then:

$$I = \sqrt{\frac{P_T}{R_1}} \tag{b}$$

Substituting Eq. (b) into Eq. (4.12) yields:

$$S_{cc} = \sqrt{P_T R_T} \tag{4.13}$$

Equations (4.9) and (4.13) indicate that the sensitivity of the potentiometer circuit is improved by a factor of $(1 + r)/r$ by using the constant-current source.

4.4 WHEATSTONE BRIDGE

4.4.1 Constant Voltage Wheatstone Bridge

The Wheatstone bridge, shown in Fig. 4.5, is another circuit commonly used to convert ΔR to an output voltage. The output voltage V_0 of the bridge can be determined by treating the top and bottom parts of the bridge as individual voltage dividers. Thus:

$$V_{AB} = \frac{R_1}{R_1 + R_2} V_s \quad \text{and} \quad V_{AD} = \frac{R_4}{R_3 + R_4} V_s \tag{a}$$

The output voltage V_0 of the bridge is given by:

$$V_0 = V_{BD} = V_{AB} - V_{AD} \qquad \text{(b)}$$

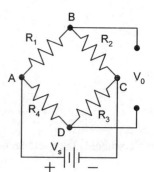

Fig. 4.5 The constant voltage Wheatstone bridge circuit.

Substituting Eqs. (a) into (b) yields:

$$V_0 = \frac{R_1 R_3 - R_2 R_4}{(R_1 + R_2)(R_3 + R_4)} V_s \qquad (4.14)$$

Equation (4.14) indicates that the initial output voltage will vanish ($V_0 = 0$) if:

$$R_1 R_3 = R_2 R_4 \qquad (4.15)$$

When Eq. (4.15) is satisfied, the bridge is in **balance**. The ability to balance the bridge (and zero V_0) represents a significant advantage, because it is much easier to measure small changes in voltage ΔV_0 from a null voltage than from an elevated voltage V_0, which may be many times greater than ΔV_0.

With an initially balanced bridge, an output voltage ΔV_0 develops when resistances R_1, R_2, R_3 and R_4 are varied by amounts ΔR_1, ΔR_2, ΔR_3 and ΔR_4, respectively. From Eq. (4.14), with these new values of resistance,

$$\Delta V_0 = \frac{(R_1 + \Delta R_1)(R_3 + \Delta R_3) - (R_2 + \Delta R_2)(R_4 + \Delta R_4)}{(R_1 + \Delta R_1 + R_2 + \Delta R_2)(R_3 + \Delta R_3 + R_4 + \Delta R_4)} V_s \qquad \text{(c)}$$

Expanding, neglecting higher-order terms, and substituting Eq. (4.14) into Eq. (c) yields:

$$\Delta V_0 = \frac{R_1 R_2}{(R_1 + R_2)^2} \left(\frac{\Delta R_1}{R_1} - \frac{\Delta R_2}{R_2} + \frac{\Delta R_3}{R_3} - \frac{\Delta R_4}{R_4} \right) V_s \qquad (4.16)$$

An equivalent form of this equation is obtained by substituting $r = R_2/R_1$ in Eq. (4.16) to give:

$$\Delta V_0 = \frac{1}{(1+r)^2} \left(\frac{\Delta R_1}{R_1} - \frac{\Delta R_2}{R_2} + \frac{\Delta R_3}{R_3} - \frac{\Delta R_4}{R_4} \right) V_s \qquad (4.17)$$

Equations (4.16) and (4.17) indicate that the output voltage from the bridge is a linear function of the resistance changes. This apparent linearity results from the fact that the higher-order terms in Eq. (d) were neglected. If the higher-order terms are retained, the output voltage ΔV_0 is a nonlinear function of the $\Delta R/R$'s, which can be expressed as:

$$\Delta V_0 = \frac{1}{(1+r)^2}\left(\frac{\Delta R_1}{R_1} - \frac{\Delta R_2}{R_2} + \frac{\Delta R_3}{R_3} - \frac{\Delta R_4}{R_4}\right)(1-\eta)V_s \qquad (4.18)$$

where

$$\eta = \frac{1}{1 + \dfrac{r+1}{\dfrac{\Delta R_1}{R_1} + \dfrac{\Delta R_4}{R_4} + r\left(\dfrac{\Delta R_2}{R_2} + \dfrac{\Delta R_3}{R_3}\right)}} \qquad (4.19)$$

In a commonly used arrangement for the bridge, $R_1 = R_2 = R_3 = R_4$. In this case, Eq. (4.19) reduces to:

$$\eta = \frac{\displaystyle\sum_{i=1}^{4}\frac{\Delta R_i}{R_i}}{\displaystyle\sum_{i=1}^{4}\frac{\Delta R_i}{R_i} + 2} \qquad (4.20)$$

The error due to the nonlinear effect depends on $\Delta R_1/R_1$ and r. The results from Eq. (4.19) with r = 1, show that $\Delta R_1/R_1$ must be less than 0.02, if the error due to the nonlinear effect is not to exceed 1%. While this limit may appear quite restrictive, the Wheatstone bridge is usually employed with transducers that exhibit very small changes in $\Delta R_1/R_1$.

The sensitivity S_c of a Wheatstone bridge with a constant-voltage power supply and a single active arm is determined from Eq. (4.17) as:

$$S_c = \frac{\Delta V_0}{\Delta R_1/R_1} = \frac{r}{(1+r)^2}V_s \qquad (4.21)$$

Again, it is clear that increasing the supply voltage produces an increase in sensitivity; however, the power P_T that can be dissipated by the transducer limits the supply voltage V_s to:

$$V_s = I_T(R_1 + R_2) = I_T R_T(1+r) = (1+r)\sqrt{P_T R_T} \qquad (4.22)$$

Substituting Eq. (4.21) into Eq. (4.22) gives:

$$S_{cv} = \frac{r}{1+r}\sqrt{P_T R_T} \qquad (4.23)$$

Equation (4.23) indicates that the circuit sensitivity of the constant-voltage Wheatstone bridge is due to two factors; the circuit efficiency [r/(1 + r)] and the characteristics of the transducer as indicated by P_T and R_T. Increasing r increases circuit efficiency; however, r should not be increased to a level requiring unusually large supply voltages. For example, a 500 Ω sensor capable of dissipating 0.2 W in a bridge with r = 4 (80% circuit efficiency) will require a supply voltage V_s = 50 V, which is higher than the capacity of most highly regulated power supplies.

The selection of a sensor with a high resistance and a high heat dissipating capability is much more effective in maximizing circuit sensitivity than increasing the circuit efficiency beyond 70 or

80%. The product $P_T R_T$ for commercially available sensors can range from about 1 W-Ω to 1,000 W-Ω; therefore, much more latitude exists for increasing circuit sensitivity S_{cv} by transducer selection than by increasing circuit efficiency.

Circuit sensitivity S_{cv} can also be increased, as indicated by Eq. (4.17), by using multiple sensors (one in each arm of the bridge). In most cases, however, the cost of the additional sensors is not warranted. Instead, it is usually more economical to use a high-gain differential amplifier to increase the output signal ΔV_0 from the Wheatstone bridge.

Load effects in a Wheatstone bridge are negligible if a high-impedance voltage-measuring instrument (such as a DVM for static signals or a computer equipped with a signal conditioning circuit board for dynamic signals) is used with the bridge. The output impedance Z_B of the bridge is given by:

$$Z_B = R_B = \frac{R_1 R_2}{R_1 + R_2} + \frac{R_3 R_4}{R_3 + R_4} \tag{4.24}$$

In most bridge arrangements, R_B is less than 10^4 Ω. Because the input impedance Z_B of modern voltage recording devices exceeds 10^6 Ω, the ratio $Z_B/Z_M < 0.01$ and loading errors are usually less than 1%.

4.4.2 Constant Current Wheatstone Bridge

Using a constant-current power supply with the potentiometer circuit improved the circuit sensitivity and eliminated nonlinear effects. There are also advantages of using a constant-current power supply with the Wheatstone bridge that are determined by replacing the voltage source in Figure 4.5 with a constant current supply. The current from the source I_s divides at point A into currents I_1 and I_2 where:

$$I_s = I_1 + I_2 \tag{a}$$

The voltage drops across resistances R_1 and R_4 are given by:

$$V_{AB} = I_1 R_1 \qquad V_{AD} = I_2 R_4 \tag{b}$$

Thus, the output voltage V_0 from the bridge is given by:

$$V_0 = V_{BD} = V_{AB} - V_{AD} = I_1 R_1 - I_2 R_4 \tag{4.25}$$

From Eq. (4.25) it is clear that the bridge will be balanced ($V_0 = 0$) if,

$$I_1 R_1 = I_2 R_4 \tag{c}$$

This balance equation is not in a useful form, because the currents I_1 and I_2 are unknowns. However, the magnitudes of these currents can be determined by observing that the voltage V_{AC} can be expressed in terms of I_1 and I_2 as

$$V_{AC} = I_1(R_1 + R_2) = I_2(R_3 + R_4) \tag{d}$$

From Eqs. (a), (c), and (d),

$$I_1 = \frac{R_3 + R_4}{R_1 + R_2 + R_3 + R_4} I_s \quad \text{and} \quad I_2 = \frac{R_1 + R_2}{R_1 + R_2 + R_3 + R_4} I_s \tag{e}$$

Substituting Eqs. (e) into Eq. (4.25) gives:

$$V_0 = \frac{I_s}{R_1 + R_2 + R_3 + R_4}(R_1 R_3 - R_2 R_4) \tag{4.26}$$

This equation shows that the balance requirement for the constant-current Wheatstone bridge is the same as that for the constant-voltage Wheatstone bridge.

The open-circuit output voltage V_0, from an initially balanced bridge ($V_0 = 0$), due to resistance changes ΔR_1, ΔR_2, ΔR_3 and ΔR_4 is determined from Eq. (4.26) as:

$$\Delta V_0 = \frac{I_s}{\sum R + \sum \Delta R}\left[\left(R_1 + \Delta R_1\right)\left(R_3 + \Delta R_3\right) - \left(R_2 + \Delta R_2\right)\left(R_4 + \Delta R_4\right)\right]$$

$$= \frac{I_s R_1 R_3}{\sum R + \sum \Delta R}\left(\frac{\Delta R_1}{R_1} - \frac{\Delta R_2}{R_2} + \frac{\Delta R_3}{R_3} - \frac{\Delta R_4}{R_4} + \frac{\Delta R_1}{R_1}\frac{\Delta R_3}{R_3} - \frac{\Delta R_2}{R_2}\frac{\Delta R_4}{R_4}\right) \tag{4.27}$$

where $\sum R = R_1 + R_2 + R_3 + R_4 = \sum \Delta R = \Delta R_1 + \Delta R_2 + \Delta R_3 + \Delta R_4$

Equation (4.27) shows that the constant-current Wheatstone bridge exhibits a nonlinear output voltage ΔV_0. The nonlinearity is due to the $\sum \Delta R$ term in the denominator and to the two second-order terms within the bracketed quantity. Consider a typical application with a transducer in arm R_1 and fixed-value resistors in the other three arms of the bridge such that

$$R_1 = R_4 = R_T, \qquad R_2 = R_3 = r\, R_T, \qquad \Delta R_2 = \Delta R_3 = \Delta R_4 = 0 \tag{f}$$

For this example, Eq. (4.27) reduces to:

$$\Delta V_0 = \frac{I_s R_T r}{2(1+r) + (\Delta R_T / R_T)}\left(\frac{\Delta R_T}{R_T}\right) \tag{4.28}$$

This can also be expressed as:

$$\Delta V_0 = \frac{I_s R_T r}{2(1+r)}\frac{\Delta R_T}{R_T}(1 + \eta) \tag{4.29}$$

where

$$\eta = \frac{\Delta R_T / R_T}{2(1+r) + (\Delta R_T / R_T)} \tag{4.30}$$

It is evident from Eq. (4.30) that increasing r can reduce the nonlinear effect. The error due to non-linearity for a constant current Wheatstone bridge is significantly less than the error for a bridge powered with a constant voltage source. Comparing the results of Eq. (4.19) and Eq. (4.30) clearly shows the advantage of the constant-current power supply in extending the range of the Wheatstone bridge circuit.

The circuit sensitivity S_c obtained from Eq. (4.29) is:

$$S_{cc} = \frac{\Delta V_0}{\Delta R_T / R_T} = \frac{I_s R_T r}{2(1+r)} \tag{4.31}$$

For this example, the bridge is symmetric; therefore, the current $I_T = I_s/2$. The power dissipated by the transducer is:

$$P_T = I_T^2 R_T = \tfrac{1}{4} I_s^2 R_T \tag{g}$$

Substituting Eq. (g) into Eq. (4.31) yields a relation that is identical with Eq. (4.23), hence, the circuit sensitivity is identical for the constant-voltage and constant-current Wheatstone bridges. **The principal advantage of a Wheatstone bridge, when compared with a potentiometer, is the initial balancing of the Wheatstone bridge to produce a zero output voltage ($V_0 = 0$).**

4.5 AMPLIFIERS

An amplifier is one of the most important components in an instrumentation system. Amplifiers are used in nearly every system to increase low-level signals from a transducer to a higher level sufficient for recording with a voltage measuring instrument or for conversion to a digital code using an analog to digital converter (ADC). An amplifier is represented in schematic diagrams of instrumentation systems by the triangular symbol shown in Fig. 4.6. The voltage input to the amplifier is V_i; the voltage output is V_0. The ratio V_0/V_i is the gain G of the amplifier. As the input voltage is increased, the output voltage increases in the linear range of the amplifier according to the relationship:

$$V_0 = G V_i \tag{4.32}$$

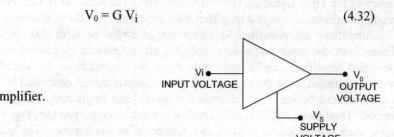

Vi •
INPUT VOLTAGE

• V₀
OUTPUT VOLTAGE

• Vs
SUPPLY VOLTAGE

Fig. 4.6 Symbol for an amplifier.

The linear range of an amplifier is finite because the supply voltage and the characteristics of the amplifier components limit the output voltage. A typical input-output graph for an amplifier is shown in Fig. 4.7. If the amplifier is driven beyond the linear range, serious errors can result if the gain G is treated as a constant.

The frequency response or bandwidth of an amplifier must also be given careful consideration during design of an instrumentation system. The gain is a function of the frequency of the input signal and there is always a high frequency where the gain of the amplifier will be less than its value at the lower frequencies. This frequency effect on amplifier gain is similar to inertia effects in a mechanical system. A finite time (transit time) is required for the input current to pass through all of the components in the amplifier and reach the output terminal. Also, time is required for the output voltage to develop because some capacitance is always present in the circuits of the amplifier and the recording instrument.

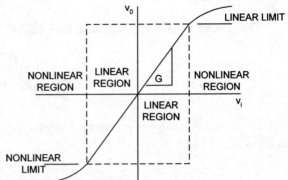

Fig. 4.7 A typical input versus output voltage for an amplifier.

The frequency response of an amplifier-recorder system can be illustrated in two different ways. First, the output voltage can be described as a function of time for a step input as shown in Fig. 4.8a. The rise in output voltage for this representation can be approximated by an exponential function of the form:

$$V_0 = G(1 - e^{-t/\tau})V_i \qquad (4.33)$$

where τ is the time constant for the amplifier.

The second method of illustrating frequency effects utilizes a graph with gain plotted as a function of frequency in Fig. 4.8b. The output of the amplifier is flat between the lower and upper frequency limits f_L and f_U. Thus, a dynamic signal with all frequency components within the band between f_L and f_U is amplified with a constant gain. DC or dc-coupled amplifiers are designed with input circuits that maintain a constant gain down to zero frequency. However, if a capacitor is placed in series with the input to the amplifier to block the dc components of the input signal, the gain G goes to zero as the frequency of the input signal decreases toward zero. The addition of the series capacitor at the input terminal produces an ac-coupled amplifier with a variable gain for frequencies between zero and f_L.

Amplifiers are classified as either single ended or with dual input. With single-ended amplifiers both the input and output voltages are referenced to ground as indicated in Fig. 4.9a. Single-ended amplifiers can be used only when the output from the signal conditioning circuit is referenced to ground, as is the case for the potentiometer circuit described in Section 4.3. The output from a Wheatstone bridge is not referenced to ground and single-ended amplifiers cannot be used with this circuit. Dual input or differential amplifiers must be employed (see Fig. 4.9b) where two separate voltages, each referenced to ground, are connected to the inputs. The output from a differential amplifier is single-ended and referenced to ground. The ideal output voltage from a differential amplifier is given by:

$$V_0 = G(V_{i1} - V_{i2}) \qquad (4.34)$$

Generally, the input voltages to a differential amplifier are expressed as:

$$V_{i1} = V + \Delta V \qquad \text{and } V_{i2} = V \qquad (a)$$

where V is the common mode voltage and ΔV is the small difference voltage that is to be amplified.

Unfortunately, due to slight differences in the amplifier's components, the output voltage V_0 is not zero as indicated by Eq. (4.34) when ΔV is zero. It is more accurate to write Eq. (4.34) as:

$$V_0 = G_d \, \Delta V + G_c \, V \tag{4.35}$$

where G_d is the gain for the difference voltage ΔV and G_c is the gain for the common mode voltage V.

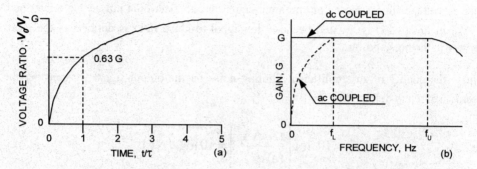

Fig. 4.8 (a) Frequency response of a typical amplifier to a step function input voltage.
(b) Gain of a typical amplifier as a function of frequency of the input voltage.

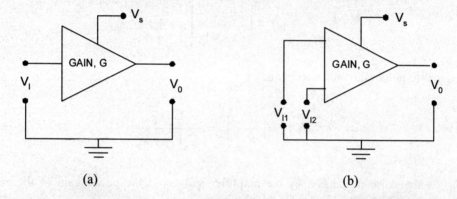

Fig. 4.9 Amplifier with single ended input voltage. (b) Amplifier with double ended input voltage.

One measure of the quality of a differential amplifier is the common mode rejection ratio (CMRR) where:

$$CMRR = \frac{G_d}{G_c} \tag{4.36}$$

To minimize G_c relative to G_d, a very high value of the CMRR is preferred. Values of CMRR ranging from 1,000 to 20,000 are typical for differential amplifiers with the lower values occurring at the higher frequencies. With CMRR > 1,000, Eq. (4.35) is closely approximated by Eq. (4.34).

A high value for the CMRR in the difference mode is important because it implies that spurious signals common to both inputs V_{i1} and V_{i2} such as noise, power supply ripple and temperature-induced drift are canceled. The ability of the differential amplifier to eliminate these undesirable components of the input signal is a significant advantage.

Another measure of the quality of an amplifier is related to the signal-to-noise ratio S/N, which is written as:

$$(S/N)_i = \left(\frac{V_i}{V_{ni}}\right)^2 \tag{4.37}$$

where V_{ni} is voltage superimposed on the input signal due to electronic noise. Note that the voltage ratio V_i/V_{ni} in Eq. (4.37) is squared because the signal-to-noise ratio is defined as the ratio of the signal power to the noise power.

To evaluate the quality of an amplifier in limiting noise on the output signal we consider the noise parameter F_n, which is defined by:

$$F_n = 10 \ \log\left[\frac{(S/N)_i}{(S/N)_0}\right] = 10\log \ (\text{NF}) \tag{4.38}$$

where NF is the noise factor given by:

$$\text{NF} = \left[\frac{(S/N)_i}{(S/N)_0}\right] > 1 \tag{4.39}$$

Note the signal-to-noise ratio on the output is:

$$(S/N)_0 = \left(\frac{V_0}{V_{n0}}\right)^2 = \frac{G_p V_i^2}{G_p V_{ni}^2 + V_{nA}^2} \tag{4.40}$$

where V_{nA} is the noise introduced by the amplifier and G_p is the power gain of the amplifier. Substituting Eqs. (4.37) and (4.40) into Eq. (4.39) gives:

$$\text{NF} = 1 + \frac{V_{nA}^2}{G_p F_{ni}^2} \tag{4.41}$$

It is important to minimize the term $[V_{nA}^2/(G_p V_{ni}^2)]$ so that the noise factor NF approaches one. If NF = 2, it is evident from Eq. (4.41) that the amplifier and input source is adding a noise signal equal to the noise in the input signal. Clearly the addition of electronic noise on the signal at any point in the instrumentation system is objectionable.

Another measure of quality of an amplifier is its dynamic range R_d that is defined as:

$$R_d = 20 \ \log\left(\frac{V_m}{V_n}\right) \tag{4.42}$$

where V_m is the maximum input signal before the amplifier becomes non-linear and $V_n = V_{nA}/G$. A high dynamic range is sought to extend the linear range of the amplifier.

4.6 OPERATIONAL AMPLIFIERS

An **operational amplifier** (op-amp) is an integrated circuit where miniaturized transistors, diodes, resistors and capacitors have been placed on a small silicon chip to form a complete amplifier circuit. Operational amplifiers serve many functions because they can easily be adapted to perform several mathematical operations with circuits involving a small number of external passive components, such as resistors or capacitors. Operational amplifiers have an extremely high gain ($G = 10^5$ is a typical value). Consequently, G is usually considered infinite in the analysis and design of circuits containing an op-amp. The input impedance (typically R = 4 MΩ and C = 8 pF) is so high that circuit loading usually is not a consideration[1]. Output resistance from the op amp, of the order of 100 Ω, is sufficiently low to be considered negligible in most applications.

The symbols used to represent the internal op-amp circuit in schematic diagrams are shown in Fig. 4.10. The two input terminals are identified as the inverting (−) terminal and the non-inverting (+) terminal. The output voltage V_0 of an op-amp is given by the expression:

$$V_0 = G(V_{i1} - V_{i2}) \qquad\qquad (4.34)$$

It is evident from Eq. (4.34) that the op-amp is a differential amplifier; however, it is not used as an instrument differential amplifier because of its extremely high gain and its **poor stability**. The op-amp can be used effectively, however, as a part of a larger circuit (with more accurate and more stable passive elements) for many applications. Several applications of the op-amp, including inverting amplifiers, voltage followers, summing amplifiers, integrating amplifiers and differentiating amplifiers are summarized in the next subsection.

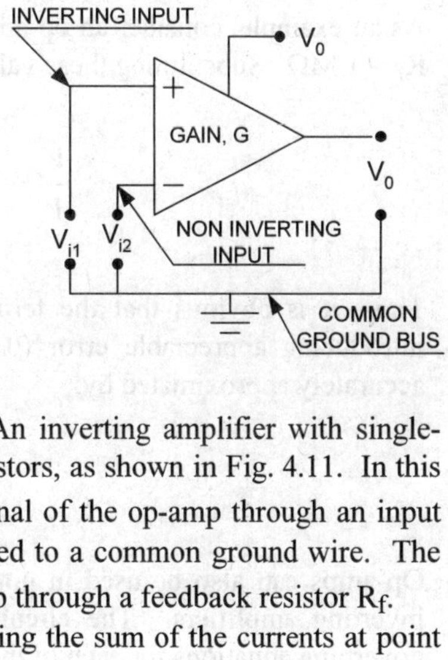

Fig. 4.10 Circuit diagram of an operational amplifier

4.6.1 Op-Amp Applications

Several applications of op-amps are described in this section. An inverting amplifier with single-ended input and output can be assembled from an op-amp and resistors, as shown in Fig. 4.11. In this circuit, the input voltage V_i is applied to the negative input terminal of the op-amp through an input resistor R_1. The positive input terminal of the op-amp is connected to a common ground wire. The output voltage V_0 is fed back to the negative terminal of the op-amp through a feedback resistor R_f. The gain of the inverting amplifier can be determined by considering the sum of the currents at point A in Fig 4.11. Thus,

$$I_1 + I_f = I_a \qquad\qquad (a)$$

if V_a is the voltage drop across the op-amp is given by:

$$I_1 = \frac{V_i - V_a}{R_1}, \qquad I_f = \frac{V_0 - V_a}{R_f}, \qquad I_a = \frac{V_a}{R_a} \qquad (b)$$

---

[1] Except for piezoelectric transducers where their output impedance is extremely high.

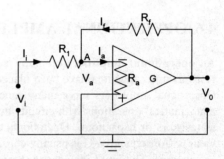

Fig. 4.11 An inverting amplifier with single ended input and output.

The voltage drop across the op-amp V_a is related to the output voltage V_0 by the gain. Therefore,

$$V_a = -\frac{V_0}{G} \qquad\qquad (c)$$

From Eqs. (a), (b), and (c),

$$\frac{V_0}{V_i} = -\frac{R_f}{R_1}\left[\frac{1}{1+\dfrac{1}{G}\left(1+\dfrac{R_f}{R_1}+\dfrac{R_f}{R_a}\right)}\right] \qquad\qquad (4.43)$$

As an example, consider an op-amp with a gain $G = 200{,}000$ and $R_a = 4\ M\Omega$, with $R_1 = 0.1\ M\Omega$ and $R_f = 1\ M\Omega$. Substituting these values into Eq. (4.43) yields:

$$\frac{V_0}{V_i} = -10\left[\frac{1}{1+5.6(10^{-5})}\right] = -9.9994400 \approx -10 \qquad\qquad (d)$$

Thus, it is obvious that the term containing the gain G in Eq. (4.43) can be neglected without introducing appreciable error (0.0056% in this example), and the gain of the circuit G can be accurately approximated by:

$$G_c = -\frac{V_0}{V_i} \approx -\frac{R_f}{R_1} \qquad\qquad (4.44)$$

Op-amps can also be used in non-inverting amplifiers and differential amplifiers in addition to the inverting amplifiers. The circuits for each of these amplifiers are shown in Fig. 4.12, and the governing equations for each of these circuits are given by:

Fig. 4.12 Amplifiers designed using op-amps.
(a) Non-inverting amplifier.
(b) Differential amplifier.

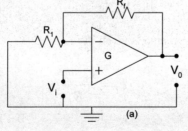

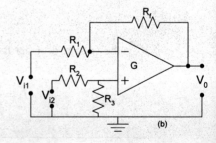

For the noninverting amplifier:

$$G_c = \frac{V_0}{V_i} = \frac{G}{1+\dfrac{GR_1}{R_1+R_f}} \approx 1 + \frac{R_f}{R_1} \tag{4.45}$$

For the differential amplifier:

$$V_0 \approx \frac{R_3}{R_2}\left(\frac{1+\dfrac{R_f}{R_1}}{1+\dfrac{R_3}{R_2}}\right)V_{i2} - \left(\frac{R_f}{R_1}\right)V_{i1} \tag{4.46}$$

If $R_f/R_1 = R_3/R_2$, then Eq. (4.46) reduces to:

$$G_c = \frac{V_0}{V_{i2}-V_{i1}} \approx \frac{R_f}{R_1} \tag{4.47}$$

The circuits shown in Fig. 4.12 have been simplified to illustrate the concept of developing an amplifier with a circuit gain G_c that is essentially independent of the op-amp gain G. In practice, these circuits must be modified to account for zero-offset voltages because, ideally, the output voltage V_0 of the amplifier should be zero when both of the inputs (+) and (−) of the op-amp are connected to the common ground buss. In typical circuits, this zero voltage is not achieved automatically, because the op-amps exhibit a zero-offset voltage. It is necessary to add a biasing circuit to the amplifier that can be adjusted to restore the output voltage to zero; otherwise, serious measurement errors can occur. Because the magnitude of the offset voltage changes (drifts) as a result of temperature, time and power-supply voltage variations, it is advisable to adjust the bias circuit periodically to restore the zero output conditions.

A biasing circuit for an inverting amplifier with single-ended input and output is shown in Fig. 4.13. Common values of resistances, R_2, R_3 and R_4 are $R_3 = R_1$, $R_2 = 10\ \Omega$ and $R_4 = 25\ k\Omega$. Voltages $V = \pm\,15$ V are often used because the zero-offset voltage of the op-amp can be either positive or negative. The magnitude of the bias voltage that must be applied to the op-amp seldom exceeds a few millivolts.

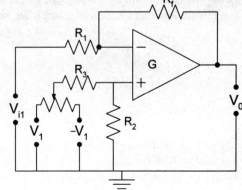

Fig. 4.13 Biasing circuit for an amplifier with a single ended input and output.

4.6.2 Additional Circuits Containing Op-amps

Voltage Follower

An op-amp can also be used to construct an instrument with very high input impedance for use with transducers that incorporate piezoelectric sensors. The high-impedance circuit, shown in Fig. 4.14, is known as a voltage follower and has a circuit gain of unity ($G_c = 1$). The purpose of a voltage follower is to adjust the impedance between the transducer and the voltage-recording instrument. The gain G_c of the voltage follower is given by:

$$G_c = \frac{V_0}{V_i} = \frac{G}{1+G} \tag{4.48}$$

When the gain G of the op-amp is very large, the gain G_c of the circuit approaches unity. The input resistance R_{ci} of the voltage follower circuit is given by:

$$R_{ci} = (1 + G)R_a \tag{4.49}$$

Because both G and R_a are very large for op-amps, the input impedance R_{ci} of the voltage follower circuit can be made quite large. In the design of a voltage follower op-amps are specified because they exhibit $G \approx 5 \times 10^4$ and $R_a \approx 10^{13}$ Ω. This circuit gives an input impedance of $R_{ci} \approx 5 \times 10^{17}$ that is sufficiently large to minimize the effect of charge drain on measurements of short duration events.

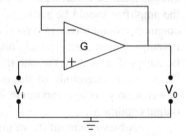

Fig. 4.14 A high input impedance voltage follower circuit.

Summing Amplifier

In some data analysis applications, signals from two or more sources are added to obtain an output signal that is proportional to the sum of the input signals. Adding can be accomplished with an op-amp circuit, known as a summing amplifier, shown in Fig. 4.15.

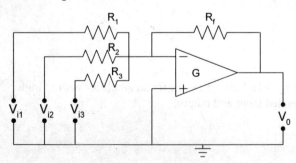

Fig. 4.15 A summing amplifier circuit designed with an op-amp.

The output voltage from this summing amplifier is given by:

$$V_0 = -R_f\left(\frac{V_{i1}}{R_1} + \frac{V_{i2}}{R_2} + \frac{V_{i3}}{R_3}\right)$$

(4.50)

Equation (4.50) indicates that the input signals V_{i1}, V_{i2} and V_{i3} are scaled by ratios R_f/R_1, R_f/R_2 and R_f/R_3, respectively, and then summed. If $R_1 = R_2 = R_3 = R_f$, the inputs sum without scaling and Eq. (4.50) reduces to:

$$V_0 = -(V_{i1} + V_{i2} + V_{i3})$$

(4.51)

Integrating Amplifier

An integrating amplifier utilizes a capacitor in the feedback loop as shown in Fig 4.14. An expression for the output voltage from the integrating amplifier can be established by following the procedure used for the summing amplifier. The output voltage of an integrating amplifier is related to the input voltage by:

$$V_0 = -\frac{1}{R_1 C_f}\int_0^t V_i\,dt$$

(4.52)

It is clear from Eq. (4.52) that the output voltage V_0 from the circuit of Fig. 4.16 is the integral of the input voltage V_i with respect to time multiplied by the constant $-1/(R_1 C_f)$.

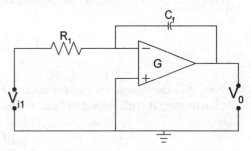

Fig. 4.16 An integrating amplifier circuit designed with an op-amp.

Differentiating Amplifier

The differentiating amplifier is similar to the integrating amplifier except that the positions of the resistor and capacitor of Fig. 4.16 are interchanged. An expression for the output voltage V_0 of the differentiating amplifier is given by:

$$V_0 = -R_f C_1 \frac{dV_i}{dt}$$

(4.53)

Considerable care must be exercised to minimize noise on the input signal when the differentiation amplifier is used. Noise superimposed on the input voltage is differentiated and contributes significantly to the output voltage producing large error. The effects of high-frequency noise can be suppressed by placing a capacitor across resistance R_f, however, the presence of this capacitor affects the differentiating process, and Eq. (4.53) must be modified to account for its effects.

4.7 FILTERS

In many instrumentation applications, the signal from the transducer is combined with noise or some other parasitic signal. These parasitic voltages can often be eliminated with a filter that is designed to attenuate the undesirable noise signals, but transmit the transducer signal without significant attenuation or distortion. Filtering of the signal is possible if the frequencies of the parasitic and transducer signals are sufficiently different. Two filters utilizing passive components that are commonly employed in signal conditioning include: the RC high-pass filter and the RC low-pass filter. Schematic diagrams of these filters are shown in Fig 4.17.

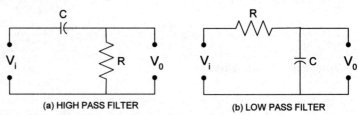

Fig. 4.17 Filter circuit that utilize
passive components R and C.

(a) HIGH PASS FILTER   (b) LOW PASS FILTER

High Pass Filter

A simple yet effective high-pass resistance-capacitance (RC) filter is illustrated in Fig. 4.17a. The behavior of this filter in response to a sinusoidal input voltage of the form:

$$V_i = Ve^{j\omega t} \tag{a}$$

V_i is determined by summing the voltage drops around the loop of Fig. 4.26a. Thus,

$$V_i - \frac{q}{C} - RI = 0 \tag{b}$$

where q is the charge on the capacitor. Equation (b) can be expressed in a more useful form by differentiating it with respect to time to obtain:

$$RC\frac{dI}{dt} + I = j\omega CV_a e^{j\omega t} \tag{c}$$

Solve Eq. (c) by letting $I = I_a e^{j\omega t}$ to obtain:

$$I = \frac{j\omega CV_a}{1 + j\omega RC} e^{j\omega t} \tag{d}$$

The output voltage V_0 is the voltage drop across the resistance R; therefore, from Eq. (d):

$$V_0 = IR = \frac{\omega RCV_a}{\sqrt{1 + (\omega RC)^2}} e^{(j\omega t + \phi)} \tag{e}$$

where the phase angle $\varphi = \pi/2 - \tan^{-1}(\omega RC)$

The ratio of the amplitudes of the output and input voltages V_0/V_i, obtained from Eqs. (a) and (e), gives the frequency response function for the high-pass filter as:

$$\frac{V_0}{V_i} = H(\omega) = \frac{j\omega RC}{1 + j\omega RC} = |H(\omega)|e^{j\phi} \qquad \text{(f)}$$

where
$$|H(\omega)| = \frac{\omega RC}{\sqrt{1 + (\omega RC)^2}} \qquad (4.54)$$

Equation (4.54) indicates that $V_0/V_i \Rightarrow 1$ as the frequency becomes large; thus, this filter is known as a high-pass filter. At zero frequency (dc), the voltage ratio V_0/V_i vanishes, which indicates that the filter completely blocks any dc component of the output voltage. This dc-blocking capability of the high-pass RC filter can be used to great advantage when a low-amplitude transducer signal is superimposed on a large dc output voltage (see, for example, the potentiometer circuit). Because the RC filter eliminates the dc voltage, a low-magnitude but a frequency dependent signal from a transducer can be amplified to produce a satisfactory display. When a high-pass RC filter is used, $\omega RC > 5$ is necessary to ensure that the input signal is transmitted through the filter with a signal attenuation of less than 2%.

Low Pass Filter

Interchanging the position of the resistor and capacitor of the high-pass RC filter produces a low-pass RC filter. This modified RC circuit, shown in Fig. 4.17b, has transmission characteristics that are opposite to those of the high-pass RC filter; namely, it transmits low-frequency signals and attenuates high-frequency signals. Using the methods of circuit analysis described in the previous, it is easy to show that the ratio of the output and input voltages for this filter is given by:

$$\frac{V_0}{V_i} = H(\omega) = \frac{1}{1 + j\omega RC} = |H(\omega)|e^{-j\phi} \qquad (4.55)$$

where
$$|H(\omega)| = \frac{1}{\sqrt{1 + (\omega RC)^2}} \quad and \quad \phi = \tan^{-1}(\omega RC)$$

These results indicate that $H(\omega)$ varies from 1 to 0 as ωRC changes from 0.1 to 100. Both limits of this response function are important. The low frequency portion is important because it controls the attenuation of the input signal. To avoid errors greater than 2%, values for R and C must be selected so that $\omega RC < 0.203$ when designing the low pass filter.

The high-frequency response of the filter is also important because it controls the attenuation of the parasitic or noise signal. A reduction of 90% in the noise signal can be achieved if $\omega_p RC = 10$ (where ω_p is the circular frequency of the parasitic signal). It is not always possible with this passive filter to simultaneously limit the attenuation of the input signal to 2% while reducing the parasitic voltages by 90%, because this reduction requires that $\omega_p/\omega_i > 20$. If $\omega_p/\omega_i < 20$, it will be necessary to accept a higher ratio of parasitic signal, or to accept a higher loss of the input signal.

Active Filters

Operational amplifiers are employed to construct active filters where select frequencies can be attenuated and the signal amplified during the filtering process. Three active filters are illustrated in Fig. 4.18. The circuit shown in Fig. 4.18a is a low-pass filter similar to that presented in Fig. 4.17b. The ratio of the amplitudes of the input and output voltage for this filter is:

$$\frac{V_0}{V_i} = -\frac{R_2}{R_1}\frac{1}{\sqrt{1+(\omega/\omega_c)}} \tag{4.56}$$

where

$$\omega_c = \frac{1}{R_2 C}$$

The addition of the operational amplifier permits the gain ($G = R_1/R_2$) of the filter to be adjusted independent of the critical frequency ω_c, which is varied by changing R_2C. For independent settings of G_c and ω_c, R_2 is fixed and C is adjusted to vary ω_c while R_2 is adjusted to vary G.

 A two-pole Bessel filter is presented in Fig. 4.18b. The ratio of the amplitudes of the input and output voltage for this filter is given by:

$$\frac{V_0}{V_i} = \frac{1}{\sqrt{\left[1-(\omega/\omega_c)^2\right]^2 + 4(\omega/\omega_c)^2}} \tag{4.57}$$

Note that $\omega_c = 2/(3RC)$ when $R_1 = R_2 = R$ and $C_1 = C_2 + C$

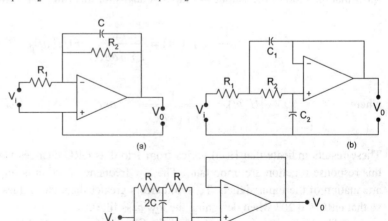

(a)   (b)   (c)

Fig. 4.18 Active filter circuits employing operational amplifiers.

The addition of the second pole (the use of a second capacitor) increases the rate of roll-off in attenuating the higher frequency signals and improves filter performance. Exercises concerning filters are given at the end of the chapter to enable one to compare performances of different types of filters.

Noise at 60 Hz, caused by the presence of motors and lights operating at line frequency, is extremely common, annoying and detrimental in most laboratories. If proper shielding does not eliminate these noise signals, a notch filter that attenuates signals at 60 Hz, can be employed. The twin-tee notch filter, shown in Fig. 4.18c, has an attenuating notch that depends on the of critical frequency $f_c = 1/(2\pi RC)$. By selecting $R = 41.9$ kΩ and $C = 0.0633$ μF, places f_c at 60 Hz. The frequencies of the input signal should be considerably lower or higher than f_c because the notch is broad.

Many other filters such as the fourth-order low-pass Butterworth filter and the Chebyshev filter are often used in signal processing applications. An excellent and extensive treatment of active filters is given in Reference [6].

4.8 AMPLITUDE MODULATION AND DEMODULATION

Amplitude modulation is a signal conditioning process in which the signal from a transducer is multiplied by a carrier signal of constant frequency and amplitude. The carrier signal can have any periodic form, such as a sinusoid, square wave, saw-tooth, or triangle. The transducer signal can be sinusoidal, transient, or random. The only requirement for mixing carrier and transducer signals is that the frequency ω_c of the carrier signal must be much higher than the frequency ω_i of the transducer signal.

The important aspects of data transmission with amplitude modulation can be illustrated by considering a case where both the carrier and transducer signals are sinusoidal. The output voltage V_0 is then given by the expression:

$$V_0 = [V_i \sin (\omega_i t)][V_c \sin (\omega_c t)] \tag{a}$$

where V_i and V_c are the amplitudes of the transducer and carrier signals, respectively.

Next, recall the trigonometric identity:

$$\sin A \sin B = \frac{1}{2}\cos(A - B) - \frac{1}{2}\cos(A + B) \tag{b}$$

Substituting Eq. (b) into Eq. (a) gives:

$$V_0 = \frac{V_i V_c}{2}\left[\cos(\omega_c - \omega_i)t - \cos(\omega_c - \omega_i)t\right] \tag{4.56}$$

Equation (4.56) indicates that the output signal is being transmitted at two discrete frequencies ($\omega_c - \omega_i$) and ($\omega_c + \omega_i$). The amplitude associated with each frequency is identical. The transmission of data at the higher frequencies permits use of high-pass filters to eliminate noise signals that usually occur at much lower frequencies. For example, consider use of a carrier frequency of 4,000 Hz with a transducer signal frequency of 60 Hz. Normally any 60-Hz noise would be difficult to eliminate because of the coincidence of the frequencies of the transducer signal and the noise. However, with amplitude modulation, the data (in this example) are transmitted at frequencies of 3,940 and 4,060 Hz and the 60-Hz noise can be easily eliminated with a high-pass filter. The results of Eq. (4.56) give an amplitude-modulated output signal V_0 that is illustrated in Fig. 4.19.

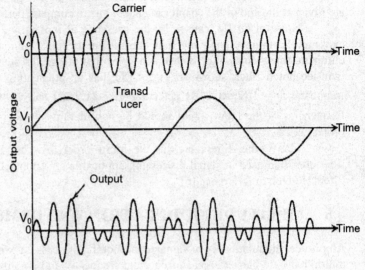

Fig. 4.19 Carrier ,transducer and amplitude-modulated output signals.

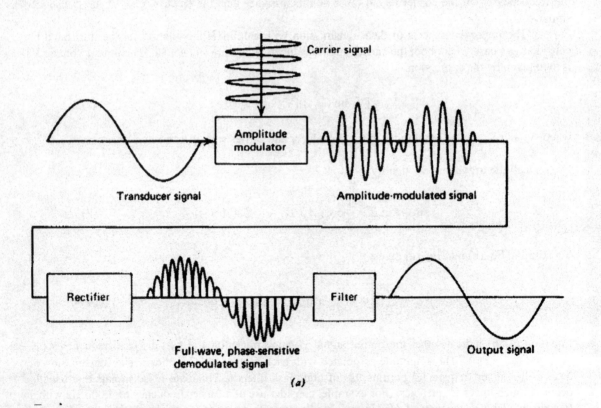

Fig. 4.20 (a) Amplitude modulation and demodulation.

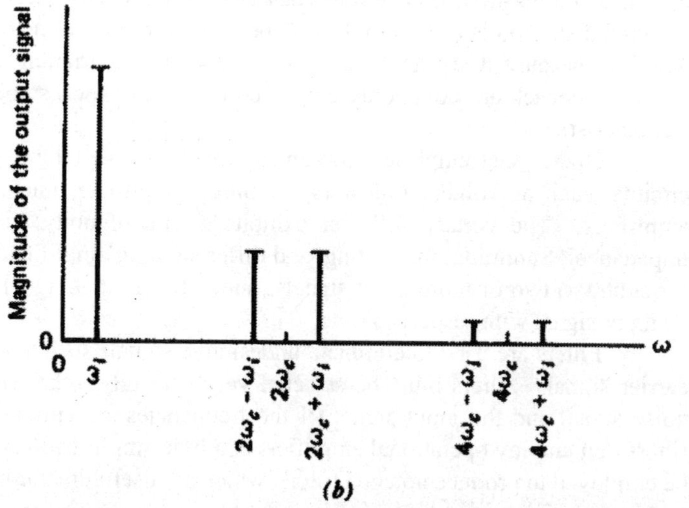

Fig. 4.20 (b) Frequency spectrum for the output from a full-wave phase-sensitive rectifier.

(b)

Although amplitude modulation offers several advantages in data transmission (stability, low power and noise suppression), the output signal is not suitable for display or interpretation until the input signal is separated from the carrier signal. The process of separating the transducer signal from the carrier signal is known as demodulation. The demodulation process is illustrated in block diagram form in Fig. 4.20a.

The first step in the demodulation process involves rectifying the signal. This is usually accomplished with a full-wave, phase-sensitive rectifier. The output from this rectifier is a series of half-sine waves with amplitude and sense corresponding to the output signal from the transducer. The frequency spectrum associated with a rectified signal is shown in Fig 4.20b. The frequency spectrum contains the input signal frequency as a single line at ω_i and four other lines that depend the carrier frequency. There are many other carrier lines at higher frequencies; however, these have been omitted since they can be easily eliminated by filtering. The transducer signal is separated with a low-pass filter that transmits ω_i and severely attenuates the frequencies $2\omega_c \pm \omega_i$, $4\omega_c \pm \omega_i$, and so on.

Carrier frequencies of 10 to 100 times the transducer frequencies are required if the carrier signal is to be eliminated by filtering. Multi-pole low-pass filters with sharp roll-off at the higher frequencies are usually employed in demodulation processes.

4.9 SUMMARY

Different signal conditioning circuits are employed in instrumentation systems and the performance of the system is markedly affected by the behavior of any of these circuits. Power supplies, both constant voltage and constant current, are commonly used in several different elements of an instrumentation system. It is imperative that the power supplies be stable over long periods of time and that noise and/or ripple be suppressed. Many portable instruments are equipped with long life batteries using Zener diodes to stabilize the supply voltage.

Both the potentiometer circuit and the Wheatstone bridge circuit convert resistance change to a voltage variation. The significant characteristics of each of these circuits have been described and equations have been derived to show their behavior. The Wheatstone bridge is widely used for converting resistance change to voltage, because it can be employed for both static and dynamic measurements.

Amplifiers are used in most instrumentation systems to increase the output signal from a transducer to a level sufficiently large for recording with a voltage-measuring instrument. Frequency response and linearity are two important characteristics of instrument amplifiers that must be adequate if signal distortion is to be avoided. A popular amplifier in instrumentation systems is the differential amplifier because it rejects common-mode signals. Instrument amplifiers that employ op-amps with resistor feedback are commonly employed because of their stability, low cost and superior operating characteristics.

Operational amplifiers (op-amps) are the active circuit element in many signal conditioning circuits, such as voltage followers, summing amplifiers, integrating amplifiers, and differentiating amplifiers. The voltage follower exhibits a gain of unity and is used because of its high input impedance. Summing, integrating, and differentiating amplifiers, as the names imply, are used to add (or subtract) two or more input signals, integrate an input signal with respect to time, or differentiate an input signal with respect to time.

Filters are used to eliminate undesirable signals such as noise, a dc signal or a high frequency carrier signal. Filters must be selected very carefully; otherwise, the filter may attenuate both the noise signal and the input signal (if the frequencies are similar) and produce serious error. Active filters that employ operational amplifiers combine amplification and filtering functions. They can also be employed to produce notched filters, which are useful in eliminating 60-Hz noise signals.

REFERENCES

1.   Ahmed, H. and P. J. Spreadbury: Analogue and Digital Electronics for Engineers, 2nd Edition, Cambridge University Press, New York, 1984.
2.   Franco: Design with Operational Amplifiers (OPAMPS) and Analog Integrated Circuits, 3rd Edition, McGraw Hill, New York, 2002.
3.   Virdee, B. S. and A. S. Virdee: Broadband Microwave Amplifiers, Artec House, New York, 2004.
4.   Doebelin, E. O.: Measurement Systems, 4th Edition, McGraw-Hill, New York, 1990.
5.   Sayed, A. H.: Fundamentals of Active Filtering, John Wiley New York, 2003.
6.   Hilburn, J. L. and D. E. Johnson: Manual of Active Filter Design, 2nd Edition, McGraw-Hill, New York, 1983.
7.   Hughes, F. W.: Op-Amp Handbook, 2nd Edition, Prentice Hall, Englewood Cliffs, NJ, 1984.
8.   Gray, P. R., P. J. Hurst, S. H. Lewis and R. J. Meyer: Analysis and Design of Analog Integrated Circuits, 5th Edition, John Wiley, New York, 2009.
9.   Palloe-Areny, R., J. G. Webster: Sensors and Signal Conditioning, Prentice-Hall, Englewood Cliffs, NJ, 2001.
10. Meiksin, Z. H.: Complete Guide to Active Filter Design, Op Amps, and Passive Components, Prentice-Hall, Englewood Cliffs, NJ, 1989.
11. Huelsman, L. H.: Active and Passive Filter Design, Prentice Hall, Englewood Cliffs, NJ,1993.
12. Carusone, T. C., D. A. Johns, K. W. Martins: Analog Integrated Circuit Design, 2nd Edition, John Wiley & Sons, New York, 2012.
13. Antoniou, A.: Digital Filters, McGraw Hill, New York, 2000.

EXERCISES

4.1   Describe the operation of the Zener controlled battery power supply shown in Fig. 4.1. If the battery supply voltage is $V_S = 9$ V and the Zener breakdown voltage is $V_Z = 5.2$ V, select R to limit the current flow to 100 mA. If a resistive load of 1,000 Ω is placed across the output terminals, describe the effect on the voltage V_0.

4.2   How and when will the power supply of Exercise 4.1 fail?

4.3   Sketch a circuit showing the output impedance of a dc power supply.

4.4   Prepare a graph showing the sensitivity S_{cv} versus r for a potentiometer circuit. Consider the product $p_T R_T$ as a variable equal to 100, 200, 500, and 1,000 Ω.

4.5   A strain gage with $R_g = 350$ Ω and $S_g = 2.00$ is used to monitor a sinusoidal signal with an amplitude of 1,200 μin./in. and a frequency of 200 Hz. Determine the output voltage V_0 if a constant-voltage potentiometer circuit is used to convert the resistance change to voltage. Assume $V_S = 8$ V and $r = 2$.

4.6   Determine the magnitude of the nonlinear term η for the data of Exercise 4.5.

4.7   If the strain gage described in Exercise 4.5 can dissipate 0.25 W, determine the input voltage V_S required to maximize the output voltage.

4.8   Determine the circuit sensitivity S_{cv} for the constant-voltage potentiometer circuit described in Exercise 4.5.

4.9   Determine the load error $\mathcal{E}$ if the output voltage V_0 of Exercise 4.5 is monitored with an oscilloscope having an input impedance of 10^6 Ω.

4.10 If a constant-current potentiometer circuit was used in Exercise 4.5 in place of the constant-voltage potentiometer circuit, determine the output voltage V_0 if $I = 3$ mA.

4.11 Determine the magnitude of the nonlinear term η for the data of Exercise 4.10.

4.12 If the strain gage described in Exercise 4.5 can dissipate 0.25 W, determine the current I that should be used with a constant-current potentiometer circuit to maximize the output voltage V_0.

4.13 Determine the circuit sensitivity S_{cc} for the constant-current potentiometer circuit of Exercise 4.10.

4.14 Determine the circuit sensitivity S_{cc} for the constant-current potentiometer circuit of Exercise 4.12.

4.15 Prepare a graph showing S_{cc} as a function of R_T from 100 to 10,000 for a constant current potentiometer circuit. Let $p = 0.1, 0.2, 0.5$ and 1 W.

4.16 A constant-voltage Wheatstone-bridge circuit is employed with a displacement transducer (potentiometer type) to convert resistance change to output voltage. If the displacement transducer has a total resistance of 2,000 Ω, then $\Delta R = \pm 1000$ Ω if the wiper is moved from the center position to either end. If the transducer is placed in arm R_1 of the bridge and, if $R_1 = R_2 = R_3 = R_4 = 1,000$ Ω, determine the magnitude of the nonlinear term η as a function of ΔR. Prepare a graph of η versus ΔR as ΔR varies from $-1,000$ Ω to $+1,000$ Ω.

4.17 Determine the output voltage v_0 as a function of ΔR for the displacement transducer and Wheatstone bridge described in Exercise 4.16 if $V_S = 8$V.

4.18 The nonlinear output voltage of Exercise 4.17 makes data interpretation difficult. How can the Wheatstone-bridge circuit be modified to improve the linearity of the output voltage V_0?

4.19 A strain gage with $R_g = 350$ Ω, $p_T = 0.25$ W, and $S_g = 2.05$ is used in arm R_1 of a constant-voltage Wheatstone bridge. Determine the values of R_2, R_3 and R_4 needed to maximize V_0 if the available power supply is limited to 15 V. Also determine the circuit sensitivity of the bridge of with these resistors.

4.20 If the strain gage of Exercise 4.19 is subjected to strain of 1,200 μin./in., determine the output voltage V_0.

4.21 Four strain gages are installed on a cantilever beam as shown in Fig.E4.21 to produce a displacement transducer:

(a) Indicate how the gages should be wired into a Wheatstone bridge to produce maximum signal output.

(b) Determine the circuit sensitivity if $R_g = 350 \, \Omega$, $p_T = 0.15$ W and S = 2.00.

(c) Determine the calibration constant $c = \delta/v_0$ for the transducer.

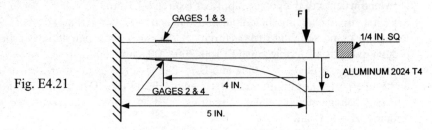

Fig. E4.21

4.22 If the cantilever beam of Exercise 4.21 is used as a load transducer, determine the calibration constant $C = P/v_0$.

4.23 A strain gage with $R_g = 350 \, \Omega$, $p_T = 0.10$ W, and $S_g = 2.00$ is used in arm R_1 of a constant-current Wheatstone bridge. Determine:

(a) Values of R_2, R_3 and R_4 needed to maximize v_0 if the available power supply can deliver a maximum of 10 mA.

(b) The circuit sensitivity of the bridge of Part (a)

(c) The output voltage v_0 if the gage is subjected to a strain of 1,500 in./in.

4.24 If the displacement transducer of Exercise 4.16 is used with a constant-current Wheatstone bridge, determine the magnitude of the nonlinear term η as a function of ΔR. Prepare a graph of η versus ΔR as ΔR varies from $-1,000 \, \Omega$ to $+1,000 \, \Omega$.

4.25 Determine the output voltage V_0 as a function of ΔR for the displacement transducer and Wheatstone bridge described in Exercise 4.24 if I = 20 mA.

4.26 Prepare a graph showing V_0/V_i for an amplifier responding to a step input voltage. Let $\tau = 10$ µs and consider gains of 10, 100, and 1,000.

4.27 Sketch simple circuits showing the difference between single ended and differential amplifiers.

4.28 If we have a common voltage of 0.1 V on the input to a differential amplifier with a gain $G_d = 500$ and we measure a voltage difference $\Delta v = 10$ mV, find the output voltage V_0 if the common mode rejection ratio is:

(a) 1,000   (c) 10,000

(b) 5,000   (d) 20,000

4.29 Prepare a graph showing the dynamic range R as a function of gain G for an amplifier with a maximum input voltage $V_i = 500$ mV. Assume the amplifier noise V_{nA} is 5 µA.

4.30 Use an op-amp with a gain of 100 dB and $R_a = 7 \, M\Omega$ to design an inverting amplifier with a gain of:

(a) 10   (b) 20   (c) 50   (d) 100

4.31 Use an op-amp with a gain of 100 dB and $R_a = 7 \, M\Omega$ to design a non-inverting amplifier with a gain of:

(a) 10   (b) 20   (c) 50   (d) 100

4.32 Use an op-amp with a gain of 100 dB and $R_a = 7 \, M\Omega$ to design a differential amplifier with a gain of:

(a) 10   (b) 20   (c) 50   (d) 100

4.33 Determine the input and output impedances for a voltage follower that incorporates an op-amp having a gain of 120 dB and $R_a = 10 \, M\Omega$.

4.34 Verify Eq. (4.49).

4.35 Verify Eq. (4.52).

4.36 Three signals V_{i1}, V_{i2} and V_{i3} are to be summed so that the output voltage V_0 is proportional to $V_{i1} + 3V_{i2} + (1/3)V_{i3}$. Select resistances R_1, R_2, R_3 and R_f to accomplish this operation.

4.37 Show that the op-amp circuit shown in Fig. E4.37 is a combined adding/scaling and subtracting/scaling amplifier by deriving the following equation for the output voltage V_0:

$$V_0 = \frac{R_f^*}{R_4}V_{i4} + \frac{R_f^*}{R_5}V_{i5} - \frac{R_f}{R_1}V_{i1} - \frac{R_f}{R_2}V_{i2} - \frac{R_f}{R_3}V_{i3}$$

where

$$R_f^* = R_f \left(\frac{\dfrac{1}{R_1} + \dfrac{1}{R_2} + \dfrac{1}{R_3} + \dfrac{1}{R_f}}{\dfrac{1}{R_4} + \dfrac{1}{R_5} + \dfrac{1}{R}} \right)$$

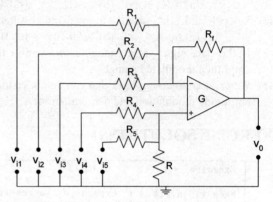

Fig. E4.37

4.38 The signals shown in Fig. E4.38 are to be used as input to an integrating amplifier having $R_1 = 1$ MΩ and $C_f = 0.5$ µF. Sketch the output signal corresponding to each of the input signals.

Fig. E4.38

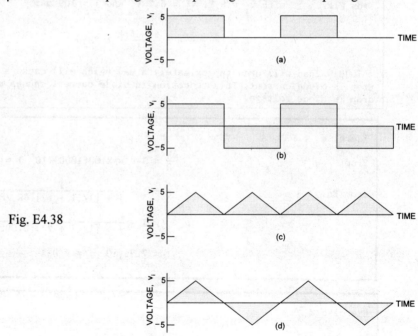

4.39 Discuss potential problem areas associated with the output voltages from signals (a) and (c) of Exercise 4.38.

4.40 Repeat Exercise 4.38 with a differentiating amplifier in place of the integrating amplifier.

4.41 Draw circuits for the simple high-pass and low-pass RC filters. Sketch response curves for these filters.

4.42 Verify Eq. (4.54).

4.43 Verify Eq. (6.55).

4.44 Select R and C for a high-pass filter so that the dc component of the output from a potentiometer circuit will be blocked, while the ac signal from a transducer will be transmitted with less than 2% attenuation if the transducer signal is

        (a) 10-Hz   (b) 20-Hz   (c) 30-Hz

4.45 Select R and C for a low-pass filter that will block 60 Hz noise but transmit the following low frequency signals with less than 1 percent loss:

        (a) 5-Hz   (b) 10-Hz   (c) 20 Hz.

4.46 Select R and C in Fig. 6.18 to give a notch filter with a critical frequency f_c of

        (a) 60-Hz   (b) 1200-Hz   (c) 10,000-Hz.

4.47 If the data signal is a triangular wave and the carrier signal is a square wave, sketch the amplitude modulated signal.

4.48 Write an engineering brief that can be understood by a business school graduate which explains amplitude modulation and demodulation.

EXERCISE SOLUTIONS

Exercise 4.1

When v_i in Fig 4.1 exceeds v_z in reverse bias, the Zener diode breaks down and the current flow increases rapidly.

From Fig. 4.1 with $v_s = 9$ V, $v_z = 5.2$ V, and $i = 100$ mA:

$$R = \frac{v_s - v_z}{i} = \frac{9 - 5.2}{0.100} = 38 \ \Omega$$

A 1000-Ω load will draw approximately 5 ma, which will cause a slight drop in diode current. This reduction in diode current causes a small drop in diode voltage.

Exercise 4.6

From

$$\frac{\Delta R}{R} = S_g \epsilon = 2.00(1200)(10^{-6}) = 0.0024$$

From Eq. 4.3

$$\eta = 1 - \frac{1}{1 + [1/(1 + r)][\Delta R_1/R_1]}$$

$$= 1 - \frac{1}{1 + [1/(1 + 2)][0.0024]}$$

$$= 7.99(10^{-4}) = 0.08\%$$

Exercise 4.7

From Eq. 4.8

$$v_s = (1 + r) \sqrt{p_g R_g}$$

$$= (1 + 2) \sqrt{(0.25)(350)} = 28.1 \text{ V}$$

Exercise 4.15

From Eq. 4.13 $$S_{cc} = \sqrt{p_T R_T}$$

R_T	Circuit Sensitivity S_{cc}			
	$p_T = 0.1$ W	$p_T = 0.2$ W	$p_T = 0.5$ W	$p_T = 1.0$ W
100	3.16	4.47	7.07	10.00
500	7.07	10.00	15.81	22.36
1000	10.0	14.14	22.36	31.62
5,000	22.36	31.62	50.00	70.71
10,000	31.62	44.72	70.71	100.00

Exercise 4.18

1. The nonlinear effects can be reduced by employing a constant-current source in place of the constant-voltage source.

2. Increasing r also decreases the nonlinear effect as indicated by Eq. (4.30). For example,

    with $\Delta R_p/R_p = 0.5$ and r = 1: $\eta = 0.111$

    with $\Delta R_p/R_p = 0.5$ and r = 5: $\eta = 0.040$

    with $\Delta R_p/R_p = 0.5$ and r = 9: $\eta = 0.024$

3. Finally ΔR_p of the potentiometer of Exercise 4.16 can be effectively reduced by placing a resistor in parallel with potentiometer. This parallel resistor produces $\Delta R_e < \Delta R_p$ which reduces the sensitivity of the circuit.

Exercise 4.27

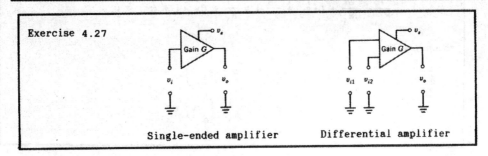

Single-ended amplifier   Differential amplifier

Exercise 4.23

From Eq.
$$v_o = \frac{i_s R_g r}{2(1 + r)} \frac{\Delta R_g}{R_g}$$

Eq. (4.29) indicates that v_o increases with r. A practical limit is about 10. Therefore:

$$R_1 = R_4 = 350 \ \Omega \qquad\qquad R_2 = R_3 = 10(350) = 3500 \ \Omega$$

$$i_{max} = \sqrt{p_T/R_g} = \sqrt{\frac{0.10}{120}} = 16.9 \ \text{mA}$$

Since 16.9 mA > 10 mA, the power supply limits the current to 10 mA.

From Eq. (4.30)
$$S_{cc} = \frac{i_s R_T r}{2(1 + r)} = \frac{10(10^{-3})(350)(10)}{2(1 + 10)} = 1.591 \ \text{V}$$

From
$$\frac{\Delta R_g}{R} = S_g \epsilon = 2.00(1500)(10^{-6})$$

$$= 3000(10^{-6}) = 0.0030$$

$$v_o = \frac{i_s R_g r}{2(1 + r)} \frac{\Delta R_g}{R_g} = \frac{10(10^{-3})(350)(10)}{2(1 + 10)} (0.0030)$$

$$= 4.77(10^{-3}) \ \text{V} = 4.77 \ \text{mV}$$

Exercise 4.35

$$i_1 = \frac{v_1 - v_A}{R_1}$$

$$q_f = C(v_o - v_A)$$

$$i_f = \dot{q}_f = C(\dot{v}_o - \dot{v}_A)$$

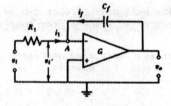

At Point A:

$$i_i + i_f = \frac{v_i - v_A}{R_1} + C(\dot{v}_o - \dot{v}_A) = 0$$

$$v_o = -Gv_A$$

$$\frac{v_i}{R_1} + \frac{v_o}{GR_1} + C(\dot{v}_o + \frac{\dot{v}_o}{G}) = \frac{v_i}{R_1} + C\dot{v}_o(1 + \frac{1}{G}) = 0$$

Which yields

$$\dot{v}_o = -\frac{1}{R_1 C} v_i$$

$$v_o = -\frac{1}{R_1 C} \int_0^t v_i \ dt$$

Exercise 4.40

From Eq. (4.53)

$$v_o = - R_f C_1 \frac{dv_i}{dt}$$

$$= (10^6)(0.5)(10^{-6}) \frac{dv_i}{dt} = 0.5 \frac{dv_i}{dt}$$

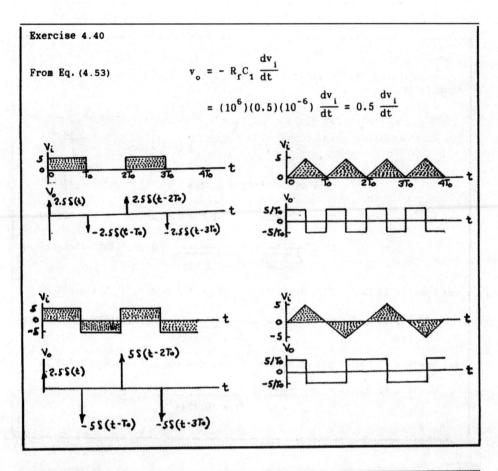

Exercise 4.41

High-pass RC filter:

Low-pass RC filter:

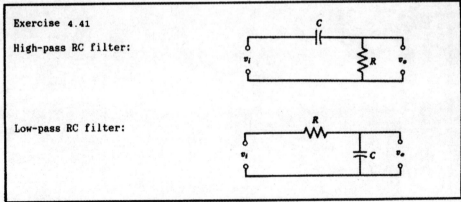

Exercise 4.45

From Eq.(4.55) $\dfrac{v_o}{v_i} = \dfrac{1}{\sqrt{1 + u^2}}$ where $u = \omega RC$

For 1% Attenuation: $\dfrac{v_o}{v_i} = 0.99 = \dfrac{1}{\sqrt{1 + u^2}}$ $u = 0.1425$

$u = \omega RC = 2\pi f RC = 0.1425$ $RC = \dfrac{0.1425}{2\pi f}$

(a) For $f = 5$ Hz: $RC = 0.004536$ If $C = 1.0\ \mu F$ $R = 4.536$ kΩ

$f = 60$ Hz: $RT = \dfrac{1}{\sqrt{1 + u^2}} = \dfrac{1}{\sqrt{1 + (1.71)^2}} = 0.505$ (49% attenuation)

(b) For $f = 10$ Hz: $RC = 0.002268$ If $C = 1.0\ \mu F$ $R = 2.268$ kΩ

$f = 60$ Hz: $RT = \dfrac{1}{\sqrt{1 + u^2}} = \dfrac{1}{\sqrt{1 + (0.855)^2}} = 0.760$ (24% attenuation)

(c) For $f = 20$ Hz: $RC = 0.001134$ If $C = 1.0\ \mu F$ $R = 1.134$ kΩ

$f = 60$ Hz: $RT = \dfrac{1}{\sqrt{1 + u^2}} = \dfrac{1}{\sqrt{1 + (0.428)^2}} = 0.919$ (8% Attenuation

CHAPTER 5

DISPLACEMENT AND VELOCITY MEASUREMENTS — FIXED REFERENCE

5.1 INTRODUCTION

Displacement and velocity measurements relative to a fixed reference are described in this chapter. The major difference between seismic- and fixed-reference motion measurements is that the reference point does not move with fixed reference measurements ($x = 0$). Later in Chapter 10, we will cover measurement methods when there is global movement of an object and a fixed reference point cannot be defined. Many different sensors are available for making displacement determinations, when a fixed reference frame is available. Variable-resistance and capacitance sensors are widely used for small static and dynamic displacement measurements (from a few micrometers to a few millimeters). Differential transformers are used for larger displacement magnitudes (from 1 to 100 mm). Resistance potentiometers are used where less accuracy but greater range (1 mm to 10 m) is required. Optical methods are available when contact with the object is not possible.

5.2 POTENTIOMETERS FOR DISPLACEMENT MEASUREMENTS

The simplest type of potentiometer, shown schematically in Fig. 5.1, is the slide-wire resistor. This sensor consists of a length l of resistance wire attached across a voltage source V_i. The relationship between the output voltage V_0 and the position x of a wiper, as it moves along the length of the wire, is expressed as:

$$V_0 = (x/l)V_i \qquad x = (V_0/V_i)l \qquad (5.1)$$

Thus, the slide-wire potentiometer can be used to measure a displacement x.

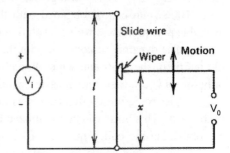

Fig. 5.1 Slide-wire resistance potentiometer.

Straight-wire resistors are not feasible for most applications, because the resistance of short lengths of wire is low and this feature imposes excessive power requirements on the voltage source. To alleviate this difficulty, high-resistance, wire-wound potentiometers are obtained by winding the resistance wire around an insulating core, as shown in Fig. 5.2. The potentiometer illustrated in Fig. 5.2a is used for linear displacement measurements. Cylindrically shaped potentiometers, similar to the one illustrated in Fig. 5.2b, are used for angular displacement measurements. The resistance of a wire-wound potentiometer can range between 10 and 10^5 ohms Ω depending upon the type and diameter of the wire used and the length of the coil.

The resistance of the wire-wound potentiometer increases in a stepwise manner as the wiper moves from one turn to the next. This step change in resistance limits the resolution of the potentiometer to L/n, where n is the number of turns in the length L of the coil. Resolutions ranging from 0.05 to 1 % are common, with the lower limit obtained by using many turns of very small diameter wire.

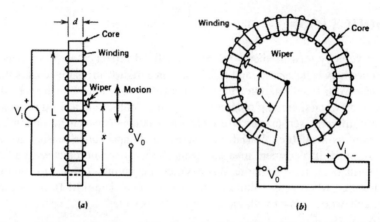

Fig. 5.2 Wire-wrapped resistance potentiometer for (a) axial displacements and (b) for angular displacements.

The active length L of the coil controls the range of the potentiometer. Linear potentiometers are available in many lengths up to about 1 m. Arranging the coil in the form of a helix can extend the range of the angular-displacement potentiometer. Helical potentiometers are commercially available with as many as 20 turns; therefore, angular displacements as large as 7,200 degrees can be measured easily.

In order to improve resolution, potentiometers have been introduced that utilize thin films with controlled resistivity instead of wire-wound coils. Thin metallic films on an insulating substrate exhibits very high resolution together with lower noise and longer life. For example, a resistance of 50 to 100 Ω/mm can be obtained with the conductive plastic films that are used for commercially available potentiometers with a resolution of 0.001 mm.

The dynamic response of both the linear and the angular potentiometer is severely limited by the inertia of the shaft and wiper assembly. Because this inertia is large, the potentiometer is used only for static or quasi-static measurements, where a high frequency response is not required.

Electronic noise often occurs as the electrical contact on the wiper moves from one wire turn to the next. This noise can be minimized by ensuring that the coil is clean and free of oxide films and by lubricating the coil with a thin film of silicone oil. Under ideal conditions, the life of a wire-wound and conductive-plastic potentiometer exceeds 1 and 10 million cycles, respectively.

Potentiometers are used primarily to measure large displacements — 10 mm or more for linear motion and 15 degrees or more for angular motion. Potentiometers are relatively inexpensive yet accurate; however, their main advantage is simplicity of operation, because only a voltage source and a DVM to measure voltage comprise the complete instrumentation system. Their primary disadvantage is limited frequency response, which precludes their use for dynamic measurements.

5.3 DIFFERENTIAL TRANSFORMERS TO MEASURE DISPLACEMENTS

Differential transformers, based on a variable-inductance principle, are also used to measure displacement. The most popular variable-inductance sensor for linear displacement measurements is the linear-variable-differential-transformer (LVDT). An LVDT, illustrated in Fig 5.3a, consists of three symmetrically spaced coils wound onto an insulated bobbin. A magnetic core, which moves through the bobbin without contact, provides a path for magnetic flux linkage between coils. The position of the magnetic core controls the mutual inductance between the center or primary coil and the two outer or secondary coils.

When an ac excitation is applied to the primary coil, voltages are induced in the two secondary coils. The secondary coils are wired in a series-opposing circuit, as shown in Fig. 5.3b. When the core is centered between the two secondary coils, the voltages induced in the secondary coils are equal but out of phase by 180°. Because the coils are in a series-opposing circuit, the voltages V_1 and V_2 in the two coils cancel and the output voltage is zero. When the core is moved from the center position, an imbalance in mutual inductance between the primary and secondary coils occurs and an output voltage, $V_0 = (V_2 - V_1)$, develops. The output voltage is a linear function of core position, as shown in Fig. 5.4, if the displacement of the core is within the operating range of the LVDT. The direction of the displacement is determined from the phase of the output voltage relative to the input voltage.

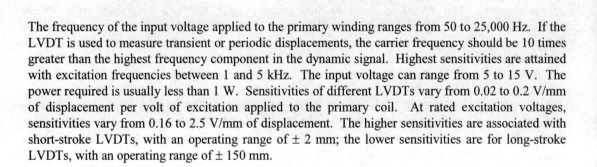

Fig. 5.3 (a) Sectional view of a linear variable differential transformer (LVDT). (b) Schematic diagram of the LVDT circuit.

The frequency of the input voltage applied to the primary winding ranges from 50 to 25,000 Hz. If the LVDT is used to measure transient or periodic displacements, the carrier frequency should be 10 times greater than the highest frequency component in the dynamic signal. Highest sensitivities are attained with excitation frequencies between 1 and 5 kHz. The input voltage can range from 5 to 15 V. The power required is usually less than 1 W. Sensitivities of different LVDTs vary from 0.02 to 0.2 V/mm of displacement per volt of excitation applied to the primary coil. At rated excitation voltages, sensitivities vary from 0.16 to 2.5 V/mm of displacement. The higher sensitivities are associated with short-stroke LVDTs, with an operating range of ± 2 mm; the lower sensitivities are for long-stroke LVDTs, with an operating range of ± 150 mm.

Because the LVDT requires ac excitation at frequencies different from common ac supplies, signal conditioning circuits are necessary. A typical signal conditioner (see Fig. 5.5) provides a power supply, a frequency generator to drive the LVDT and a demodulator to convert the ac output signal from the LVDT to an analog dc output voltage. A dc amplifier is incorporated in the signal conditioner to increase the magnitude of the output voltage.

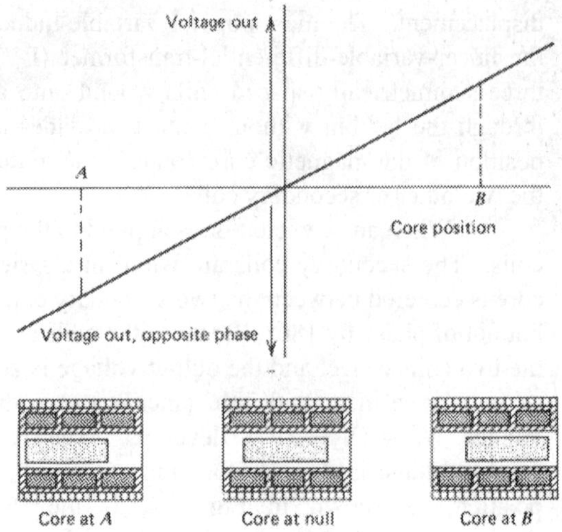

Fig. 5.4 Phase-referenced voltage as a function of LVDT core position.

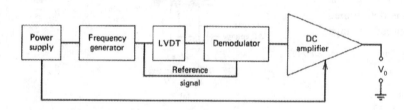

Fig. 5.5 Block diagram of the signal conditioning circuit for a LVDT.

Microelectronic circuits have been developed that permit miniaturization of the signal conditioners so that they can be packaged within the case of an LVDT. The result is a small self-contained sensor known as a direct current differential transformer (DCDT). A DCDT operates from a battery or a regulated power supply and provides an amplified output signal that can be monitored on either a DVM or an oscilloscope. The output impedance of a DCDT is relatively low (about 100 Ω).

Both the LVDT and the DCDT are used to measure linear displacement. An analogous device known as a rotary variable differential transformer (RVDT) has been developed to measure angular displacements. The RVDT consists of two primary coils and two secondary coils wound symmetrically on a large-diameter insulated bobbin. A cardioid-shaped rotor, fabricated from a magnetic material, is mounted on a shaft that extends through the bobbin and serves as the core. As the shaft rotates and turns the core, the mutual inductance between the primary and secondary windings varies and produces an output voltage versus rotation response that resembles a modified sinusoid.

Although the RVDT is capable of a complete rotation (360 degrees), the range of linear operation is limited to about ± 40°. The linearity of a typical RVDT, having a range of ± 40°, is about 0.5% of the range. Reducing the operating range improves its linearity; an RVDT operating within a range of ± 5° exhibits a linearity of about 0.1%.

LVDTs, DCDTs, and RVDTs have many advantages[1] as sensors for measuring displacement. There is no contact between the core and the coils; therefore, friction and hysteresis are eliminated. Because the output is continuously variable with input, resolution is often determined by the characteristics of the voltage recorder. No contact between the core and the coils ensures that its life will be long with no significant deterioration of performance over this period[2]. The small core mass and freedom from friction give the sensor a limited capability for dynamic measurements. Finally, the sensors are not damaged by over travel; therefore, they can be employed as feedback transducers in servo-controlled systems where over-travel may occur due to accidental deviations beyond the control band. A commercially available RVDT is presented in Fig. 5.6.

Fig. 5.6 A commercially available rotary variable differential transformer (RVDT). Courtesy of Moog Components Group.

5.4 CAPACITANCE SENSORS TO MEASURE DISPLACMENTS

The capacitance sensor, illustrated in Fig. 5.7a, consists of a target plate and a second plate termed as the sensor head. These two plates are separated by an air gap of thickness h and form the terminals of a capacitor that exhibits a capacitance C given by:

$$C = \frac{kKA}{h} \tag{5.2}$$

where C is the capacitance in picofarad (pF); A is the area of the sensor head ($\pi D^2/4$); K is the relative dielectric constant for the medium in the gap (K = 1 for air) and k = 0.225 is a constant for dimensions in in. and k = 0.00885 for dimensions in mm.

If the separation between the head and the target is changed by an amount Δh, then the capacitance C becomes:

$$C + \Delta C = \frac{kKA}{h + \Delta h} \tag{a}$$

which can be written as:

$$\frac{\Delta C}{C} = \frac{\Delta h / h}{1 + (\Delta h / h)} \tag{5.3}$$

---

[1] Typical electrical and mechanical performance characteristics for LVDTs and DCDTs are listed at http://www.meas-spec.com/position-sensors.aspx.
[2] Mean time between failures for a typical DCDT is 33,000 h.

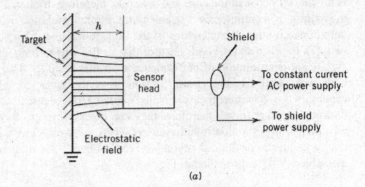

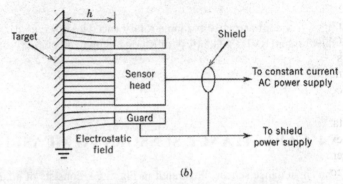

Fig. 5.7 Capacitor sensors: (a) without a guard ring, where edge effects in the electrostatic field affect the range of linearity, and (b) with a guard ring to extend its linear range.

This result indicates that $(\Delta C/C)$ is non-linear because of the presence of $\Delta h/h$ in the denominator of Eq. (5.3). To avoid the difficulty of employing a capacitance sensor with a non-linear output, we measure its change in the impedance. Note that the impedance Z_C of a capacitor is given by:

$$Z_C = -j/(\omega C) \qquad\qquad\text{(b)}$$

With a capacitance change ΔC it can be shown that:

$$Z_C + \Delta Z_C = -\frac{j}{\omega}\left[\frac{1}{C+\Delta C}\right] \qquad\qquad\text{(c)}$$

Substituting Eq. (b) into Eq. (c) and solving for $\Delta Z/Z$ gives:

$$\frac{\Delta Z_C}{Z_C} = -\frac{\Delta C/C}{1+\Delta C/C} \qquad\qquad\text{(5.4)}$$

Finally, substituting Eq. (5.3) into Eq. (5.4) yields:

$$\frac{\Delta Z_C}{Z_C} = -\frac{\Delta h}{h} \qquad\qquad\text{(5.5)}$$

From Eq. (5.5) it is clear that the capacitive impedance Z_C is linear in Δh and that methods of measuring ΔZ_C permits simple plates (the target as ground and the sensor head as the positive terminal) to act as a sensor to measure the displacement Δh. Cylindrical sensor heads provide linear output signals and Eq. (5.5) is valid provided $0 < h < D/4$, where D is the diameter of the sensor head. Fringing in the electric field produces non-linearity if $(h + \Delta h)$ exceeds D/4. The linear range can be extended to $h \approx D/2$ if a guard ring surrounds the sensor as shown in Fig. 5.7b. The guard ring essentially moves the distorted edges of the electric field to the outer edge of the guard, significantly improving the uniformity of the electric field over the sensor area and extending its linear range.

The sensitivity of the capacitance probe is given by Eqs. (b), (5.2) and (5.5) as:

$$S = \frac{\Delta Z_C}{\Delta h} = \left| \frac{Z_C}{h} \right| = \left| \frac{1}{\omega Ch} \right| = \frac{1}{\omega kKA} \tag{5.6}$$

Sensitivity can be improved by reducing the area A of the probe; however, as noted previously, the range of the probe is limited by linearity to about D/2. Clearly, there is a range-sensitivity trade-off. Of particular importance is the circular frequency ω term in Eq. (5.6). Low frequency improves sensitivity but limits frequency response of the instrument, another trade-off. It is also important to note that the frequency of the ac power supply must remain constant to maintain a stable calibration constant.

The capacitance sensor has several advantages. It is non-contacting and can be used with any target material provided the material exhibits a resistivity less than $100\ \Omega/\text{cm}$. The sensor is extremely rugged and can be subjected to high shock loads (5,000 g's) and intense vibratory environments. Their use as a sensor at high temperature is particularly impressive. They can be constructed to withstand temperatures up to 2,000 °F and they exhibit a constant sensitivity S over an extremely wide range of temperature (74 to 1,600 °F). Examination of the relation for S in Eq. (5.6) shows that the dielectric constant K is the only parameter that can change with temperature. Because K is constant for air over a wide range of temperature, the capacitance sensor has excellent temperature characteristics.

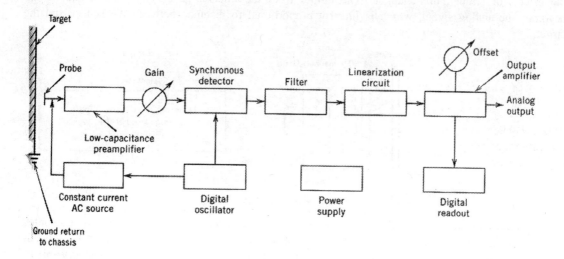

Fig. 5.8 Schematic diagram of an instrument system for monitoring the output of a capacitor sensor.

The change in the capacitive impedance Z_C is usually measured with the circuit illustrated schematically in Fig. 5.8. The probe, its shield and guard ring are powered with a constant current ac supply. A digital oscillator is used to drive the ac supply and to maintain a constant frequency. This oscillator also provides the reference frequency for the synchronous detector. The voltage drop across the probe is detected with a low capacitance preamplifier. The signal from the preamplifier is then amplified again with a fixed-gain instrument amplifier. The high voltage ac signal from the instrument amplifier is rectified and given a sign in the synchronous detector. The rectified signal is filtered to eliminate high frequency ripple and give a dc output voltage related to Δh. A linearizing circuit is used to extend the range of the sensor by accommodating for the influence of the fringes in the electrostatic field. Finally, the signal is passed through a second instrument amplifier where the gain and zero offset can be varied to adjust the sensitivity and the zero reading of the DVM display. When the gain and zero offset are properly adjusted, the DVM reads Δh directly to the scale selected by the operator.

5.5 EDDY CURRENT SENSORS TO MEASURE DISPLACEMENTS

An eddy current sensor measures the distance between the sensor head and an electrically conducting surface, as illustrated in Fig. 5.9. The sensor operation is based on eddy currents that are induced at the conducting surface when magnetic flux lines from the sensor intersect with the surface of the conducting material. The magnetic flux lines are generated by the active coil in the sensor, which is driven at a high frequency (1 MHz). The magnitude of the eddy current produced at the surface of the conducting material is a function of the distance between the active coil and the surface. The eddy currents increase as the separation gap decreases.

Changes in the eddy currents are sensed with an impedance (inductance) bridge. Two coils in the sensor are used for two arms of the bridge. The other two arms are housed in an associated electronic package illustrated in Fig. 5.9. The first coil in the sensor (active coil), which changes inductance with target movement, is wired into the active arm of the bridge. The second coil is wired into an opposing arm of the same bridge, where it serves as a compensating coil to balance and cancel the effects of temperature change. The output from the impedance bridge is demodulated and becomes the analog signal, which is linearly proportional to distance between the sensor and the target.

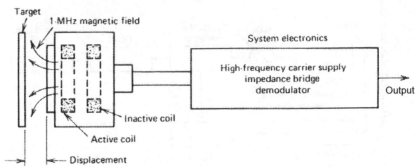

Fig. 5.9 Schematic diagram for an eddy current sensor.

The sensitivity of the sensor is dependent upon the target material with higher sensitivity associated with high conductivity materials. The output for a number of materials is shown as a function of specific resistivity in Fig. 5.10. For aluminum targets, the sensitivity is typically 100 mV/mil (4 V/mm). Thus, it is apparent that eddy current sensors are high-output devices if the specimen material is non-magnetic. Note in Fig. 5.10 that the sensitivity decreases significantly if the specimen material is magnetic.

For non-conducting, poorly conducting or magnetic materials, it is possible to bond a thin film of aluminum foil to the surface of the target at the location of the sensor to improve its sensitivity. Because the penetration of the eddy currents into the material is minimal, the thickness of the foil can be as small as 0.0007 in. (ordinary kitchen type aluminum foil).

Fig. 5.10 Relative output from an eddy-current sensor as a function of the resistivity of the target material.

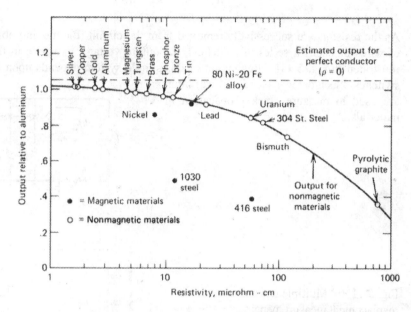

The effect of temperature on the output of the eddy current sensor is small. The sensing head with dual coils is temperature compensated; however, a small error can be produced by temperature changes in the target material since the resistivity of the target material is a function of temperature. For instance, if the temperature of an aluminum target is increased by 500 °F, its resistivity increases from 0.03 to 0.06 $\mu\Omega$-m. From Figure 5.10 it is evident that the bridge output is reduced by about 2% for this change in resistivity. For aluminum, the temperature sensitivity of the eddy current sensor is 0.004% per °F.

The range of the sensor is controlled by the diameters of the coils, with the larger sensors exhibiting the larger ranges. The range to diameter ratio is usually about 0.25. Linearity is typically better than 0.5% and resolution is better than 0.05% of full scale. The frequency response (bandwidth) is typically 20 kHz, although small-diameter coils can be used to increase this response to 50 kHz.

The fact that an eddy current sensor does not require contact for measuring displacement is important. As a result of this feature, these sensors are often used in transducer systems for automatic control of dimensions in fabrication processes. They are also applied extensively to determine thicknesses of non-conducting organic coatings that are bonded to metals.

5.6 DISPLACEMENT MEASUREMENTS WITH MULTIPLE RESISTORS

Another variable-resistance, displacement-measuring device consists of a sequence of resistors in parallel, as shown in the circuit of Fig. 5.11. With a fixed supply voltage V_s, the initial output voltage V_0 of the circuit is given by the expression:

$$V_0 = \frac{R_0}{R_0 + R_e} V_s \qquad (5.7)$$

where

$$\frac{1}{R_e} = \frac{1}{R_1} + \frac{1}{R_2} + \frac{1}{R_3} + \cdots + \frac{1}{R_n}$$

As the resistors are successively removed from the circuit (the moving object either breaks the series of wires or opens a series of switches), the output voltage V_0 varies in the descending step fashion illustrated in Fig. 5.11b. Resolution of this simple system depends upon the spacing of the wires or switches. Such devices (see Fig. 5.1c) often are used to measure crack propagation in materials.

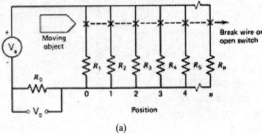

(a)

Fig. 5.11 (a) Multiple resistor circuit for displacement measurements.
(b) Output voltage position trace as resistors are opened.
(c) Parallel resistance gage that is bonded to a fracture specimen to record crack tip position during a fracture process.

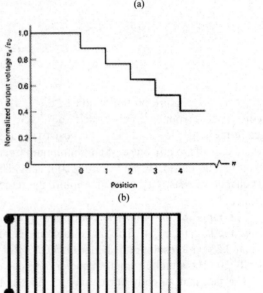

(b)

(c)

5.7 OPTICAL DISPLACEMENT MEASUREMENTS

A wide range of optical methods are available to measure displacements. These methods range from Moiré gratings which give interference patterns for measuring displacements to high-speed photography using video digitization and high-speed computers. A major advantage of optical methods is that contact is not necessary and the object under investigation is not influenced by the size or the mass of a sensor. Several of the displacement measuring methods using optical methods are described below.

5.7.1 Photoelectric Displacement Transducers

A light source, an opaque object, and a photo-detector can be combined to produce a very useful displacement measuring system that does not require contact with an object in motion. Exact implementation depends on the type of photoelectric sensor to be used. For photo-emissive and photo-conductive sensors, which generate a current that is proportional to the illumination imposed on the sensitive area of the sensor, a system similar to the one illustrated schematically in Fig 5.12 is used. In this system, a parallel beam of light is generated by using a point light source and a collimating lens. An opaque flag, whose position in the parallel beam is related to the displacement, interrupts the light beam and controls the illumination falling on the focusing lens and ultimately on the sensitive area of the photo-detector.

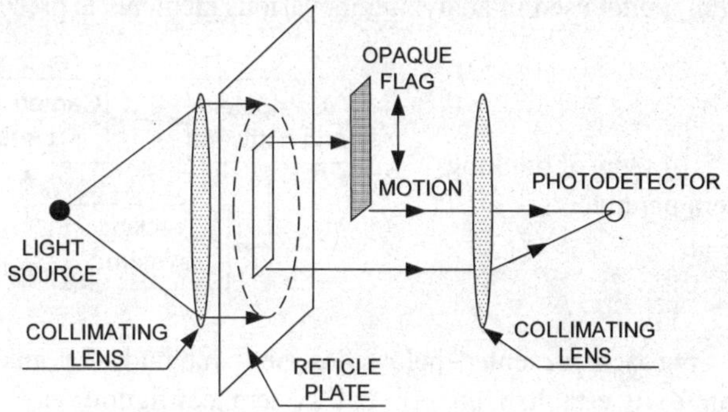

Fig. 5.12 Schematic diagram of a photo-detector system for measuring displacements.

The focusing lens and photo-detector of Fig. 5.12 are often replaced by a flat photovoltaic cell that exhibits the behavior of a current generator in parallel with a capacitor as shown in Fig. 5.13a. The output V_0 from the circuit of Fig. 5.13a depends on the load resistance R_M of the instrument used to record the voltage. For an open-circuit condition ($R_M \Rightarrow \infty$), the output V_0 varies logarithmically with illumination. Dynamic response and linearity can be improved by introducing an op-amp into the circuit as a current amplifier, as shown in Fig. 5.13b. In this circuit, the feedback resistor R_f is adjusted to give the best linear output over the signal range. The inherent capacitance of the sensor is effectively removed with this circuit because the voltage across the capacitor is very small due to the large open-loop gain G of the op-amp.

Errors with this system result from light source and lens imperfections that tend to produce variations in intensity over the field. However, non-contacting measurements with accuracies better than ± 5 % can be made at low cost using this technique.

Fig. 5.13 Circuits used with photovoltaic sensors.

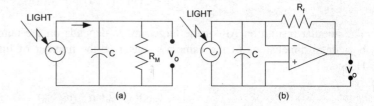

(a)   (b)

5.7.2 Optical Tracker System

An optical tracking system consists of 3 subsystems that include an optical imaging camera, a mechanical tracking arrangement and a tracking computer. The optical imaging system acquires light from the target converting it into a digital image that the tracking computer processes. This imaging system is usually a standard digital camera or a high resolution camera mounted on a telescope. The camera determines the upper-limit of the range of the tracking system.

The mechanical tracking arrangement maintains the optical image in the field of view of the camera. The response of the mechanical tracking system together with the camera determines the tracking system's ability to maintain its lock on a target that often changes direction and velocity. A computer records the images from the camera and performs an analysis to establish the target position with respect to time. It also provides the feedback signals necessary to control the movement of the tracking system to maintain its lock on the target. Tracking a target that is moving with high velocity and changing direction or orientation is not a trivial task.

An optical tracking system can be viewed as a collection of interdependent subsystems that must be analyzed in determining their effect on its overall performance of the integrated system. The system model used in analyzing its various elements is presented in Fig. 5.14.

Fig. 5.14 Optical tracking system parameters

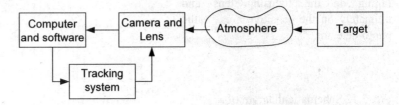

The approach presented below describes methods for analyzing some of the important parameters required to establish an optimal system configuration. Target characteristics and environmental parameters that must be considered include the following:

- Size
- Dynamics
- Target Radiance
- Spectral Region
- Range
- Background Radiance
- Atmospheric Attenuation

Let's first consider the effects on the target image based on the size and range of the target, camera's focal length and sensor size and pixel density. The angular field of view α of the target image depends on the camera's sensor size L and the focal length of its lens f. Accordingly:

$$\alpha = 2 \tan^{-1} (L/2f) \tag{5.8}$$

The angular resolution AR of the target image depends on the number of pixels per line N_h in the horizontal dimensions of the camera's sensor or the number of lines N_v in its vertical dimension. Hence:

$$AR_h = 2 \tan^{-1} (\alpha_h/N_h)$$

$$AR_v = 2 \tan^{-1} (\alpha_v/N_v) \tag{5.9}$$

The target's angular capability φ depends on the target size H and its range S (horizontal distance from the camera's lens to the target).

$$\varphi = \tan^{-1} (H/S) \tag{5.10}$$

Finally, the number of pixels N_p or the number of lines N_L imposed on the camera's sensor is given by:

$$N_p = \varphi/(AR_h)$$

$$N_L = \varphi/(AR_v)$$

(5.11)

Consider an optical tracking system with a camera equipped with a sensor having a horizontal dimension of 12.7 mm and a vertical dimension of 9.6 mm. The sensor has 640 pixels in its horizontal direction and 480 in its vertical direction. Its lens has a focal length of 1,000 mm. The target, which is 5 m in size, is positioned at a range of 2 km. Let's determine the pixel count in the image to ascertain if the count is sufficient for measurement of displacement or velocity.

Using Eq. (5.8) to determine the angular field of view gives:

$$\alpha_h = 2 \tan^{-1} [(12.7)/(2000)] = 0.7276° \qquad \text{(a)}$$

$$\alpha_v = 2 \tan^{-1} [(9.6)/(2000)] = 0.5500° \qquad \text{(b)}$$

The angular resolution AR in the horizontal and vertical directions is calculated from Eq. (5.9) as:

$$AR_h = 2 \tan^{-1} (0.7276/640) = 0.001137 \text{ degrees/pixel} \qquad \text{(c)}$$

$$AR_v = 2 \tan^{-1} (0.5500/480) = 0.00146 \text{ degrees/line} \qquad \text{(d)}$$

The target's angular dimension is given by Eq. (5.10) as:

$$\varphi = \tan^{-1} (5/2,000) = 0.1432° \qquad \text{(e)}$$

Finally, the pixel count for the target is given by Eq. (5.11) as:

$$N_p = \varphi/(AR_h) = (0.1432)/(0.001137) = 104.5 \text{ pixels} \qquad \text{(f)}$$

$$N_L = \varphi/(AR_v) = (0.1432)/(0.00146) = 98.1 \text{ lines} \qquad \text{(g)}$$

These results indicate that the image will contain about 10^4 pixels, which should be sufficient to provide data for image analysis used to determine the displacement or velocity of the target. If higher resolution is required (more pixels) the range could be reduced to increase the target's angular dimension. Alternatively, a camera with a high pixel count sensor could be employed.

The design of the tracking system depends on the velocity and the range of the target. For low speed objects or long-range tracking, the target can be tracked manually where the operator keeps the target within the field of view. In this approach, the target is viewed through a telescope or with a TV monitor, and the results depend on the skill of the operator.

For high speed objects that move rapidly within the field of view, it is necessary to use closed loop control of the mechanical tracking mechanism. There are two aspects to closed loop control of the tracking mechanism. The first is the image analysis of the target's image in the field of view. The image analysis program establishes the position of the centroid of the target relative to the center point in the field of view. The difference in these two positions provides an error signal to the servo system that adjusts the mechanical tracker to bring the centroid of the target and the center-point of the field of view into closer correspondence. Because of the use of high-framing-rate-cameras, the image analysis must be performed in milliseconds requiring high-speed computers for adequate tracking control.

The demands on the mechanism to adjust the target elevation and bearing angles depend on the target speed, range and altitude. For high velocity applications servo-control valves with wide bandwidth are used to drive hydraulic cylinders that respond rapidly to adjust the elevation and bearing angles to maintain the target in the field of view of the camera.

The major advantage of optical trackers is the ability to measure the motion of high velocity vehicles in space and to simultaneously inspect the surfaces of the vehicles.

5.7.3 Video Camera Motion Analysis

The development of high-performance video cameras coupled with video recorders and digital computers has produced a new generation of full-field displacement-measurement systems. The major elements of these systems, shown in Fig. 5.15, include a video camera, a video recorder, a video monitor, a video processor, a computer with disk storage, a graphics workstation and a printer/plotter unit.

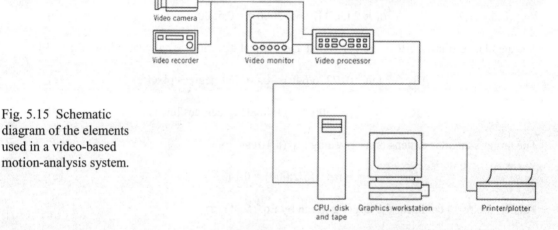

Fig. 5.15 Schematic diagram of the elements used in a video-based motion-analysis system.

Motion analysis with a video system consists of a number of basic steps. The first step involves recording of the images of interest. Numerous camera options are available that support a wide range of illumination conditions, fields of view, and picture frame rates ranging from one to hundreds of thousands of frame/s. The data representing the image are usually stored on a video cassette by the video recorder for the slower cameras or on RAM for the high speed video recorders. These data are available for editing, display or video processing.

Fig. 5.16 A high speed video camera capable of 150,000 frames/s.
Courtesy of Olympus

The second step involves reducing the vast amount of data available in a given frame to that data required for the motion analysis. A video processor is used to define those pixels needed to describe the object being recorded. A video image composed of 1,024 rows by 1,280 columns has 1.31×10^6 picture elements (pixels) that each contains 10 bits to define the light intensity of the pixel. The video processor and monitor allow the operator to observe the moving object in outline form before the video image is digitized. This preview permits undesirable lighting and background effects to be eliminated from the image. Once adjustments are made, only data from selected points are digitized and stored in the computer memory. By using only selected pixels, that define the motion of the object in the field of view, much less data is stored and analyzed.

The third step is to analyze positions of points, lines, area centroids, etc. that are of interest. This analysis involves developing displacement-time histories for each feature on the object of interest. From these displacement-time histories, linear velocity and acceleration as well as angular position, velocity and acceleration are determined. A computer performs the numerical computations in the differentiation processes and displays the results on a monitor. A printer/plotter is used to prepare hard copies for oral presentations and written reports.

Video technology is developing rapidly and is applicable to a wide variety of measurements in engineering and other fields. While the method has limitations, it is versatile and is adaptable to numerical processing.

5.8 GPS MEASUREMENTS OF DISPLACEMENT

The **Global Positioning System (GPS)** is a space-based global navigation satellite system (GNSS) that provides location and time information on or near the Earth, where there is a clear line of sight to four or more GPS satellites. It is maintained by the U S government and is accessible by anyone with a GPS receiver. The GPS system was created by the U.S. Department of Defense and became operational in 1994.

A GPS receiver calculates its position by precisely timing the signals sent by GPS satellites. The satellites continually transmit messages that include:

- The time the signal was transmitted
- Precise orbital information
- The orbits of the GPS satellites

The receiver uses this data to calculate the transit time of each signal and then computes the distance from the receiver to each of the satellites. These distances together with the satellites' locations are used with an algorithm to compute the position of the receiver. This position is then displayed as the receiver's latitude and longitude. Some GPS receivers display additional information such as direction and speed that are derived from position changes with respect to time.

Using signals received from a minimum of four visible satellites, a GPS receiver is able to determine the times the signals were sent and then the satellite positions corresponding to these times. The x, y, and z components of position, and the time sent, are designated as x_i, y_i, z_i, t_i, where the subscript i is the satellite number 1, 2, 3, or 4. Because the receiver incorporates an accurate clock, the time the message was received t_r is known. The receiver computes the transit time of the signal as ($t_r - t_i$). Assuming the message traveled at the speed of light, the distance traveled R is determined from:

$$R_i = (t_r - t_i)\, c \qquad (5.12)$$

where c is the speed of light.

A satellite's position and the distance the signal has travelled define a sphere, centered on the satellite, with radius equal to R_i. The position of the receiver is somewhere on the surface of this sphere. With four satellites, the position of the receiver is near the intersection of the surfaces of four spheres. In the ideal case with no errors, the receiver would be at a precise intersection of the four surfaces.

One of the most significant error sources is the clock on the GPS receiver. Because of the large value of the speed of light c, the estimated distance d from the receiver to the satellite is very sensitive to errors in the receiver clock. For example, an error of one microsecond corresponds to an error of 300 m or 980 ft. This suggests that an extremely accurate and expensive clock is required for the GPS receiver to provide accurate estimates of position. However, manufacturers fabricate inexpensive GPS receivers for mass markets, avoiding the expensive clock by developing a correction based on the way the spherical surfaces intersect in the GPS problem.

It is probable that the surfaces of three of the spheres intersect, because the circle of intersection of the first two spheres is normally quite large. Hence, the third spherical surface will probably intersect this large circle. However, the surface of the sphere corresponding to the fourth satellite may not intersect either of the two points of intersection of the first three, because clock error may cause it to miss intersecting either of these points. It is possible to compute a correction using the estimate of GPS receiver position to the surface of the sphere corresponding to the fourth satellite. The correction is based on the difference from the estimate of the receiver's distance from the fourth satellite and the range established by the intersections of the three spheres due to the first three satellites. This difference ΔS is divided by the speed of light c to yield a correction to the clock time Δt given by:

$$\Delta t = \Delta S/c \tag{5.13}$$

Adjusting the receiver's clock time by Δt enables the processor in the receiver to markedly improve the accuracy of the position of the receiver. The position is usually given in terms of latitude and longitude. Position errors are usually less than about 3 m or 10 ft for commercial products with access to the wide area augmentation system. This accuracy is usually adequate when measuring large displacements of a moving object or large distances between two stationary objects.

5.9 INTERFEROMETRIC DISPLACEMENT MEASUREMENTS

Constructive and destructive interference produces an interference pattern due to the combining of two collinear waves. Newton's rings are an example of collinear interference. To examine the interference of collinear waves, consider two plane waves of light propagating along the z axis, as illustrated in Fig. 5.17. The light associated with both waves is coherent, so that the two waves are in phase except for a small delay of wave #2 relative to wave #1 that is associated with z_0. Because both waves are produced by the same coherent source, their wavelengths are identical.

It is possible to express the magnitude E of the two light vectors as:

$$E_1 = a\cos\frac{2\pi}{\lambda}(z - ct)$$

$$E_2 = a\cos\frac{2\pi}{\lambda}(z - ct - z_0) \tag{5.14}$$

Because the two waves are collinear, the two components E_1 and E_2 can be superimposed to obtain:

$$E' = a\left\{ \cos\frac{2\pi}{\lambda}(z-ct) + \cos\frac{2\pi}{\lambda}(z-ct-z_0) \right\} \qquad (5.15)$$

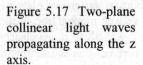
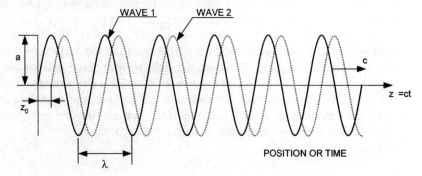

Figure 5.17 Two-plane collinear light waves propagating along the z axis.

Recall the trigometric identity:

$$\cos A + \cos B = 2\cos\left(\frac{A+B}{2}\right)\cos\left(\frac{A-B}{2}\right) \qquad (a)$$

Substitute Eq. (a) into Eq. (5.15) and simplifying gives:

$$E' = 2a\cos\left(\frac{\pi z_0}{\lambda}\right)\cos\left[\left(\frac{2\pi}{\lambda}\right)(z-ct-z_0)\right] \qquad (5.16)$$

Examination of Eq. (5.16) indicates that the amplitude of the superimposed waves is $2a\cos\dfrac{\pi z_0}{\lambda}$. Squaring this term gives the light intensity I as:

$$I = 4a^2\cos^2\left(\frac{\pi z_0}{\lambda}\right) \qquad (5.17)$$

From Eq. (5.17), it is clear that the argument of the cosine function yields the maximum and the minimum values for the intensity I. The maximum intensity ($I = 4a^2$) occurs when the interference is constructive and the argument of the cosine function is given by:

$$z_0/\lambda = k \qquad (k = 0, 1, 2, \ldots\ldots) \qquad (5.18a)$$

The minimum intensity ($I = 0$) occurs when the interference is destructive and the argument of the cosine function is given by:

$$z_0/\lambda = (2k+1)/2 \qquad (k = 0, 1, 2, \ldots\ldots) \qquad (5.18b)$$

5.9.1 Newton's Rings

The most commonly observed fringe pattern associated with the interference produced by two plane collinear waves are Newton's rings. Newton's rings are visible when two nearly flat plates of glass are brought into contact and observed in normal incidence. This interference phenomenon is illustrated with a diagram of the interfering light waves presented in Fig. 5.18.

Reference to Fig. 5.18 shows an incident light wave illuminating two glass plates at normal incidence. The partial reflection of the light from the top surface of plate #1 is ignored, because it does not affect the results. However, the light waves reflecting from the bottom surface of plate #1 and the top surface of plate # 2 are shown as R_1 and R_2, respectively. The axes of propagation of the two waves coincide; however, the two axes are inclined and separated in Fig. 5.18 to more clearly depict the reflecting surfaces. There is a space between the two reflecting surfaces that is filled with air. A gap g characterizes the distance between these reflecting surfaces.

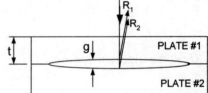

Figure 5.18 Light wave reflections from the contacting surfaces of two glass plates with a small gap.

The light waves reflecting from the two surfaces interfere to produce fringes that are known as Newton's rings. The theory associated with the formation of the rings is similar to that presented in developing Eq. (5.17) with one exception—there is a phase change associated with the reflection from the surface of plate #2. Because the light acts like a wave, it undergoes a phase change of π upon reflection, if the reflecting medium has a higher index of refraction than the medium in which the wave is propagating. Accordingly, reflection occurs at the lower surface of plate #1 without a phase change, but a phase change of π occurs upon reflection from plate #2.

Because of the phase change of π for the wave associated with R_2, it is easy to show that the intensity of the light produced by the interference of waves R_1 and R_2 is given by:

$$I = 4a^2 \sin^2 \frac{\pi z_0}{\lambda} \qquad (5.19)$$

From Eq. (5.19) it is clear that the argument of the sine function yields the maximum and the minimum values for the intensity I. The maximum intensity ($I = 4a^2$) occurs when the interference is constructive and the argument of the sine function is given by:

$$z_0 / \lambda = (2k + 1)/2 \qquad (k = 0, 1, 2, \ldots\ldots) \qquad (a)$$

Recognize that $z_0 = 2g$, because the light travels though the gap twice. Substitute this quantity into Eq. (a) to obtain:

$$g = \frac{2k+1}{4} \lambda \qquad (k = 0, 1, 2, \ldots\ldots) \qquad (5.20a)$$

The minimum intensity ($I = 0$) occurs when the interference is destructive and the argument of the sine function is given by:

$$z_0 / \lambda = k \qquad (k = 0, 1, 2, \ldots\ldots) \qquad (b)$$

The relation for the dimension of the gap which produces destructive interference (extinction) is given by:

$$g = \frac{k\lambda}{2} \qquad (k = 0, 1, 2, \ldots\ldots) \qquad (5.20b)$$

Clearly, the intensity of the light from the superimposed waves R_1 and R_2 provide a means or measuring small gaps between one transparent plate and another plate (of any material) with a reflecting surface.

  Consider next the optical arrangement shown in Fig. 5.19, which enables an observer to measure surface irregularities using the interference patterns produced when two surfaces are in close proximity to one another.

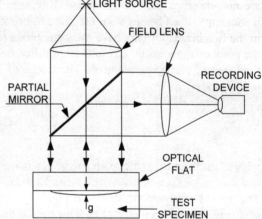

Figure 5.19 Optical arrangements for measuring surface imperfections using Newton's rings.

The light from the source is collected and collimated by a field lens and directed toward the test specimen at normal incidence. The incident light passes through a partial mirror and through an optical flat that serves as plate #1. The optical flat, as the name implies, is plane to within a fraction of a wavelength of light over its entire area. It serves as a reference plane from which surface deviations in the test specimen are measured. The incident light is reflected from the bottom surface of the optical flat and the top surface of the specimen. Both of these waves propagate to the partial mirror where they are reflected at an angle of 90°. This light is then focused by another field lens onto the lens of a camera where an image of the fringe pattern is recorded.

  If the surface imperfection of the test specimen shown in Fig. 5.19 is represented by a spherical depression, the resulting fringe pattern would appear as illustrated in Fig. 5.20. The fringe order N corresponds to k with the zero order k = N = 0 corresponding to the outside ring where contact occurs between the optical flat and the test specimen. The maximum fringe order occurs in the center in this example with N = k = 3 where the gap g = 3λ/2.

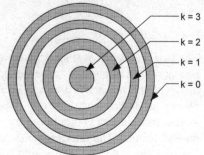

Figure 5.20 Appearance of Newton's rings for a test specimen with a spherical depression.

5.9.2 The Interferometer

An interferometer is an optical instrument that is used to measure lengths or changes in length with great accuracy by means of interference fringes. The modulation of intensity of light by superposition of light waves provides an interference effect. The intensity of the wave resulting from the superposition of two waves of equal amplitude was shown in Eq. (5.17) to be a function of the phase difference between the waves. A fundamental requirement for the existence of well-defined interference fringes is that the light waves producing the fringes have a clearly defined phase difference that remains constant during the recording interval.

When light beams from two independent light sources are superimposed, interference fringes are not observed because the phase difference between the beams varies randomly (the beams are incoherent). Two beams from the same light source will interfere, because the individual wave trains in the two beams initially have the same phase (the beams are coherent). Any difference in phase, at the point of superposition, results from differences in optical path lengths (OPL), which occurs as the light beams propagate along different legs of an interferometer. The optical-path length OPL is defined as:

$$OPL = \sum_{i=1}^{m} n_i L_i$$

(5.21)

where L_i is the mechanical-path length in a material having an index of refraction n_i.

The optical arrangement, shown in Fig. 5.21, illustrates the essential elements involved in the design of a generic interferometer. The light for the instrument is provided by a coherent source—a helium-neon laser. The beam is immediately divided into two parts: one following the reference path and the other following the active path. Usually a neutral density filter (not shown in Fig. 5.21 is inserted into the reference path to adjust the intensity of the reference beam until the intensity of both beams is equal. The active beam passes through a specimen and undergoes retardation due to the optical characteristics of the specimen.

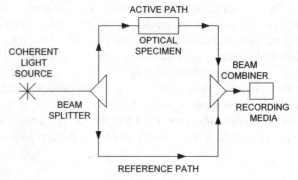

Figure 5.21 The concept of a generic interferometer, after Cloud.

The two beams arrive at an optical element that combines the two beams. In all probability, these two beams are out of phase because the optical path lengths between the active and reference paths may be different and the active beam is retarded by the test specimen. Because the two beams are out of phase, an interference pattern develops when the beams are combined (superimposed). The interference pattern is monitored by some type of recording device such as a digital camera, film or a photodetector. The interferometer provides a means to measure the difference in optical path length between the reference and active paths. In this sense, the interferometer is a type of micrometer capable of measuring in fractions of a wavelength of light.

5.9.3 Commercial Interferometers

A commercial interferometer, shown in Fig. 5.22, employs a coherent and stable laser light source. The laser stability is typically ±0.02 ppm over a period of one hour. Linear measurement accuracy is ±0.5 ppm over a range of temperatures from 0 °C to − 40 °C. Measurements are taken at 50 kHz and with a linear resolution of 1 nm.

Commercial systems are often connected to a laptop computer through an USB port to give a laser-to-PC interface. The laser is often configured with an analog signal output and it accepts a trigger signal input to synchronize recording the output data.

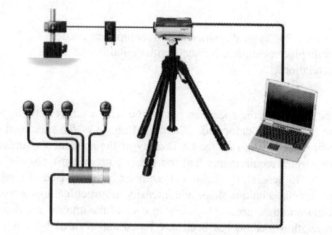

Fig. 5.22 A commercial interferometric displacement measuring system.

The design of advanced interferometric systems employ temperature sensors that are attached to the material being measured, allowing the output to be normalized to a standard material temperature of 20 °C. The signals from both the air and material temperature sensors are processed by integral microprocessors in the laser package before sending digital displacement measurements to the laptop computer.

Advanced systems are capable of dynamic measurement at rates of 10 Hz to 50 kHz. Software provided with the system provides displacement, velocity and acceleration data and a Fast Fourier Transform (FFT) package for frequency analysis.

The greatest uncertainty in most laser based interferometers is due to variations in environmental parameters including air temperature, air pressure and humidity. Even small variations in these parameters will change the laser wavelength and the resulting measurement. For example, increasing the air temperature by 0.26° C will increase laser wavelength by 0.25 ppm. To avoid these errors advanced systems use a compensation unit for the laser and very accurate environmental sensors to correct the effects of temperature and atmospheric pressure changes on the laser wavelength.

5.10 DIGITAL IMAGE CORRELATION

Digital image correlation represents a different approach that is less demanding optically than other techniques such as interferometry. Ordinary incoherent light is sufficient, a vibration isolation table is not required, and the optical components such as beam splitters, prisms, spatial filters, piezoelectric actuators, etc. are eliminated. However, digital image correlation does require at least one high-resolution digital camera and for three-dimensional displacement measurements, two cameras are required. These cameras must be equipped with distortion free lenses to avoid lens induced errors.

Also, a suitable computer with adequate memory and a frame grabbing circuit card to digitize the output from the camera is required. To illustrate the concepts a brief description of the digital image correlation technique is presented. Further details of the technique can be found in [2].

In concept the method is simple. A digital camera[3] is employed to photograph the surface of a plane (two-dimensional) specimen as indicated in Fig. 5.23. The image is downloaded from the camera to a frame grabbing circuit card where the analog signals from the CCD array are digitized. These data are then stored in memory for subsequent processing.

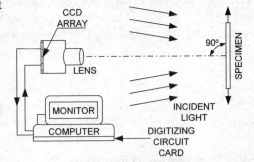

Figure 5.23 Typical arrangement of equipment used for displacement measurements with digital image correlation.

The surface of the specimen is covered with a target pattern, which is photographed before and after the specimen is deformed. The digital image of the specimen will contain intensity measurements at each pixel location on the CCD array of the specimen's surface before and after deformation. There are certain requirements that the target pattern must possess in order for the technique to properly work. In general, the target pattern must be comprised of a whole field of unique targets where each speckle has a unique shape and intensity. If target features are sufficient to identify a number of unique points and their precise locations in each of the images, the displacement field can be established. The correlation method has been developed and refined by a number of different researchers to locate unique points and to establish their locations in the x-y plane to within about 0.02 pixels.

5.10.1 Calibration

Calibration of the camera-specimen arrangement is required to provide numerical factors necessary in the analysis of the data and for the conversion of pixel count to units of displacement. For two-dimensional studies, four calibration factors must be determined.

1. The aspect ratio λ for the camera-digitizing circuit board combination.
2. The magnification M used in the experiment.
3. The location of the center of the lens relative to the center of the specimen.
4. The distortion coefficient for the lens.

The aspect ratio is related to the vertical and horizontal dimensions of the light sensitive cells in the CCD array. It also depends on the design of the digitizing circuit board; however, λ is a constant for a specific combination of camera and digitizing circuit board. Hence, it is only necessary to measure this parameter one time. Several techniques may be used to measure λ.

Of the several techniques, which may be used to measure λ, two will be described here. The first technique involves the preparation of a target plate with a notch as shown in Fig. 5.24. Also shown in Fig. 5.24 is a group of pixels illustrating the size, shape and spacing of the light sensitive cells in the CCD array. The size of the target is such that it will cover (block the light) of several pixels as it is translated.

---

[3] Usually a digital camera with a CCD array is used to capture the image. CCD arrays with small photosensitive cells and high pixel count have significant advantages.

The target plate is mounted on a precision x-y stage[4] so that it can be translated by controlled amounts in the x and y directions. Images are recorded after a series of translations of Δx in the x direction and a series of translation of Δy in the y direction. Comparisons of the gray level intensities recorded in the pixels covered by translations of Δx and Δy, provide the data needed to determine the aspect ratio λ.

The second method for determining λ utilizes a calibration grid placed on the plane of the specimen. A contact measuring reticule, with a 10×10 mm grid divided into 100 squares, serves as a suitable grid. Accuracy of the spacing of the intersecting grid lines on a quality reticule is typically $\pm$ 4 μm with line thickness of about 30 μm. Many images of the grid are acquired at relatively high magnification so that the grid area fills several cells on the CCD sensor array. By using image analysis software, the locations of the grid points are established from image threshold intensities [13] and least square curve fitting. A large number (about 20) of these image points are selected, and a $5 \times$ 5 pixel subset that surrounds each of these image points is analyzed. The value of the ratio of $\Delta y/\Delta x$ of alternate diagonal vertices in the 5×5 subsets is measured. An example of the dimensions Δx and Δy are shown in Fig. 5.25. The value of the aspect ratio λ is then determined by averaging as indicated by:

$$\lambda = \frac{1}{k}\sum_{1}^{k}\frac{\Delta y}{\Delta x} \qquad (5.22)$$

where k is the number of image points considered in determining the average.

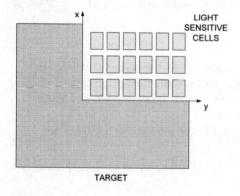

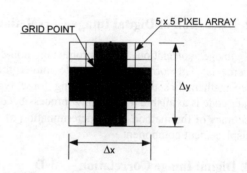

Fig. 5.24 Notch target on a translating plate.

Fig. 5.25 Dimensions of the 5×5 pixel array surrounding the grid point.

Determining the Magnification Factor

The magnification factor M relates a dimension on the specimen to a corresponding dimension on the image plane of the camera. Again, two methods of determining M are employed. One method uses a target plate with a high contrast speckle pattern that is translated by known increments in the x and y directions. Images of the speckle pattern are taken after each translation. The images are analyzed to determine the distance moved by a specific point before and after motion. This motion measured in pixels is compared to the known translations and a magnification factor giving the number of pixels per mm of translation is determined.

---

[4] Precision translation stages are capable of incremental translations Δx or Δy with a least count accuracy of $\pm$ 1.0 μm.

A second approach is to attach a standard scale to the surface of the specimen. An image of the scale is recorded and an edge detecting routine [13] is employed to locate the pixel positions of two marks on the scale which have a known spacing. The grid on the measuring reticule described in Section 15.5.1 serves well as a standard scale to measure the magnification factor in both the x and y directions.

Locating the Lens Center

To reduce the effect of any lens distortion, the center of the camera lens should coincide with the center of the area of interest on the specimen. Centering the lens is easily accomplished by placing a black single point target on a white background at the center of the area of interest on the specimen. An image of the single point target is acquired and the intensities of the pixels near the center of the CCD array are monitored. The center pixels in the array should show the lowest intensities. If the centers do not coincide, either the camera or the specimen should be translated until the two centers coincide.

Lens Distortion

To minimize the effect of lens distortion, high-quality lenses with relatively long focal lengths are employed with the CCD cameras. Lenses with focal length ranging from 200 to 300 mm are commonly employed to minimize the effect of distortion. If sufficient light is available, the lens is stopped down so that only its central region is used in focusing the image on the CCD sensor array. Limiting the use of the lens to its central region greatly reduces the distortion effects.

5.10.2 Discussion of Digital Image Correlation —2-D

Digital image correlation is a promising non-contacting method for measuring whole field displacements. The correlation method to convert the digital images to whole field displacement maps involves mathematics that is challenging for a typical experimentalist; however, when a suitable computer code is available the mapping process becomes automatic.

The accuracy of the method in the determination of displacements is often quoted at $\pm$ 0.02 pixels for each displacement component

5.10.3 Digital Image Correlation — 3-D

The measurement of the three displacement components on a specimen is much more difficult than two dimensional measurements. Stereo imaging techniques, which require two digital cameras, are employed. The typical camera arrangement is illustrated in Fig. 5.26. This drawing shows the pan angles θ_{p1} and θ_{p2} of the cameras, their spacing d_{12} and the distance s from the cameras to the specimen. Also defined in Fig. 5.26 are three coordinate systems—the one centered at the specimen O-XYZ is the reference system. The other two are coordinate systems are centered on the two camera lenses at C_1 and C_2.

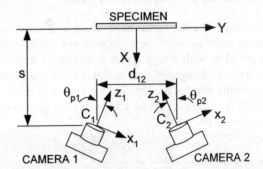

Fig. 5.26 Stereo camera arrangement for 3-dimensional displacement measurements.

The procedure is to record images with both cameras of the initial state of the specimen and then to load the specimen and to acquire images with both cameras after the specimen has deformed. Before beginning the digital image correlation process for the 3-dimensional data recorded as gray scale images, it is necessary to develop the stereo imaging equation. This development is due to P. F. Luo, Y. J. Chao, M. A. Sutton and W. H. Peters, which is described in References [14, 15].

5.10.4 Stereo Imaging Relations

The position of the camera relative to the specimen in the two-dimensional measurements was simple. The plane of the specimen was parallel to the image plane in the camera and the camera was centered on the area of interest on the specimen. However, for three-dimensional measurements, the simplicity of the camera-specimen arrangement vanishes and is replaced with a more complex arrangement with camera spacing, pan angles, camera stand-off and seven coordinate systems. A drawing showing the coordinate systems, specimen and camera images is presented in Fig. 5.27.

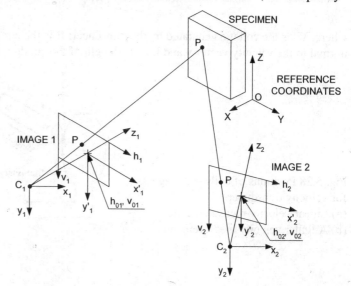

Fig. 5.27 Drawing showing the coordinate systems used in analyzing stereo images.

The drawings in Figs. 5.26 and 5.27 differ to some degree because the latter contains more detail. Definitions are provided below to clarify the various coordinates shown in Fig. 5.27.

The reference coordinates O-XYZ define all points in space. These coordinates may be positioned anywhere in space although it is common practice to place their origin on the specimen.

A coordinate system with its origin at C_i is defined for each camera, where C_i is the lens center of the camera. For camera #1, the coordinates are x_1, y_1 and z_1. Each point in the image plane of camera #1 has coordinates relative to C_1 of x_1, y_1 and f, where f is the focal point of the system. An identical coordinate system is established for camera #2.

Another coordinate system is placed on the image plane with coordinates x'_i, y'_i and 0. This system is identical to the camera system of coordinates except it is shifted in the positive z direction by the distance f.

A second coordinate system on the image plane with coordinates (h_i, v_i) is introduced with its origin at the upper left hand corner of the pixel array. This is the standard coordinate system for computer-image systems. The origin of the first image plane coordinate system for camera #1 relative to the computer image coordinate system is h_{01} and v_{01} as shown in Fig. 5.27.

Pixel coordinates for each camera are converted into physical dimension on the specimen by determining two magnification factors M_x and M_y for each camera.

Due to the more complex arrangement of the camera system used in three-dimensional studies, the calibration procedure become more complex in nature and the details can be found in [2].

5.11 VELOCITY MEASUREMENTS

The principle of electromagnetic induction provides the basis for design of direct-reading, linear- and angular-velocity measuring transducers. The principle of operation for these is shown in Fig. 5.28. For the linear-velocity measurements, a magnetic field associated with the permanent magnet moves with a velocity referenced to a fixed conductor. For the angular-velocity measurements, a moving conductor associated with the velocity moves with respect to a fixed magnetic field. In either case, a voltage is generated that can be related to the unknown velocity. The basic equation relating voltage generated to velocity of a conductor in a magnetic field can be expressed as:

$$V_T = BLv \tag{5.23}$$

where V_T is the voltage generated by the transducer; B is the component of the magnetic field strength normal to the velocity vector **v** and L is the length of the conductor and v is its velocity.

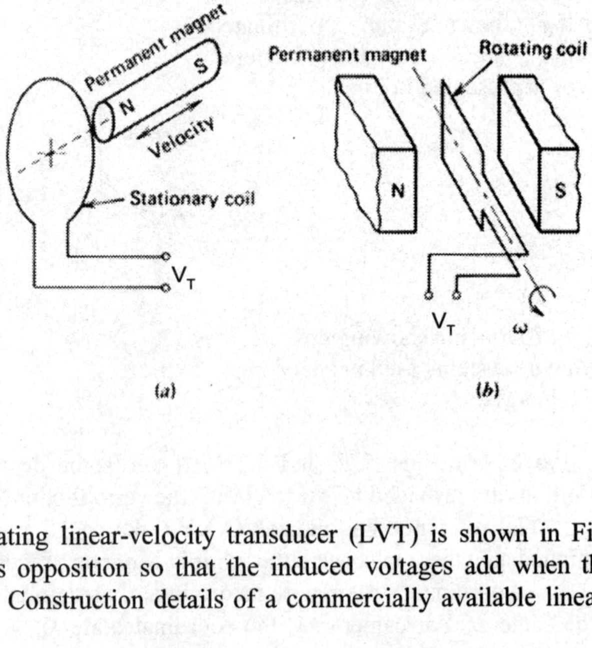

Fig. 5.28 Positions of coils and magnets for velocity transducers.
(a) Linear velocity measurements.
(b) Angular velocity measurements.

5.11.1 Linear Velocity Measurements

A schematic representation of a self-generating linear-velocity transducer (LVT) is shown in Fig. 5.29a. The windings are installed in series opposition so that the induced voltages add when the permanent magnet moves through the coil. Construction details of a commercially available linear-velocity transducer are shown in Fig. 5.29b.

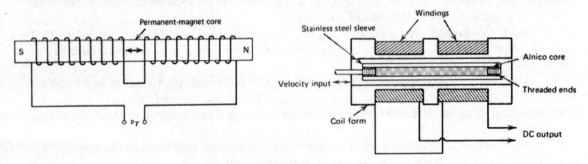

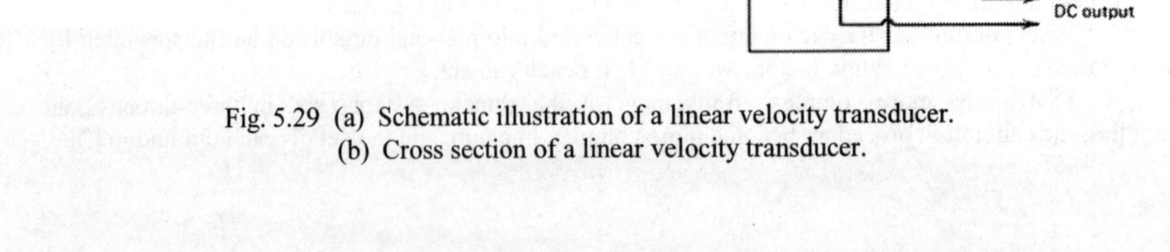

Fig. 5.29 (a) Schematic illustration of a linear velocity transducer.
(b) Cross section of a linear velocity transducer.

The LVT is equivalent to a voltage generator connected in series with an inductance L_T and a resistance R_T, as shown in Fig. 5.30. The governing differential equation for this circuit with an LVT sensor and a recording instrument having an input resistance R_M is:

$$L_T \frac{dI}{dt} + (R_T + R_M)I = S_v v \tag{5.24}$$

where S_v is the voltage sensitivity of the transducer [mV/(in./s)], v is the time-dependent velocity and
$\quad$ I is the time-dependent current flowing in the circuit.

The frequency response function of an LVT is obtained by assuming a sinusoidal input velocity and output current in exponential notation as done previously. Substitution of these relations into Eq. (2.47) yields:

$$I_0 = \frac{S_v v_0}{(R_M + R_T) + jL_T \omega} \tag{a}$$

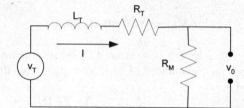

Fig. 5.30 Equivalent circuit for a linear velocity transducer.

where v_0 is the magnitude of the velocity and I_0 is the magnitude of the current. The current lags the velocity by a phase angle ϕ that is given by the expression:

$$\tan \phi = \frac{L_T \omega}{R_M + R_T} \tag{b}$$

The output voltage V_0 from the circuit shown in Fig. 5.25 is given by:

$$V_0 = IR_M = \frac{R_M S_v v_0}{(R_M + R_T) + jL_T \omega} e^{j\omega t} \tag{5.25}$$

The corresponding frequency response function for the circuit is:

$$H(\omega) = \frac{V_0}{v} = \frac{V_0}{v_0 e^{j\omega t}} = \frac{R_M S_v}{(R_M + R_T) + jL_T \omega}$$

$$= \frac{R_M S_v r^{-j\phi}}{\left[(R_M + R_T)^2 + (L_T \omega)^2 \right]^{1/2}} \tag{5.26}$$

Equation (5.26) also indicates that the output will be attenuated and the phase will be shifted relative to the input at the higher frequencies. The break frequency ω_c for a circuit controlled by a first-order differential equation occurs when the real and imaginary parts of the frequency response function are equal. This equality occurs when:

$$\omega_c = \frac{R_M + R_T}{L_T} = \frac{R_M}{L_T}\left(1 + \frac{R_T}{R_M}\right) \tag{5.27}$$

Measurement error at the break frequency (− 3 dB or 30 % with a 45° phase shift) is much too large for most practical applications. A more realistic value of 2% error with a phase shift of 15.9° occurs when $\omega = 0.28 \, \omega_c$. Magnitude errors are less than 5 % if use of the transducer is limited to frequencies below one-third of the break frequency.

Equations (5.25) and (5.26) clearly indicate that the sensitivity and frequency response of an LVT is dependent upon the input resistance R_M of the recording instrument. The output voltage of an LVT sensor is relatively large [10 to 100 mV/(in./s)]; therefore, signal amplification is not usually required. Linearity within ± 1% can usually be achieved over the rated range of motion of the transducer. Common values for R_T are less than 10 Ω.

5.11.2 Angular Velocity Measurements

Angular velocities can be measured by using ac generators. The frequency of the generated voltage is dependent on the number of field coil pairs and the speed at which the generator is operated, as indicated below:

$$f = (Nn)/60 \tag{5.28}$$

where f is the frequency in Hz, N is the rotor velocity in RPM and n is the number of field coil pairs.

Clearly a simple counter can be used to measure frequency and/or angular velocity of the rotor.

The measurement of instantaneous angular velocities is accomplished with a rotary encoder. A high resolution encoder is attached to the shaft of the rotary device and its output (counts per unit time) provides an instantaneous measure of the angular velocity. If a continuous record of the angular velocity is required, the frequency measurement from the encoder is converted to voltage by using a frequency to voltage converter.

5.11.3 Laser-Doppler System

A Michelson interferometer is used in a non-contacting optical method for measuring velocities. The operating principle of the interferometric measurement method is illustrated in Fig. 5.31 where the laser beam is divided into two beams; namely, an internal reference beam and a signal beam. The signal beam is focused on the moving surface by a computer controlled scanning mirror so that various points can be selected in a prescribed pattern. Back-reflected light from the signal beam is recombined with the reference beam. The signal beam path length changes as the reflecting surface moves so that the light intensity is modulated from bright to dark as the light from the two beams reinforce and cancel one another. One complete cycle in intensity variation occurs with a surface displacement of half of a wave length; or $\lambda/2 = 314$ nm for a Helium-Neon laser. The reflected signal beam undergoes a Doppler shift with a Doppler frequency f_d given by:

$$f_d = 2v/\lambda \tag{5.29}$$

where v is the velocity of the moving surface. The direction of the velocity of the moving surface is resolved by using two detectors that are spaced one quarter wave length apart. One detector is called the cosine detector while the other is called the sine detector. By using frequency modulation and detection schemes, an output voltage is available that gives the sign and magnitude of the surface velocity.

Typical instruments employ a 1-mW Helium-neon laser and are effective with most surfaces up to a distance of 200 m. The instruments are designed with several velocity ranges with accuracies of ±3% of the full-scale range. While accurate measurements can be made without contact with this instrument, its major disadvantage is its relatively high cost.

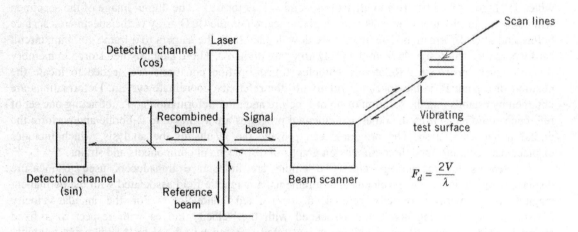

Fig. 5.31 Schematic diagram illustrating the operating principle of a laser-Doppler velocity system.

5.12 SUMMARY

Several transducers are available for measurements of either displacement or velocity from a fixed reference. For displacements the potentiometer, linear differential transformer (LVDT), capacitance sensor and eddy current sensor all provide effective methods of measurement. The advantages and disadvantages of each transducer are described. For angular measurements the potentiometer and the rotary differential (RVDT) transformer are employed. The potentiometer is used for larger rotations of as much as up to 7,200° and the RVDT is used to measure smaller rotations up to 40°.

A wide range of optical methods are available to measure displacements. These methods include interference patterns for measuring displacements to high-speed photography using video digitization and high-speed computers. A major advantage of optical methods is that contact is not necessary; therefore, they do not disturb the system under investigation. The optical methods for measuring displacements include: photoelectric transducers; optical tracker systems and video camera motion analysis.

The Global Positioning System (GPS) is a space-based global navigation satellite system (GNSS) that provides location and time information on or near the Earth, where there is a clear line of sight to four or more GPS satellites. A GPS receiver calculates its position by precisely timing the signals sent by GPS satellites. The GPS receiver uses this data to calculate the transit time of each signal and then computes the distance from the receiver to each of the satellites. This data are used with an algorithm to compute the position of the receiver. This position is then displayed as the receiver's latitude and longitude. Changes in the position of the receiver provide displacement data, but its accuracy is limited to ± 2 to 3 meters.

An interferometer is an optical instrument that is used to precisely measure displacement by means of interference fringes. The modulation of intensity of light by superposition of light waves provides an interference effect. The light for these instruments is provided by a coherent source, usually a helium-neon laser. Commercial interferometers give linear measurement with an accuracy of ±0.5 ppm over a range of temperatures from 0 °C to – 40 °C. Commercial systems are often connected to a laptop computer through an USB port providing a laser-to-PC interface.

Digital image correlation represents a different approach that is less demanding optically than other techniques for measuring in-plane and out-of-plane displacements. Digital image correlation requires at least one high-resolution digital camera and for three-dimensional displacement measurements, two cameras are required. The surface of the specimen is covered with a target pattern, which is photographed before and after the specimen is deformed. The digital image of the specimen will contain intensity measurements at each pixel location on the CCD array of the specimen's surface before and after deformation. The images are downloaded from the camera to a frame grabbing circuit card where the analog signals from the CCD array are digitized. These data are then stored in memory for subsequent processing. Relatively complex transformation equations are needed to locate the position of a point P on the specimen relative to the reference coordinate system. Deformations are obtained by establishing the location of point P before and after deformation and subtracting one set of reference coordinates from the other. Commercial programs are available to calibrate and perform the digital image correlation. The programs can provide the results of the analysis, which includes displacement contours, and three-dimension graphs of displacement components and strains.

Sensors for measuring velocity resemble the inductance transducers used to measure displacements. For the linear-velocity measurements, a magnetic field associated with the permanent magnet moves with a velocity referenced to a fixed conductor. For the angular-velocity measurements, a moving conductor associated with the velocity moves with respect to a fixed magnetic field. In either case, a voltage is generated that can be related to the unknown velocity. Angular velocities are measured by using ac generators. The frequency of the generated voltage is dependent on the number of field coil pairs and the RPM of the generator. A simple counter can be used to measure frequency and/or angular velocity of its rotor. The measurement of instantaneous angular velocities is accomplished with a rotary encoder. A high resolution encoder is attached to the shaft of the rotary device and its output (counts per unit time) provides an instantaneous measure of the angular velocity.

A Michelson interferometer is used in a non-contacting optical method for measuring velocities. The interferometer incorporates laser light which is divided into two beams; namely, an internal reference beam and a signal beam. The signal beam is focused on the moving surface by a computer controlled scanning mirror so that various points can be selected in a prescribed pattern. Back-reflected light from the signal beam is recombined with the reference beam. The signal beam path length changes as the reflecting surface moves so that the light intensity is modulated from bright to dark as the light from the two beams reinforce and cancel one another. One complete cycle in intensity variation occurs with a surface displacement of half of a wave length; or $\lambda/2 = 314$ nm for a Helium-Neon laser. The reflected signal beam undergoes a Doppler shift. By using frequency modulation and detection schemes, an output voltage is available that gives the sign and magnitude of the surface velocity.

REFERENCES

1. Beckwith, T. G., R. D. Marangoni and J. H. Lienhard V: Mechanical Measurements, 6th ed., Prentice Hall, Englewood Cliffs, NJ, 2007.
2. Shukla, A, Dally, J. W. and W. F. Riley: Experimental Solid Mechanics, College House Ent., Knoxville, TN 2010.
3. Doebelin, E. O.: Measurement Systems Application and Design, International Edition, Tata McGraw-Hill, New York, 2004.
4. Holman, J. P.: Experimental Methods for Engineers, 8th ed., McGraw-Hill, 2011.
5. Wheeler, A. J., A. R. Ganji, Introduction to Engineering Experimentation, Prentice Hall, Englewood Cliffs, NJ, 2009.
6. Figliola, R. S., D. E. Beasley, Theory and Design for Mechanical Measurements, 5th Edition, John Wiley & Sons, New York, 2011.
7. Irwin, J. D., and R. M. Nelms, Basic Engineering Circuit Analysis, 10th Edition, Wiley, New York, 2011.
8. Dally, J. W., Riley W. F. and K. G. McConnell: Instrumentation for Engineering Measurements, Wiley, New York, 1993.
9. Palloe-Areny, R., J. G. Webster: Sensors and Signal Conditioning, Prentice-Hall, Englewood Cliffs, NJ, 2001.
10. Wilson, J. S., Sensor Technology Handbook, Elsevier Science and Technology, Oxford, UK, 2005.
11. Fraden, J., Handbook of Modern Sensors, 4th Edition, Springer, New York, 2010.
12. Solomon, S., Sensor Handbook, 2nd Edition, McGraw Hill, New York, 2010.
13. Morimoto, Y., "Digital Image Processing," Chapter 21, Handbook on Experimental Mechanics, 2nd Revised Edition, Edited by A. S. Kobayashi, VCH Publishers, New York, pp. 969-1027, 1993.
14. Lou, P. F., Y. J. Chao, M. A. Sutton and W. H. Peters, "Accurate Measurements of Three-Dimensional Deformations in Deformable and Rigid Bodies Using Computer Vision," Experimental Mechanics, Vol. 33, pp. 123-132, 1993.
15. Lou, P. F., Y. J. Chao and M. A. Sutton, "Application of Stereo Vision to Three-Dimensional Deformation Analysis in Fracture Experiments," Optical Engineering, Vol. 33, pp. 991-990, 1994.

EXERCISES

5.1 A slide-wire potentiometer having a length of 100 mm is fabricated by winding wire with a diameter of 0.10 mm around a cylindrical insulating core. Determine the resolution limit of this potentiometer.

5.2 If the potentiometer of Exercise 5.1 has a resistance of 2,000 Ω and can dissipate 2 W of power, determine the voltage required to maximize the sensitivity. What voltage change corresponds to the resolution limit?

5.3 A 20-turn potentiometer with a calibrated dial (100 divisions/turn) is used as a balance resistor in a Wheatstone bridge. If the potentiometer has a resistance of 20 kΩ and a resolution of 0.05%, what is the minimum incremental change in resistance ΔR that can be read from its calibrated dial?

5.4 Why are potentiometers limited to static or quasi-static applications?

5.5 List several advantages of the conductive-film type of potentiometer.

5.6 A 20-kΩ single-turn potentiometer has been incorporated into a displacement measuring system as shown in Fig. E5.6. The potentiometer consists of 0.008-in.-diameter wire wound onto a 1.25-in.-diameter ring, as shown in the figure. The pulley diameters are 2.00 in. Determine:

  (a) The minimum load resistance that can be used if nonlinearity error must be limited to 0.25%.

  (b) The smallest motion x that can be detected with this system.

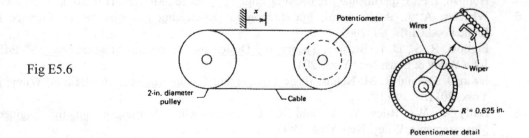

Fig E5.6

5.7 The potentiometer circuit shown in Fig. E5.7 is used to measure angular position θ. The capacitor C is used to reduce contact bounce and the op-amp isolates the potentiometer from long lead wires and recording instrument resistance loading. The potentiometer being used can rotate 320 degrees, has a resistance R_p = 4.0 kΩ, and is capable of dissipating 0.02 W of power in most environments. Show that:

  (a) The maximum voltage that can be applied to the potentiometer is 8.94 V.

  (b) The value of series resistor R_S in order to protect the potentiometer if V_S = 15.0 volts is 2.71 kΩ.

  (c) The output sensitivity S is given by

$$S = \left(\frac{R_M}{R_M + 2R_W}\right)\left(\frac{R_P}{R_P + 2R_S}\right)\frac{V_S}{\theta_T}$$

where θ_T is the range of the potentiometer in degrees.

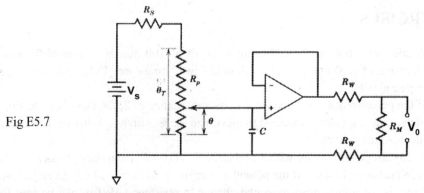

Fig E5.7

5.8 The circuit in Exercise 5.7 is to have a minimum sensitivity of 10.0 mV/degree when 400 ft of AWG 28 copper lead wires (66.2 Ω per 1000 ft) is being used. The op-amp is capable of driving an output circuit continuously at 20 mA and a 10.0-volt dc power supply is to be used.

(a) What value of RM and Rs would you select to achieve the desired sensitivity?

(b) What electrical components would you add to the circuit to easily adjust the circuit's sensitivity?

(c) How would you calibrate the system?

5.9 Assume that the current generated by the photoelectric sensor in Fig. 5.13a and Fig. 5.13b is given by I = Ky. Show that the governing differential equation for the sensor is:

$$R_M C \dot{V}_0 + V_0 = R_M Ky \qquad \text{For Figure 5.13a}$$

and

$$\frac{R_f C}{G} \dot{V}_0 + \frac{1+G}{G} V_0 = -R_f Ky \qquad \text{For Figure 5.13b}$$

where G is the op-amps open loop gain. Compare circuit behavior when G is large (>10,000) and $R_M = R_f$. Why is the high frequency performance improved?

5.10 A new elevator must be tested to determine its performance characteristics. Design a displacement transducer that utilizes a 20-turn potentiometer to monitor the position of the elevator over its 100-m range of travel.

5.11 Compare the potentiometer and LVDT as displacement sensors with regard to the following characteristics: range, accuracy, resolution, frequency response, reliability, complexity and cost.

5.12 Prepare a block diagram representing the electronic components in a LVDT. Describe the function of each component.

5.13 Prepare a sketch of the output signal as a function of time for an LVDT with its core located in a fixed off-center position if:

(a) The demodulator is functioning.

(b) The demodulator is removed from the circuit.

5.14 Prepare a sketch of the output signal as a function of time for an LVDT with its core moving at constant velocity from one end of the LVDT through the center to the other end if:

(a) The demodulator is functioning.

(b) The demodulator is removed from the circuit.

5.15 Describe the basic differences between an LVDT and a DCDT.

5.16 Compare the cylindrical potentiometer (heli-potentiometer) and the RVDT as sensors for measuring angular displacement.

5.17 Prepare a graph of the sensitivity S of a capacitance sensor as a function of its frequency ω. Assume the dielectric in the gap is air and consider probe diameters of 1, 2, 5 and 10 mm.

5.18 Write an engineering brief describing the advantages and disadvantages of capacitance sensors.

5.19 Describe the operating principles of the instrument, shown in Fig. 5.8, which is used to monitor the output of a capacitance sensor.

5.20 Can eddy current sensors be employed with the following target material?

(a) Magnetic materials

(b) Polymers

(c) Non-magnetic metallic foils

(d) Indicate procedures that permit usage of the sensor in these three cases.

5.21 Write an engineering brief with sketches showing the operating principle of a photoelectric displacement transducer.

5.22 Describe the decisions you would make if you were to write the engineering specification for an optical tracking system to observe the launch of a space satellite.

5.23 Prepare the information necessary for a purchasing agent to obtain quotations for a high-speed video camera capable of 100,000 frames/s or more.

5.24 Write a letter to your younger brother explaining how the global positioning system functions. Indicate the accuracy of the system.

5.25 A linear-velocity transducer (LVT) has an inductance of 16.5 mH, a resistance of 6.2 Ω and a sensitivity of 30 mV/(in./s). Evaluate the performance of this sensor when it is used in conjunction with a recording instrument having an input resistance of (a) 100 Ω and (b) 1,000 Ω if the measurement errors are limited to 5 % magnitude and 10 degrees in phase.

5.26 A shaft has a 128 tooth gear mounted on it and is rotating at 2,650 rpm. A magnetic proximity sensor gives a series of pulses as an output signal as the gear rotates beneath it. What is the fundamental frequency of these pulses in Hz?

5.27 Determine the Doppler shift frequency when a Helium-Neon laser is being used to measure a 100 mm/s velocity.

5.28 For the fringe pattern illustrated in Fig. 5.20, determine the maximum dimension of the gap if the wavelength of the light source was $\lambda = 543$ nm.

5.29 Prepare a sketch of a generic interferometer and describe the optical elements used in this arrangement.

EXERCISE SOLUTIONS

Exercise 5.2

Recall:
$$p = \frac{v^2}{R}$$

Therefore:
$$v_{max} = \sqrt{pR} = \sqrt{2(2000)} = 63.2 \text{ V}$$

$$\Delta v = \frac{63.2}{100/0.10} = 0.0632 \text{ V} = 63.2 \text{ mV}$$

Exercise 5.9

For the circuit shown Fig. 5.13a :

$$i = Ky \qquad i_1 = C \frac{dv_0}{dt} \qquad i_2 = \frac{v_0}{R_M}$$

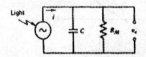

$$i_1 + i_2 = i$$

$$C \frac{dv_0}{dt} + \frac{v_0}{R_M} = Ky$$

$$R_M C \frac{dv_0}{dt} + v_0 = R_M Ky$$

For the circuit shown Fig. 5.13b :

$$i = Ky \qquad v_0 = -Gv_1 \qquad v_1 = -\frac{v_0}{G}$$

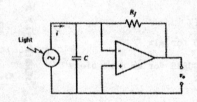

$$i_1 = C \frac{dv_1}{dt} = -\frac{C}{G} \frac{dv_0}{dt}$$

$$i_2 = \frac{v_1 - v_0}{R_f} = -\frac{(1 + G)v_0}{GR_f}$$

$$i_1 + i_2 = i$$

$$-\frac{C}{G} \frac{dv_0}{dt} - \frac{(1 + G)}{G} \frac{v_0}{R_f} = Ky$$

$$\frac{CR_f}{G} \frac{dv_0}{dt} + \frac{1 + G}{G} v_0 = -R_f Ky$$

For large G: $v_0 \approx -R_f Ky$ (small time derivative effects).

For the circuit of Fig. 5.13a :

$$[1 + jRC\omega] \, v_0 = R_M Ky_0$$

$$\uparrow_{\text{decay with high freq.}}$$

For the circuit of Fig. 5.13b with G > 10,000 and $R_M = R_f$:

$$\left(1 + j \frac{RC\omega}{G}\right) v_0 = -R_f \, k \, y_0$$

$$\uparrow_{\text{decay reduced by 10,000 (open loop gain)}}$$

Thus, using an op-amp improves high frequency response.

Exercise 5.11

Characteristic	Potentiometer	LVDT
Range	Large	Small
Accuracy	Good	Fair
Resolution	Good	Good
Freq. Response	Poor	Fair
Reliability	Excellent	Good
Complexity	Simple	Moderate
Cost	Low	Moderate

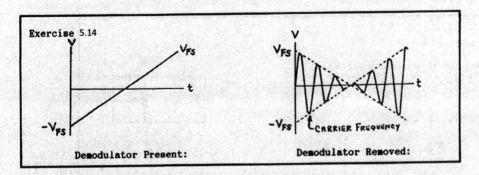

Exercise 5.14

Demodulator Present:

Demodulator Removed:

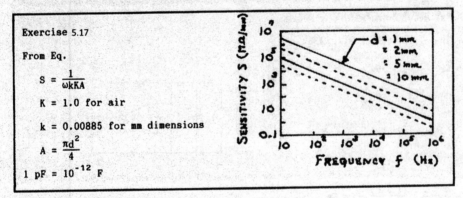

Exercise 5.17

From Eq.

$$S = \frac{1}{\omega kKA}$$

$K = 1.0$ for air

$k = 0.00885$ for mm dimensions

$$A = \frac{\pi d^2}{4}$$

$1 \text{ pF} = 10^{-12} \text{ F}$

CHAPTER 6

MEASURING STRAIN

6.1 INTRODUCTION

Over the past 60 years, the electrical resistance strain gage has become the most popular method to measure strain. However, strain gages based on mechanical, optical, electrical, acoustical, and even pneumatic principles are sometimes employed. A strain gage has several characteristics that should be considered in judging its adequacy for a particular application. These characteristics are:

1. The calibration constant for the gage should be stable; it should not vary with either time, temperature or other environmental factors.
2. The gage should be able to measure strains with an accuracy of ± 1 μin./in. (μm/m) over a large strain range ($\pm 10\%$).
3. The gage size (the gage length L_0 and width w_0) should be small so that strain (a point quantity) is approximated with small error.
4. The frequency response (bandwidth) of the gage, largely controlled by its inertia, should be sufficient to permit recording of dynamic strains with frequency components exceeding 100 kHz.
5. The gage system should permit both on-location and remote readout.
6. The output from the gage during the readout period should be independent of temperature and other environmental parameters.
7. The gage and the associated auxiliary equipment should be low in cost.
8. The gage system should be easy to install and operate.
9. The gage should exhibit a linear response to strain over a wide range.
10. The gage should be suitable for use as the sensing element in other transducer systems where an unknown quantity is measured in terms of strain.

The electrical resistance strain gage, when properly installed, closely meets all of the required characteristics listed above.

6.2 ETCHED-FOIL STRAIN GAGES

Electrical resistance strain gages are thin metal-foil grids, shown in Fig. 6.1, which are adhesively bonded to the surface of a component or structure. When the component or structure is subjected to loads, strains develop that are transmitted to the foil grid. The resistance of the foil grid changes in proportion to the load-induced strain. The strain sensitivity of metals, first observed in copper and iron by Lord Kelvin in 1856, is explained by the following analysis.

The resistance R of a uniform metallic conductor can be expressed as:

$$R = \rho L/A \qquad (6.1)$$

where ρ is the specific resistance of the metal (Ω - cm), L is the length of the conductor and A is the cross-sectional area of the conductor.

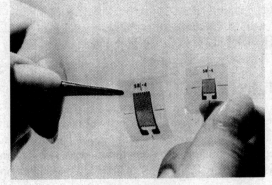

Fig. 6.1 The thin metallic foil, in the form of a grid is supported on a thin plastic carrier.

Differentiating Eq. (6.1) and dividing by the resistance R gives:

$$dR/R = d\rho/\rho = dL/L - dA/A \qquad \text{(a)}$$

The term dA represents the change in cross-sectional area of the conductor resulting from the applied load. For a conductor subjected to a uniaxial state of tensile stress, recall that

$$\varepsilon_a = dL/L \qquad \text{and} \qquad \varepsilon_t = -\nu\varepsilon_a = -\nu dL/L \qquad \text{(b)}$$

where ε_a is the axial strain in the conductor; ε_t is the transverse strain; ν is Poisson's ratio of the metallic foil.

If the diameter of the conductor is d_0 before application of the axial strain, the diameter of the conductor d_f after it is strained is given by:

$$d_f = d_0\left(1 - \nu\frac{dL}{L}\right) \qquad \text{(c)}$$

From Eq. (c) it is clear that the change in area is given by:

$$\frac{dA}{A} = -2\nu\frac{dL}{L} + \nu^2\left(\frac{dL}{L}\right)^2 = -2\nu\frac{dL}{L} \qquad \text{(d)}$$

Substituting Eq. (d) into Eq. (a) and simplifying yields:

$$\frac{dR}{R} = \frac{d\rho}{\rho} + \frac{dL}{L}(1 + 2\nu) \qquad (6.2)$$

which can be written as:

$$S_A = \frac{dR/R}{\varepsilon_a} = \frac{d\rho/\rho}{\varepsilon_a} + (1 + 2\nu) \qquad (6.3)$$

The quantity S_A is defined as the sensitivity of the metal or alloy used for the conductor. It is evident from Eq. (6.3) that it is possible to measure strain with a straight length of wire, if the change in resistance is monitored when the wire is subjected to a strain. The circuits required to measure dR (in practice ΔR) have power supplies with limited current capabilities and the power dissipated by the gage itself must be limited. As a result, strain gages are usually manufactured with a resistance of 120 or 350 Ω or preferably more. These high values of gage resistance, in most cases, preclude fabrication of a strain gage from a straight length of wire, because the length of the gage becomes excessive. To reduce the length of the strain gage its conductor is formed into a grid configuration.

A strain gage exhibits a resistance change $\Delta R/R$ that is related to the strain ε in the direction of the grid by the expression:

$$\Delta R/R = S_g\, \varepsilon \qquad\qquad (6.4)$$

where S_g is the gage factor or calibration constant for the gage.

The gage factor S_g is always less than the sensitivity of the metallic alloy S_A because the grid configuration of the gage with the transverse conductors is less responsive to axial strain than a straight uniform conductor.

When electrical resistance strain gages were first introduced (1936—1956), the gage element was produced by forming a grid configuration with very-fine-diameter wire. Since the late 1950s, most gages have been fabricated from ultra-thin metal foil by using a precise photoetching process. Because this process is quite versatile, a wide variety of gage sizes and grid shapes are produced. Gages as small as 0.20 mm in length are commercially available. Standard gage resistances are 120 Ω and 350 Ω; but in some configurations, resistances of 500, 1,000 and 5,000 Ω are available. The foil gages are normally fabricated from Advance, Karma, or Isoelastic alloys (see Table 6.1). In addition, high-temperature gages are available in several heat-resistant alloys.

Table 6.1
Strain sensitivity S_A for common strain-gage alloys

Material	Composition (%)	S_A
Advance or Constantan	45 Ni, 55 Cu	2.1
Nichrome V	80 Ni, 20 Cr	2.1
Isoelastic	36 Ni, 8 Cr, 0.5 Mo, 55.5 Fe	3.6
Karma	74 Ni, 20 Cr, 3 Al, 3 Fe	2.0
Armour D	70 Fe, 20 Cr, 10 Al	2.0
Platinum-Tungsten	92 Pt, 8 W	4.0

The etched metal-film grids are very fragile and easy to distort or tear. To avoid these difficulties, the metal film is bonded to a thin sheet of plastic (see Fig. 6.1), which serves as a backing material and carrier, before the photoetching process is performed. The carrier contains markings for the centerlines of the gage's length and width to facilitate installation. It also serves to electrically insulate the metal grid from the specimen when it is installed.

For general-purpose strain-gage applications, a polyimide polymer (Kapton) that is tough and flexible is used for the carrier. For transducer applications, where precision and linearity are extremely important, a very thin, brittle, high-modulus epoxy is used for the carrier. Glass-fiber-reinforced epoxy is used when the gage will be exposed to high-level cyclic strains or when the gage will be employed at higher temperatures [750 °F (400 °C) maximum].

For very-high-temperature applications, gages with strippable carriers are available. The carrier is removed during installation of the gage. A ceramic adhesive is used to bond the gage and to electrically insulate its grid from the specimen.

6.3 STRAIN-GAGE INSTALLATION

The bonded electrical resistance strain gage is a high-quality precision resistor that must be mounted to a specimen using the correct adhesive and employing proper bonding procedures. The adhesive serves a vital function in a strain-measuring system, because it must transmit the surface displacements from the specimen to the gage grid without distortion. Initially it appears that this function can be accomplished with almost any high-strength adhesive; however, experience has shown that improperly selected and cured adhesives can seriously degrade a gage installation by changing the gage factor and/or the initial resistance of the gage. Improperly cured or viscoelastic adhesives also produce hysteresis and signal loss due to stress relaxation. The best results are obtained with a high-strength, low-viscous, completely-cured adhesive that forms a thin-elastic-bond line.

The surface of the component in areas where gages are to be positioned must be carefully prepared before the gages are installed. This preparation consists of removal of surface films, such as paint and/or rust, followed by sanding to obtain a smooth but not polished surface. Solvents are then used to eliminate all traces of grease and oil. Finally, the surface is treated with a basic solution to give it the correct chemical affinity for the adhesive.

Next, the gage location is marked on the specimen with very light scribe lines and the gage, without adhesive, is positioned by using a rigid transparent tape in the manner illustrated in Fig. 6.2. The position and orientation of the gage are maintained by the tape as the adhesive is applied. The gage is then pressed into place using the tape as a carrier and the excess adhesive is squeezed-out from under the gage producing a very thin bond line.

Fig. 6.2 The tape method for installing strain gages.

(a) Position the gage on the work-piece and overlay it with transparent tape.

(b) Peel the tape back to expose the gage's bonding area.

(c) Apply a thin coating of adhesive over the bonding area.

(d) Replace tape in the overlay position with a wiping action to squeeze-out excessive adhesive.

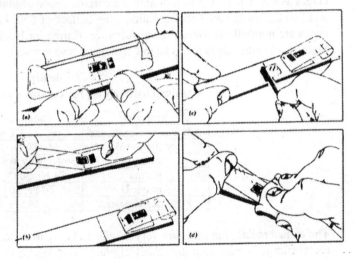

When the gage is positioned, the adhesive must be subjected to a combination of pressure and temperature for the time required to ensure a complete cure. The curing process is quite critical because the adhesive will expand during heating, experience a volume change during polymerization, exhibit contraction while cooling and sometimes exhibit post-cure shrinkage. The adhesive is sufficiently rigid to affect deformation of the gage; hence, changes in the volume of the adhesive influences the resistance of the gage. Of particular importance is post-cure shrinkage, which influences the gage resistance long after the adhesive is supposed to be completely cured. If a long-term measurement of strain is made with a gage bonded with an adhesive that has not completely polymerized, the signal from the gage will drift with time and accuracy of the data will be seriously impaired.

For most strain-gage applications, either cyanoacrylate or epoxy adhesives are used. The cyanoacrylate adhesive has the advantage of being easier to apply, because it requires no heat, cures with a gentle pressure that can be applied with one's thumb and requires only about 10 min for complete polymerization. Its disadvantages include deterioration of strength with time, water absorption and elevated temperatures. The epoxy adhesives are superior to cyanoacrylates; however, they are more difficult to apply because they require a pressure of 5 to 20 psi (35 to 140 kPa) and often require curing at elevated temperature for an hour or more while the pressure is applied. After the adhesive is completely cured, the gage is waterproofed with a light overcoat of crystalline wax or polyurethane coating.

Lead wires are attached to the terminals of the gage so that its change in resistance can be monitored with a suitable instrumentation system. Because the foil strain gages are fragile, even when bonded to a structure, care must be exercised when the lead wires are attached to the soldering tabs. Intermediate anchor terminals, shown in Fig. 6.3, which are much more rugged than the strain gage tabs, are used to protect the gage from damage. A small-diameter wire (32 to 36 gage) with a strain relief loop is used to connect the gage tabs to the anchor terminals. Three lead wires soldered to the anchor terminal, provide for temperature compensation of the lead wires used to connect the strain gages into the Wheatstone bridge (see Section 6.7).

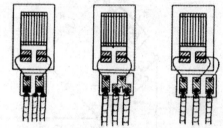

Fig. 6.3 A strain gage installation with anchor terminals to anchor lead wires.

6.4 WHEATSTONE BRIDGE SIGNAL CONDITIONING

The basic equations governing the balance condition, output voltage, nonlinearity and sensitivity of Wheatstone bridges with constant-voltage and constant-current power supplies were developed in Chapter 4. Because the Wheatstone bridge is the most commonly employed circuit to convert the resistance change $\Delta R/R$ from a strain gage to an output voltage V_0, its application for this purpose is considered in detail in this section. The position of the strain gage or gages within the bridge is an important consideration. Consider the four common bridge arrangements shown in the four cases depicted in Fig. 6.4.

Case 1:

This bridge arrangement utilizes a single active gage in position R_1 and it is often employed for both static and dynamic strain-gage measurements, if temperature compensation is not required. The resistance R_1 equals R_g and the other three resistances are selected to maximize the circuit sensitivity while maintaining the balance condition $R_1R_3 = R_2R_4$.

The sensitivity S_s of the strain-gage Wheatstone-bridge system is defined as the product of the sensitivity of the gage S_g and the sensitivity of the bridge circuit S_c. Thus:

$$S_s = S_g S_c = \frac{\Delta R_g / R_g}{\varepsilon} \left(\frac{\Delta V_0}{\Delta R_g / R_g} \right) = \frac{\Delta V_0}{\varepsilon} \qquad (6.5)$$

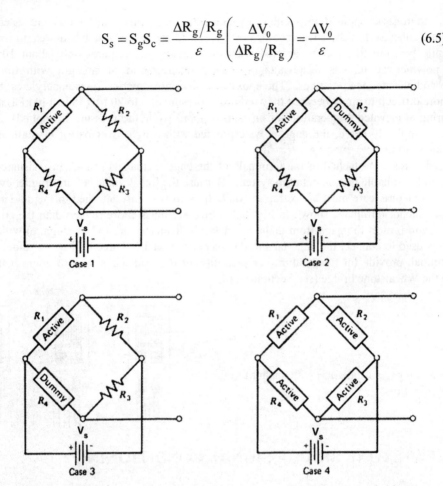

Fig. 6.4 Four common strain-gage arrangements in a Wheatstone bridge.

From Eqs. (4.23) and (6.5),

$$S_s = \frac{r}{1+r} S_g \sqrt{P_g R_g} \qquad (6.6)$$

Equation (6.6) indicates that the sensitivity of the system is controlled by the circuit efficiency $r/(1 + r)$ and the characteristics of the strain gage S_g, P_g and R_g. The more important of these two factors is the characteristics of the strain gage (S_g, P_g and R_g), which vary widely with gage selection. The gage factor S_g is about 2 for gages fabricated from Advance or Karma alloys and about 3.6 for gages fabricated from Isoelastic alloy. Resistances of 120 and 350 Ω are available for most grid configurations, and resistances of 500, 1,000 and 5,000 Ω are available for some grid configurations. Power density P_D is more difficult to specify because it depends upon the conductivity and heat-sink capacity of the specimen to which the gage is bonded. Power density P_D is defined as:

$$P_D = \frac{P_g}{A} \qquad (6.7)$$

where P_g is the power that is dissipated by the gage and A is the area of the grid of the gage.

Recommended power densities for specimens made from different materials are given in Table 6.2.

Table 6.2
Recommended Power Densities

Power Density P_D		Specimen Conditions
W/in^2	W/mm^2	
5-10	0.008-0.016	Heavy Al or Cu sections
2-5	0.003-0.008	Heavy steel sections
1-2	0.0015-0.003	Thin steel sections
0.2-0.5	0.0003-0.0008	Fiberglass, glass, ceramics
0.02-0.05	0.00003-0.00008	Unfilled plastics

A graph showing bridge supply or input voltage V_s as a function of grid area, for a large number of different gage configurations, is shown in Fig. 6.5. The bridge voltage V_S, specified in Fig. 6.5, is for a four-equal-arm bridge with r = 1. In this case, the bridge voltage is given by:

$$V_s = 2\sqrt{AP_D R_g} \qquad (6.8)$$

When r ≠ 1, the bridge voltage is given by:

$$V_s = (1+r)\sqrt{AP_D R_g} \qquad (6.9)$$

The power that is dissipated by a gage will vary over very wide limits. A small gage with a grid area of 0.001 in.^{2} bonded to an insulating material such as a ceramic (P_D = 0.2 W/in.^{2}) dissipates about 0.2 mW. On the other hand, a large strain gage with A = 0.2 in.^{2} mounted on a heavy aluminum section (P_D = 10 W/in.^{2}) dissipates about 2 W.

System sensitivity can be maximized by selecting high-resistance gages with the largest grid area consistent with allowable error due to gage-length and gage-width effects. Specification of Isoelastic alloys to obtain S_g = 3.6 should be limited to dynamic strain measurements, where temperature stability of the gage is not a consideration.

The second factor controlling system sensitivity is circuit efficiency r/(1 + r). The value of r should be selected to increase circuit efficiency, but not so high that the bridge voltage V_s given by Eq. (6.9) increases beyond reasonable limits. Values of r ranging from 3 and 5 give circuit efficiencies between 75% and 83%; while maintaining V_s at reasonable values. For this reason most bridges are designed with r in this range.

Case 2:

This bridge arrangement contains a single active gage in arm R_1, a dummy gage in arm R_2, and fixed-value resistors in arms R_3 and R_4. The active gage and the dummy gage must be identical (preferably two gages from the same production lot), must be applied with the same adhesive and must be subjected to the same curing cycle. The dummy gage can be mounted in a stress-free region of the specimen or on a small block of the specimen material that is placed in the same thermal environment as the specimen. In the Wheatstone bridge, the output from the dummy gage serves to cancel any active gage output due to temperature fluctuations during the test interval. The manner in which this bridge arrangement compensates for temperature changes is illustrated by considering the resistance changes experienced by the active and dummy gages during a test. Thus:

$$\left(\frac{\Delta R_g}{R_g}\right)_A = \left(\frac{\Delta R_g}{R_g}\right)_\varepsilon + \left(\frac{\Delta R_g}{R_g}\right)_{\Delta T}$$

$$\left(\frac{\Delta R_g}{R_g}\right)_D = \left(\frac{\Delta R_g}{R_g}\right)_{\Delta T}$$

(a)

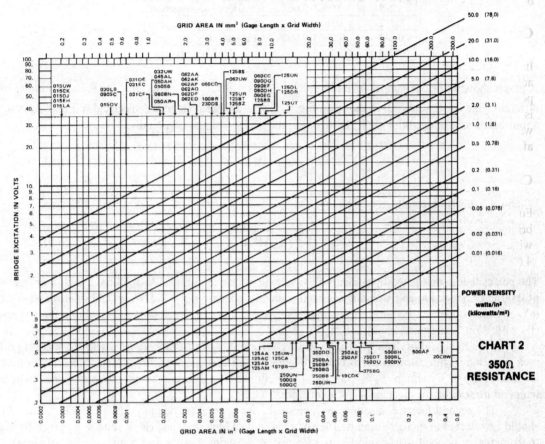

Fig. 6.5 Allowable bridge voltage as a function of grid area for different power densities.
Courtesy of Micro Measurements.

In Eq. (a) the subscripts A and D refer to the active and dummy gages, respectively, while the subscripts ε and ΔT refer to the effects of strain and temperature changes. Substituting Eq. (a) into Eq. (4.4) and noting that $\Delta R_3 = \Delta R_4 = 0$ (fixed-value resistors) gives:

$$\Delta V_0 = V_s \frac{r}{(1+r)^2}\left[\left(\frac{\Delta R_g}{R_g}\right)_\varepsilon + \left(\frac{\Delta R_g}{R_g}\right)_{\Delta T} - \left(\frac{\Delta R_g}{R_g}\right)_{\Delta T}\right]$$

(6.10)

Because the last two terms in the bracketed quantity cancel, the output ΔV_0 is due only to the strain applied to the active gage, and temperature compensation is achieved. With this bridge arrangement, r must equal 1 to satisfy the bridge balance requirement; therefore, the system sensitivity obtained from Eq. (6.6) is:

$$S_s = \frac{1}{2} S_g \sqrt{P_g R_g}$$

(6.11)

Equation (6.11) indicates that placement of a dummy gage in arm R_2 of the Wheatstone bridge to affect temperature compensation reduces the circuit efficiency to 50%. This undesirable feature can be avoided by use of the bridge arrangement described in Case 3.

Case 3:

In this bridge arrangement, the dummy gage is inserted in arm R_4 of the bridge instead of arm R_2. The active gage remains in arm R_1 and fixed value resistors are used in arms R_2 and R_3. With this positioning of the dummy gage, r is not restricted by the balance condition and the system sensitivity is the same as that given by Eq. (6.6). Temperature compensation is achieved in the same manner that was illustrated in Case 2, but without loss of circuit efficiency. When a dummy gage is to be used to affect temperature compensation, arm R_4 of the bridge is the preferred location for the dummy gage.

Case 4:

Four active gages are used in this Wheatstone-bridge arrangement: one active gage in each arm of the bridge (thus, r = 1). When the gages are placed on a specimen, such as a cantilever beam in bending, with tensile strains on gages 1 and 3 (top surface of the beam) and compressive strains on gages 2 and 4 (bottom surface of the beam), then:

$$\left(\frac{\Delta R_1}{R_1} \right) = \left(\frac{\Delta R_3}{R_3} \right) = -\left(\frac{\Delta R_2}{R_2} \right) = -\left(\frac{\Delta R_4}{R_4} \right)$$

(a)

Substituting Eq. (a) into Eq. (4.18) gives:

$$\Delta V_0 = \frac{1}{4} V_s \left(4 \frac{\Delta R_g}{R_g} \right) = V_s \frac{\Delta R_g}{R_g}$$

(6.12)

The Wheatstone bridge has added the four resistance changes to increase the output voltage; therefore, the system sensitivity is given by:

$$S_s = \frac{1}{2} \left(4 S_g \sqrt{P_g R_g} \right) = 2 S_g \sqrt{P_g R_g}$$

(6.13)

This arrangement (with four active gages) has doubled the system sensitivity of Cases 1 and 3 and has quadrupled the sensitivity of Case 2. Also, this bridge arrangement provides temperature compensation. The use of multiple gages to gain sensitivity is not usually recommended because of the costs involved in procuring the additional gages and the increased cost for installing the extra gages. High-quality, high-gain differential amplifiers usually provide a more economical method to increase the magnitude of output signals.

Examination of these four bridge arrangements shows that the system sensitivity can be varied from $1/2$ to 2 times the quantity $S_g\sqrt{P_gR_g}$. Temperature compensation is best achieved by placing the dummy gage in position R_4 to avoid loss of system sensitivity. System sensitivity can be improved by using multiple gages; however, the costs involved for the added gages and their installation is usually not warranted except for transducer applications, where the additional gages serve other purposes.

6.5 RECORDING INSTRUMENTS FOR STRAIN GAGES

The selection of a recording system for strain-gage applications depends primarily upon the nature of the strain to be measured (static or dynamic) and upon the number of strain gages to be monitored. Static recording is by far the easiest and least expensive. Dynamic recording is more difficult and much more expensive. Noise problems arise as a result of the higher level of amplification needed for dynamic recording and the complex multi-channel dynamic recorders increase the costs of making the measurements.

Many different recording instruments can be used to monitor the output of the Wheatstone bridge. In this section, we describe four different instrumentation systems that have been specifically adapted for strain-gage applications, which are widely used in industry.

6.5.1 Direct-Reading Strain Indicator

A direct-reading strain indicator, shown in Fig. 6.6, uses an integrating digital voltmeter to record the system output. This system also contains a Wheatstone bridge that is initially balanced by a potentiometer connected parallel to the output terminals. The voltage output from the bridge is amplified and then displayed on a 4½-digit DVM which gives a range of 20,000 με. The bridge excitation is 2 V dc, which is low enough to avoid gage heating in most applications. System calibration is performed with shunt resistors switched across either 120 or 350 Ω dummy gages to yield an output signal equivalent to 5,000 με. Another potentiometer is used to adjust the gage factor. The gage factor adjustment attenuates the output of the instrument amplifier so that the DVM reads directly in terms of με.

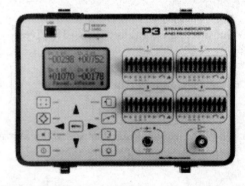

Fig. 6.6 A small portable strain indicator. Courtesy of Vishay Precision Group

The strain measuring instrument shown in Fig. 6.6 is portable, with battery power. It is capable of simultaneously accepting four inputs from quarter-, half-, and full bridge strain-gage circuits, including strain-gage-based transducers. The instrument incorporates a Wheatstone bridge, an amplifier and a large LCD display providing direct readout in terms of strain.

An extensive, easy-to-use menu-driven user interface operates through a front-panel keypad to configure the instrument. Selections for setup include active input and output channels, bridge configuration, measurement units, bridge balance, calibration method and recording options. Bridge or strain gage connections to the instrument are affected through lever release terminal blocks.

Data, recorded at a user-selectable rate of up to 1 reading per channel per second, is stored on a removable RAM card and is transferred by USB to a host computer for subsequent storage, reduction and presentation. The instrument can also be configured to operate directly from a PC with compatible software.

The instrument exhibits a stable measurement circuit with a regulated bridge excitation supply. The gage factor is set into the instrument to enable measurements of ±0.1% accuracy and 1 µε resolution. Bridge completion resistors of 120, 350 and 1,000 ohms are built in for quarter-bridge operation. Also, input connections and switches are provided for remote shunt calibration of transducers and full-bridge circuits. The battery supply consists of two D cells. Battery life depends upon mode of operation but ranges up to 600 hours of continuous use for a single channel. The instrument can also be powered with an external battery, a dc power supply or from a computer's USB port.

6.5.2 Strain Gage Signal Conditioners

Complete strain gage signal conditioners that include an internal half-bridge, an instrument amplifier, an adjustable-output regulated power supply and a low-pass filter are commercially available. A typical signal conditioner for strain gages, presented in Fig. 6.7, which is packaged in a chip carrier, shows the compactness of this integrated unit.

The instrument amplifier has an adjustable gain that is varied from 2 to 5,000 by selecting the resistance across two accessible terminals. The common mode rejection of the differential amplifier is 140 dB when the gain is set at 1,000. The excitation can be adjusted with external resistors to provide bridge supply voltages between 4 and 15 V. A two-pole low-pass filter is set for a cut-off frequency of 1 kHz, although the cut-off frequency is variable between limits of 10 Hz and 20 kHz with external resistors or capacitors. These integrated strain gage signal conditioners are recommended, because they provide four well matched circuits (bridge, power supply, amplifier and filter) at remarkably low cost ($188.24 in lots of 100) for the complete package.

FUNCTIONAL BLOCK DIAGRAM

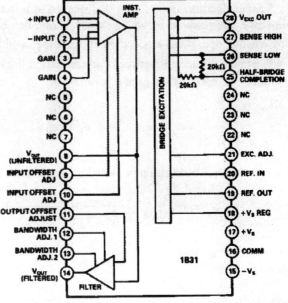

Fig. 6.7 Functional block diagram and pin-out for a high quality signal conditioning unit. Courtesy of Analog Devices.

6.5.3 Wheatstone Bridge and Oscilloscope

When strain gages are used to measure high-frequency dynamic strains at a limited number of locations, the oscilloscope is probably the most suitable recording instrument. A typical Wheatstone bridge-oscilloscope arrangement is shown in Fig. 6.8. The connection from the bridge to the oscilloscope is direct if the oscilloscope has a differential amplifier with sufficient gain. Many single-ended amplifiers and power supplies cannot be used, because they ground point D of the bridge. This grounding seriously affects the output voltage of the bridge and introduces major errors in the strain measurements.

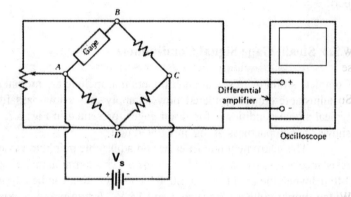

Fig. 6.8 A Wheatstone bridge-oscilloscope strain-measurement system.

The input impedance of an oscilloscope is quite high (one to ten MΩ); as a consequence, loading errors are negligible for the Wheatstone bridge- oscilloscope combination because $R_s/R_m < 0.001$. The bandwidth of an oscilloscope is extremely high and even inexpensive models, with a 10 MHz bandwidth, greatly exceed the requirements for mechanical strain measurements that rarely exceed 100 kHz. The observation interval depends upon the oscilloscope's sweep rate and can range from about one μs to 50 s. With digital oscilloscopes, the observation period depends on the number of words that can be stored and its sampling rate.

Strain as a function of time is displayed as a trace on the face of the display. With a digital oscilloscope, the readings of voltage and/or strain can be taken directly from the display. With an analog oscilloscope, strain ε is computed from the height d_s of the strain-time pulse, as illustrated in Fig. 6.9, and the distance d_c between two calibration lines produced by shunt calibration of the bridge. The strain ε_g indicated by the gage is given by:

$$\varepsilon_g = \frac{d_s}{d_c}\varepsilon_c \qquad (6.14)$$

where ε_g is the equivalent strain produced by shunt calibration.

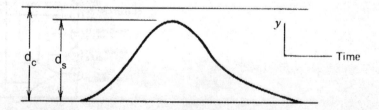

Fig. 6.9 Method to determine strain from an oscilloscope trace.

If the shunt calibration technique is not used, the strain must be computed from the output voltage of the bridge. For example, consider the output voltage ΔV_0 from a single gage (see Fig. 6.9) that is given by using Eqs. (6.4) and (4.5) as:

$$\Delta V_0 = \frac{r}{(1+r)^2} V_s S_g \varepsilon \tag{a}$$

This output voltage can be expressed in terms of oscilloscope parameters as:

$$\Delta V_0 = S_R d_s \tag{b}$$

where d_s is the height of the strain-time pulse in divisions measured on the display and S_R is the sensitivity of the oscilloscope in volts per division.

Substituting Eq. (b) into Eq. (a) and solving for the strain gives:

$$\varepsilon_g = \frac{(1+r)^2}{r} \frac{S_R d_s}{V_s S_g} \tag{6.15}$$

With a digital oscilloscope the strain is determined using the on board microprocessor to perform the multiplication indicated in Eq. (6.15).

6.5.4 Data Acquisition Systems with Circuit Cards and PCs

A more elaborate method for measuring the output from one or more strain gages involves a digital data acquisition system (DAQ), as shown in Fig. 6.10. This data acquisition system is assembled on a printed circuit board (PCB), which provides integrated signal conditioning for measuring bridge-based sensors, such as strain gages, load cells, and pressure transducers. A typical DAQ accommodates eight channels with 24-bit analog-to-digital converters (ADCs) per channel and 25 kS/s sampling rate for simultaneous high-frequency measurements. Each channel incorporates digital filters to reduce noise. Anti-aliasing filters are also used to avoid errors due to improper sampling. The excitation voltage for each channel is programmable from 0.625 to 10 V. Additionally, the instrument provides remote sensing, internal bridge completion with quarter, half and full bridge completion, and shunt calibration for each channel. The accuracy is specified as 0.02% of the recorded strain. Many other DAQs are available packaged in a similar manner.

Some units can be plugged directly into PCs utilizing their power supplies and buss structures.

Fig. 6.10 An eight channel data acquisition system (DAQ) mounted on a printed circuit board (PCB). Courtesy of National Instruments.

6.6 CALIBRATION METHODS

A strain-measurement system, shown in Fig. 6.9, usually includes one or more strain gages, a power supply, circuit-completion resistors, an amplifier, and a recorder. It is possible to calibrate such a system by precisely measuring R_1, R_2, R_3, R_4, V_S, the gain G of the amplifier, and the sensitivity S_R of the recorder. The system calibration constant C for the entire system is then given by:

$$C = \frac{(1+r)^2 S_A S_R}{r V_s S_g} \qquad (6.16)$$

where S_A is the amplifier sensitivity and S_R is the recorder sensitivity (volts per division).

The strain recorded with the system is given in terms of the system calibration constant as:

$$\varepsilon = C d_s \qquad (6.17)$$

where d_s is the deflection of the recorder in divisions.

This procedure is time consuming and is subject to errors in measuring each of the quantities in Eq. (6.16). A more direct, less time-consuming, and more accurate procedure is to calibrate the complete system. This may be accomplished by applying a known strain in the bridge (either mechanically or electrically), measuring d_s resulting from this known strain, and determining the system calibration constant C from Eq. (6.17).

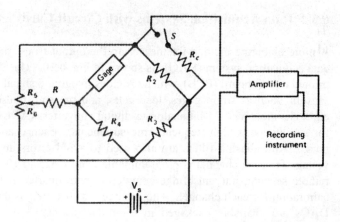

Fig. 6.11 Schematic diagram of the shunt method of calibrating a strain measuring system.

Mechanical calibration is performed by mounting a strain gage (which must have the same gage factor S_g as the gages employed in the measurements) on a cantilever beam, connecting this calibration gage into arm R_1 of the Wheatstone bridge, and observing the deflection of the trace on the recorder as the known strain is applied to the gage. If the free end of a cantilever beam is deflected an amount δ, the calibration strain ε_c induced in the calibration gage is given by:

$$\varepsilon_c = \frac{3hx}{2L^3}\delta = k\delta \qquad (6.18)$$

where h is the depth of the cantilever beam; L is the length of the cantilever beam; x is the distance from the load point to the center of the gage and $k = (3hx)/(2L^3)$ is a constant

The voltage output from an initially balanced bridge is recorded before and after the beam is deflected (for example, note the two horizontal traces shown in Fig. 6.9). The distance between these two lines d_c is used with the calibration strain ε_c to determine the calibration constant C. Thus,

$$C = \frac{\varepsilon_c}{d_c} \qquad (6.19)$$

Electrical calibration is performed in a similar manner, except that the calibration strain is induced by shunting a calibration resistor R_c across arm R_2 of the Wheatstone bridge, as shown in Fig. 6.11. The effective resistance of arm R_2 with R_c in place is given by:

$$R_{2e} = \frac{R_2 R_c}{R_2 + R_c} \qquad (6.20)$$

The change of resistance $\Delta R_2/R_2$ is then given by:

$$\frac{\Delta R_2}{R_2} = \frac{R_{2e} - R_2}{R_2} = -\frac{R_2}{R_2 + R_c} \qquad (6.21)$$

The output voltage produced by shunting R_c across R_2 is obtained by substituting Eq. (6.21) into Eq. (4.18) to give:

$$\Delta V_0 = V_s \frac{R_1 R_2}{(R_1 + R_2)^2} \left(\frac{R_2}{R_2 + R_c} \right) \qquad (a)$$

The output from a single active gage in arm R_1 of a bridge due to the calibration strain is given by Eq. (4.18) as:

$$\Delta V_0 = V_s \frac{R_1 R_2}{(R_1 + R_2)^2} S_g \varepsilon_c \qquad (b)$$

Equating Eqs. (a) and (b) and solving for ε_c gives:

$$\varepsilon_c = \frac{R_2}{S_g (R_2 + R_c)} \qquad (6.22)$$

After ε_c is determined, the calibration constant C is found by using Eq. (6.19). The shunt calibration technique is accurate and simple to use. It provides a single calibration constant for the complete system that incorporates the sensitivities of all components. Unfortunately, the effect of lead wire resistance is not accounted for when the calibration resistor is shunted over resistance R_2 (see Section 6.7.1 for details).

6.7 EFFECTS OF LEAD WIRES, SWITCHES, AND SLIP RINGS

The resistance change from a strain gage is a small quantity; therefore, any disturbance that produces a resistance change within the bridge circuit is extremely important, because it affects the output voltage. Components within the bridge include gages, soldered joints, terminals, lead wires, and binding posts. Often switches and slip rings are also included. Because the effects of lead wires, switches and slip rings are the most important, they will be covered in this section. The effects of soldered joints, terminals, and binding posts must not be neglected because they can also produce significant errors; however, if cold-soldered connections are avoided and if binding posts are clean and tight, then joint resistances are negligibly small.

6.7.1 Lead Wires

Frequently, a strain gage is mounted on a component that is located a significant distance from the bridge and recording system. Suppose the gage is connected to the bridge with two long lead wires, as shown in Fig. 6.12a. With this arrangement, two detrimental effects occur: (1) signal attenuation and (2) loss of temperature compensation. Both effects seriously compromise the accuracy of the measurements.

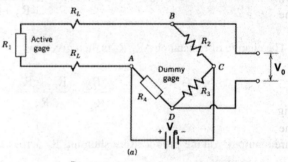

Fig. 6.12 Gage connections to a Wheatstone bridge.
  (a) Two-lead wire system.
  (b) Three-lead wire system.

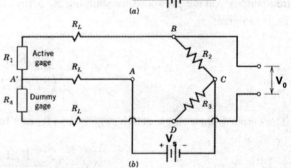

Signal attenuation or loss due to the resistance of the two lead wires can be determined by noting in Fig. 6.12a that:

$$R_1 = R_g + 2R_L \qquad (a)$$

where R_L is the resistance of a single lead wire.

The added resistance in arm R_1 of the bridge (due to the lead wires) leads to the expression:

$$\frac{\Delta R_1}{R_1} = \frac{\Delta R_g}{R_g + 2R_L} = \left[\frac{1}{\left(1 + \left(2R_L / R_g\right)\right)} \right] \qquad (b)$$

Equation (b) can be rewritten in terms of a signal loss factor $\mathcal{L}$ as:

$$\frac{\Delta R_1}{R_1} = \frac{\Delta R_g}{R_g}(1 - \mathcal{L}) \qquad (c)$$

where

$$\mathcal{L} = \frac{2\,R_L/R_g}{1 + (2\,R_L/R_g)} \qquad (6.23)$$

Signal loss factor $\mathcal{L}$ is shown as a function of resistance ratio R_L/R_g in Fig. 6.13. Error due to lead wires can be reduced to less than 1% if $R_L/R_g < 0.005$. The resistance of a 100-ft (30.5-m) length of solid copper lead wire and the associated signal loss factor as a function of gage size is listed in Table 6.3. It is obvious from the data in Table 6.3 that long lengths of small-diameter wire must be avoided in strain-gage measurements.

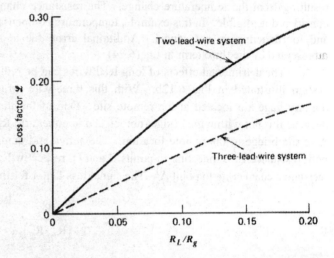

Fig. 6.13 Loss factor $\mathcal{L}$ as a function of the resistance ratio R_L/R_g for two- and three-lead wire systems.

Table 6.3
Resistance (Ohms per 100 ft) of Solid-Conductor Copper Wire
and Signal Loss Factor $\mathcal{L}$ for gages with $R_g = 120\ \Omega$.

Gage Size	R_L	$2R_L/R_g$	$\mathcal{L}$ (%)
12	0.159	0.00265	0.26
14	0.253	0.00422	0.42
16	0.402	0.00670	0.67
18	0.639	0.01065	1.05
20	1.015	0.01692	1.67
22	1.614	0.0269	2.62
24	2.567	0.0428	4.10
26	4.081	0.0670	6.28
28	6.490	0.1082	9.76
30	10.31	0.1718	14.7
32	16.41	0.2735	21.5
34	26.09	0.4348	30.3
36	41.48	0.6913	40.9
38	65.96	1.0993	52.4
40	104.9	1.7483	63.6

The second detrimental effect due to lead wires is the loss of temperature compensation. For example, consider a Wheatstone bridge with an active gage and two long lead wires in arm R_1 and a dummy gage with two short lead wires in arm R_4. If both gages and all lead wires are subjected to the same temperature change ΔT during the time interval when strain is being monitored, the output of the bridge is given by Eq. (4.18) as:

$$\Delta V_0 = V_s \frac{r}{(1+r)^2} \left[\left(\frac{\Delta R_g}{R_g + 2R_L} \right)_\varepsilon + \left(\frac{\Delta R_g}{R_g + 2R_L} \right)_{\Delta T} + \left(\frac{2\Delta R_L}{R_g + 2R_L} \right)_{\Delta T} - \left(\frac{\Delta R_g}{R_g} \right)_{\Delta T} \right] \quad (6.24)$$

The first and second terms in the brackets are due to the resistance change in the active gage from strain and temperature changes, respectively. The third term is the resistance change in the lead wires of arm R_1 due to the temperature change. The fourth term is the resistance change in the dummy gage resulting from the temperature change. The resistance change in the short lead wires to arm R_4 is considered negligible. In this example, temperature compensation is not achieved, because the second and fourth terms do not cancel. Additional error due to resistance changes in the lead wires is represented by the third term in Eq. (6.24).

The detrimental effects of long lead wires can be reduced by employing the simple three-wire system illustrated in Fig. 6.12b. With this three-wire arrangement, both the active gage and the dummy gage are located at the remote site. One of the three wires is not considered a lead wire, because it is not within the bridge (not located in either arm R_1 or R_4) and serves only to transfer point A of the bridge to the remote location. The active and dummy gages each have one long lead wire with resistance R_L connecting to points B and D, respectively, and one short lead wire with negligible resistance connecting to point A'. The signal loss factor for the three-wire system is given by:

$$\mathcal{L} = \frac{R_L / R_g}{1 + (R_L / R_g)} \quad (6.25)$$

A comparison of Eqs. (6.23) and (6.25) indicates that signal attenuation due to lead-wire resistance is reduced by a factor of nearly 2 by using the three-wire system. (This fact is also evident from the results shown in Fig. 6.13).

The temperature-compensating feature of the Wheatstone bridge is retained when the three-wire system is used. In this case, Eq. (6.24) is modified to read:

$$\Delta V_0 = V_s \frac{r}{(1+r)^2} \left[\left(\frac{\Delta R_g}{R_g + R_L} \right)_\varepsilon + \left(\frac{\Delta R_g}{R_g + R_L} \right)_{\Delta T} + \left(\frac{\Delta R_L}{R_g + R_L} \right)_{\Delta T} - \left(\frac{\Delta R_g}{R_g + R_L} \right)_{\Delta T} - \left(\frac{\Delta R_L}{R_g + R_L} \right)_{\Delta T} \right]$$

$$(6.26a)$$

which reduces to:

$$\Delta V_0 = V_s \frac{r}{(1+r)^2} \left(\frac{\Delta R_g}{R_g + R_L} \right)_\varepsilon \quad (6.26b)$$

It is clear from Eq. (6.26b) that temperature compensation is achieved because all of the temperature-dependent terms in the bracketed quantity cancel. In all cases where lead-wire resistance causes appreciable signal attenuation, the calibration resistor should be placed across the remote dummy gage to include the effects of the lead wires in the system calibration constant.

6.7.2 Switches

Frequently, a large number of gages are necessary in evaluating a structure. Moreover, the output of each gage is read several times during a typical test. In this application, the number of gages is too large to employ a separate measurement system for each gage. Instead, a single instrument system is used and the gages are switched in and out of this system according to some schedule. Two different switching arrangements are commonly employed with multiple-gage installations.

The most common and least expensive arrangement is illustrated in Fig. 6.14. Here, one side of each active gage is switched, in turn, into arm R_1 of the bridge, while the other side of each active gage is connected to the terminals of the bridge with a common lead wire. This arrangement places the switch in arm R_1 of the bridge; therefore, a high-quality switch with a small and reproducible contact resistance (less than 500 $\mu\Omega$) must be employed. Low resistance is achieved by solid state switches or silver-tipped contacts and two or more parallel contacts per switch on mechanical devices. If the switch resistance is not reproducible, the change in switch resistance ΔR_s adds to the strain-induced change in gage resistance ΔR_ε to produce an apparent strain ε', which can be expressed as:

$$\varepsilon' = \frac{\Delta R_s / R_g}{S_g} \tag{6.27}$$

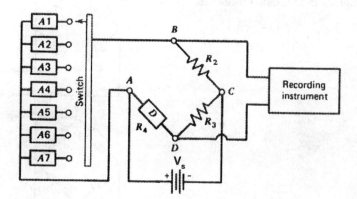

Fig. 6.14 Switching a large number of gages into arm R_1 of a Wheatstone bridge with a single pole switch.

The quality of a switch can be easily checked, because non-reproducible switch resistance results in a shifting of the zero reading. Mechanical switches must be cleaned regularly, because even high-quality switches will begin to perform erratically when the contacts become dirty or when surface films develop on its contacts due to chemical reactions with the atmosphere.

A second switching arrangement, shown in Fig. 6.15, employs a three-pole switch to transfer terminals A, B, and D to the power supply and the recording instrument. Terminal C of each bridge is grounded in common with the power supply with a single common lead wire. Because the switches are not located within the bridge, switch resistance is much less important. However, switching the complete bridge requires separate dummy gages and two bridge completion resistors for each active gage.

A major disadvantage of all switching schemes is the thermal drift due to heating of the gages and resistors when power is suddenly applied to the bridge as it is switched into the instrument system. Depending upon the thermal capacity of the specimen, this drift may continue for tens of seconds before thermal equilibrium at the gage site is achieved.

6.7.3 Slip Rings

When strain gages are used on rotating members, slip rings are often used to transfer lead-wire connections, as shown in Fig. 6.16a. The slip rings are usually mounted on a shaft that is attached to the rotating member so that the axes of rotation of this shaft and member coincide. The outer shell of the slip ring assembly is stationary and carries one or more brushes per ring to transfer the signal from the rotating rings to terminals on the stationary shell. Satisfactory operation up to speeds of 24,000 rpm is possible with well designed slip ring assemblies.

Brush contact and dirt collecting on the slip rings cause brush wear and tend to produce significant fluctuations in resistance. It is possible to reduce these fluctuations by using multiple brushes in parallel for each lead wire. However, even with multiple brushes, fluctuation in resistance between rings and brushes tend to be so large that slip rings are rarely placed within the arms of the bridge. Instead, a complete bridge is assembled for each active gage on the rotating member, as shown in Fig. 6.16a. The slip rings are used only to connect the bridge to its power supply and the bridge's output signal to its recording instrument. This arrangement minimizes the effect of resistance fluctuations produced by the slip rings and provides a means for accurately recording strain-gage signals from rotating members.

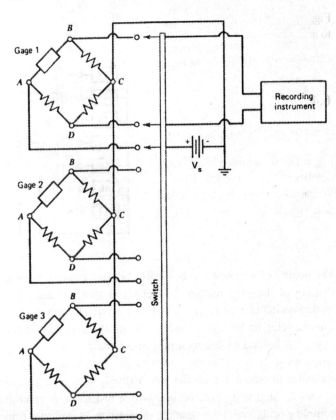

Fig. 6.15 Switching several complete bridges into the power supply and the recording instrument with a three pole switch.

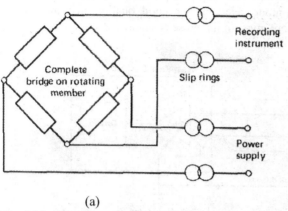

(a)

Fig. 6.16 Slip ring connections to Wheatstone bridge.

(b)

Commercial slip ring assembly.

6.8 ELECTRICAL NOISE

The output voltage from a Wheatstone bridge due to the resistance change $\Delta R/R$ of a strain gage is usually only a few millivolts. Because of this very small output voltage V_0, electrical noise is frequently a problem. Electrical noise occurs as a result of magnetic fields generated by current flow in wires in close proximity to the lead wires or the Wheatstone bridge, as shown in Fig. 6.17. When current from an ac supply line flows in an adjacent wire, a 60 Hz magnetic field is produced, which cuts both wires of the signal circuit and induces a voltage (noise) in the signal loop. The magnitude of this noise signal is proportional to the current I flowing in the disturbing wire and the area enclosed by the signal loop, and is inversely proportional to the distance between the disturbing wire and the strain-gage lead wires (see Fig. 6.17). In some cases, the voltage induced by the magnetic field is so large that the signal-to-noise ratio becomes excessive and it is difficult to separate the noise and the strain-gage signals.

Fig. 6.17 Schematic diagram showing generation of electrical noise.

Three precautions can be taken to minimize noise. First, all lead wires can be twisted together or arranged in a ribbon conductor to minimize the area of the signal loop. Second, only shielded cables should be used. The shields should be grounded only at the negative terminal of the power supply to the bridge, as shown in Fig. 6.18. With this arrangement, the shield is grounded without forming a ground loop and any noise voltage generated in the shield is maintained at ground potential. The power supply is floated relative to the system ground, which is the third conductor in the power cord, to avoid a ground loop at the supply. Third, differential amplifiers should be used to reduce noise by common-mode rejection. If the lead wires are twisted, the noise signal developed on both lead wires will be equal and will occur simultaneously. A differential amplifier rejects these noise signals and only the strain signal is amplified. Common-mode rejection for good quality, instrumentation amplifiers is about 100 to 150 dB at 60 Hz; therefore, most of the noise is suppressed.

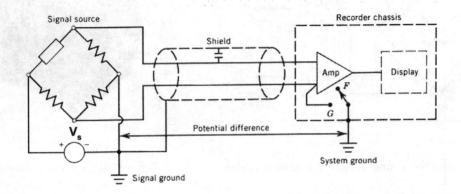

Fig. 6.18 Shielding and single point grounding to eliminate electrical noise.

If these three techniques for suppressing noise are employed, the signal-to-noise ratio can be maximized and low magnitude strain signals can be recorded even at locations with adverse electrical conditions.

6.9 TEMPERATURE COMPENSATED GAGES

Temperature compensation within the Wheatstone bridge was discussed in Section 6.4; however, temperature compensation within the gage is possible. In static applications, both the bridge and the gage should be compensated to nullify any signal due to temperature variations during the test period. When the ambient temperature changes, four effects occur that influence the signal $\Delta R/R$ from the gage:

1. The gage factor S_g changes with temperature.
2. The grid undergoes an elongation or contraction ($\Delta L/L = \alpha \Delta T$).
3. The specimen elongates or contracts ($\Delta L/L = \beta \Delta T$).
4. The resistance of the gage changes ($\Delta R/R = \gamma \Delta T$).

The strain sensitivities S_A of the two most commonly used alloys (Advance and Karma) are linear functions of temperature as shown in Fig. 6.19. The slope of the $S_A - T$ line indicates that $\Delta S_A/\Delta T$ equals 0.0000735/°C and −0.0000975/°C for Advance and Karma alloys, respectively. Because these changes are small (less than 1% for $\Delta T = 100$ °C), variations in S_A with temperature are usually neglected if temperature variations are less than 50 °C. However, in thermal stress studies where temperature variations of several hundred degrees are common, changes in S_A become significant and must be considered.

The remaining three effects are much more significant and combine to produce a change in resistance of the gage which can be expressed as:

$$\left(\frac{\Delta R}{R}\right)_{\Delta T} = (\beta - \alpha)S_g\Delta T + \gamma\Delta T \qquad (6.28)$$

where α is the thermal coefficient of expansion of the gage alloy, β is the thermal coefficient of expansion of the specimen material and γ is the temperature coefficient of resistivity of the gage alloy.

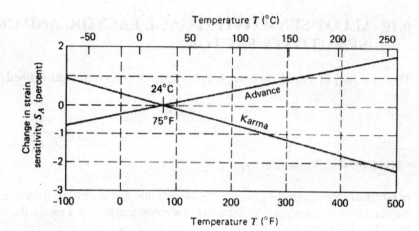

Fig. 6.19 Sensitivity as a function of temperature for Advance and Karma alloys.

A differential expansion between the gage grid and the specimen due to a temperature change ($\alpha \neq \beta$) subjects the gage to a thermally induced mechanical strain $\varepsilon_T = (\beta - \alpha)\Delta T$, that does not occur in the specimen. The gage responds to the strain ε_T in the same way that it responds to a load-induced strain ε in the specimen. Unfortunately, it is impossible to separate the component of the response due to temperature change from the response due to the mechanical strain.

If the gage alloy is matched to the specimen ($\alpha = \beta$), the first term in Eq. (6.28) does not produce a response; however, the second term causes a response and indicates an apparent strain that does not exist in the specimen. A temperature-compensated gage is obtained only if both terms in Eq. (6.28) are zero or if they cancel.

The values of α and γ are quite sensitive to the composition of the alloy and the degree of cold working imparted during the rolling the foil. It is common practice for the strain-gage manufacturers to measure the thermal-response characteristics of sample gages made from each roll of foil in their inventories. Because of variations in α and γ between melts and rolls of foil, it is possible to select gage alloys from inventory that are temperature compensated for almost any specimen material. These gages are known as selected-melt or temperature-compensated gages.

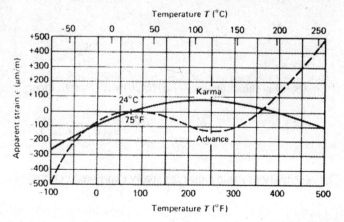

Fig. 6.20 Apparent strain as a function of temperature for Advance and Karma alloys.

Unfortunately, selected-melt gages are not perfectly compensated over a wide range of temperature because of nonlinear terms that were omitted in Eq. (6.28). A typical selected-melt strain gage exhibits an apparent strain with temperature as shown in Fig. 6.20. The apparent strain produced by a temperature change of a few degrees in the neighborhood of 75 °F (24 °C) is small (less than 0.5 $\mu\varepsilon/°C$); however, when the temperature change is large, the apparent strain generated by the gage becomes significant and corrections to account for this apparent strain are necessary.

6.10 ALLOY SENSITIVITY, GAGE FACTOR, AND CROSS-SENSITIVITY FACTOR

The sensitivity of a single, uniform length of conductor to strain was defined (see Section 6.1) as:

$$S_A = \frac{dR/R}{\varepsilon} = \frac{\Delta R/R}{\varepsilon} \tag{6.4}$$

where S_A is the alloy sensitivity.

In a typical strain gage, the conductor is formed into a grid configuration to minimize its length. Also, the conductor is usually not uniform over its entire length. As a result, the alloy sensitivity S_A differs from the gage factor S_g.

A better understanding of the response of a grid-type strain gage can be obtained by considering a gage mounted on a specimen that is subjected to a biaxial strain field. For this situation:

$$\frac{\Delta R}{R} = S_a \varepsilon_a + S_t \varepsilon_t + S_s \gamma_{at} \tag{6.29}$$

where ε_a is the normal strain along the axial direction of the gage; ε_t is the normal strain along the transverse direction; γ_{at} is the shearing strain associated with the a and t directions; S_a is the sensitivity of the gage to axial strain; S_t is the sensitivity of the gage to transverse strain and S_s is the sensitivity of the gage to shearing strain.

The gage sensitivity to shearing strain is believed to be small and is neglected. The gage sensitivity to transverse strain is usually not small enough to neglect; therefore, the strain gage manufacturers provide a transverse sensitivity factor K_t for each gage which is defined as:

$$K_t = \frac{S_t}{S_a} \tag{6.30}$$

If Eq. (6.30) is substituted into Eq. (6.29) with $S_s = 0$, then:

$$\frac{\Delta R}{R} = S_a(\varepsilon_a + K_t \varepsilon_t) \tag{6.31}$$

The sensitivity of strain gages is usually expressed in terms of a gage factor S_g previously defined by:

$$\frac{\Delta R}{R} = S_g \varepsilon_a \tag{6.4}$$

The gage factor S_g is determined by the manufacturer by measuring $\Delta R/R$ for a sample of gages drawn from each production lot. In calibration, the sample gages are mounted on a beam with a Poisson's ratio $\nu_0 = 0.285$. A known axial strain ε_a is applied to the beam which produces a transverse strain ε_t given by:

$$\varepsilon_t = - \nu_0 \varepsilon_a \tag{6.32}$$

The response of the gage in calibration is obtained by substituting Eq. (6.32) into Eq. (6.31) to give:

$$\frac{\Delta R}{R} = S_a \varepsilon_a (1 + \nu_0 K_t) \tag{6.33}$$

Equating Eqs. (6.33) and (6.4) gives the gage factor S_g in terms of S_a and K_t as:

$$S_g = S_a (1 - \nu_0 K_t) \tag{6.34}$$

The simplified form of the $\Delta R/R$ versus ε_a relationship given by Eq. (6.4) is usually used to interpret strain-gage response. It is very important to recognize that this equation is approximate unless either $K_t = 0$ or $\varepsilon_t = - \nu_0 \varepsilon_a$. The magnitude of the error incurred by using Eq. (6.4) can be determined by considering the response of a gage in a general biaxial strain field. If Eq. (6.34) is substituted into Eqs. (6.31), the gage response is given as:

$$\frac{\Delta R}{R} = \frac{S_g \varepsilon_a}{1 - \nu_0 K_t} \left(1 + K_t \frac{\varepsilon_t}{\varepsilon_a} \right) \tag{6.35}$$

The true value of strain ε_a is then written as:

$$\varepsilon_a = \frac{\Delta R/R}{S_g} \left[\frac{1 - \nu_0 K_t}{1 + K_t (\varepsilon_t / \varepsilon_a)} \right] \tag{6.36}$$

The apparent strain ε_a', obtained by using Eq. (6.4), is given by:

$$\varepsilon_a' = \frac{\Delta R/R}{S_g} \tag{a}$$

Substituting Eq. (a) into Eq. (6.36) gives

$$\varepsilon_a = \varepsilon_a' \left[\frac{1 - \nu_0 K_t}{1 + K_t (\varepsilon_t / \varepsilon_a)} \right] \tag{6.37}$$

The percent error $\mathcal{E}$ incurred by neglecting the transverse sensitivity of a strain gage in a general biaxial strain field is obtained from Eq. (6.36) and Eq. (a) as:

$$\mathcal{E} = \frac{\varepsilon_a' - \varepsilon_a}{\varepsilon_a}(100) = \frac{K_t(\varepsilon_t/\varepsilon_a + v_0)}{1 - v_0 K_t}(100) \tag{6.38}$$

Some representative values of $\mathcal{E}$ as a function of K_t for different biaxial ratios $\varepsilon_t/\varepsilon_a$ are illustrated in Fig. 6.21.

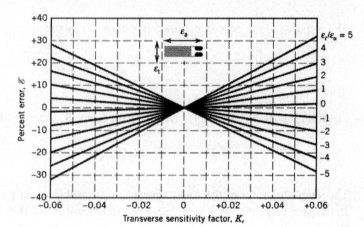

Fig. 6.21 Percent error as a function of transverse sensitivity factor for several different ratios of transverse to axial strain.

Two different procedures are used to correct for the error involved with the use of Eq. (6.4). First, if the biaxiality ratio $\varepsilon_t/\varepsilon_a$ is known a priori (in a thin-walled cylinder under internal pressure, for example), the bracketed term in Eq. (6.37) can be viewed as a correction factor C_f that modifies the apparent strain ε_a' to give the true strain ε_a. The factor by which all apparent strain values must be multiplied to give true strains is given by:

$$C_f = \frac{1 - v_0 K_t}{1 + K_t(\varepsilon_t/\varepsilon_a)} \tag{6.39}$$

Alternatively, a corrected gage factor S_g^* can be used in place of S_g to adjust the bridge before readings are taken. The corrected gage factor as determined from Eqs. (6.4) and (6.37) is given by:

$$S_g^* = S_g \frac{1 + K_t(\varepsilon_t/\varepsilon_a)}{1 - v_0 K_t} = \frac{S_g}{C_f} \tag{6.40}$$

The second correction procedure is used when the biaxiality ratio $\varepsilon_t/\varepsilon_a$ is not known. If apparent strain ε'_{xx} and ε'_{yy} are recorded in orthogonal directions, then from Eqs. (6.31) and (6.4), we may write:

$$\varepsilon'_{xx} = \frac{1}{1 - v_0 K_t}(\varepsilon_{xx} + K_t \varepsilon_{yy})$$

$$\varepsilon'_{yy} = \frac{1}{1 - v_0 K_t}(\varepsilon_{yy} + K_t \varepsilon_{xx}) \tag{6.41}$$

Solving Eqs. (6.41) for the true strains ε_{xx} and ε_{yy} yields:

$$\varepsilon_{xx} = \frac{1-\nu_0 K_t}{1-K_t^2}\left(\varepsilon'_{xx} + K_t \varepsilon'_{yy}\right)$$

$$\varepsilon_{yy} = \frac{1-\nu_0 K_t}{1-K_t^2}\left(\varepsilon'_{yy} + K_t \varepsilon'_{xx}\right)$$

(6.42)

6.11 DATA REDUCTION METHODS

Strain gages are normally bonded on the free surface of a specimen ($\sigma_{zz} = \tau_{zx} = \tau_{zy} = 0$) to determine the stresses at specific points when the specimen is subjected to a system of loads. The conversion from strains to stresses requires knowledge of the elastic constants E and ν of the specimen material and, depending upon the state of stress at the point, from one to three normal strains. Three different stress states are considered in the following subsections. Data analysis methods and special-purpose strain gages are described for each stress state.

6.11.1 The Uniaxial State of Stress ($\sigma_{xx} \neq 0$, $\sigma_{yy} = 0$, $\tau_{xy} = 0$)

In a uniaxial state of stress (encountered in tension members and in beams in pure bending), the stress σ_{xx} is the only nonzero stress component and its direction is known. In this case, a single-element strain gage (see Figs. 6.1 and 6.3) oriented with its axis in the x direction is used to determine the strain ε_{xx}. The stress is then given by the uniaxial form of Hooke's law as:

$$\sigma_{xx} = E\varepsilon_{xx} \qquad\qquad \sigma_{yy} = \tau_{xy} = 0 \qquad\qquad (6.43)$$

One principal direction coincides with the x axis; and the directions perpendicular to the x axis are principal directions.

6.11.2 The Biaxial State of Stress ($\sigma_{xx} \neq 0$, $\sigma_{yy} \neq 0$, $\tau_{xy} = 0$)

If the directions of the principal stresses are known at the gage location (on a loading axis with geometric symmetry), two strain measurements in perpendicular directions provide sufficient data to determine the stresses at the point. Special strain gages known as two-element rectangular rosettes, shown in Fig. 6.22, are available for this measurement.

Fig. 6.22 A two-element rectangular rosette with strain gages oriented in the x and y directions. Courtesy of Micro-Measurements Vishay Precision Group

The two-element rosette should be oriented on the specimen with its axes coincident with the principal stress directions in order to determine the two principal strains ε_1 and ε_2. The stresses are then given by the biaxial form of generalized Hooke's law as:

$$\sigma_1 = \frac{E}{1-v^2}(\varepsilon_1 + v\varepsilon_2)$$

$$\sigma_2 = \frac{E}{1-v^2}(\varepsilon_2 + v\varepsilon_1)$$

(6.44)

6.11.3 The General State of Stress ($\sigma_{xx} \neq 0$, $\sigma_{yy} \neq 0$, $\tau_{xy} \neq 0$)

In the most general case, the principal stress directions are not known; therefore, three unknowns σ_1, σ_2, and the principal angle ϕ_1 must be determined in order to specify the state of stress at a point. Three-element rosettes, shown in Fig. 6.23, are used in these cases to obtain the required strain data.

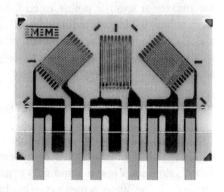

Fig. 6.23 A three-element rectangular rosette with strain gages oriented at 45, 90 and 135 degrees.
Courtesy of Micro-Measurements Vishay Precision Group

The fact that three strain measurements are sufficient to determine the state of strain at a point on a free surface is demonstrated by considering three gages aligned along axes A, B, and C, as shown in Fig. 6.24. Using one of the equations of strain transformation we write:

$$\varepsilon_A = \varepsilon_{xx} \cos^2 \theta_A + \varepsilon_{yy} \cos^2 \theta_A + \gamma_{xy} \sin \theta_A \cos \theta_A$$

$$\varepsilon_B = \varepsilon_{xx} \cos^2 \theta_B + \varepsilon_{yy} \cos^2 \theta_B + \gamma_{xy} \sin \theta_B \cos \theta_B$$

(6.45)

$$\varepsilon_C = \varepsilon_{xx} \cos^2 \theta_C + \varepsilon_{yy} \cos^2 \theta_C + \gamma_{xy} \sin \theta_C \cos \theta_C$$

Fig. 6.24 Three strain gages oriented at angles θ_A, θ_B and θ_C with respect to the x axis.

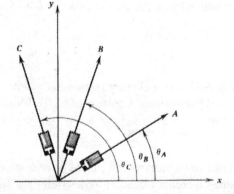

The Cartesian components of strain ε_{xx}, ε_{yy}, and γ_{xy} are determined by solving Eqs. (6.45). The principal strains ε_1, ε_2 and the principal direction ϕ_1 are then determined from:

$$\varepsilon_1 = \frac{1}{2}\left(\varepsilon_{xx} + \varepsilon_{yy}\right) + \frac{1}{2}\sqrt{\left(\varepsilon_{xx} - \varepsilon_{yy}\right)^2 + \gamma_{xy}^2}$$

$$\varepsilon_2 = \frac{1}{2}\left(\varepsilon_{xx} + \varepsilon_{yy}\right) - \frac{1}{2}\sqrt{\left(\varepsilon_{xx} - \varepsilon_{yy}\right)^2 + \gamma_{xy}^2} \qquad (6.46)$$

$$\phi_1 = \frac{1}{2}\tan^{-1}\frac{\gamma_{xy}}{\varepsilon_{xx} - \varepsilon_{yy}}$$

where ϕ_1 is the angle between the principal direction for ε_1 and the x axis.

Two of the most commonly employed rosettes are the delta rosette and the three-element rectangular rosette. The three-element rectangular rosette is discussed here, while the analysis of the delta rosette is left as an exercise. The three-element rectangular rosette is designed with $\theta_A = 0°$, $\theta_B = 45°$, $\theta_C = 90°$. With these fixed angles, Eqs. (6.45) reduce to:

$$\varepsilon_A = \varepsilon_{xx} \qquad\qquad \varepsilon_B = \tfrac{1}{2}\left(\varepsilon_{xx} + \varepsilon_{yy} + \gamma_{xy}\right) \qquad\qquad \varepsilon_C = \varepsilon_{yy} \qquad (a)$$

From Eqs. (a) it is clear that

$$\gamma_{xy} = 2\varepsilon_B - \varepsilon_A - \varepsilon_C \qquad (b)$$

The principal strains ε_1 and ε_2 and the principal angle ϕ_1 are obtained in terms of ε_A, ε_B and ε_C from Eqs. (a), (b) and (6.46) as:

$$\varepsilon_1 = \frac{1}{2}\left(\varepsilon_A + \varepsilon_C\right) + \frac{1}{2}\sqrt{\left(\varepsilon_A - \varepsilon_C\right)^2 + \left(2\varepsilon_B - \varepsilon_A - \varepsilon_C\right)^2}$$

$$\varepsilon_2 = \frac{1}{2}\left(\varepsilon_A + \varepsilon_C\right) - \frac{1}{2}\sqrt{\left(\varepsilon_A - \varepsilon_C\right)^2 + \left(2\varepsilon_B - \varepsilon_A - \varepsilon_C\right)^2} \qquad (6.47)$$

$$\phi_1 = \frac{1}{2}\tan^{-1}\frac{2\varepsilon_B - \varepsilon_A - \varepsilon_C}{\varepsilon_A - \varepsilon_C}$$

Equations (6.47) yields two values for the angle ϕ. One value ϕ_1 refers to the angle between the x axis and the axis of ε_1, while the second value ϕ_2 refers to the angle between the x axis and the axis of ε_2. A classification procedure, shown in Eqs. (6.48), is employed to define the angle ϕ_1 as:

$$0° < \phi_1 < 90° \qquad\qquad \text{when } \varepsilon_B > \tfrac{1}{2}\left(\varepsilon_A + \varepsilon_C\right)$$

$$-90° < \phi_1 < 90° \qquad\qquad \text{when } \varepsilon_B < \tfrac{1}{2}\left(\varepsilon_A + \varepsilon_C\right)$$

$$\phi_1 = 0° \qquad\qquad\qquad \text{when } \varepsilon_A > \varepsilon_C \text{ and } \varepsilon_A = \varepsilon_1 \qquad (6.48)$$

$$\phi_1 = \pm 90° \qquad\qquad\quad \text{when } \varepsilon_A < \varepsilon_C \text{ and } \varepsilon_A = \varepsilon_2$$

Finally, the principal stresses are determined in terms of ε_A, ε_B, and ε_C by substituting into Eqs. (6.47) and using the classification procedure given in Eqs. (6.48) to obtain:

$$\sigma_1 = E\left[\frac{\varepsilon_A + \varepsilon_C}{2(1-v)} + \frac{1}{2(1+v)}\sqrt{(\varepsilon_A - \varepsilon_C)^2 + (2\varepsilon_B - \varepsilon_A - \varepsilon_C)^2}\right]$$

$$\sigma_2 = E\left[\frac{\varepsilon_A + \varepsilon_C}{2(1-v)} - \frac{1}{2(1+v)}\sqrt{(\varepsilon_A - \varepsilon_C)^2 + (2\varepsilon_B - \varepsilon_A - \varepsilon_C)^2}\right]$$

$$(6.49)$$

While derivation of these equations is tedious, they are simple and easy to employ. As a result, rosettes are widely used to establish the complete state of stress at a point on the free surface of a body when the directions of the principal stresses are not known in advance.

6.12 HIGH TEMPERATURE STRAIN MEASUREMENTS

The behavior of strain gages under a wide range of temperature was described in Section 6.9 and results showing changes in alloy sensitivity and apparent strain with temperature were presented in Figs 6.19 and 6.20. It is important to note that these results are not provided for temperatures above 500 °F (260 °C). The use of strain gages at elevated temperatures becomes more difficult as the temperature increases beyond this limit. At elevated temperature, the response of a resistance strain gage must be considered to be a function of temperature T and time t in addition to strain. Recasting Eq. (6.4) to accommodate time and temperature gives:

$$\frac{\Delta R}{R} = S_g \varepsilon + S_T \Delta T + S_\tau \Delta t$$

$$(6.50)$$

where S_T is the gage sensitivity to temperature and S_τ is its sensitivity to time.

Examination of Fig. 6.20 indicates that S_g changes with temperature for both Advance and Karma alloys and Fig. 6.20 shows that S_T becomes larger for both of these alloys at higher temperatures. Indeed S_T becomes so large for Advance alloy that its use is not recommended above 180 °C.

The gage sensitivity with time S_τ, which is quite small at or near room temperature, becomes significant at higher temperature. This term $S_\tau \Delta t$, often termed strain-gage drift, must be taken into account in all static strain measurements at elevated temperatures. An example of strain-gage drift for a Karma alloy gage at 560 °F (293 °C) is presented in Fig. 6.25.

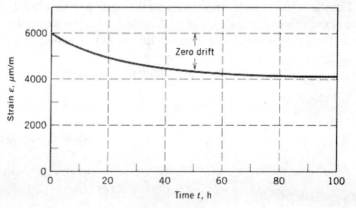

Fig. 6.25 Strain gage drift as a function of time for Karma-alloy strain gage with glass-fiber epoxy-phenolic carrier at 560 °F (from data by Hayes)

Stability or drift is affected by stress relaxation in the adhesive bond and carrier material and by metallurgical changes (phase transformations and annealing) in the strain-gage alloy. Drift rates or the magnitude of S_τ depend upon the gage alloy, adhesive and carrier materials, strain level and temperature. For high temperature strain measurements, it is suggested that a series of strain-time calibration curves (like the one shown in Fig. 6.25) be developed to cover the range of strains and temperatures to be encountered in the actual experiment. Corrections can then be taken from the appropriate curve to eliminate the $S_\tau \Delta t$ term in Eq. (6.50).

The stability problem becomes much less critical as the observation period decreases and for times of a few seconds or less, zero-drift due to time can usually be neglected. Also, for short observation times, the temperature changes are small and apparent strains due to the $S_T \Delta T$ term tends to vanish. Thus, dynamic measurement of strain, even at very high temperatures (to 1600 °F), are possible. For the dynamic measurement, $\Delta T = \Delta t \approx 0$ and Eq. (6.50) reduces to $\Delta R/R = S_g$.

Strain measurements above 500 °F (260 °C) are usually performed by modifying the gage and installation procedures. Polymeric carriers are not satisfactory and are stripped from the gage after a face down installation. Polymeric adhesives are replaced with ceramic adhesives to avoid the degradation that occurs when polymers are exposed to high temperatures. Metallurgically stable alloys such as Armour D (70 Fe, 20 Cr and 10 Al) or alloy 479 (92 Pt and 8 W) are used in fabricating the gage grids to avoid phase changes or oxidation at the higher temperatures.

6.13   MECHANICAL STRAIN GAGES

Mechanical strain gages such as the Huggenberger tensometer, or the Berry strain gage are rarely used today because the electrical-resistance strain gages are more accurate, lower in cost and easier to use. Mechanical gages often called extensometers are still widely used today in material test systems.

However, these extensometers utilize electrical devices such as displacement transformers or resistance strain gages for sensors. A typical extensometer, shown in Fig. 6.26, is employed in the conventional tensile test where the stress-strain diagram is recorded. The extensometer is equipped with knife-edges and a wire spring that forces the knife-edges into the tension specimen. Elongation or compression of the specimen causes movement of the arms. As these arms move they bend a small cross-flexural element insuring center-point bending over the entire range of the extensometer. The cross-flexural member, which is the sensing element, also provides good lateral stability and requires low actuating forces (about 50 g). Electrical-resistance strain gages, bonded to the cross-flexural element, sense the bending strains and give a signal output that is proportional to the contraction or extension of the tensile specimen. The extensometer provides an accurate response to specimen strain with maximum non-linearity of 0.3% of its range and maximum hysteresis of only 0.1% of its range.

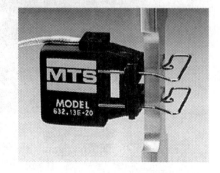

Fig. 6.26 An extensometer for measuring average strain on a tensile specimen. (Courtesy of MTS Systems Corporation.)

6.14 OPTICAL STRAIN GAGES

During the past 40 years, considerable research effort has been devoted to the area of optical methods of experimental stress analysis. The availability of gas and ruby lasers as monochromatic, collimated and coherent light sources as well as fiber optics has led to several new developments in strain gages. Three of these developments—the diffraction strain gage, the interferometric strain gage and the fiber optic strain gages—are described in this chapter to indicate the capabilities of optical gages that use coherent light.

6.14.1 The Pryor and North Diffraction Gage

The diffraction strain gage is quite simple in construction; it consists of two blades that are bonded or welded to the specimen, as illustrated in Fig. 6.27. The two blades are separated by a distance b to form a narrow aperture and are fixed to the specimen along its edges to give a gage length L_0. A beam of collimated monochromatic light from a helium-neon laser is directed onto the aperture to produce a diffraction pattern that can be observed as a line of dots on a screen a distance R from the aperture. An example of a diffraction pattern is illustrated in Fig. 6.28.

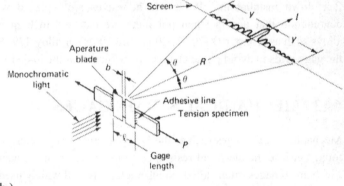

Fig. 6.27 Schematic of a diffraction-type strain gage.
(After T. R. Pryor and W. P. T. North.)

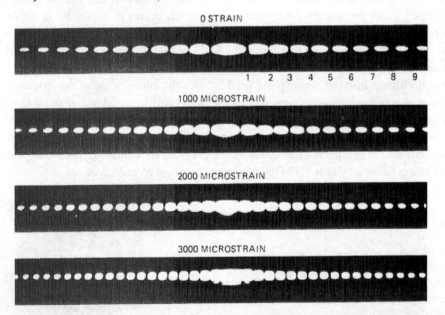

Figure 6.28 Diffractograms showing changes in the diffraction pattern with increasing strain.
(Courtesy of T. R. Pryor and W. P. T. North.)

When the distance R to the screen is very large compared with the aperture width b, the distribution of the intensity I of light in the diffraction pattern is given by:

$$I = A_0^2 \frac{\sin^2 \beta}{\beta^2} \tag{6.51}$$

where A_0 is the amplitude of the light on the centerline of the pattern ($\theta = 0$) and

$$b = \frac{\pi b}{\lambda} \sin \theta \tag{6.52}$$

where θ is defined in Fig. 6.27 and λ is the wavelength of the light. If the analysis of the diffraction pattern is limited to short distances y from the centerline of the system, $\sin \theta$ is small enough to be represented by y/R and Eq. (6.52) becomes:

$$\beta = \frac{\pi b}{\lambda} \frac{y}{R} \tag{6.53}$$

The intensity I vanishes according to Eq. (6.51) when $\sin \beta = 0$ or when $\beta = n\pi$, where n = 1, 2, 3, . By considering those points in the diffraction pattern where I = 0, it is possible to obtain a relationship between their location in the pattern and the aperture width b. Thus:

$$b = \frac{\lambda R n}{y} \tag{6.54}$$

where n is the order of extinction in the diffraction pattern at the position located by y.

As the specimen is strained, the deformation results in a change in the aperture width $\Delta b = \varepsilon L$ and a corresponding change in the diffraction pattern as indicated in Fig. 6.28. The magnitude of this strain ε can be determined from Eq. (6.54) and measurements from the two diffraction patterns. As an example, consider the diffraction pattern after deformation and note

$$b + \Delta b = \frac{\lambda R n^*}{y_1} \tag{a}$$

where n* is a specified order of extinction. Clearly, the diffraction pattern before deformation gives:

$$b = \frac{\lambda R n^*}{y_0} \tag{b}$$

Subtracting Eq. (b) from Eq. (a) and simplifying gives the average strain ε over the gage length L as:

$$\varepsilon = \frac{\Delta b}{L} = \frac{\lambda R n^*}{L} \frac{y_0 - y_1}{y_0 y_1} \tag{6.55}$$

In practice, the order of extinction n* is selected as high as possible consistent with the optical quality of the diffraction pattern. When the higher orders of extinction are used, the distance y can be measured with improved accuracy with a number of different instruments.

In an automated read out system, a linear array of CCD cells replaces the screen in Fig. 6.27. The charge on each cell is proportional to the light intensity and the value of y for each extinction order is determined by locating each cell, which exhibits a minimum intensity. The output from the linear CCD array is monitored with an online computer in real time.

The diffraction strain gage is extremely simple to install and use provided the component can be observed during the test. The method has many advantages for strain measurement at high temperature because it is automatically temperature-compensated if the blades forming the aperture are constructed of the same material as the specimen.

6.14.2 Sharpe's Diffraction Grating Gage

A second optical method of strain measurement utilizes the interference patterns produced when coherent, monochromatic light from a source such as a helium-neon laser is reflected from two shallow V-grooves ruled on a highly polished portion of the specimen surface. The V-grooves are usually cut with a diamond to a depth of approximately 0.000040 in. (0.001 mm) and are spaced approximately 0.005 in. (0.125 mm) apart. Alternatively, indentations produced with a Vickers's diamond indenter can be used to produce reflecting surfaces that make an angle of about 110° with the surface of the specimen.

When the grooves, which serve as reflective surfaces, are small enough to cause the light to diffract and close enough together to permit the diffracted light rays to superimpose, an interference pattern is produced. The intensity of light in the pattern is given by the expression:

$$I = 4A_0^2 \frac{\sin^2 \beta}{\beta^2} \cos^2 \phi \qquad (6.56)$$

where $\beta = (\pi b/\lambda)\sin \theta$; $\phi = (\pi d/\lambda)\sin \theta$; b = width of groove: d = width between grooves and θ = angle from central maximum, as previously defined in Fig. 6.27.

As the light is reflected from the sides of the V grooves, two different interference patterns are formed, as indicated in Fig. 6.29. In an actual experimental situation, the fringe patterns appear as a row of dots on screens located approximately 8 in. (200 mm) from the grooves. The diameter of the dots is consistent with the diameter of the impinging beam of coherent light from a laser.

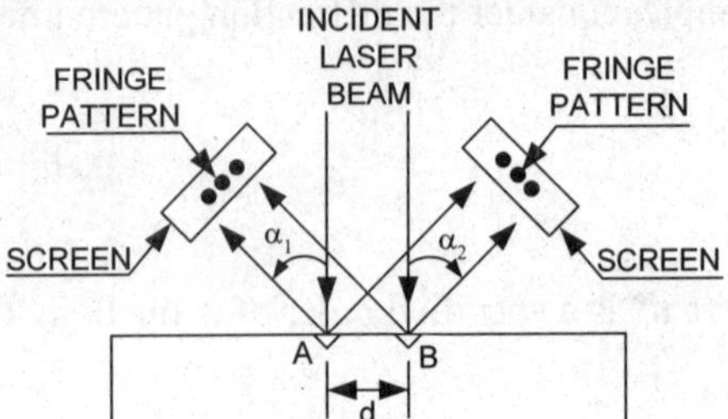

Fig. 6.29 Schematic diagram of Sharpe's interferometric strain gage.

The intensity in the interference pattern goes to zero and a dark spot is produced whenever $\beta = n\pi$, with n = 1, 2, 3, or when $\phi = (m + \frac{1}{2})\pi$, with m = 0, 1, 2, ... When the specimen is strained, both the distance d between grooves and the width b of the grooves change. These effects produce shifts in the fringes of the two interference patterns that can be related to the average strain between the two grooves. The proof is beyond the scope of this presentation; however, it is shown in Reference 24 that:

$$\varepsilon = \frac{(\Delta N_1 - \Delta N_2)\lambda}{2d\sin\alpha} \qquad (6.57)$$

where ΔN_1 and ΔN_2 are the changes in fringe order in the two patterns produced by the strain and α is the angle between the incident light beam and the diffracted rays which produce the interference pattern as shown in Fig. 6.29.

More recently, Sharpe has adapted this experimental approach to the measurement of strain in tensile tests of very small samples of polysilicon films 3.5 μm thick. As the films are too thin and brittle, the placement of grooves is not possible. However, gold lines 1 μm wide by 0.5 μm high and 200 μm long are deposited on the polysilicon films during manufacture. The sides of the lines are angled relative to the surface of the specimen; thus, they serve the same function as the grooves or diamond indentations as indicated in Fig. 6.29.

The interferometric gage offers a method for measuring strain without attaching or bonding a device, thus eliminating any reinforcing effects or bonding difficulties. Of course, it is necessary to polish the surface of the specimen and to place grooves, indentations or elevated lines on the specimen's surface. Because no contact is made, the method can be employed on rotating parts or in hostile environments. Temperature compensation is automatic and the method can be employed at very high temperatures. Also, photodiode arrays can be employed to monitor the changes in the fringe patterns with strain eliminating the need to photograph fringe patterns.

6.15 FIBER-OPTIC STRAIN GAGES

While measurements of strain are usually performed with electrical resistance strain gages, there are some inherent advantages of fiber-optic strain gages that should be considered in select applications. These advantages include:

- Lightweight and small size
- Passive with low power requirements
- Free from electromagnetic interference
- High sensitivity
- Environmentally robust
- Stable for extremely long periods of time.

Strain gages constructed from optical fibers are relatively new because their development was dependent on low loss, single mode optical fibers that were not commercially available prior to the 1970s. The first fiber optic strain gage was developed in 1978; since that time a number of different gage designs have evolved.

Optical fiber strain sensors usually based on a change in amplitude (intensity) of light or a change in phase as the light propagates through an optical fiber wave guide. Both amplitude and phase can change as a function of the strain applied to some part of an optical fiber or the sensing element. Fiber optic strain gages are called intrinsic devices because they do not require an external component element in addition to the optical fiber. Fiber-optic strain gages are classified as Mach-Zehnder, Fabry-Perot, Michelson, polarimetric, modal-domain, twin-core, and Bragg grating types. All except the Mach-Zehnder gage can be designed to be insensitive to optical effects in the leads. Accordingly, short gage length measurements are possible. Intrinsic optical fiber strain sensors usually employ a sensing fiber and a reference fiber, either or both of which can be exposed to the strain field. However, the geometric or optical properties of the two fibers must be different if both the reference and sensing fibers are exposed to strain. Each optical arrangement is composed of an input fiber, which carries light from a light source to the strain-sensitive active fiber, followed by an output fiber, which transmits the light from the active fiber to an optical detector. The input and output fibers are also sensitive to the strain; hence, gage designs with insensitive input and output fibers are important and will be described in the following subsections.

The feature common to all intrinsic optical fiber sensors is that they are constructed using only fiber components—fiber couplers replace beam splitters, aluminum-coated fiber ends replace mirrors, optical fiber retarders replace wave plates, etc. The only non-fiber components in a strain sensing system are the light source and detection electronics. These components designed for use with fiber optics are attached directly to the fibers, effectively forming a fully guided optical system. The strain gage becomes a completely closed optical system with the optical fiber laser and the optical phase detection method. While optical fiber strain gages can be produced from suitable combinations of fiber and conventional optics, these hybrid designs are generally more cumbersome to use because the conventional optical components introduce instabilities. The electronic detection schemes employed with optical fiber sensors are as varied as the sensors and are beyond the scope of this textbook.

6.15.1 Mach-Zehnder, Michelson and Fabry-Perot Strain Gage

The Mach-Zehnder Strain Gage

The Mach-Zehnder, Michelson and Fabry-Perot strain sensors use fiber versions of the classical interferometers. The Mach-Zehnder optical fiber sensor, illustrated in Fig. 6.30, is probably the best known, since it was introduced early in the development cycle. The Mach-Zehnder strain interferometer acts in the classic sense—the light propagating in the reference arm is optically interfered with the light propagating in the sensing arm [1]. This resulting coherent interference occurs in the second 2 × 2 coupler that is shown in Fig. 6.30. The intensity and phase shift is modulated by a change in the optical path length due to strain. The change in optical path length is due to a change in the segment length caused by the applied strain and the birefringent effect. The birefringence is a result of a slight dependence of the refractive index on strain. Both these contributions to the change in optical path length are integrated over the active gage length of the fiber. The phase shift is measured by directly counting the fringes, or by using homodyne or heterodyne techniques that will be discussed later.

It is possible to actually form interferometric fringes in space to determine the strain-induced phase change; however, this approach is not recommended, because it introduces instability to the optical arrangement. Instead, the second 2 × 2 coupler is added to provide a stable interference location. A photo-detector records the intensity, which varies as a sinusoid with increasing or decreasing strain as shown in Fig. 6.31. The results also serve to illustrate the difficulties encountered when attempting to count the fringe orders directly with an interferometer. The intensity-time trace is a sinusoid and unless the strain-time record is monotonic, it is necessary to employ the more advanced detection schemes, such as the active homodyne, to determine the sign of the strain or when the strain changes sign. This constraint applies to all fiber interferometers that undergo a phase shift exceeding 2π, as the intensity monitored by a detector is a periodic function of phase.

Various strain gages, stress gages, and strain rosettes have been developed by using the Mach-Zehnder fiber interferometer by simply making appropriate alterations to the geometry of either the reference or the sensing fiber. Unfortunately, the Mach-Zehnder strain gage has a serious disadvantage, which is the difficulty in isolating the leads from external strain fields.

---

[1] A segment of the sensing fiber is adhesively bonded to a specimen and the strain is transmitted through the bond to increase or decrease the length of the bonded segment.

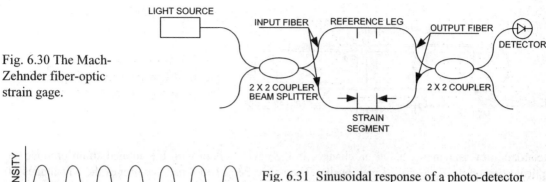

Fig. 6.30 The Mach-Zehnder fiber-optic strain gage.

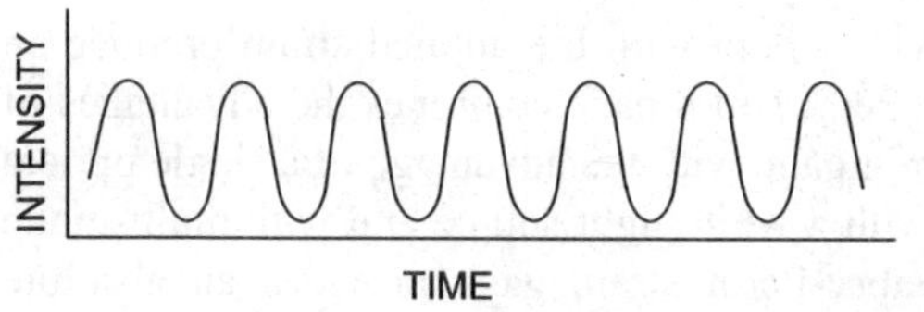

Fig. 6.31 Sinusoidal response of a photo-detector illustrating the difficulty of establishing the phase angle when it exceeds 2π.

The Michelson Strain Gage

The Michelson optical fiber strain sensors are Mach-Zehnder strain sensors operating in reflection as illustrated in Fig. 6.32. The optical fibers are cleaved after the first 2×2 coupler, and mirrors are formed on the optical fibers by depositing a thin film of aluminum on the cleaved fiber ends. As with Mach-Zehnder strain gages, lead-insensitive Michelson sensors are difficult to design. The most common approach is to subject the input and output fibers to nearly identical strain fields, thus canceling strain or temperature induced effects. This approach to localized measurements works well only when the strain on the surface containing the input and output fibers is small. The sensitivity of the Michelson strain sensor is relatively high, so that gage lengths on the order of a few millimeters are practical.

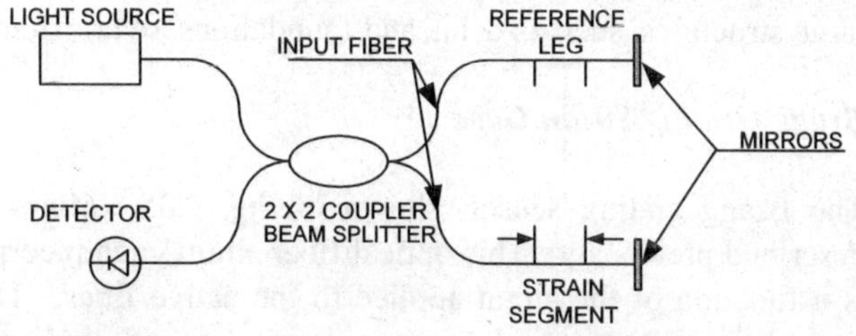

Fig. 6.32 The Michelson optical fiber strain gage.

The Fabry-Perot Strain Gage

When the application for embedded optical-fiber strain gages developed, it became important to reduce the number of optical leads required. The Fabry-Perot optical fiber strain sensor is designed so that a single optical fiber carries the optical signal in and out of the strain sensitive cavity. The all-fiber Fabry-Perot strain gage arranged in the reflection mode is shown in Fig. 6.33. The details of the Fabry-Perot cavity, which results in multiple interference of the light entering and leaving it, is shown in Fig. 6.34. This gage is commercially available [2] in gage lengths that range from 6 to 13 mm. The glass capillary tube that encases the cavity is 250 μm in diameter.

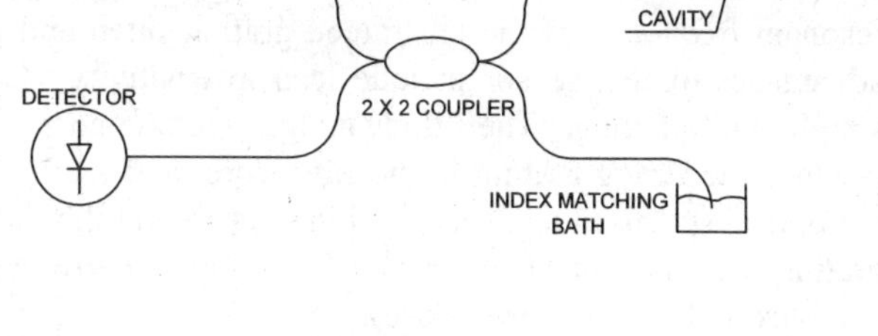

Fig. 6.33 The Fabry-Perot strain gage arranged in the reflection mode.

[2] FISO Technologies, 500 St-Jean-Baptiste, Suite 195, Quebec, Canada, G2E-5R9.

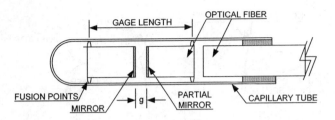

Fig. 6.34 Fabry-Perot fiber-optic sensor for measuring strain.

Retardation measurements based on changes in the cavity length with the applied strain produce an optical phase shift, as described previously. The Fabry-Perot strain gage combines the advantages of high sensitivity of the Mach-Zehnder and Michelson strain gage with the advantage of a single optical lead. It has an added advantage in that it can be used with a white light source and with multi-mode fibers. Coupled with a Fizeau interferometer, the Fabry-Perot strain gage provides an absolute measurement of the phase change in the light signal produced by changes in the length of the cavity due to strain.

Another advantage of the Fabry-Perot strain gage is its very small sensitivity to temperature changes ($- 0.1$ με/°C) prior to bonding the gage to a specimen. The glass capillary tube that encases the fiber has nearly the same coefficient of thermal expansion as the fiber. For this reason, the tube and fiber expand or contract together and the cavity length does not change with temperature fluctuations.

The most significant advantage of the Fabry-Perot strain gage is its stability over extended periods of time when the gage is monitored with a Fizeau interferometer. The readout provides the absolute cavity length and this measurement is not affected by any electronic instabilities. Consequently, the Fabry-Perot strain gage is currently being employed to monitor the state of strain in large structures, such as dams and foundations, over extended periods of time.

Bragg Grating Strain Gage

The Bragg grating sensor, shown in Fig. 6.35, differs markedly from the interferometric sensors described previously. This optical fiber strain gage incorporates a diffraction grating with a pitch that is a function of the strain applied to the active fiber. The grating is written in a germanium-doped optical fiber using high-intensity, ultraviolet, and dual-beam interference that spatially modulates the index of refraction of the fiber core. The pitch of the grating is controlled by adjusting the angle between the two coherent beams forming the interference pattern imposed on the fiber as illustrated in Fig. 6.36. The Bragg grating gage can be monitored with either a narrow-or broadband coherent light source. The narrowband sources offer a high temporal bandwidth signal, while the broadband sources provide the opportunity to multiplex gages that are designed with a single fiber.

Multiplexing is accomplished by producing a fiber with a several spatially separated gratings, each with a different pitch. The output of the multiplexed sensor is processed in an optical spectrum analyzer, and the optical signal associated with a specified pitch is centered at the 1/p location in the spectral domain. A strain-induced change in grating pitch is monitored as a perturbation of the resonant frequency of the unstrained grating pitch and provides a direct measure of the strain. The advantages of this sensor include lead insensitivity, very short gage lengths, and the capability for simple multiplexing. The disadvantages include cost of the ultraviolet, high-power laser required to produce the Bragg grating in the fiber core, and the high expense and limited frequency response of the optical spectrum analyzer used in interpreting the output signal. The frequency response of Bragg grating sensors can be improved by using a narrowband source, but this practice requires more complex multiplexing procedures.

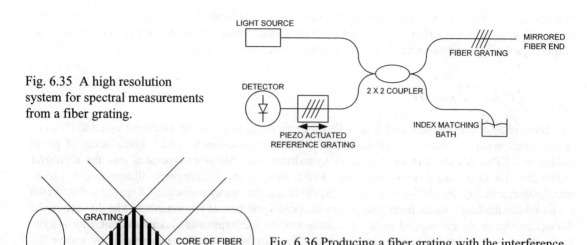

Fig. 6.35 A high resolution system for spectral measurements from a fiber grating.

Fig. 6.36 Producing a fiber grating with the interference pattern from two crossed laser beams.

6.15.2 Interpreting Optical-fiber Strain Gage Output

There are a number of methods used to characterize the wavelength and intensity of the light output from fiber-optic sensors, including optical spectrum analyzers, heterodyne methods and spectral interferometric systems. Consider first the optical spectrum analyzers.

Optical Spectrum Analyzers

An optical spectrum analyzer performs power versus wavelength measurements, and is usually employed for characterizing broadband sources such as light emitting diodes (LEDs) and semiconductor lasers. It is also useful in interpreting the signal output from a fiber-optic sensor where either the intensity or the wavelength of the optical signal is a function of the quantity (strain) being measured.

The principal of operation of a spectrum analyzer is beyond the scope of this textbook; however, the commercial instruments are equipped with a display that shows the power level or mode spacing of the signal as a function of wavelength. The capability of these instruments is remarkable, as the resolution of the wavelength associated with a spectral peak can be measured to ± 0.030 nm. The mode spacing is particular useful when employing Bragg grating strain gages that exhibit shifts in their spectral peaks with applied strain.

Homodyne Interferometry

For a fiber-optic sensor arranged as an interferometer, the intensity of the signal output will vary as a sinusoid as the strain transmitted to the sensing segment increases or decreases. In this case a photodetector will convert the optical signal to an electrical signal that can be recorded relative to time. It is possible to count the peaks on the voltage-time record to establish the magnitude of the unknown quantity if a calibration constant for the strain gage is known. This is a very simple technique that is effective if a large number of fringes (peaks) are developed during the measurement. If the number of peaks is limited, it is usually necessary to employ a modern electronic phase meter that can resolve phase to about 0.1 degree, which corresponds to resolving a fringe (peak) into 3,600 parts. Photodetectors are also useful in interpreting signals from fiber-optic sensors that provide an output signal with an intensity variation as a function of the unknown quantity.

Fizeau-CCD-Array Converter

The conversion of the optical signal from a Fabry-Perot strain gage into an electrical signal that can be readily interpreted is often accomplished with a Fizeau interferometer and a linear array of photo diodes or CCDs, as shown in Fig. 6.37. A cylindrical lens that is incorporated into the converter collimates the light signal from the Fabry-Perot strain gage. This light illuminates a Fizeau interferometer that is about 25 mm in diameter. This interferometer consists of a spatially distributed cavity whose thickness varies from almost zero to about some tens of micrometers. The dimensions of the wedge-like cavity correspond to the same values as the minimum and maximum dimensions of the Fabry-Perot cavity of the fiber-optic strain gage. The purpose of the Fizeau wedge is to resolve the spectrum into its wavelength components. The maximum intensity of light is transmitted through the Fizeau cavity at the exact location where its thickness is equal to the length of the cavity in the Fabry-Perot sensor. Thus, the Fizeau interferometer provides an instantaneous measurement of the optical signal for the entire range of gap measurement possible with the Fabry-Perot strain gage. Electronic processing locates the position of the maximum response with the data from the linear CCD array thus establishing the absolute cavity length. This measurement of cavity length is termed absolute because it corresponds to the true cavity length of the Fabry-Perot interferometer at the time of the measurement of the optical signal. The ability to make absolute measurements is critical in applications where long term or static measurements are required. The optical signal is converted in cavity length at a frequency given by the sampling rate of the conversion unit, which can approach 1,000 Hz. The conversion is accurate to ± 1 nm over a working range of 15,000 nm. This corresponds to an accuracy of 0.0067% of full scale for a strain gage

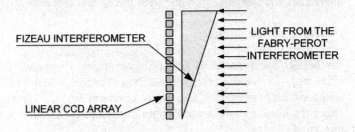

Fig. 6.37 A Fizeau interferometer and a CCD array used in optical signal analysis.

6.16 CAPACITANCE STRAIN GAGES

The capacitance sensor, illustrated in Fig. 6.38, consists of a target plate and a second plate termed as the sensor head. These two plates are separated by an air gap of thickness h and form the two terminals of a capacitor that exhibits a capacitance C given by:

$$C = \frac{kKA}{h} \qquad (6.58)$$

where   C is the capacitance in picofarad (pF) and A is the area of the sensor head ($\pi D/4$).
K is the relative dielectric constant for the medium in the gap (K = 1 for air).
k = 0.225 is a proportionality constant for dimensions specified in in.
k = 0.00885 for dimensions given in mm.

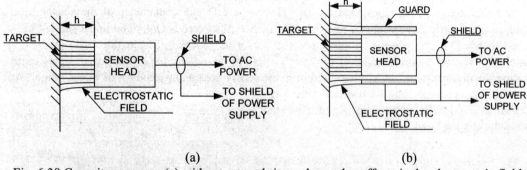

(a)   (b)

Fig. 6.38 Capacitor sensors: (a) without a guard ring, where edge effects in the electrostatic field affect the range of linearity, and (b) with a guard ring to extend the range of linearity.

If the separation between the head and the target is changed by an amount Δh, then the capacitance C becomes:

$$C + \Delta C = \frac{kKA}{h + \Delta h} \qquad \text{(a)}$$

Equation (a) can be written as:

$$\frac{\Delta C}{C} = -\frac{\Delta h / h}{1 + (\Delta h / h)} \qquad (6.59)$$

This result indicates that $(\Delta C/C)$ is non-linear because of the presence of Δ/h in the denominator of Eq. (6.59). To avoid the difficulty of employing a capacitance sensor with a non-linear output, the change in the impedance due to the capacitor is measured. Note that the impedance Z_C of a capacitor is given by:

$$Z_C = -j/(\omega C) \qquad \text{(b)}$$

With a capacitance change ΔC, it can be shown that:

$$Z_C + \Delta Z_C = -\frac{j}{\omega}\left[\frac{1}{C + \Delta C}\right] \qquad \text{(c)}$$

Substituting Eq. (b) into Eq. (c) and solving for $\Delta Z_C/Z_C$ gives:

$$\frac{\Delta Z_C}{Z_C} = -\frac{\Delta C / C}{1 + \Delta C / C} \qquad (6.60)$$

Finally, substituting Eq. (6.59) into Eq. (6.60) yields:

$$\frac{\Delta Z_C}{Z_C} = -\frac{\Delta h}{h} \qquad (6.61)$$

From Eq. (6.61) it is clear that the capacitive impedance Z_C is linear in Δh and that methods of measuring ΔZ_C will permit extremely simple plates (the target as ground and the sensor head as the positive terminal) to act as a sensor to measure the displacement Δh. Cylindrical sensor heads are linear and Eq. (6.61) is valid provided $0 < h < D/4$ where D is the diameter of the sensor head. Fringing in the electric field produces non-linearity if $(h + \Delta h)$ exceeds $D/4$. The linear range can be extended to $h \approx D/2$ if a guard ring surrounds the sensor as shown in Fig. 6.38b. The guard ring essentially moves the distorted edges of the electric field to the outer edge of the guard, significantly improving the uniformity of the electric field over the sensor area and extending its linear range. An example of a button type head for a capacitance gage, presented in Fig. 6.39, show the guard ring that surround the sensing head.

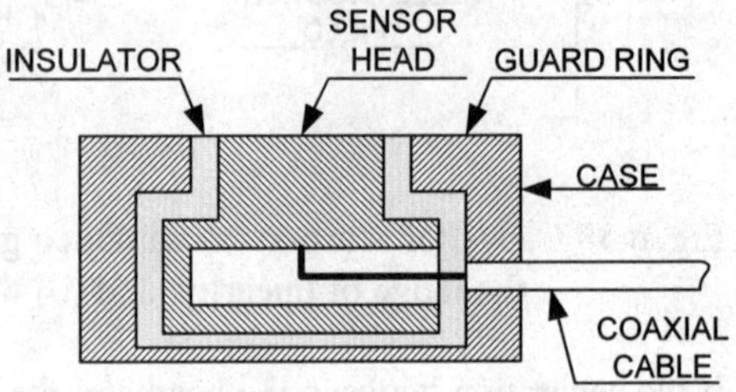

Fig. 6.39 A button capacitor gage showing the guard ring and other construction details.

The sensitivity of the capacitance probe is given by Eqs. (b), (6.58), and (6.61) as:

$$S = \frac{\Delta Z_C}{\Delta h} = \left|\frac{Z_C}{h}\right| = \left|\frac{1}{\omega\, Ch}\right| = \left|\frac{1}{\omega\, KkA}\right| \tag{6.62}$$

The sensitivity can be improved by reducing the area of the probe; however, as noted previously, the range of the probe is limited by linearity to about $D/2$. Clearly there is a range-sensitivity trade-off. Of particular importance is the circular frequency ω in Eq. (6.62). Low frequency improves sensitivity but limits frequency response of the instrument, another trade-off. It is also important to note that the frequency of the ac power supply must remain constant to maintain a stable calibration constant.

The capacitance sensor has several advantages. It is non-contacting and can be used with any target material provided the material exhibits a resistivity less than 100 Ω-cm (any metal). The sensor is extremely rugged and can be subjected to high shock loads (5,000 g's) and intense vibratory environments. Their use as a sensor at high temperature is particularly impressive. They can be constructed to withstand temperatures up to 2,000° F and they exhibit a constant sensitivity S over an extremely wide range of temperature (74 to 1,600° F). Examination of the relation for S in Eq. (6.62) shows that the dielectric constant K is the only parameter that can change with temperature. Because K is constant for air over a wide range of temperature, the capacitance sensor has excellent temperature stability.

The change in the capacitive impedance Z_C is usually measured with the circuit illustrated schematically in Fig. 6.40. The probe, its shield, and guard ring are powered with a constant current ac supply. A digital oscillator is used to drive the ac supply and to maintain a constant frequency at 15.6 kHz. This oscillator also provides the reference frequency for the synchronous detector. The voltage drop across the probe is detected with a low capacitance preamplifier. The signal from the preamplifier is then amplified again with a fixed-gain instrument amplifier. The high voltage ac signal from the instrument amplifier is rectified and given a sign in the synchronous detector. The rectified signal is filtered to eliminate high frequency ripple and give a dc output voltage related to Δh. A linearizing circuit is used to extend the range of the sensor by accommodating for the influence of the fringes in the electrostatic field. Finally, the signal is passed through a second instrument amplifier where the gain and zero offset can be varied to adjust the sensitivity and the zero reading on a DVM display. When the gain and zero offset are properly adjusted, the DVM reads Δh directly to a scale selected by the operator.

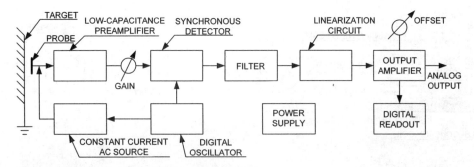

Fig. 6.40 Schematic diagram of an instrument system employed with a capacitance sensing system.

6.17   INDUCTANCE STRAIN GAGE

Of the many types of inductance measuring systems, which could be employed to measure strain or displacement, the differential-transformer system is the most commonly used. The linear differential transformer is an effective sensor for converting mechanical displacement into an electrical signal. It can be employed in a large variety of transducers including: strain, displacement, pressure, acceleration, force and temperature. A schematic illustration of a linear differential transformer employed as a strain-gage transducer is shown in Fig. 6.41. Mechanical knife-edges are displaced over the gage length L_0 by the strain induced in the specimen. This displacement is transmitted to the core, which moves relative to the coils and an electrical output is produced across the coils.

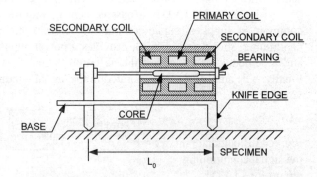

Fig. 6.41 Schematic illustration of a linear differential transformer employed as a strain transducer.

The most popular variable-inductance sensor for linear displacement measurements is the linear variable differential transformer (LVDT). A LVDT, illustrated in Fig. 6.42a, consists of three symmetrically spaced coils wound onto an insulated bobbin. A magnetic core, which moves through the bobbin without contact, provides a path for magnetic flux linkage between coils. The position of the magnetic core controls the mutual inductance between the center or primary coil and the two outer or secondary coils.

When ac excitation is applied to the primary coil, voltages are induced in the two secondary coils. The secondary coils are wired in a series-opposing circuit, as shown in Fig. 6.42b. When the core is centered between the two secondary coils, the voltages induced in the secondary coils are equal but out of phase by 180 degrees. Because the coils are in a series-opposing circuit, the voltages V_1 and V_2 in the two coils cancel and the output voltage is zero. When the core is moved from the center position, an imbalance in mutual inductance between the primary and secondary coils occurs and an output voltage, $V_0 = V_2 - V_1$, develops. The output voltage is a linear function of core position if the motion of the core is within the operating range of the LVDT. The direction of motion can be determined from the phase of the output voltage relative to the input voltage.

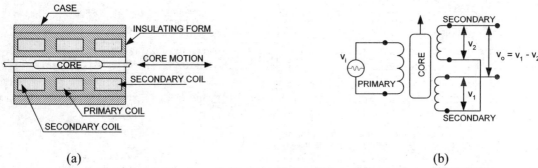

(a)   (b)

Fig. 6.42 (a) Sectional view of a linear variable differential transformer (LVDT).
(b) Schematic circuit diagram for the LVDT coils.

The frequency of the voltage applied to the primary winding can range from 50 to 25,000 Hz. If the LVDT is used to measure transient or periodic displacements, the carrier frequency should be 10 times greater than the highest frequency component in the dynamic signal. The highest sensitivities are attained with excitation frequencies between 1 and 5 kHz. The input voltage can range from 3 to 15 V rms. The power required is usually less than 1 W. Sensitivities of different LVDTs vary from 0.02 to 0.2 V/mm of displacement per volt of excitation applied to the primary coil. At rated excitation voltages, sensitivities vary from about 30 to 350 mV per V_i – mm of displacement. The higher sensitivities are associated with short-stroke LVDTs, with an operating range of ± 0.13 mm; the lower sensitivities are for long-stroke LVDTs, with an operating range of ± 254 mm.

      Because the LVDT, a passive sensor, requires ac excitation at a frequency different from common ac supplies, signal-conditioning circuits are needed for its operation. A typical signal conditioner, shown in Fig. 6.43, provides a power supply, a frequency generator to drive the LVDT, and a demodulator to convert the ac output signal from the LVDT to an analog dc output voltage. Finally, a dc amplifier is incorporated in the signal conditioner to increase the magnitude of the output voltage.

Fig. 6.43 Block diagram of
the signal conditioning
circuit for a LVDT.

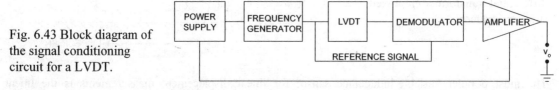

Many different types of LVDTs are commercially available today. They are designed for normal applications, for rugged environments, for high temperature (220 °C) and high-pressure measurements and to monitor motion sensitive mechanisms. Most of the LVDTs are packaged in a stainless steel tube that encases the coils and shields the electronics from noise.

      With the development of microelectronics, circuits have been developed that permit miniaturization of the signal conditioner shown in Fig. 6.43. These miniaturized circuits are packaged within the case of an LVDT to produce a small self-contained sensor known as a direct current differential transformer (DCDT). A DCDT operates from a battery or a regulated power supply ($\pm$ 15VDC nominal) and provides an amplified output signal that can be monitored on either a digital voltmeter (DVM) or an oscilloscope. The output impedance of a DCDT is relatively low (about 100 Ω).

      The LVDT and the DCDT have many advantages as sensors for measuring displacement. There is no contact between the core and the coils; therefore, friction and hysteresis are eliminated. Because the output is continuously variable with input, resolution is determined by the characteristics of the voltage recorder. Non-contact also ensures that life will be very long with no significant deterioration of performance over this period. The small core mass and freedom from friction give the sensor a limited capability for dynamic measurements. Finally, the sensors are not damaged by over travel; therefore, they can be employed as feedback transducers in servo-controlled systems where over travel may occur due to accidental deviations beyond the control band.

In more recent years, the DCDT has been equipped with an analog to digital converter (A/D) to provide a digitized output. Their input voltage may be varied from 8.5 to 30 V, and their output signal has a resolution of at least 15 bits or 1 part in 32,768.

6.18 ACOUSTICAL STRAIN GAGES

Acoustical strain gages have been employed in a variety of forms since the late 1920s; however, they have been largely supplemented by the electrical-resistance strain gage with one important exception. They are unique among all forms of strain gages in view of their long-term stability and freedom from drift over extended time periods. The acoustical gage described here was developed in 1944 and today is still representative of the devices currently being employed. The strain-measuring system is based on the use of two identical gages identified as a test gage and a reference gage. The significant parts of a gage are shown schematically in Fig. 6.44.

In this illustration it is evident that the gage has the common knife-edges for mounting the device. One knife-edge is mounted to the main body, which is fixed, while the other knife-edge is mounted in a bearing suspension and is free to elongate with the specimen. The gage length L_0 is 3 in. (76 mm). One end of a steel wire is attached to the movable knife-edge while the other end of the wire passes through a small hole in the fixed knife-edge and is attached to a tension screw. The movable knife-edge is connected to a second tension screw by a leaf spring. This arrangement permits the initial tension in the wire to be applied without transmitting the wire preload to the knife-edges.

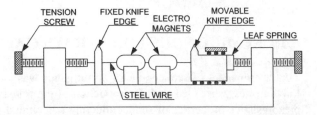

Fig. 6.44 Schematic drawing illustrating design features of an acoustical strain gage.

The wire passes between the pole pieces of two small electromagnets. One of these magnets is used to keep the wire vibrating at its natural frequency; the other is employed to monitor the frequency of the system. Electrically both magnets operate together—the signal from the monitoring magnet is amplified and fed back into the driving magnet to keep the string excited in its natural frequency.

The reference gage is identical to the test gage except that the knife-edges are removed and a micrometer is used to tension the wire. A helical spring is employed in series with the wire to permit larger rotations of the micrometer head for small changes of stress in the wire.

To operate the system, the test gage is mounted and adjusted and the reference gage is placed in a location suitable for compensating for temperature effects. Both gages are energized and each wire emits a musical note. If the frequency of vibrations from the two gages is not the same, beats will occur. The micrometer setting is varied on the reference gage until the beat frequency decreases to zero. The reading of the micrometer is then taken and the strain is applied to the test gage. The change in tension in the wire of the test gage produces a change in frequencies and it is necessary to adjust the reference gage with the micrometer until the beats are eliminated. This new micrometer reading is proportional to the strain.

If the test gage is located in a remote position and the beat signals from the test and reference gages cannot be by the operator, it is possible to balance the two gages by using an oscilloscope. The voltage output from the pickup coils of each gage is displayed while operating the oscilloscope in the xy mode. The resulting Lissajous figure provides the display enabling the adjustment of the micrometer on the reference gage to match the frequency of the test gage.

The natural frequency f of a wire held between two fixed points is given by the expression:

$$f = \frac{1}{2L}\sqrt{\frac{\sigma}{\rho}} \tag{6.63}$$

where L is the length of wire between supports; σ is the stress and ρ is the density of the wire, respectively. In terms of strain in the wire, the frequency is governed by the following equation, which comes directly from Eq. (6.63):

$$f = \frac{1}{2L}\sqrt{\frac{E\varepsilon}{\rho}} \tag{6.64}$$

where E is the modulus of elasticity.

The sensitivity of this instrument is very high, with possible determinations of displacements of the order of 0.1 μin. (2.5 μm). The range is limited to about one-thousandth of the wire length before over or under stressing of the sensing wire becomes critical. The gage is temperature-sensitive unless the thermal coefficients of expansion of the base and wire are closely matched over the temperature range encountered during a test. Finally, the force required to drive the transducer is relatively large and it should not be employed in high compliance systems where the large driving force will affect its accuracy.

6.19 SEMICONDUCTOR STRAIN GAGES

The development of semiconductor strain gages was an outgrowth of research at the Bell Telephone Laboratories, which led to the introduction of the transistor in the early 1950s. Smith determined the piezoresistive properties of semiconducting silicon and germanium in 1954. Further development of semiconductor transducers by Mason and Thurston in 1957 eventually led to the commercial marketing of piezoresistive strain gages in 1960.

Basically, the semiconductor strain gage consists of a small, thin rectangular filament of single crystal silicon. The semiconducting materials exhibit a very high strain sensitivity S_A, with values ranging from 50 to 175 depending upon the type and amount of impurity diffused into the pure silicon crystal. The resistivity ρ of a single-crystal semiconductor with impurity concentrations of the order of 10^{16} to 10^{20} atoms/cm^3 is given by:

$$\rho = \frac{1}{eN\mu} \tag{6.65}$$

N is number of charge carriers, which depends on the concentration of the impurity, and μ is the mobility of the charge carriers, which depends on the strain and its direction relative to the crystal axes.

Piezoresistive strain gages occupy a niche in the strain-gage market. Their advantage of a high sensitivity is balanced by several disadvantages, which include higher cost, limited range, and large temperature effects.

The importance of Eq. (6.65) can be better understood if it is considered in terms of the sensitivity S_A of a semiconductor to strain, which can be written as:

$$S_A = 1 + 2v + \frac{d\rho/\rho}{\varepsilon} \qquad (6.66)$$

For metallic conductors, $1 + 2v \approx 1.6$ and ranges from 0.4 to 2.0 for the common strain-gage alloys. For semiconductor materials $(d\rho/\rho)/\varepsilon$ can be varied between -125 and $+175$ by selecting the type and concentration of the impurity. Thus, very high conductor sensitivities are possible where the resistance change is about 100 times larger than that obtained for the same strain with metallic-alloy gages. Also, negative gage factors are possible which permit large electrical outputs from Wheatstone-bridge circuits where multiple strain gages are employed.

The semiconductor materials have another advantage over metallic alloys for strain-gage applications. The resistivity of P-type silicon is of the order of 5,000 $\mu\Omega$-cm, which is 1,000 times greater than the resistivity of Advance or Constantan, which is 49 $\mu\Omega$-cm. Because of this very high resistivity, semiconductor strain gages often do not utilize grid geometries. They are usually very short single elements with leads as shown in Fig. 6.45.

In producing semiconductor strain gages, ultra pure single-crystal silicon is employed. Boron is used as the trace impurity in producing the P-type (positive gage factor) piezoresistive material. Arsenic is used to produce the N-type (negative gage factor) material. The very high sensitivity of semiconductor gages to strain and their high resistivity have led to their application in measuring extremely small strains, in miniaturized transducers and in very-high-signal-output transducers.

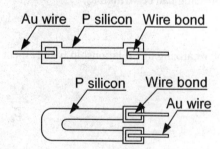

Fig. 6.45 Construction details for semiconductor strain gages.

6.19.1 Piezoresistive Properties of Semiconductors

A crystal of a semiconducting material is electrically anisotropic; consequently, the relation between the potential gradient E and the current density I is formulated relative to the directions of the crystal axes to give components E_1, E_2, and E_3 of the vector E. Thus

$$E_1 = \rho_{11} I_1 + \rho_{12} I_2 + \rho_{13} I_3$$

$$E_2 = \rho_{21} I_1 + \rho_{22} I_2 + \rho_{23} I_3 \qquad (6.67)$$

$$E_3 = \rho_{31} I_1 + \rho_{32} I_2 + \rho_{33} I_3$$

where the first subscript of each resistivity coefficient indicates the component of the voltage field to which it contributes and the second identifies the component of current. The single crystal will permit isotropic conduction only if:

$$\rho_{11} = \rho_{22} = \rho_{33} = \rho$$

$$\rho_{12} = \rho_{13} = \rho_{21} = \rho_{23} = \rho_{31} = \rho_{32} = 0$$

Because this situation exists for unstressed cubic crystals, Eqs. (6.67) reduce to

$$E_1 = \rho I_1 \qquad\qquad E_2 = \rho I_2 \qquad\qquad E_3 = \rho I_3 \qquad\qquad\qquad (6.68)$$

When a state of stress is imposed on the crystal, it responds by exhibiting a piezoresistive effect that can be described by the expression:

$$\rho_{ij} = \delta_{ij}\, \rho + \pi_{ijkl}\, \square_{kl} \qquad\qquad\qquad (6.69)$$

where the subscripts i, j, k, and l range from 1 to 3 and π_{ijkl} is a fourth-rank piezoresistivity tensor, which is a function of the crystal and the level and type of the impurities. A complete discussion of the results obtained from Eq. (6.69) is beyond the scope of this text. Fortunately, several reductions in the complexity of Eq. (6.69) are possible for the P and N doped single crystal silicon used in the fabrication of semiconductor strain gages. It can be shown that the sensitivity π_g of the gage to stress can be varied by changing the orientation of the gage axis relative to the crystal axes or by changing the doping (N or P) and the doping concentration.

The difference in voltage gradient ΔE across the semiconductor element before and after stressing can be written as:

$$\Delta E/\rho = I_g(1 + \pi_g \sigma_g) - I_g = I_g \pi_g \sigma_g \qquad\qquad\qquad (6.70)$$

Normalizing this relationship with respect to the voltage gradient in the unstressed state gives:

$$\frac{\Delta E_g}{E_g} = \frac{\Delta R_g}{R_g} = \pi_g \sigma_g \qquad\qquad\qquad (6.71)$$

Because a uniaxial state of stress exists in the gage element,

$$\sigma_g = E\, \varepsilon \qquad\qquad\qquad (a)$$

where E is the modulus of elasticity of the semiconducting silicon and ε is the strain transmitted to the element from the specimen. Substituting Eq. (a) into Eq. (6.71) gives:

$$\Delta R_g/R_g = \pi_g E \varepsilon = S_{sc}\, \varepsilon \qquad\qquad\qquad (6.72)$$

where $S_{sc} = \pi_g E$ is the strain sensitivity of the piezoresistive material due to strain-induced changes in resistivity. It should be noted that S_{sc} is sufficiently large (≈ 100) such that the net effect of changing length and cross sectional area on the sensitivity of the conducting element is very small (≈ 1.5).

6.19.2 Temperature Effects on Semiconductor Strain Gages

The results of the previous discussion indicated that the response of a semiconductor strain gage is linear with respect to strain. Unfortunately, this is a simplification that is not true in the general case. For lightly doped semiconducting materials (10^{19} atoms/cm^3 or less), the sensitivity S_A is markedly dependent upon both strain and temperature with

$$S_A = \frac{T_0}{T}(S_A)_0 + C_1\left(\frac{T_0}{T}\right)^2 \varepsilon + C_2\left(\frac{T_0}{T}\right)^3 \varepsilon^2 + \cdots \qquad (6.73)$$

where $(S_A)_0$ is the room-temperature zero-strain sensitivity, as defined in Eq. (6.66).

T is the temperature, with $T_0 = 294$ °K.

C_1, C_2 are constants, which depend on the type of impurity, the level of doping and the orientation of the element with respect to the crystal axes.

The variation of the semiconductor sensitivity S_A as a function of doping level for P-type silicon is shown in Fig. 6.46. As the impurity concentration is increased from 10^{16} to 10^{20} atoms/cm^3, the sensitivity S_A decreases from 155 to 50. Two significant advantages related to the temperature effect compensate for this loss of sensitivity:

1. The effect of temperature on the sensitivity S_A is greatly diminished (because the temperature coefficient of sensitivity approaches zero) when the impurity concentration approaches 10^{20} atoms/cm^3, as shown in Fig. 6.46.
2. The temperature coefficient of resistance decreases from 0.009/°C for impurity concentrations of 10^{16} atoms/cm^3 to 0.00036/°C for impurity concentrations of 10^{19} atoms/cm^3.

Experiments with P-type strain gages indicate that the effects of temperature are minimized with impurity concentrations of 10^{19} atom/cm^3 that results in a sensitivity $S_A = 109$. However, temperature compensation of single element P-type semiconductor strain gages is not possible because the gage responds to temperature and the gage factor changes. As a result, a temperature induced apparent strain occurs.

Fig. 6.46 Alloy sensitivity and temperature coefficient of sensitivity as a function of dopant concentration for P-type silicon.

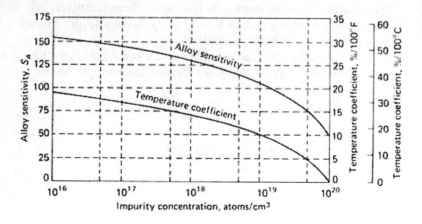

6.19.3 Linearity and Strain Limits

It is clear from Eq. (6.73) that the response of semiconductor strain gages may be nonlinear with respect to strain. For piezoresistive materials with a low impurity concentration, the non-linearity is significant. Increasing the impurity level to 10^{19} to 10^{20} atoms/cm^3 markedly improves the linearity. Unfortunately, most commercial gages are P-type with a gage factor of about 140, which corresponds to an impurity level of 10^{17} atoms/cm^3 that is below the optimum for linearity. Typical linearity specifications are $\pm 0.25\%$ to 600 $\mu\varepsilon$ $\pm 1.5\%$ to 1,500 $\mu\varepsilon$.

The small elements used in fabricating semiconductor strain gages are removed from a single crystal of silicon by a slicing. The single crystal is sectioned and then sliced with a diamond saw to produce thin plates of P-type silicon with their plane in the [111] crystal axis. The thin plates are lapped and etched to eliminate flaws induced by sawing and to improve the surface finish. The small sensing elements are then etched from the plate by using photoresist images to protect the sensing elements.

While silicon exhibits a very high strength, it is glasslike and accordingly semiconductor strain gages must be treated with care during mounting. On flat surfaces, installation presents no problems, and the gages can be subjected to approximately 3,000 $\mu\varepsilon$ before the gages begin to fail by brittle fracture. When semiconductor gages are installed in a fillet and bending stresses are imposed during installation, extreme care must be exercised to avoid rupture of the element. Gages can be mounted on fillet radii from 0.1 to 0.25 in. (2.5 to 6 mm); however, the strains induced in the element during installation reduce its strain range in subsequent experiments.

The fatigue life of semiconductor gages is rated at 10^7 cycles for cyclic strains of ± 500 $\mu\varepsilon$. This is considerably less than the capability of metallic-foil-type gages; however, semiconductor strain gages are usually employed in low-magnitude strain fields, so that the relatively low strain limits placed on single-cycle and multiple-cycle measurements usually are not a significant concern.

6.20 SUMMARY

The principles employed in the construction of strain gages are typically used as the basis for classifying them. The different types of strain gages available include electrical, mechanical, optical, and acoustical; where electrical strain gages are the most widely used. Other types include fiber-optic, capacitance, acoustical, inductance and semi conductor strain gages.

The electrical resistance strain gage nearly satisfies all of the optimum requirements for a strain gage; therefore, it is widely employed in stress analysis and as the sensing element in other transducers. While the strain gage is inexpensive and relatively easy to use, care must be exercised in its installation to ensure that it is properly bonded to the specimen, water-proofed, and properly connected into the Wheatstone bridge.

The voltage that can be applied to a Wheatstone bridge, having a single active gage, is limited by the power the gage can dissipate. The maximum supply voltage is:

$$V_s = (1+r)\sqrt{AP_D R_g} \qquad (6.9)$$

With this voltage applied, the system sensitivity is

$$S_s = \frac{r}{1+r} S_g \sqrt{P_g R_g} \qquad (6.6)$$

The bridge can provide temperature compensation if a temperature-compensating gage (dummy gage) is used in arm R_4 of the bridge.

Digital voltmeters and oscilloscopes are high-impedance recording instruments that can be used with the Wheatstone bridge to measure the output voltage V_0 without introducing appreciable loading errors. Both electrical and mechanical procedures are used to calibrate a strain measuring system. For electrical calibration, the calibration strain ε_c is simulated by shunting a calibration resistor R_c across arm R_2 of the bridge. The magnitude of the calibration strain is given by:

$$\varepsilon_c = \frac{R_2}{S_g(R_2 + R_c)} \tag{6.22}$$

The strain is obtained by comparing deflections of the recorder trace induced by the calibration strain and the load-induced strain. Thus:

$$\varepsilon_g = \frac{d_s}{d_c}\varepsilon_c = Cd_s \tag{6.18}$$

Lead wires, slip rings and switches, commonly employed with strain gages, can in some cases seriously degrade the instrumentation system. The detrimental effects of long lead wires are reduced appreciably by using a three-wire system. Signal loss $\mathcal{L}$, due to long lead wires in a three-wire system, is

$$\mathcal{L} = \frac{R_L/R_g}{1+(R_L/R_g)} \tag{6.25}$$

Long lead wire effects on calibration can be eliminated by shunt calibration at the remote gage location. Only high-quality switches should be used in the arms of a Wheatstone bridge; otherwise, errors due to variations in switch resistance will occur. Slip rings should not be used within the arms of the bridge to transmit signals from rotating members. Instead, complete bridges are assembled on the rotating member and the supply voltage and output voltage are transmitted with the slip rings.

Noise in strain-gage circuits is common and can be minimized by employing twisted leads with a properly grounded shield. Also, the use of differential amplifiers with high common-mode rejection ratios further reduce the noise- to-signal ratio.

Temperature-compensating strain gages are available for a wide range of specimen materials and should be used for all tests where large temperature changes are expected to occur.

Strain gages exhibit sensitivity to both axial and transverse strains given by:

$$\frac{\Delta R}{R} = \frac{S_g\varepsilon_a}{1-v_0K_t}\left(1+K_t\frac{\varepsilon_t}{\varepsilon_a}\right) \tag{6.35}$$

If the transverse sensitivity of the gage is neglected, the response from the gage is related to the axial strain by the simple but approximate expression:

$$\frac{\Delta R}{R} = S_g\varepsilon_a \tag{6.4}$$

The percent error resulting from use of this approximate relation is

$$\mathcal{E} = \frac{\varepsilon_a' - \varepsilon_a}{\varepsilon_a}(100) = \frac{K_t(\varepsilon_t/\varepsilon_a + \nu_0)}{1 - \nu_0 K_t}(100) \tag{6.38}$$

If the ratio $\varepsilon_t/\varepsilon_a$ is known, a corrected gage factor S_g^* is used to eliminate error due to the transverse sensitivity of the gage. The corrected gage factor S_g^* is given by:

$$S_g^* = S_g \frac{1 + K_t(\varepsilon_t/\varepsilon_a)}{1 - \nu_0 K_t} = \frac{S_g}{C_f} \tag{6.40}$$

If the ratio $\varepsilon_t/\varepsilon_a$ is not known, transverse sensitivity errors are eliminated by measuring two orthogonal apparent strains ε_{xx}' and ε_{yy}' with a two-element rectangular rosette and computing true strains by using the equations:

$$\varepsilon_{xx} = \frac{1 - \nu_0 K_t}{1 - K_t^2}\left(\varepsilon_{xx}' + K_t \varepsilon_{yy}'\right)$$
$$\varepsilon_{yy} = \frac{1 - \nu_0 K_t}{1 - K_t^2}\left(\varepsilon_{yy}' + K_t \varepsilon_{xx}'\right) \tag{6.42}$$

Strain measurements can be converted to stresses for a uniaxial state of stress by using the simple expression:

$$\sigma_{xx} = E\varepsilon_{xx} \tag{6.43}$$

In more complex strain fields, where a three-element rectangular rosette is used to record strains ε_A, ε_B and ε_C, the principal stresses σ_1 and σ_2 and their directions ϕ are obtained from these three strains by using the equations:

$$\sigma_1 = E\left[\frac{\varepsilon_A + \varepsilon_C}{2(1-\nu)} + \frac{1}{2(1+\nu)}\sqrt{(\varepsilon_A - \varepsilon_C)^2 + (2\varepsilon_B - \varepsilon_A - \varepsilon_C)^2}\right]$$
$$\sigma_2 = E\left[\frac{\varepsilon_A + \varepsilon_C}{2(1-\nu)} - \frac{1}{2(1+\nu)}\sqrt{(\varepsilon_A - \varepsilon_C)^2 + (2\varepsilon_B - \varepsilon_A - \varepsilon_C)^2}\right] \tag{6.49}$$
$$\phi_1 = \frac{1}{2}\tan^{-1}\frac{2\varepsilon_B - \varepsilon_A - \varepsilon_C}{\varepsilon_A - \varepsilon_C}$$

To employ strain gages at elevated temperatures, the relation for $\Delta R/R$ must be modified in order to account for sensitivity to temperature changes and instabilities with time to:

$$\frac{\Delta R}{R} = S_g \varepsilon + S_T \Delta T + S_t \Delta t \tag{6.50}$$

The mechanical strain gages are rarely used, except as extensometers that also employ resistance strain gages for sensors.

The optical strain gages are generally non-invasive and are preferred in applications requiring high resolution. They are more difficult to use and require extensive training.

The fiber optic strain gages are light weight, free from electromagnetic interference and incorporate all the advantages of fiber optic technology including multiplexing. They are delicate and require care in handling. The choice of the type of fiber-optic strain gage is dependent on the application involved in the study, the optical equipment available and the level of expertise of the user. Clearly tradeoffs exist between performance and difficulty in implementation. While optical fiber strain gages have not reached the level of commercialization of resistance strain gages, the intrinsic Fabry-Perot, Bragg grating as well as other sensors, are commercially available from a number of companies. It is anticipated that many of the difficulties encountered in performing difficult measurements with fiber optic strain gages will be resolved in the future as methods and hardware are optimized. Optical fiber strain gages are finding applications in niche areas not well suited for resistance gages. This is particularly true in electromagnetic noise environments, explosive environments (where electrical sparks cannot be tolerated), and applications requiring monitoring of structures over extended periods of time.

Semiconductor strain gages have the advantage of a high gage factor and a high resistivity, which leads to miniaturization of the sensing element. They have the disadvantage of exhibiting significant temperature effects. The primary application of semiconductor gages is as sensors for very rigid miniature transducers which provide high output signals and very wide bandwidth. In these applications, the mechanical element in the transducer is fabricated from single crystal silicon. The semiconductor gages are usually implanted by a diffusion process into this silicon element. Semiconductor gages are less suited as sensors in the more common general purpose high-accuracy transducers that incorporate mechanical elements fabricated from metal. The semi-conductor gage has very high strain sensitivity and is suitable for measuring small strains.

REFERENCES

1. Brace, W.F.: "Effect of Pressure on Electrical-Resistance Strain Gages," Experimental Mechanics, vol. 4, no. 7, 1964, pp 212-216.
2. Shukla, A. and J. W. Dally: Experimental Solid Mechanics, College House Enterprises, Knoxville, TN, 2010.
3. Freynik, H.S., and G.R. Dittbenner: Strain Gage Stability Measurements for a Year at 75° C in Air, University of California Radiation Laboratory Report 76039, 1975.
4. Measurements Group, Inc., Strain Gage Installations, Instruction Bulletin B-128-5, April, 1996.
5. Measurements Group, Inc., Noise Control in Strain Gage Measurements, Technical Note 501-2, 1992, pp. 1-6.
6. Measurements Group, Inc., Optimizing Strain Gage Excitation Levels, Technical Note 502, 1979, pp. 1-5.
7. Measurements Group, Inc., Temperature-Induced Apparent Strain and Gage Factor Variation in Strain Gages, Technical Note 504-1, 1993, pp. 1-10.
8. Measurements Group, Inc., Strain Gage Selection Criteria, Procedures, Recommendations, Technical Note 505-4, 1989, pp. 1-14.
9. Measurements Group, Inc., Fatigue Characteristics of Micro-Measurements Strain Gages, Technical Note 508-1, 1991, pp. 1-8.
10. Measurements Group, Inc., Errors Due to Transverse Sensitivity in Strain Gages, Technical Note 509, 1993, pp 1-8.
11. Measurements Group, Inc., Errors Due to Misalignment of Strain Gages, Technical Note 511, 1983, pp. 1-4.

12. Measurements Group, Inc., Errors Due to Wheatstone Bridge Nonlinearity, Technical Note 507-1, 1992, pp. 1-4.

13. Measurements Group, Inc., Shunt Calibration of Strain Instrumentation, Technical Note 514, 1988, pp. 1-16.

14. Measurements Group, Inc., Errors Due to Shared Lead Wires in Parallel Strain Gage Circuits, Technical Note 516, 1990, pp. 1-4.

15. Measurements Group, Inc., Strain Gage Rosettes—Selection, Application and Data Reduction, Technical Note 515, 1990, pp. 1-10.

16. Simmons, E. E., Jr.: Material Testing Apparatus, U. S. Patent 2,292,549, February 23, 1940.

17. Telinde, J.C.: "Strain Gages in Cryogenics and Hard Vacuum," Proceedings of the Western Regional Strain Gage Committee, 1968, pp. 45-54.

18. Telinde, J.C.: "Strain Gages in Cryogenic Environment," Experimental Mechanics, vol. 10, no. 9, 1970, pp. 394-400.

19. Thompson, W. (Lord Kelvin): On the Electrodynamic Qualities of Metals, Philosophical Transactions of the Royal Society (London), vol. 146, 1856, pp. 649-751.

20. Tomlinson, H.: The Influence of Stress and Strain on the Action of Physical Forces, Philosophical Transactions of the Royal Society (London), vol. 174, 1883, pp. 1-172.

21. Weymouth, L. J. "Strain Measurement in Hostile Environment," Applied Mechanics Reviews, vol. 18, no.1, 1965, pp. 1-4.

22. Pryor, T. R., and W. P. T North: "The Diffractographic Strain Gage," Experimental Mechanics, Vol. 11, No. 12, pp. 565-578, 1971.

23. Sharpe, W. N. Jr.: "The Interferometric Strain Gage," Experimental Mechanics, Vol. 8, No. 4, pp. 164-170, 1968.

24. Sharpe, W.N. Jr. et al: "Measurements of Young's Modulus, Poisson's Ratio and Tensile Strength of Polysilicon," Proceedings of the Tenth International Workshop on Micromechanical Systems, Nagoya Japan, 1997, pp. 424-429.

25. Harting, D. R.: "Evaluation of a Capacitive Strain Measuring System for use to 1500 °F", Instrument Society of America, ASI Publication No. 75251, pp. 289-297, 1975.

26. Foster R. L. and S. P. Wnuk Jr.: "High Temperature Capacitive Displacement Sensing", Instrument Society of America, Paper # 85-0123, 0096-7238, pp. 245-252, 1985.

27. Herceg, E. E.: Handbook of Measurement and Control, Schaevitz Engineering, Pennsauken, N.J., 1976.

28. Shepherd, R.: "Strain Measurement Using Vibrating-Wire Gages", Experimental Mechanics, Vol. 4, No. 8, pp. 244-248, 1964.

29. Mason, W. P., and R. N. Thurston: "Piezoresistive Materials in Measuring Displacement, Force, and Torque," Journal Acoustical Society America, Vol. 29, No. 10, pp. 1096-1101, 1957.

30. Geyling, F. T., and J. J. Forst: "Semiconductor Strain Transducers," Bell System Technical Journal., Vol. 39, 1960.

31. Mason, W. P.: "Semiconductors in Strain Gages," Bell Laboratory Record., Vol. 37, No.1, pp. 7-9, 1959.

32. Smith, C. S.: "Piezoresistive Effect in Germanium and Silicon," Physical Review, Vol.94, pp. 42-49, 1954.

33. Padgett, E. D., and W. V. Wright: "Silicon Piezoresistive Devices," pp. 1-20, in M. Dean and R. D. Douglas (eds.), Semiconductor and Conventional Strain Gages, Academic Press, Inc., New York, 1962.

34. O'Regan, R.: "Development of the Semiconductor Strain Gage and Some of Its Applications," pp. 245-257, in M. Dean and R. D. Douglas (eds.), Semiconductor and Conventional Strain Gages, Academic Press, Inc., New York, 1962.

35. Mason, W. P., J. J. Forst, and L. M. Tornillo: "Recent Developments in Semiconductor Strain Transducers," pp. 109-120, in M. Dean and R. D. Douglas (eds.), <u>Semiconductor and Conventional Strain Gages</u>. Academic Press, Inc., New York, 1962.

36. Kurtz, A. D.: "Adjusting Crystal Characteristics to Minimize Temperature Dependence," pp. 259-272, in M. Dean and R. D. Douglas (eds.), <u>Semiconductor and Conventional Strain Gages</u>, Academic Press, Inc., New York, 1962.

37. Sanchez, J. C., and W. V. Wright: "Recent Developments in Flexible Silicon Strain Gages," pp. 307-346, in M. Dean and R. D. Douglas (eds.), <u>Semiconductor and Conventional Strain Gages</u>, Academic Press, Inc., New York, 1962.

38. Durelli, A. J., J. W. Dally, and W. F. Riley: "Developments in the Application of the Grid Method to Dynamic Problems," Journal Applied Mechanics, Vol.26, No. 4, pp. 629-634, 1959.

39. Butter, C. D. and G. B. Hocker: "Fiber Optics Strain Gage," Applied Optics, Vol. 17, No. 18, pp. 2868-2869, 1978.

40. Sirkis, J. S. and C. E. Taylor: "Interferometric Fiber Optic Strain Sensor," Experimental Mechanics, Vol. 28, No. 2, pp. 170-176, 1988.

41. Meltz, G. R., W. W. Morey, and W. H. Glen: "Formation of Bragg Gratings in Optical Fibers by a Transverse Holographic Method," Optical Letters, Vol. 14, pp823-825, 1989.

42. Udd, E. et al: "Progress on Multidimensional Strain Field Measurements Using Fiber Optic Grating Sensors," Proceedings SPIE Smart Structures Symposia Conference, Newport Beach, March 6-9, 2000.

43. Schultz, W. L. et al: "Single and Multiaxis Fiber Grating Based Strain Sensors for Civil Structure Applications," Proceedings SPIE, Vol. 3586, p. 41, 1999.

44. Choquet, P., F. Juneau and J. Bessette: "New Generation of Fabry-Perot Fiber Optic Sensors for Monitoring of Structures," Proceedings SPIE Smart Structures Symposia Conference, Newport Beach, March 6-9, 2000.

45. Lee, C. E. et al: "Optical-fiber Fabry-Perot Embedded Sensors, Optical Letters," Vol. 13, No. 21, pp. 1225-1227, 1989.

46. Rashleigh, S. C.: "Origins and Control of Polarization in Single Mode Optical Fibers," Journal Lightwave Technology, Vol. 1, No. 2, pp. 312-331, 1983.

47. Stetson, K. A.: "Optical Heterodyning," Chapter 10, <u>Handbook on Experimental Mechanics</u>, 2nd Ed., ed. A. S. Kobayashi, VCH Publishers, New York, pp. 477-490, 1993.

48. Narendran, N., A. Shukla and S. Letcher: "Application of Fiber Optic Sensor to a Fracture Mechanics Problem," Eng. Fracture Mech. 1991, Vol. 38, 491-498.

49. Narendran, N., A. Shukla and S. Letcher: "Determination of Fracture Parameters Using Embedded Fiber Optic Sensors. Experimental Mechanics," 1991, Vol. 31, 360-365.

EXERCISES

6.1 A strain gage is to be fabricated from Advance wire having a diameter of 0.001 in. and a resistance of 25 Ω/in. The gage is to have a gage length of 2.0 in. and a resistance of 500 Ω. Design a grid configuration.

6.2 Write an engineering brief describing the characteristics of an optimum strain gage.

6.3 Write a concise description of a foil type resistance strain gage. Include the alloys employed and cover the role of the carrier and the tabs.

6.4 Write a specification describing the procedure to be followed by a laboratory technician in installing strain gages on metallic components.

6.5 Write a specification describing the procedure to be followed by a laboratory technician in installing strain gages on components fabricated from engineering polymers.

6.6 Prepare a graph showing system sensitivity S_S as a function of the power P_g dissipated by the gage. Let $r = 3.0$, $S_g = 2$ and consider $R_g = 120, 350, 500$ and $1,000\ \Omega$.

6.7 Determine the system sensitivity for a bridge with a single active gage having $R_g = 350\ \Omega$ and $S_g = 2.05$, if $r = 3.0$ and if the bridge voltage is 5 V.

6.8 If the gage in Exercise 6.7 can dissipate 0.01 W, is the bridge voltage correct? If not, what is the correct voltage?

6.9 Determine the voltage output from a Wheatstone bridge if a single active gage is used in an initially balanced bridge to measure a stain of 1,200 μm/m. Assume that a digital voltmeter will be used to measure the voltage and that $S_g = 2.06$, $r = 1$, and $V_S = 6$ V.

6.10 Prepare a graph showing bridge voltage V_S as a function of gage area A if $r = 1$ and $R_g = 350\ \Omega$. Consider $P_D = 0.1, 0.2, 0.5, 1, 2, 5$ and 10 W/in.^{2}

6.11 A 350 Ω strain gage with $S_g = 2.07$ is employed in a single arm Wheatstone bridge with $r = 1$. If the gage is subjected to a strain of 1,600 μm/m determine the reading on a 4 ½ digit digital voltmeter if:

	V_S (V)	Amplifier gain G.
(a)	2	10
(b)	4	10
(c)	6	100
(d)	5	50

6.12 Four strain gages ($R_g = 500\ \Omega$, $S_g = 2.06$) are attached to a bar to produce a load cell. The supply voltage $V_S = 4$ V and the amplifier (with a variable gain 10 to 100) is set at G = 20. When a load of 10,000 lb is applied to the bar the 4 ½ digit DVM provides a count of 6,280. What adjustments are required to make the count correspond to the applied load?

6.13 An oscilloscope with an input impedance of $10^6\ \Omega$ is connected to a Wheatstone bridge with one active gage ($R_g = 350\ \Omega$, $S_g = 3.35$, and $r = 5$). The bridge is powered with a 9-V constant-voltage supply. If the gage responds to a dynamic strain pulse having a magnitude of 900 μm/m, determine the sensitivity setting on the oscilloscope that will give a trace deflection of four divisions.

6.14 If the bridge and gage of Exercise 6.13 respond to a strain of 1,400 μm/m, determine the trace deflection if an oscilloscope having a sensitivity of 1 mV/div is used for the measurement.

6.15 If the bridge, gage, and oscilloscope of Exercise 6.14 record a trace deflection of 5.2 divisions, determine the strain at the gage location.

6.16 Determine the value of the calibration constant C for a gage-bridge-amplifier-recorder system if $S_g = 2.04$, $r = 2$, $V_S = 4$ V, G = 50, and $S_R = 10$ mV per division.

6.17 Determine the resistance R_c that must be shunted across arm R_2 of the listed Wheatstone bridges to produce the given calibration strains.

	ε_c (μm/m)	r	R_g (Ω)	S_g
(a)	600	3	350	2.06
(b)	1,000	2	500	2.07
(c)	900	1	120	2.05
(d)	2,000	2	350	2.09

6.18 Design a displacement fixture to be used with a strain gage mounted on a cantilever beam to mechanically produce a calibration strain ε_c ranging from 0 to 2,000 μm/m in 500 μm/m increments.

6.19 A 120 Ω strain gage is connected into a single arm bridge using 190 feet of twin lead wire. What is the signal loss factor if the wire is gage:

        (a) 30   (b) 26   (c) 20   (d) 14

6.20 Solve Exercise 6.19 if a 350 Ω gage is used in place of the 120 Ω gage.

6.21 Solve Exercise 6.19 if a three wire system is employed to connect the gage into the bridge.

6.22 A switch similar to the one shown in Fig. 6.14 is employed to switch a series of 120 Ω gages ($S_g = 2.09$) in and out of a single arm bridge. Prepare a graph showing the apparent strain ε' as a function of switch resistance ΔR_s. Let ΔR_s range from 100 μΩ to 100 mΩ.

6.23 Write an engineering brief describing the operation of a set of slip rings to be employed with a rotating shaft.

6.24 Write an engineering specification describing grounding procedures to minimize noise pick-up on strain gage leads.

6.25 What three precautions used to minimize noise must be included in the specification of Exercise 6.24.

6.26 Determine the error that results if a strain gage compensated for aluminum [$\alpha = 13.0 \times 10^{-6}/$ °F] is used on steel [$\alpha = 6.0 \times 10^{-6}/$°F]. The total response of the gage was 200 μm/m and the temperature change between the zero and final reading was 30 °F. Assume that a dummy gage was not used in the bridge.

6.27 Determine the axial sensitivity S_a of a strain gage if $S_g = 2.04$ and $K_t = 0.02$.

6.28 Determine the error involved if transverse sensitivity is neglected in a measurement of hoop strain in a thin-walled steel ($E = 29,000$ ksi and $\nu = 0.29$) cylindrical pressure vessel when K_t for the gage is 0.03.

6.29 If strain gages with $S_g = 2.03$ and $K_t = 0.04$ are used to determine the apparent strains ε'_{xx} and ε'_{yy}, determine the true strains ε_{xx} and ε_{yy}.

Case No.	ε'_{xx} (μm/m)	ε'_{yy} (μm/m)
1	800	1,200
2	640	−720
3	1,200	−240
4	−560	2,400
5	240	1,440

6.30 Determine the error produced by ignoring transverse sensitivity effects if strain gages with $K_t = 0.03$ are employed in a simple tension test to measure Poisson's ratio of a material.

6.31 Assume that K_t for an ordinary strain gage is zero. Show how this gage could be used to measure stress in a specified direction. Clearly indicate all assumptions made in your derivation.

6.32 A stress gage is fabricated with two grids each of which exhibit an axial sensitivity $S_a = 2.00$. Determine the output from the gage in terms of $\Delta R/R$ if it is mounted on a steel specimen and subjected to a stress $\sigma = 50,000$ psi.

6.33 Determine the uniaxial state of stress associated with the following strain measurements:

ε (μm/m)	Material
800	Steel ($E = 29,000$ ksi, $\nu = 0.29$)
1,100	Aluminum ($E = 10,000$ ksi, $\nu = 0.33$)
1,620	Titanium ($E = 14,000$ ksi, $\nu = 0.25$)

6.34 Determine the biaxial state of stress associated with the following strain measurements:

ε_1 (μm/m)	ε_2 (μm/m)	Material
−600	−900	Aluminum
1,220	−470	Titanium
1,115	820	Steel

See Exercise 6.33 for material properties.

6.35 Determine the general state of stress associated with the following strain measurements made with a 0°, 45°, 90° rosette. See Exercise 6.33 for material properties.

ε_A (μm/m)	ε_B (μm/m)	ε_C (μm/m)	Material
600	1,200	−300	Aluminum
1,050	1,050	1,050	Titanium
−450	−900	1,350	Steel

6.36 Beginning with Eqs. (6.45) verify Eqs. (6.47) for the three-element rectangular rosette.

6.37 Derive relations of the same form as Eq. (6.43) that give ε_1, ε_2 and ϕ in terms of ε_A, ε_B, and ε_C for a three element delta rosette.

6.38 Continue Exercise 6.37 and expand the solution to show:

   (a) The classification procedure for the principal angles in terms of ε_A, ε_B, and ε_C —similar to Eqs. (6.48).

   (b) The relations for the principal stresses in terms of ε_A, ε_B, and ε_C — similar to Eqs. (6.45).

6.39 Use Mohr's strain circle to verify the classification procedure for a three-element rectangular rosette described by Eqs. (6.48).

6.40 Write an engineering brief which describes our capabilities of measuring strain at high temperatures by employing electrical resistance strain gages.

6.41 A helium-neon laser (λ = 632.8 nm) is used to illuminate a diffraction type strain gage with a gage length of 20 mm. The diffraction pattern is displayed on a screen, which is located 3 m from the aperture. The initial aperture width b is 0.1 mm.

   (a) Determine the density n/y of the diffraction pattern.

   (b) If the gage is subjected to a strain of 1,000 με, what are the new aperture width and the new density n/y_1?

   (c) Suppose the diffraction pattern is sufficiently well defined for the +8 and −8 orders of extinction to be clearly observed before and after subjecting the gage to the strain. If distances y_0 and y_1 can be determined from scale measurements on the screen to ± 1 mm, estimate the percent error in the measurement of strain.

6.42 Cite the disadvantages of measuring strain with fiber-optic strain gages.

6.43 Sketch the optical arrangement for the Mach-Zehnder fiber-optic sensor.

6.44 Sketch the optical arrangement for the Michelson fiber-optic sensor.

6.45 Sketch the optical arrangement for the Fabry-Perot fiber-optic sensor.

6.46 Design an acoustical strain gage, which can be installed in a concrete dam and monitored over the life (estimated to exceed two centuries), of the dam. The gage will be monitored periodically to record the change in strain with rising and falling head, to record any change in effective modulus of the concrete due to cracking or other deterioration of the concrete, and to estimate damage to the structure after any natural occurrence such as an earthquake. Items to be considered in the design include selection of materials for the components of the gage, gage length, wire size, wire type, and frequency range during operation. Estimate the accuracy of the strain measurement and comment on the ability of the gage to detect structural damage or deterioration of the concrete.

EXERCISE SOLUTIONS

Exercise 6.1

Given: $d = 0.001$ in., $L_g = 2.00$ in., $R_g = 500 \; \Omega$, and $R_w = 25 \; \Omega/$in.

$$L_w = \frac{R_g}{R_w} = \frac{500}{25} = 20.0 \text{ in.}$$

Number of segments $= \dfrac{L_w}{L_g} = \dfrac{20.0}{2.00} = 10$

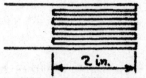

2 in.

Exercise 6.8

From Eq. (6.7): $p_g = A \, p_D$

From Eq. (6.9): $v_s = (1 + r) \sqrt{A p_D R_g}$

$$= (1 + r) \sqrt{p_g R_g}$$

$$= (1 + 3) \sqrt{0.01(350)} = 7.48 \text{ V}$$

The bridge voltage ($v_s = 5$ V) is satisfactory; could use as much as $v_s = 7.48$ V.

Exercise 6.16

From Eq. (6.16):

$$C = \frac{(1 + r)^2 S_A S_R}{r v_s S_g} = \frac{(1 + 2)^2 (10)(10^{-3})}{2(4)(2.04)(50)}$$

$$= 110.3(10^{-6}) \text{ (m/m)/div} = 110.3 \text{ (}\mu\text{m/m)/div}$$

Exercise 6.22

From Eq. (6.27):

$$\varepsilon' = \frac{\Delta R_s / R_g}{S_g}$$

With $R_g = 120\ \Omega$ and $S_g = 2.09$:

$$\varepsilon' = \frac{\Delta R_s}{120(2.09)} = 0.003987 \Delta R_s$$

$\Delta R_s\ (\mu\Omega)$	$\varepsilon'\ (\mu in./in.)$
100	0.4
1000	4.0
10,000	39.9
100,000	398.7

Exercise 6.28

For a thin-walled cylindrical pressure vessel:

$$\sigma_a = \frac{pr}{2t} \qquad \sigma_h = \frac{pr}{t} \qquad \sigma_h = 2\sigma_a$$

$$\varepsilon_a = \frac{1}{E}\left[\sigma_a - \nu(2\sigma_a)\right] = \frac{\sigma_a}{E}(1 - 2\nu)$$

$$\varepsilon_h = \frac{1}{E}\left[2\sigma_a - \nu\sigma_a\right] = \frac{\sigma_a}{E}(2 - \nu)$$

Therefore:

$$\frac{\varepsilon_a}{\varepsilon_h} = \frac{1 - 2\nu}{2 - \nu}$$

For steel $\nu = 0.29$:

$$\frac{\varepsilon_a}{\varepsilon_h} = \frac{1 - 2\nu}{2 - \nu} = \frac{1 - 0.58}{2 - 0.29} = 0.2456$$

From Eq. (6.38):

$$\mathcal{E} = \frac{K_t(\varepsilon_a/\varepsilon_h + \nu_0)}{1 - \nu_0 K_t}(100) = \frac{0.03(0.2456 + 0.285)}{1 - 0.285(0.03)}(100) = 1.606\%$$

CHAPTER 7

MEASURING FORCE, TORQUE AND PRESSURE

7.1 INTRODUCTION

Transducers that measure force, torque, or pressure often contain an elastic member that converts these mechanical quantities to a deflection or strain. A deflection sensor, or alternatively, an arrangement of strain gages is then used to give an electrical signal proportional to the quantity of interest (force, torque, or pressure). Characteristics of the transducer, such as range, linearity and sensitivity, are determined by the size and shape of the elastic member, the material used in its fabrication and the sensors employed.

A wide variety of transducers are commercially available for measuring force (load cells), torque (torque cells), and pressure. The different elastic members employed in the design of these transducers include links, columns, rings, beams, cylinders, tubes, washers, diaphragms, shear webs, and other shapes for special-purpose applications. Strain gages are commonly used as the sensor; however, linear potentiometers and linear variable-differential transformers (LVDTs) are sometimes used for static or quasi-static measurements. A large capacity load cell using strain gages as the sensors is presented in Fig. 7.1.

Fig. 7.1 A shear-web type transducer capable of measuring large forces. Courtesy of Interface, Inc.

In the first part of this chapter, we consider the quasi-static measurements, where the loads are applied slowly to the elastic member contained in the transducer. If the time required for the load to reach its maximum value exceeds the period of the natural frequency of the elastic element by a factor of 10 or more, the dynamic response of the transducer is not a serious consideration.

Later in this chapter, we will introduce a spring-mass-dashpot representation of a transducer that enables us to examine its response to terminated-ramp and periodic input functions. Later in Chapter 10, a seismic transducer model is introduced. This model is important because it is used to describe dynamic behavior of transducers in measuring displacement, velocity, acceleration, force and pressure that vary rapidly with time.

7.2 FORCE MEASUREMENTS (Load Cells)

The elastic members commonly used in load cells are links, beams, and shear webs. The operating characteristics for load cells with these elastic members are developed in the following subsections.

7.2.1　Link-Type Load Cells

A simple link-type load cell with strain gages as the sensor is shown in Fig. 7.2a. The load P can be either tensile or compressive. Four strain gages are bonded to the link, with two in the axial direction and two in the transverse direction. The four gages are wired into a Wheatstone bridge with the axial gages in arms 1 and 3 of the bridge and the transverse gages in arms 2 and 4, as shown in Fig. 7.2b.

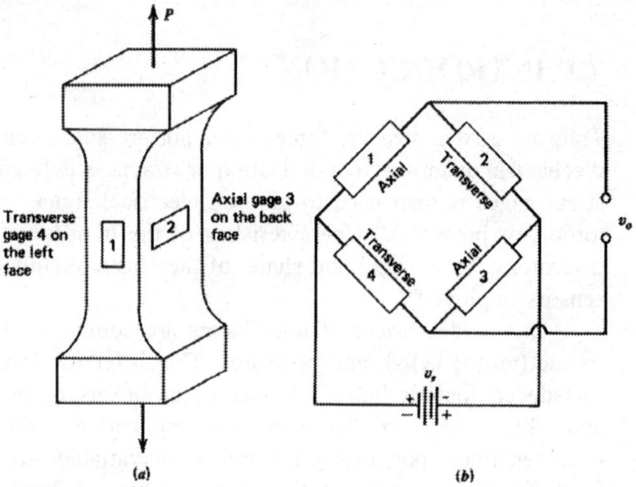

Fig. 7.2　Link type load cell.
(a) Elastic element with strain ages.
(b) Gage positions in a Wheatstone bridge.

When the load P is applied to the link, axial and transverse strains, ε_a and ε_t respectively, develop in the link. They are related to the load by the expressions:

$$\varepsilon_a = \frac{P}{AE} \qquad \varepsilon_t = -\frac{\nu P}{AE} \qquad (a)$$

where A is the cross-sectional area of the link, E is its modulus of elasticity and ν its Poisson's ratio.

The response of the gages to the applied load P is given by Eqs. (6.4) and Eq. (a) as:

$$\frac{\Delta R_1}{R_1} = \frac{\Delta R_3}{R_3} = S_g \varepsilon_a = \frac{S_g P}{AE}$$

$$\frac{\Delta R_2}{R_2} = \frac{\Delta R_4}{R_4} = S_g \varepsilon_t = -\frac{\nu S_g P}{AE} \qquad (b)$$

The output voltage V_0 from the Wheatstone bridge is expressed in terms of the load P by substituting Eqs. (b) into Eq. (4.17). If the four strain gages on the link are identical, then $R_1 = R_2$ and Eq. (4.17) yields:

$$V_0 = \frac{S_g P (1 + \nu) V_s}{2 AE} \qquad (7.1)$$

or

$$P = \frac{2 AE V_0}{S_g (1 + \nu) V_s} = C V_0 \qquad (7.2)$$

Equation (7.2) indicates that the load P is linearly proportional to the output voltage V_0 and that its constant of proportionality or calibration constant C is:

$$C = \frac{2AE}{S_g(1+v)V_s} \tag{7.3}$$

The sensitivity of the load cell-Wheatstone bridge combination is given by $S = V_0/P$; therefore, from Eq. (7.3), we obtain:

$$S = \frac{V_0}{P} = \frac{1}{C} = \frac{S_g(1+v)V_s}{2AE} \tag{7.4}$$

Clearly, the sensitivity of the link-type load cell depends upon the link's cross sectional area (A), the elastic constants of the material used in fabricating it (E and v), the gage factor of the gages (S_g) and the input voltage applied to the Wheatstone bridge (V_s).

The range of a link-type load cell is determined by the cross-sectional area of the link and by the fatigue strength S_f of the material used in its fabrication. Thus:

$$P_{max} = S_f A \tag{7.5}$$

Because both sensitivity and range depend upon the cross-sectional area A of the link; higher sensitivities are associated with low-capacity load cells, while lower sensitivities are associated with higher-capacity load cells.

The voltage ratio at maximum load (V_0/V_s) for the link-type load cell is obtained from Eqs. (7.5) and (7.1) as:

$$\left(\frac{V_0}{V_s}\right)_{max} = \frac{S_g S_f(1+v)}{2E} \tag{7.6}$$

Most load-cell links are fabricated from a high strength steel (E = 30,000,000 psi and v = 0.30) that is heat treated to give a fatigue strength $S_f \approx 180,000$ psi. Because $S_g \approx 2$ for metal foil strain gages, Eq. (7.6) gives $(V_0/V_s)_{max} = 3.47$ mV/V. Many link-type load cells are rated at $(V_0/V_s) = 3$ mV/V at the full-scale value of the load (P = P_{max}). With this full-scale specification of voltage ratio $(V_0/V_s)^*$, the load P on the load cell is given by:

$$P = \frac{(V_0/V_s)}{(V_0/V_s)^*} P_{max} \tag{7.7}$$

The supply voltage applied to the bridge in the load cell is typically about 10 V which gives an output voltage at the maximum rated load of approximately 30 mV. This output is monitored with a digital voltmeter or, if the signal is dynamic, it is displayed on the monitor of a computer or an oscilloscope. A link-type load cell has a high spring rate and a high natural frequency; however, the mass attached to its ends degrade the load cell's natural frequency.

7.2.2 Beam-Type Load Cell

Beam-type load cells are commonly employed for measuring smaller forces where the link-type load cell is not sufficiently sensitive. A simple cantilever beam serves as the elastic member (see Fig. 7.3a). Two strain gages on the top surface and two strain gages on the bottom surface (all oriented along the axis of the beam) are the sensors. The gages are connected into a Wheatstone bridge as shown in Fig. 7.3b.

The load P produces a moment M = Px at the gage location x, which produces equal and opposite strains given by:

$$\varepsilon_1 = -\varepsilon_2 = \varepsilon_3 = -\varepsilon_4 = \frac{6M}{Ebh^2} = \frac{6Px}{Ebh^2} \tag{a}$$

where b is the width of the cross section of the beam and h is the height of its cross section.

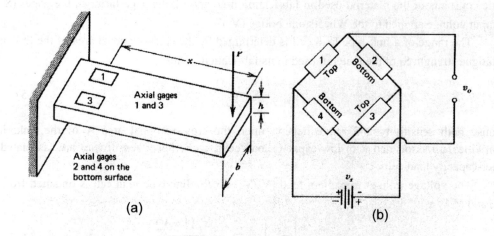

(a) (b)

Fig. 7.3 (a) Beam type load cells incorporate an elastic element with four strain gages.
(b) Gage positions in the Wheatstone bridge.

The response of the strain gages is obtained from Eqs. (6.4) and (a). Thus:

$$\frac{\Delta R_1}{R_1} = -\frac{\Delta R_2}{R_2} = \frac{\Delta R_3}{R_3} = -\frac{\Delta R_4}{R_4} = \frac{6S_g Px}{Ebh^2} \tag{b}$$

The output voltage V_0 from the Wheatstone bridge, due to the force P, is obtained from Eq. (b). If the four strain gages on the beam are identical, the bridge output voltage V_0 becomes:

$$V_0 = \frac{6S_g Px V_s}{Ebh^2} \tag{7.8}$$

or

$$P = \frac{Ebh^2 V_0}{6S_g x V_s} = CV_0 \tag{7.9}$$

and the sensitivity is:

$$S = \frac{V_0}{P} = \frac{1}{C} = \frac{6S_g x V_s}{Ebh^2} \tag{7.10}$$

The sensitivity of the beam-type load cell depends upon the shape of the beam cross section (b and h), the modulus of elasticity of the material used in its fabrication (E), the location of the load with respect to the gages (x), the strain gage factor (S_g) and the input voltage applied to the Wheatstone bridge (V_s).

The range of a beam-type load cell depends upon the dimensions of the cross section of the beam, the location of the point of application of the load and the fatigue strength of the material from which the beam is fabricated. If the gages are located at or near the beam support, then $M_{gage} \approx M_{max}$ and

$$P_{max} = \frac{S_f bh^2}{6x} \tag{7.11}$$

Equations (7.10) and (7.11) indicate that both the range and the sensitivity of a beam-type load cell can be changed by varying the point of application of the load. Maximum sensitivity and minimum range occurs as x approaches the length L of the beam. The sensitivity decreases and the range increases as the point of load application moves nearer the gages. The voltage ratio at maximum load (V_0/V_s) is obtained from Eqs. (7.11) and (7.8) as

$$\left(\frac{V_0}{V_s}\right)_{max} = \frac{S_g S_f}{E} \tag{7.12}$$

Comparison of Eq. (7.12) with Eq. (7.6) shows that the beam-type load cell is approximately 50 percent more sensitive than the link-type load cell. Beam-type load cells are commercially available with ratings of $(V_0/V_s)^*$ between 4 and 5 mV/V at full capacity.

7.2.3   Shear-Web-Type Load Cell

The shear-web-type load cell (also known as a low-profile or flat load cell) is useful for applications where space is limited along the line of action of the force. The flat load cell consists of an inner loading hub and an outer supporting flange connected by a continuous shear web (see Fig. 7.4). Strain gages that respond to shear strain are used as the sensor. The strain gages are installed in small holes drilled into the neutral surface of the web (see Fig. 7.4). Some characteristics of flat load cells are shown in Table 7.1.

The shear-web-load cell is compact and stiff; therefore, it can be used to measure dynamic loads at higher frequencies than the beam-type load cell. The effective weight w_e in Table 7.1 consists of the inner hub and a portion of the shear web. The natural frequencies presented in Table 7.1 are for a rigidly mounted load cell with no mass attached; therefore, these values represent the upper frequency limit. The attachment of any additional mass will reduce this natural frequency and will also reduce the frequency range of the transducer. The manufacturer recommends the following equation for estimating the natural frequency of these load cells.

$$f_n = 3.13 \sqrt{\frac{k}{w_e + w_x}} \qquad\qquad (7.13)$$

where f_n is the transducer's natural frequency (Hz); k is its spring rate (lb/in); w_e is the effective weight of its hub assembly (lb) and w_x is the weight attached to the hub (lb).

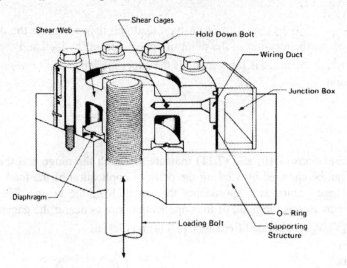

Fig. 7.4 Construction details of a shear web type load cell.

Table 7.1
Mechanical Properties of Flat Load Cells

Force Capacity P (lb)	Spring Rate k (kip/in.)	Weights w_x and w_e (lb)	Natural Frequency f_n (Hz)
250	920	0.25—0.023	5,700
500	920	0.50—0.023	4,150
1,000	1,310	1.0—0.020	3,550
5,000	5,880	5.0—0.091	3,300
10,000	11,300	10.0—0.224	3,300
50,000	21,400	50.0—1.62	2,000
100,000	32,600	100.0—6.35	1,730
400,000	68,000	400.0—32.2	1,250

Courtesy of Strainsert Company (from technical bulletin No. 365-4MP)

The natural frequencies listed in Table 7.1 were calculated assuming that no external weight ($w_x = 0$) was attached to the load cell. With external weight attached to the load cell, the frequency limit will be lowered. A complete discussion of the performance of force transducers under dynamic loading is presented later in Section 7.7.

It should be recognized that the frequency response of the load cells described above is limited. The exact natural frequency is difficult to predict because of the effect of the mass that is added to the load cell in connecting it to the load train. Piezoelectric force transducers with significantly better frequency response are described in a later in Chapter 10.

7.3   TORQUE MEASUREMENT (Torque Cells)

Torque cells are transducers that convert an applied torque to an electrical output signal. The two types of torque cells in common usage include those installed on fixed shafts and those on rotating shafts. The latter type is more difficult to utilize, because the electrical signal must be transmitted from the rotating shaft to a stationary instrument station. This problem of signal transmission is treated after the design concepts associated with torque cells are discussed.

7.3.1   Torque Cells-Design Concepts

Torque cells are very similar to load cells. They contain a mechanical element, usually a shaft with a circular cross section, and a sensor, usually electrical resistance strain gages. A circular shaft with four strain gages mounted on two perpendicular 45-degree helixes is shown in Fig. 7.5. Gages 1 and 3, mounted on the right-hand helix, measure positive strains, while gages 2 and 4, mounted on the left-hand helix, measure negative strains. The two 45-degree helixes define the principal stress and strain directions for a circular shaft subjected to pure torsion.

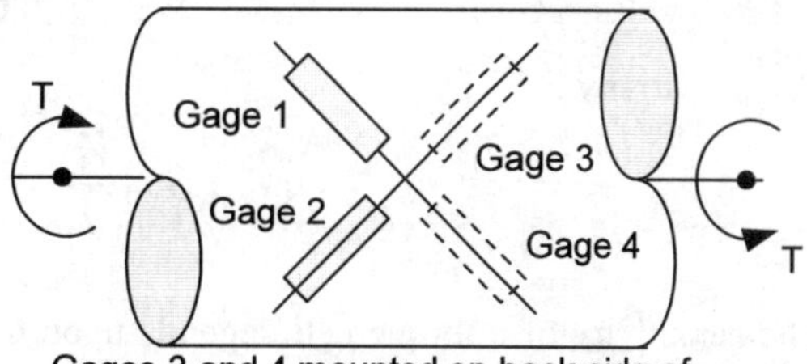

Fig. 7.5 A circular shaft with four strain gages used as sensors in a torque cell.

Gages 3 and 4 mounted on back side of the shaft

The shearing stress τ in the circular shaft is related to the applied torque T by the equation:

$$\tau_{xz} = \frac{TD}{2J} = \frac{16T}{\pi D^3} \tag{7.14}$$

where D is the diameter of the shaft and J is the polar moment of inertia of the circular cross section.

Because the normal stresses $\sigma_{xx} = \sigma_{yy} = \sigma_{zz} = 0$ for a circular shaft subjected to pure torsion, it is easy to show that:

$$\sigma_1 = -\sigma_2 = \tau_{xz} = \frac{16T}{\pi D^3} \tag{7.15}$$

Principal strains ε_1 and ε_2 are obtained by using Eqs. (7.15) and Hooke's law for the plane stress. Thus,

$$\varepsilon_1 = \frac{16T}{\pi D^3}\left(\frac{1+v}{E}\right) \qquad \varepsilon_2 = -\frac{16T}{\pi D^3}\left(\frac{1+v}{E}\right) \tag{7.16}$$

The response of the strain gages is obtained by substituting Eqs. (7.16) into the equations describing the response from a Wheatstone bridge to obtain:

$$\frac{\Delta R_1}{R_1} = -\frac{\Delta R_2}{R_2} = \frac{\Delta R_3}{R_3} = -\frac{\Delta R_4}{R_4} = \frac{16T}{\pi D^3}\left(\frac{1+v}{E}\right)S_g \qquad \text{(a)}$$

If the gages are connected into a Wheatstone bridge, as illustrated in Fig. 7.3b, the relationship between output voltage V_0 and torque T is obtained by substituting Eq. (a) into Eq. (4.18) to give:

$$V_0 = \frac{16T}{\pi D^3}\left(\frac{1+v}{E}\right)S_g V_s \qquad (7.17)$$

or

$$T = \frac{\pi D^3 E}{16(1+v)S_g V_s}V_0 = CV_0 \qquad (7.18)$$

where

$$C = \frac{\pi D^3 E}{16(1+v)S_g V_s} \qquad \text{(b)}$$

The sensitivity is:

$$S = \frac{V_0}{T} = \frac{1}{C} = \frac{16(1+v)S_g V_s}{\pi D^3 E} \qquad (7.19)$$

The sensitivity of a torque cell depends upon the diameter of the shaft (D), the shaft material (E and v), the gage factor (S_g), and the voltage applied to the Wheatstone bridge (V_s). The range of the torque cell depends upon the diameter D of the shaft and the proportional limit S_τ of the material in torsion. For static applications, the range is given by Eq. (7.14) as

$$T_{max} = \frac{\pi D^3 S_\tau}{16} \qquad (7.20)$$

The voltage ratio at maximum torque $(V_0/V_s)_{max}$ is obtained from Eqs. (7.19) and (7.20) as

$$\left(\frac{V_0}{V_s}\right)_{max} = \frac{S_\tau S_g(1+v)}{E} \qquad (7.21)$$

If the torque cell is fabricated from heat-treated steel ($S_\tau \approx 60,000$ psi), then $(V_0/V_s)_{max} = 5.2$ mV/V. Typically, commercial torque cells are rated at values of (V_0/V_s) between 4 and 5 mV/V. The torque T corresponding to an output voltage V_0 is then determined from Eq. (7.19).

7.3.2   Transmission of Torque-Cell Signals

Frequently, torque is measured on a rotating shaft, which necessitates transmission of the signal from a Wheatstone bridge located on the rotating shaft and a stationary instrumentation center. Signal transmission between a rotating body and a fixed instrument is accomplished with slip rings, rotating joints or telemetry.

Signal Transmission with Slip Rings

A schematic illustration of a slip-ring connection between a Wheatstone bridge on a rotating shaft and a recording instrument at a stationary location is shown in Fig. 7.6. The slip-ring assembly contains a series of insulated rings mounted on a shaft and a companion series of insulated brushes mounted in the case. High-speed bearings between the shaft and the case enable the case to remain stationary, while the shaft rotates with the torque cell. A commercial slip-ring assembly is shown in Fig. 7.7.

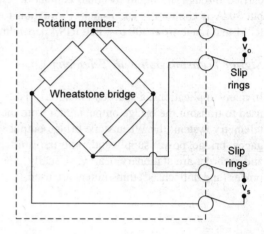

Fig. 7.6 Wheatstone bridge connections on a rotating shaft using slip rings.

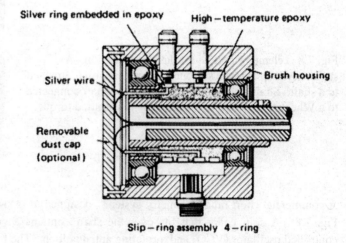

(a) Brush housing	(b) Design details

Fig. 7.7 Slip ring assembly

The major problem in using slip rings is noise (generated by contact resistance variations between the rings and brushes). These contact resistance variations can be maintained within acceptable limits (100 mΩ) by fabricating the rings from silver or Monel (a copper-nickel alloy) and the brushes from a silver-graphite mixture. Also, it is important to maintain the ring-brush contact pressure between 50 and 100 psi. Current carrying capacity for instrument slip rings is often specified at 500 mA. The maximum RPM of slip-ring assemblies depends on the concentricity between the shaft and the slip ring's case and by the quality of its bearings. Slip-ring units with speed ratings of 12,000 RPM are commercially available.

Signal Transmission with Rotating Electrical Connectors

Rotating electrical connectors[1] operate on a different principle from slip rings. The electrical conduction path is a liquid metal (mercury) that is molecularly bonded to the contact tracks. Because of the liquid interface between the contacting surfaces and ball bearing construction, they have a long maintenance free life. Moreover the electrical resistance is extremely low (less than 1 mΩ) and it is constant. Hence, the electrical noise is much lower than that developed with slip rings. The current carried through the liquid-to-liquid contact depends on the number of channels contained in the unit, but 30 A is common. The primary limitation for instrument applications is the maximum allowable RPM that range from 300 to 1,800 RPM depending on the diameter of its rotor.

Signal Transmission with Telemetry

In many applications, a shaft end is not available for mounting the slip-ring assembly and telemetry is used to transmit the bridge output signal from the rotating shaft to a recording instrument. In a simple telemetry system, the Wheatstone bridge output voltage is used to modulate a radio signal. The strain gages, bridge, power supply and radio transmitter are mounted on the rotating shaft while the receiver and recorder are stationary nearby. Usually, the signal is transmitted only a few feet; therefore, low-power (and unlicensed) transmitters are used.

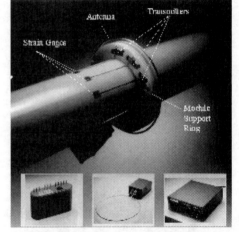

Fig. 7.8 Telemetry system for data transmission. A stationary loop antenna surrounds a rotating collar attached to a shaft. Strain gages are mounted on the shaft connected to a Wheatstone bridge to measure the transmitted torque.

A commercial short-range telemetry system[2], designed to measure rotating shaft torques, is shown in Fig. 7.8. A split collar that fits over the shaft contains a power supply, a modulator, a voltage-controlled oscillator (VCO) and a rotating antenna loop. The bridge signal modulates the pulse width of a constant- amplitude 5-kHz square wave (i.e. the time width of the positive part of the square wave is proportional to bridge output while the square wave period remains the same). The square wave is used to vary the VCO frequency that is varied from 10.7 to 16.0 MHz. The VCO signal is transmitted at low power by the rotating antenna located in the split collar. A stationary loop antenna that encircles the split collar, as shown in Fig. 7.8, receives this signal. The transmitting unit is completely self-contained and receives its power through inductive coupling of a 160 kHz signal from the stationary antenna loop.

---

[1] Commercially available from Mercotac®, Inc. Carlsbad, CA.
[2] Commercially available from Honeywell-Sensotec, Columbus, OH.

7.4 COMBINED MEASUREMENTS OF F, M OR T

Some experiments require two or more quantities be measured simultaneously. For example, a six component transducer used in wind tunnel measurements must simultaneously measure three orthogonal forces and three orthogonal moments. These combined measurements are accomplished by using two or more separate strain-gage bridges mounted on an elastic element or by using selected gage combinations to form a single bridge. Many different gage and bridge combinations can be designed. To illustrate the concepts while limiting the length of this section, only two combined-measurement transducers are discussed—a force-moment transducer and a force-torque transducer.

7.4.1 Force-Moment Measurements

A common force-moment transducer uses an elastic link, as shown in Fig. 7.9. For simplicity, consider the link with a square cross section ($A = h^2$), strain gages bonded on the centerline of each side and aligned with the longitudinal (P_z) direction. An axial force P_z is measured by connecting gages A and C into Wheatstone bridge arm positions 1 and 3, as shown in Fig. 7.10a. Resistances R_2 and R_4 are equal fixed-value resistors with $R_2 = R_4 = R_g$. Under these conditions, Eq. (4.17) reduces to:

$$V_0 = \frac{1}{4}\left(\frac{\Delta R_1}{R_1} + \frac{\Delta R_3}{R_3}\right)V_s \qquad (a)$$

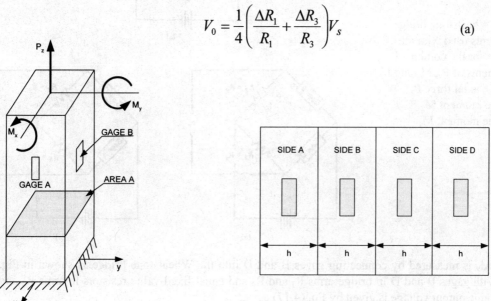

(a) Elastic element with strain gages.　　　(b) Developed surface showing strain gage positions.

Fig. 7.9 Transducer for the combined measurement of an axial force P_z and moments M_x and M_y.

The corresponding strain gage response is given by Eq. (6.4) as:

$$\frac{\Delta R_1}{R_1} = \frac{\Delta R_3}{R_3} = S_g \varepsilon = \frac{S_g P_z}{AE} \qquad (b)$$

Substitution of Eq. (b) into Eq. (a) gives the output voltage as a function of the applied load as

$$V_0 = \left(\frac{S_g V_s}{2AE}\right)P_z = S_a P_z \tag{7.22}$$

where the term in parentheses is the force-voltage sensitivity S_a.

A sensitivity comparison between this two-gage load cell and a four-gage load cell [see Eq. (7.4)] shows a sensitivity loss of $[1/(1 + v)]$ or about 25%. This sensitivity loss is the cost for having gages B and D available for moment M_x measurements.

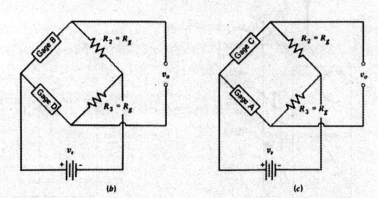

Fig. 7.10 Wheatstone bridge arrangements used with the transducer for the combined measurements of P_z, M_x and M_y
(a) For the axial force P_z
(b) For the moment M_x
(c) For the moment M_y

Moment M_x is measured by connecting gages B and D into the Wheatstone bridge as shown in Fig. 7.10b. With gages B and D in bridge arms R_1 and R_4 and equal fixed-value resistors in arms R_2 and R_3, the bridge output voltage is given by Eq. (4.17) as:

$$V_0 = \frac{1}{4}\left(\frac{\Delta R_1}{R_1} - \frac{\Delta R_3}{R_3}\right)V_s \tag{c}$$

The corresponding strain gage response is given by Eq. (6.4) as:

$$\frac{\Delta R_1}{R_1} = -\frac{\Delta R_4}{R_4} = S_g\varepsilon = \frac{6S_g M_x}{Eh^3} \tag{d}$$

Substitution of Eq. (d) into Eq. (c) gives an input-output of:

$$V_0 = \left(\frac{3 S_g V_s}{E h^3} \right) M_x = S_x M_x \qquad (7.23)$$

where the bracketed term is the moment-voltage sensitivity S_x.

Similarly, moment M_y can be measured by connecting gages C and A into bridge arms R_1 and R_4, respectively, and using equal fixed-value resistors in arms R_2 and R_3, as indicated in Fig. 7.10c. Thus,

$$V_0 = \left(\frac{3 S_g V_s}{E h^3} \right) M_y = S_y M_y \qquad (7.24)$$

where the bracketed term is the moment voltage sensitivity S_y.

A comparison of Eqs. (7.23) and (7.24) shows equal voltage sensitivities for the x and y directions because the cross-section used in designing the link was square. Transducers designed for combined measurements are usually equipped with switch boxes that contain the required bridge completion resistors and the connections needed to switch the gages into the correct bridge locations. Care must be exercised during certain measurements, because temperature compensation within the Wheatstone bridge is not maintained.

7.4.2 Force-Torque Measurements

A transducer designed to measure both axial force P_z and torque M_z is shown in Fig. 7.11. The load link has a circular cross section. For measuring axial force P_z, gages A and C are connected to bridge arms R_1 and R_3, respectively, and equal fixed-value resistors are used in the other two arms. This arrangement is identical to that shown in Fig. 7.10a; therefore, Eq. (7.22) applies to this case.

Torque is measured by connecting gages B and D into bridge arms R_1 and R_4 as shown in Fig. 7.11b. With equal fixed-value resistors in the other two bridge arms, Eq. (4.18) reduces to Eq. (c). The strain gage response for this case becomes:

$$\frac{\Delta R_1}{R_1} = -\frac{\Delta R_4}{R_4} = S_g \varepsilon = \frac{16(1+v) S_g M_z}{\pi D^3 E} \qquad (e)$$

Substitution of Eq. (e) into Eq. (c) gives

$$V_0 = \left(\frac{8(1+v) S_g V_s}{\pi D^3 E} \right) M_z = S_z M_z \qquad (7.25)$$

A comparison of Eq. (7.25) for two active strain gages with Eq. (7.19) for a standard four-gage torque cell indicates that the combined transducer has one-half the sensitivity of the standard cell. This loss in sensitivity results from using only half as many strain gages in the Wheatstone bridge.

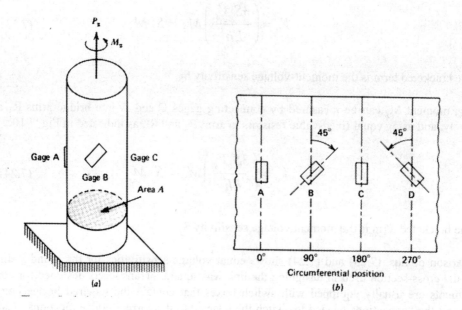

Fig. 7.11 Combined measurement transducer used to measure axial load P_z and moment M_z.
(a) Elastic element with strain gages. (b) Developed surface showing strain gage locations.

7.5 PRESSURE MEASUREMENTS (Pressure Transducers)

Pressure transducers are devices that convert an applied pressure into an electrical signal by measuring either displacement, strain or a piezoelectric or piezoresistive response. The quasi-static operating characteristics for each of these transducer types are covered in the following subsections. The dynamic operating characteristics of pressure transducers are covered in Section 7.7.

7.5.1 Diaphragm-Type Pressure Transducers

A strain sensing pressure transducer utilizes either a clamped circular plate (diaphragm) or a hollow cylinder as its elastic element and electrical resistance strain gages as its sensors. Diaphragms are used for low- and middle-pressure ranges (0 to 30,000 psi), while cylinders are mostly used for the high- and very-high-pressure ranges (30,000 to 100,000 psi). The strain distribution resulting from a uniform pressure on the face of a clamped circular plate of constant thickness is given by:

$$\varepsilon_{rr} = \frac{3p(1-v^2)}{8Et^2}\left(R_0^2 - 3r^2\right) \qquad \varepsilon_{\theta\theta} = \frac{3p(1-v^2)}{8Et^2}\left(R_0^2 - r^2\right) \qquad (7.26)$$

where p is the pressure; t is the thickness of the diaphragm; R_0 is its outside radius and r is a position parameter.

Examination of Eqs. (7.26) indicates that the circumferential strain $\varepsilon_{\theta\theta}$ is always positive and is a maximum at r = 0. The radial strain ε_{rr} is positive in some regions, but negative in others, and assumes its maximum negative value at r = R_0. Both distributions are shown in Fig. 7.12.

A special-purpose diaphragm strain gage, which has been designed to take advantage of this strain distribution, is widely used in diaphragm-type pressure transducers. Circumferential elements are employed in the central region of the diaphragm where $\varepsilon_{\theta\theta}$ is a maximum. Similarly, radial elements are employed near the edge of the diaphragm where ε_{rr} is a maximum. Also, the circumferential and radial elements are each divided into two parts, as shown in Fig. 7.13. It is evident that this special-purpose gage actually consists of four separate strain gages. The individual gages are connected into a Wheatstone bridge with the circumferential elements in arms R_1 and R_3 and radial elements in arms R_2 and R_3. If the strains are averaged over the areas of the circumferential and radial elements, and if the average values of $\Delta R/R$ (with a gage factor $S_g = 2$) obtained from Eq. (6.4) are substituted into Eq. (4.18), the output voltage V_0 is given by:

$$V_0 = 0.82 \frac{pR_0^2(1 - v^2)}{Et^2} V_s = S_p p \tag{7.27}$$

where the pressure-voltage sensitivity S_p depends on the geometry (R_0 and t), material properties (E and v), and supply voltage (V_0).

The power that is supplied to a Wheatstone bridge is controlled by the power P_T that can be dissipated by the gage elements. The voltage-power relationship of a four-arm Wheatstone bridge is given by Eq. (6.24) as:

$$V_S = 2(P_T R_T) \tag{a}$$

Substituting Eq. (a) into Eq. (7.27) and solving for S_p gives

$$S_p = 1.64 \frac{R_0^2(1 - v^2)\sqrt{P_T R_T}}{Et^2} \tag{7.28}$$

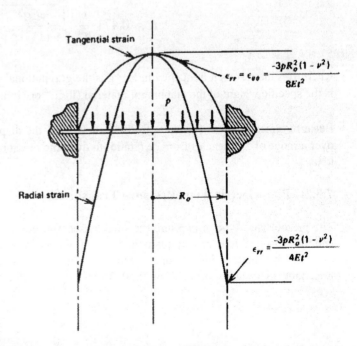

Fig. 7.12 Strain distribution in a thin clamped circular plate (diaphragm) due to a uniform transverse pressure.

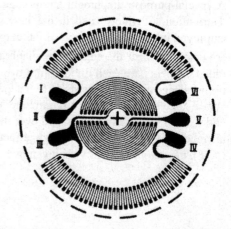

Fig. 7.13 Special purpose four-element strain gage for diaphragm-type pressure transducers.

Clearly, Eq. (7.28) shows that a diaphragm-type pressure gage can be designed with a wide range of sensitivities by varying the (R_0/t) ratio. Unlike most other transducers, diaphragm deflection rather than yield strength controls the limit of (R_0/t). The relationship between pressure and output voltage will be linear within 0.3 percent if the center deflection is limited to be less than $t/4$. Using this deflection criterion, one can show that the maximum sensitivity becomes:

$$\left(S_p\right)_{max} = 2.19\left(\frac{t}{R_0}\right)^2 \frac{\sqrt{p_T R_T}}{p_{max}}$$
(7.29)

The amount of damping in a diaphragm pressure transducer is highly dependent on the fluid in contact with the diaphragm's surface. Also, the effective seismic mass of the diaphragm is dependent on the density of the contacting fluid. The upper resonant natural frequency can be estimated by using the expression:

$$f_r = 0.471 \frac{t}{R_0^2} \sqrt{\frac{Eg}{w(1-v^2)}}$$
(7.30)

where f_r is the resonant frequency in Hz; g is the gravitational constant (386 in./s^2 or 7.81 m/s^2) and w is the specific weight of the diaphragm material (lb/in.^{3} or N/mm^3).

Because typical values of f_r range from 10 to 50 kHz, the diaphragm pressure transducer can be used over a range of frequencies from dc (static) to dynamic measurements involving frequencies of 2 to 10 kHz.

7.5.2 Piezoelectric-Type Pressure Transducers

The piezoelectric type of pressure transducer uses a piezoelectric material as both the elastic element and the sensor. Single crystal quartz is the most widely used piezoelectric material because of its high modulus of elasticity, high resonant frequency, linearity over a wide range, and very low hysteresis. Resonant frequencies of 0.25 to 0.50 MHz can be achieved while maintaining relatively high sensitivity.

A photograph of a piezoelectric pressure transducer is shown in Fig. 7.14. The quartz crystal is enclosed in a cylindrical shell that has a thin pressure-transmitting diaphragm on one end and a rigid support base for the crystal on the other end. As pressure is applied to the face of the crystal in contact with the diaphragm, an electrostatic charge is generated. The magnitude of the charge depends upon the pressure, the size of the crystal and the orientation of the crystal axes. Miniature pressure transducers that utilize a quartz crystal having a diameter of 6 mm and a length of 6 mm exhibit a sensitivity of approximately 1 pC/psi, and those with larger crystals (11-mm diameter and 12-mm length) have sensitivities of 5 pC/psi. Piezoelectric transducers can be used for very-high-pressure (up to 100,000 psi) measurements and for pressure measurements at temperatures as high as 350 °C. If water-cooling is used to protect the crystal and its insulation, the temperature range can be extended.

Piezoelectric sensors all exhibit extremely high output impedance. Because of this high output impedance, a charge amplifier or cathode follower must be inserted between the sensor and any conventional voltage-measuring instrument. A charge amplifier converts the charge on the crystal to a voltage, amplifies this voltage, and provides an output impedance of approximately 100 Ω, which is satisfactory for most voltage measuring instruments. With the advent of microelectronics many of the pressure sensors are available with signal conditioning circuits built into the case of the transducer. With these transducers, the output impedance is reduced many orders of magnitude, but power must be supplied to the signal conditioning circuits.

Fig. 7.14 Photograph of a piezoelectric pressure transducer that incorporates a quartz sensor.

The low frequency response characteristics of piezoelectric sensors depend on the effective time constant of the measuring circuit. The time constant depends on the input impedance of the charge amplifiers or built-in voltage-followers that are employed with the sensor. Usually piezoelectric pressure transducers are used in measurements where the pressure fluctuates rapidly. The performance characteristics of a high sensitivity dynamic pressure transducer with a quartz sensor are given in Table 7.2.

Table 7.2
Characteristics of Piezoelectric Pressure Transducers
PCB Piezotronics Model 101A (100 psi)

Parameter	US Customary	SI
Range	0 to 100 psi	0 to 689 kPa
Sensitivity	50 mV/psi	7.3 mV/kPa
Resolution	2×10^{-3} psi	0.014 kPa
Resonance Frequency	≥ 250 kHz	≥ 250 kHz
Rise Time	≤ 2.0 μs	≤ 2.0 μs
Non-Linearity	≤ 1.0 % Full Scale	≤ 1.0 % Full Scale

7.5.3 Piezoresistive-Type Pressure Transducers

With the advent of doping techniques with semiconductor silicon, manufacturers of pressure gages and accelerometers have introduced transducers incorporating piezoresistive sensors. These sensors consist of a thin elastic element of silicon. Piezoresistive strain gages are implanted in the silicon by either diffusion or ion implantation techniques. Both P and N type doping elements[3] are employed to provide strain gages with both positive and negative gage factors. There are two significant advantages to this approach. First, the sensing element is small and light, enabling the production of a transducer with a very high frequency response. Second, adjusting the concentration of the dopant for both N and P type semiconductors provides a method to control the gage factor. Hence, semiconductor strain gages with very high gage factors can be produced.

The elastic element is usually formed from a silicon chip processed using the same methods as used in the manufacture of microelectronic components. Four small strips of P and N dopants are implanted in a silicon chip as indicated in Fig. 7.15. The strips are connected together with thin lines of aluminum or copper to form a Wheatstone bridge. Leads are attached to the chip to provide the necessary supply voltage and to conduct the output voltage V_0 to a suitable connector.

Typical performance parameters for a piezoresistive type pressure transducer are presented in Table 7.3. The sensitivity is lower than that obtained with a piezoelectric sensing element; however, the piezoresistive transducer can be used for either static or dynamic pressure measurements. Recall that the piezoelectric sensors are limited to dynamic measurements because of charge leakage from the piezoelectric elements with time.

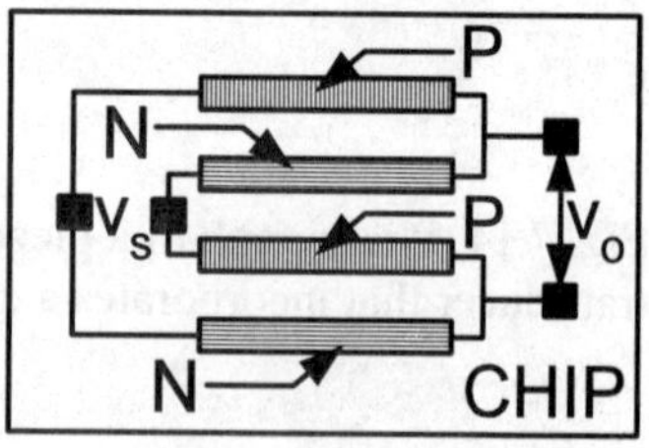

Fig. 7.15 Layout of a four arm Wheatstone bridge on a silicon chip using P and N doped strips as strain gages.

Table 7.3
Characteristics of Piezoresistive Pressure Transducers
Endevco Piezoresistive Pressure Transducer Model 8530B-200 (200 psi)

Parameter	US Customary
Range	0 to 200 psia
Sensitivity	1.5 ± 0.5 mV/psi
Resonance Frequency	750 kHz
Non-Linearity	≤ 0.2 % Full Scale
Thermal Zero Shift From 0 to 200 °F	± 3.0 % Full Scale
Thermal Sensitivity Shift From 0 to 200 °F	± 4.0 % Full Scale
Burst Pressure (Diaphragm)	800 psia

---

[3] Dopant elements with five valence electrons in the outer shell such a phosphorous, arsenic and antimony are used to produce N type semiconductors. If elements with three valence electrons such as boron, aluminum or gallium are used the semiconductor is classified as a P type.

The sensitivity of the piezoresistive pressure gages is about ten times greater than pressure sensors fabricated with metallic alloy strain gages. The only significant disadvantage associated with using the piezoresistive sensor is its sensitivity to changes in temperature during the measurement interval. If large changes in temperature are anticipated during the measurement interval temperature induced zero shifts and sensitivity variations can occur.

7.6 MINIMIZING ERRORS IN TRANSDUCERS

Most transducers designed to measure force, torque, or pressure utilize electrical resistance strain gages as sensors because they are inexpensive, easy to install, and provide an output voltage V_0 (when used as elements of a Wheatstone bridge) that can be related easily to the load, torque, or pressure. In applications of strain gages to stress analysis, accuracies of $\pm 2\%$ are usually acceptable. When strain gages are used as sensors in transducers, accuracy requirements are an order of magnitude more stringent; therefore, more care must be exercised in the selection and installation of the gages and in the design of the Wheatstone bridge. Typical performance specifications for general-purpose, improved-accuracy, and high-accuracy load cells are listed in Table 7.4.

Table 7.4
Specifications for Load-Cell Accuracies*

Characteristic	General Purpose Load Cell	Improved Accuracy Load Cell	High-Accuracy Load Cell
Calibration inaccuracy	0.50%	0.25%	0.10%
Temperature effect on zero	$\pm 0.005\%/°F$	$\pm 0.0025\%/°F$	$\pm 0.0015\%/°F$
Zero-balance error	$\pm 5\%$	$\pm 2.5\%$	$\pm 1\%$
Temperature effect on span	$\pm 0.01\%/°F$	$\pm 0.005\%/°F$	$\pm 0.008\%/°F$
Nonlinearity	0.25%	0.10%	0.05%
Hysteresis	0.1%	0.05%	0.02%
Non-repeatability	0.1%	0.05%	0.02%
System inaccuracy	1.0%	0.5%	0.15%

*All percentages are relative to full scale measurements.

Errors that degrade the accuracy of a transducer include dual sensitivity, zero shift with temperature change, bridge balance, span adjust and span change with temperature change. Each of these sources of error is discussed in the following subsections together with procedures for minimizing error.

7.6.1 Dual Sensitivity

All transducers exhibit a dual sensitivity, to some small degree, which means that the output voltage is due to both a primary quantity, such as force, torque, or pressure, and a secondary quantity, such as temperature or a secondary force or moment. Provision must be made during design of the transducer to minimize these secondary sensitivities.

A. Dual Sensitivity-Temperature

As an example of dual sensitivity due to temperature, consider a link-type load cell subjected to both a load P_z and a temperature change ΔT that occurs during the measurement period. The strain gages on the link will respond to both the strain ε produced by the load and the apparent strain ε', due to the temperature change. The total response of each gage will appear as:

$$\left.\frac{\Delta R_1}{R_1} = \frac{\Delta R_g}{R_g}\right]_{P_z} + \left.\frac{\Delta R_g}{R_g}\right]_{\Delta T} = S_g(\varepsilon_1 + \varepsilon'_1) \qquad \text{(a)}$$

Similar expressions will apply for the other three gages. If the strain gages are identical and if the temperature change for each gage is the same, Eq. (4.18) indicates that the response of the gages due to temperature will cancel and the output of the Wheatstone bridge will be a function only of the load-induced strains in the elastic element (link) of the transducer. In this example, the signal summing property of the Wheatstone bridge provides temperature compensation of the load cell.

B. Dual Sensitivity-Secondary Load

When link-type load cells are used for force measurements, it is usually difficult to apply the load P_z coincident with the centroidal axis of the link. As a consequence, both the load P_z and a bending moment M are imposed on the link and it is necessary to design the transducer with a very low sensitivity to M while maintaining a high sensitivity to P_z. This objective is accomplished in the link-type load cell by proper placement of the strain gages.

As an example, consider that an arbitrary moment M is being applied to the cross section of the elastic element of the load cell, as shown in Fig. 7.16. If the moment M is resolved into Cartesian components M_x and M_y, the effect of M_x will be to bend the element about its x axis such that:

$$\varepsilon_{a1} = -\varepsilon_{a3} \qquad \text{(a)}$$

Because the transverse gages are on the neutral axis for bending about the x axis:

$$\varepsilon_{a2} = -\varepsilon_{a4} = 0 \qquad \text{(b)}$$

Equations (a) and (b) indicate that the response of the gages to a moment M_x will be:

$$\frac{\Delta R_1}{R_1} = -\frac{\Delta R_3}{R_3} \quad \text{and} \quad \frac{\Delta R_2}{R_2} = \frac{\Delta R_4}{R_4} = 0 \qquad \text{(c)}$$

When Eq. (c) is substituted into Eq. (4.18), the output resulting from the strain-gage response to moment M_x vanishes. Because neither M_x or M_y produce an output, any arbitrary moment M can be applied to the load cell without affecting the measurement of the load P_z. In this example, proper placement of the strain gages eliminates any sensitivity to the secondary load.

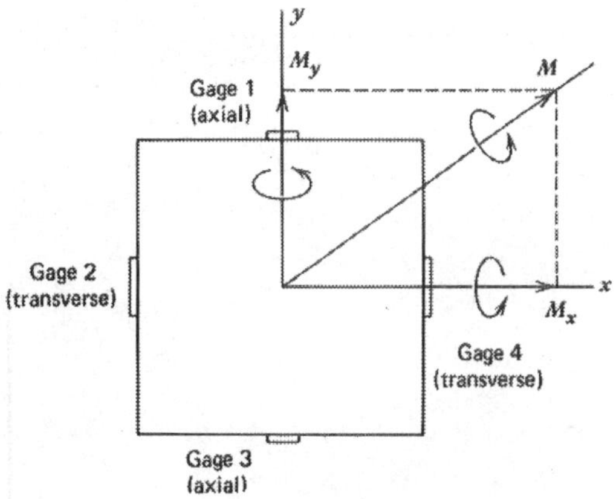

Fig. 7.16 An arbitrary moment applied to a cross section of an elastic element in a link-type load cell.

7.6.2 Zero Shift with Temperature Change

It was shown previously that some electrical resistance strain gages are temperature compensated (resistance changes due to temperature change are minimized through proper selection of the gage alloy) over a limited range of temperature. When temperature variations are large, changes in resistance occur and zero output under zero load is not maintained.

Zero shift with temperature change is reduced by using either half or full Wheatstone bridges, as discussed previously. Here, temperature-induced resistance changes are partially canceled by the summing properties of the Wheatstone bridge. However, because strain gages are never identical, some zero shift persists.

A third compensation procedure for reducing zero shift in transducers is illustrated in Fig. 7.17. Here, a low-resistance copper ladder gage is inserted between arms 3 and 4 of the Wheatstone bridge. Because the ladder gage is a part of both arms, it increases both ΔR_3 and ΔR_4 when the temperature is increased. During calibration (which involves temperature cycling of the transducer over its specified range of operation), the ladder gages are trimmed by cutting one or more rungs to adjust ΔR_3 and ΔR_4 to temperature changes until the zero shift for the transducer is within acceptable limits.

7.6.3 Bridge Balance

In general, transducers should exhibit zero output under no-load conditions. Unfortunately, the strain gages employed as sensors do not have exactly the same resistance; therefore, the Wheatstone bridge is usually out-of-balance under the no-load condition. Balance can be achieved by inserting a compensation resistor between arms 1 and 2 of the bridge, as shown in Fig. 7.17. The compensation resistor is a double-ladder gage that can be trimmed to add either ΔR_1 or ΔR_2 until nearly perfect balance is achieved.

7.6.4 Span Adjust

Span refers to the sensitivity of the transducer. In instrumentation systems where transducers are often interchanged or replaced, it is important to have transducers with identical span. The span is usually adjusted by using a temperature insensitive resistor (ladder gage) in series with the voltage supply, as indicated in Fig. 7.17. Because the ladder gage reduces the supply voltage applied to the bridge, the span of the transducer is adjusted to the specified value (usually 3 mV/V full scale).

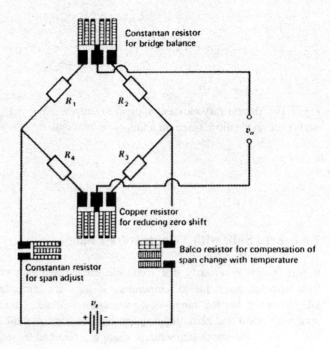

Fig. 7.17 Compensation resistors introduced into the Wheatstone bridge of a transducer to minimize the effects of temperature changes.

7.6.5 Span Change with Temperature

Compensation of span change with temperature is difficult because the procedure involves simultaneous application of the load and cycling of the temperature. Usually, temperature compensation of the span is achieved by inserting a resistor that changes with temperature (a nickel-iron alloy known as Balco) in the second lead from the voltage supply, as shown in Fig. 7.17. This ladder resistor is trimmed to give a resistance change with temperature that compensates for changes in sensitivity with temperature.

Considerable fine tuning of a transducer is required to achieve the accuracies specified in Table 7.4. Also, periodic recalibration is needed to ensure that the transducer is operating within specified limits of accuracy. If these high accuracies are not required, then some of the compensation procedures will not be necessary and lower cost transducers can be specified.

7.7 FREQUENCY RESPONSE (BANDWIDTH) OF TRANSDUCERS

There are two different approaches employed in describing the frequency response of transducers in applications involving measurements of mechanical quantities that vary with time. One approach assumes that a fixed point exists where the base of the transducer is attached. The loads or pressure are applied to elastic members, which deforms relative to this fixed point. The second approach does not utilize a fixed reference point. Instead, the base and a representative mass in the transducer both move in response to the dynamic input. The relative motion between the base and the mass is used to sense kinematic quantities such as displacement, velocity, and acceleration, when a fixed reference point is not available.

In this section, we employ the first approach and assume that the base of the transducer is mounted to a rigid surface that remains stationary during the dynamic application of force to the elastic member. In Chapter 10 we will introduce the seismic transducer model. This model accommodates the motion of the base of the transducer and must be used if it is not possible to attach the base of the transducer to a fixed reference surface. The dynamic response of recording instruments was considered previously in Chapter 3 to illustrate the importance of frequency response characteristics to the measurement process. The frequency response of a transducer are equally important because serious errors can be introduced in dynamic measurements if the bandwidth of the transducer is not adequate.

Transducers for measuring load, torque, and pressure are all second-order systems; therefore, their dynamic behavior can be described by a second-order differential equation. The application of second-order theory to transducers will be illustrated by considering a link-type load cell with a uniaxial elastic member such as the one illustrated in Fig. 7.18. The dynamic response of this load cell can be described by the differential equation of motion for the mass-spring-dashpot combination shown in Fig. 7.18. The elastic member of the load cell is represented by the spring. The spring modulus or spring rate k is given by the expression:

$$k = \frac{P}{\delta} = \frac{AE}{L} \tag{7.31}$$

where P is the load; δ is the extension or contraction of the elastic member; A is its cross-sectional area; E is its modulus of elasticity and L is the length of the link.

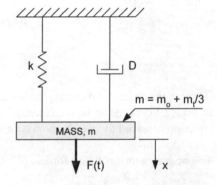

Fig. 7.18 A spring-mass-dashpot representation of a link type load cell.

The dashpot represents the parameters in the transducer system (such as internal friction) that produce damping. In load and torque cells, damping is usually a very small quantity; however, in diaphragm pressure transducers, damping is larger because the fluid interacts with the diaphragm. The mass is a lumped mass consisting of the mass of the object to which the transducer is attached plus the effective mass of the elastic element of the transducer. The force F(t) acts on the moving mass and is the quantity being measured. The position parameter x describes the motion (displacement) of the mass m as a function of time. The dynamic response of this second-order system is described by the differential equation:

$$\frac{1}{\omega_n^2} \frac{d^2 x}{dt^2} + \frac{2d}{\omega_n} \frac{dx}{dt} + x = \frac{F(t)}{k} \tag{7.32}$$

where ω_n is the natural frequency of the system, $\omega_n = \sqrt{\dfrac{k}{m}}$.

The natural frequency ω_n of the system depends upon the mass of the object attached to the load cell and the effective mass of the elastic element. For the link-type load cell, the effective mass m of the system is approximated as:

$$m = m_0 + m_t/3$$

where m_0 is the mass of the attached object and m_t is the mass of the elastic element in the transducer.

Clearly, both the mass of the elastic element and the mass of the object affect the fidelity of the measurement of the dynamic force F(t).

7.7.1 Response of a Force Transducer to a Terminated Ramp Function

The fidelity of a force measurement depends primarily on the rise time associated with F(t). In the treatment of electronic recording instruments, F(t) is usually considered to be a step function, because electrical signals can be applied almost instantaneously. In mechanical systems, however, it is not realistic to consider F(t) as a step function because application of F(t) requires some finite time even in the most severe dynamic application. For this reason, a more realistic forcing function for mechanical systems is the terminated-ramp function shown in Fig. 7.19. This terminated-ramp function can be expressed in equation form as:

$$F(t) = \frac{F_0 t}{t_0} \qquad for \quad 0 \le t \le t_0$$

$$F(t) = F_0 \qquad for \quad t > t_0 \tag{7.33}$$

Because the degree of damping in the link-type load cell is very small, only the under-damped solution to Eq. (7.32) needs to be considered. After Eq. (7.33) is substituted into Eq. (7.32), the differential equation is solved to yield homogeneous and particular solutions:

The homogeneous solution for Eq. (7.32) is given by:

$$x_h = e^{-d\omega_n t}\left(C_1 \sin\sqrt{1-d^2}\ \omega_n t + C_2 \cos\sqrt{1-d^2}\ \omega_n t\right) \tag{a}$$

The particular solution for Eq. (7.32) is:

$$x_p = \frac{F_0}{kt_0}\left(t - \frac{2d}{\omega_n}\right) \qquad for\ 0 \le t \le t_0$$

$$x_p = \frac{F_0}{k} \qquad for\ t > t_0 \tag{b}$$

The coefficients C_1 and C_2 in Eq. (a) are obtained by using the initial conditions for the system, which are:

$$x = 0 \quad and \quad dx/dt = 0 \quad at \quad t = 0 \tag{c}$$

The general solution for the ramp region ($x_r = x_p + x_h$) is obtained from Eqs. (a), (b), and (c) as:

$$\frac{x_r(t)}{x_0} = \left(\frac{t}{t_0} - \frac{\tau}{t_0}\right) - \frac{e^{-at}}{bt_0}\sin(bt - \phi) \qquad \text{for } t < t_0 \qquad (7.34)$$

where

$$\tau = \frac{2d}{\omega_n} \qquad \qquad x_0 = \frac{F_0}{k}$$

$$a = d\omega_n \qquad \qquad \phi = \tan^{-1}\left(\frac{2d\sqrt{1-d^2}}{1-2d^2}\right) \qquad (7.35)$$

$$b = \omega_n\sqrt{1-d^2}$$

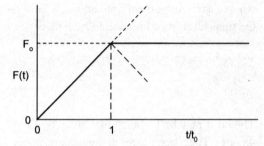

Fig. 7.19 A force F(t) that is characterized by a terminated ramp function.

The terminal portion of the input in Fig. 7.19 is composed of the initial ramp with a second ramp being subtracted starting at $t = t_0$, as shown by the dashed lines. Thus,

$$x_h(t) = x_r(t) - x_r(t - t_0) \qquad (d)$$

Substituting Eq. (7.34) into Eq. (d) gives:

$$\frac{x_h(t)}{x_0} = 1 - \frac{e^{-at}}{bt_0}\left\{\sin(bt - \phi) - e^{-at}\sin[b(t - t_0) - \phi]\right\} \qquad \text{for } t < t_0 \quad (7.36)$$

Equations (7.34), (7.35), and (7.36) provide the information needed to determine the error introduced by a load cell while tracking a terminated-ramp function if the degree of damping d is known.

In most force transducers, the degree of damping d is very low (less than 0.02); therefore, $\phi \approx 0$ and Eqs. (7.34), (7.35), and (7.36) reduce to:

$$\frac{x_r(t)}{x_0} = \frac{t}{t_0} - \frac{\sin\omega_n t}{\omega_n t_0} \qquad \text{for } t < t_0 \qquad (7.37)$$

$$\frac{x_h(t)}{x_0} = 1 - \frac{1}{\omega_n t_0}[\sin\omega_n t - \sin\omega_n(t - t_0)] \qquad \text{for } t > t_0$$

$$(7.38)$$

$$= 1 + \frac{\sqrt{2(1 - \cos\omega_n t_0)}}{\omega_n t_0}\sin(\omega_n t + \theta)$$

$$\theta = \tan^{-1}\left(\frac{\sin\omega_n t_0}{1 - \cos\omega_n t_0}\right) \tag{7.39}$$

The first term in Eq. (7.38) represents the ramp while the second term represents an oscillation about the ramp that has an amplitude of $1/(\omega_n t_0)$. This amplitude is the maximum deviation from the ramp as illustrated in Fig. 7.20. The deviation is minimized by ensuring that $1/(\omega_n t_0)$ is small compared to the peak response of 1. The maximum error that can occur in the measurement after the peak response is given by Eq. (7.38) as:

$$\mathcal{E} = \frac{2}{\omega_n t_0} \tag{7.40}$$

where $\omega_n t_0$ is an odd multiple of π. To limit the error to a specified amount $\mathcal{E}$, the natural frequency of the transducer must be selected such that:

$$\omega_n \ge \frac{2.0}{\mathcal{E}\, t_0} \tag{7.41}$$

The error may be less than that given by Eq. (7.40) if $\omega_n t_0$ is near to an even multiple of π such as 2π, 4π, etc. The precise error at the peak response is obtained from Eq. (7.38) as:

$$\mathcal{E} = \frac{\sqrt{2(1 - \cos\omega_n t_0)}}{\omega_n t_0} \tag{7.42}$$

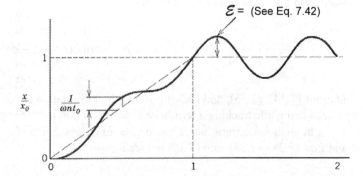

Fig. 7.20 Response of a load transducer with d = 0 to a terminated ramp function as an input.

Because ω_n and t_0 are not always known prior to the measurement, Eq. (7.40) is usually employed to judge the adequacy of a transducer for measuring the peak of a terminated ramp function with a rise time of t_0. Consider, for example, a load cell and mass system with a natural frequency of 5,000 Hz intended to measure a dynamic load with a rise time of 1 ms. The maximum error in the peak response that can occur is given by Eq. (7.40) as 0.0636 or 6.4 percent. If this error is acceptable, the measurement can be made with confidence. However, if the error is too high, a transducer with a higher natural frequency must be utilized for the measurement.

7.7.2 Response of a Force Transducer to a Sinusoidal Forcing Function

The dynamic response of transducers to a periodic forcing function can be studied by letting $F(t) = F_0 \sin \omega t$ in Eq. (7.32). Thus,

$$\frac{1}{\omega_n^2} \frac{d^2 x}{dt^2} + \frac{2d}{\omega_n} \frac{dx}{dt} + x = \frac{F_0}{k} \sin \omega t \qquad (7.43)$$

where ω is the circular frequency of the applied force.

If the damping coefficient d is small (as with most transducers), Eq. (7.43) reduces to:

$$\frac{1}{\omega_n^2} \frac{d^2 x}{dt^2} + x = \frac{F_0}{k} \sin \omega t \qquad (7.44)$$

Because the forcing function is periodic, the complementary solution to Eq. (7.44) has no significance and the particular solution gives the steady-state response of the transducer as:

$$x_p = \frac{1}{1 - (\omega / \omega_n)^2} \frac{F_0}{k} \sin \omega t \qquad (7.45)$$

Equation (7.45) can be expressed in terms of the periodic forcing function $F(t)$ as:

$$k x_p = \frac{1}{1 - (\omega / \omega_n)^2} F_0 \sin \omega t = A \sin \omega t \qquad (7.46)$$

where $A = F_0 / [1 - (\omega/\omega_n)^2]$ is an amplification factor that relates the steady-state response to the amplitude of the forcing function.

The error ε associated with a measurement of F_0 is determined from Eq. (7.46) in terms of the frequency ratio as

$$\varepsilon = \frac{A - F_0}{F_0} = \frac{(\omega / \omega_n)^2}{1 - (\omega / \omega_n)^2} \qquad (7.47)$$

Equation (7.47) indicates that substantial error can occur in a measurement of force, torque, or pressure unless the frequency ratio ω/ω_n is very small. For example, if $\omega/\omega_n = 0.142$, an error of 2% occurs. Similarly, if $\omega/\omega_n = 0.229$, the error is 5%. If the error is to be maintained within reasonable limits, the natural frequency of the transducer system (including all attached mass) must be 5 to 10 times higher than the frequency of the forcing function.

The dynamic response of transducers to other common inputs, such as the impulse function, should also be studied. This case is covered in Exercise 7.32.

7.8 CALIBRATION OF TRANSDUCERS

All transducers must be calibrated periodically to ensure that their sensitivity has not changed with time or due to misuse. Calibration of load cells and torque cells is usually accomplished with a testing machine with a scale certified to be accurate within specified limits. After the transducer is mounted in the testing machine, load is applied in increments that cover the range of the transducer. The output from the transducer is compared to the load indicated by the testing machine at each level of load, and differences (errors) are recorded. If the error is small, the calibration constant for the transducer is verified and the transducer can be used with confidence. If the error is excessive but consistent (i.e., the response is linear, but the slope is not correct), the calibration constant can be adjusted to correct the error. In cases where the calibration constant requires correction, the calibration test should be repeated to ensure that the new calibration constant is reproducible and correct. In some cases it will be observed that the error is not consistent and the output from the transducer is erratic. If the instrumentation system is checked and found to be operating properly, then the transducer is malfunctioning and cannot be calibrated. Such transducers should be removed from service immediately and returned to their manufacturer for repair.

A second method of calibrating load cells and torque cells is commonly employed in instances where a testing machine, certified to the required accuracy limits, is not available. This method utilizes two transducers connected in series. One transducer is a "standard" that is used only for calibration purposes; the other is the working transducer. With this method, the calibration forces are obtained from the standard transducer instead of the testing machine.

For low-capacity load cells and torque cells, deadweight loads are frequently used in the calibration process. The standard weights (traceable to the National Institute of Standards and Technology or certified by weighing with a calibrated scale) are applied directly to the transducer to provide the known input. The transducer output is compared to the known input as discussed previously. While deadweight loading in calibration has many advantages and is usually preferred, it is not practical when the range or capacity of the load cell exceeds a few hundred pounds (about 1 kN). Also, dead weight calibration is dependent on the local acceleration due to gravity; a quantity that varies with location and altitude.

Pressure transducers are usually calibrated with a deadweight pressure source, such as the one illustrated schematically in Fig. 7.21. The calibration pressures are generated by adding standard weights to the piston tray. The calibration pressure is related to the weight by the expression:

$$p = w/A \qquad (7.48)$$

where w is the total weight of the piston, tray, and standard weights and A is the cross-sectional area of the piston.

After the weights are placed on the piston tray, a screw-driven plunger is forced into the hydraulic oil chamber to reduce its volume and to lift the piston-weight assembly. The piston-weight assembly is then rotated to eliminate frictional forces between the piston and the cylinder. By adding weights incrementally to the piston tray, it is possible to generate 10 to 12 calibration pressures that cover the operating range of the transducer. Comparisons are made between the calculated calibration pressures and the pressures indicated by the transducer in order to certify the calibration constant. Because deadweight testers are relatively inexpensive to operate over a very wide range of pressures, they are preferred in calibrating pressure gages over methods that utilize a standard transducer. The cost associated with the purchase of a number of standard transducers to cover a wide range of pressures exceeds the cost of a deadweight tester to cover the same range.

Fig. 7.21 Schematic illustration of a deadweight calibration system for calibrating pressure transducers.

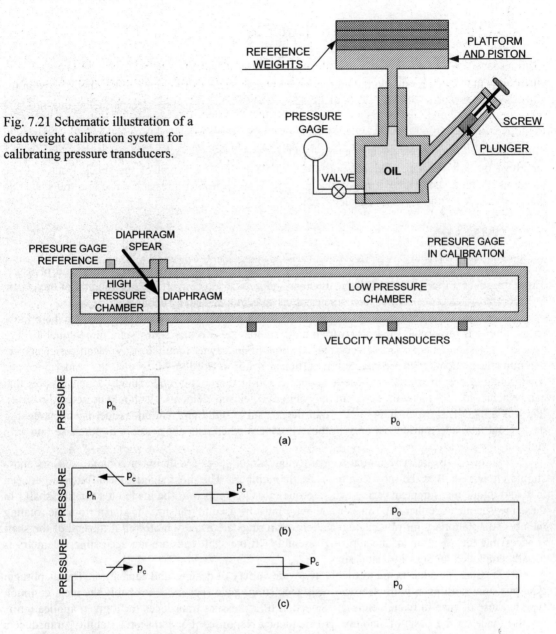

Fig. 7.22 Drawing of a shock tube used to generate pressure pulses for transducer calibration.
    (a)   Pressure distribution with diaphragm intact.
  (b)   Pressure distribution before reflection of the rarefaction wave.
  (c)   Pressure distribution after reflection of the rarefaction wave.

Dynamic calibration of pressure transducers is usually accomplished with a shock tube. A shock tube is simply a closed section of smooth-walled tubing that is divided by a diaphragm into a short high-pressure chamber and a longer low-pressure chamber. When the diaphragm is ruptured, a shock wave propagates into the low-pressure chamber as illustrated schematically in Fig. 7.22.

The pressure associated with the shock wave (the dynamic calibration pressure p_c), with air as the gas in the shock tube, is given by the expression:

$$p_c = p_h\left(\frac{5}{6} - \frac{v}{c}\right) \tag{7.49}$$

where p_h is the static pressure in the high-pressure chamber; v is the velocity of the shock wave in the low-pressure chamber and c is the velocity of sound at the static pressure p_h in the low-pressure chamber.

The velocity v of the shock wave is determined by placing a number of pressure transducers along the length of the low-pressure chamber and measuring the time of arrival of the shock front at these positions. With a shock tube, it is possible to apply a sharp-fronted pressure pulse to a transducer so that its dynamic response can be characterized.

7.9 SUMMARY

A wide variety of transducers are commercially available for measuring load, torque and pressure. These transducers incorporate an elastic member and a sensor to convert the deformation of the elastic member into an electrical signal. Accuracies of 0.1 to 0.2% are usually achieved.

Most load cells use strain gages as the sensor; however, for static measurements, where long-term stability is important, the linear variable-differential transformer sensors are more suitable. For dynamic measurements, where a very high natural frequency is required, piezoelectric sensors are recommended. Load cells are covered in sufficient detail in Section 7.2 to give the reader adequate background to design special-purpose transducers and to thoroughly understand the sensitivities that can be achieved with many of the commonly employed elastic elements. It should be noted, however, that it is usually less expensive to buy a transducer than to build one, and the reader is encouraged to design and fabricate transducers only in those instances when it is not possible to purchase one with suitable characteristics.

Torque cells are very similar to load cells. Strain gages are the most common sensors and a simple circular shaft is the most common elastic member. The most significant difference between load and torque measurements arises when torque measurements must be made on a rotating shaft. In these measurements, either slip rings or telemetry must be used to transmit the signal from the rotating member to a stationary instrumentation station. Slip rings are usually preferred if the end of the shaft is accessible for mounting of the slip-ring assembly. If the shaft ends are not accessible, telemetry is usually employed for signal transmission.

Pressure transducers are available in a wide variety of designs and capacities. The diaphragm type pressure transducer, with electrical resistance strain-gage sensors, is probably the most common type because of ease in manufacturing. Selection of a pressure transducer for a given application is usually made on the basis of stability and frequency response. For long-term stability, transducers with linear variable-differential transformer (LVDT) sensors are usually preferred. For quasi-static and medium-frequency measurements, the diaphragm-type pressure transducer with strain-gage sensors has advantages. For extremely high-frequency measurements, transducers with piezoelectric sensors are used.

Considerable care must be exercised in all dynamic measurements to ensure that the desired quantities are recorded with the required accuracy. The capability of a transducer to record a dynamic signal depends primarily upon its natural frequency, because its damping is very small. Error increases in proportion to the frequency ratio ω/ω_n; hence piezoelectric and piezoresistive sensors with natural frequencies of 100 kHz have significant advantages.

The form of the dynamic signal is important. The errors occurring in measuring a terminated-ramp function and a periodic-input function are:

For the terminated ramp input:

$$\mathcal{E} = \frac{2}{\omega_n t_0} \tag{7.40}$$

For the sinusoidal input:

$$\mathcal{E} = \frac{A - F_0}{F_0} = \frac{(\omega/\omega_n)^2}{1 - (\omega/\omega_n)^2} \tag{7.47}$$

Periodic transducer calibration and complete system calibration must be performed to ensure continued satisfactory performance. Calibration must be regarded as the most important step in the measurement process.

REFERENCES

1. Beckwith, T. G., R. D. Marangoni and J. H. Lienhard: <u>Mechanical Measurements</u>, 6th Ed. Prentice Hall , Upper Saddle, NJ, 2007.
2. Doeblin, E. O.: Measurement Systems, Application and Design, International Edition, Tata, McGraw-Hill, New York, 2004.
3. Shukla, A and J. W. Dally: <u>Experimental Solid Mechanics</u>, College House Enterprises, Knoxville, TN, 2010.
4. Holman, J. P.: <u>Experimental Methods for Engineers</u>, 8th Ed., McGraw-Hill, 2011.
5. Dyer, S. A. <u>Survey of Instrumentation and Measurement</u>, John Wiley & Sons, New York, 2001.
6. Klaassen, K. B. and S Gee, <u>Electronic Measurement and Instrumentation</u>, Cambridge University Press, New York, 1996.
7. Wheeler, A. J., A. R. Ganji, <u>Introduction to Engineering Experimentation</u>, Prentice Hall, Englewood Cliffs, NJ, 2009.
8. Figliola, R. S., D. E. Beasley, <u>Theory and Design for Mechanical Measurements</u>, 5th Edition, John Wiley & Sons, New York, 2011.
9. Tandeske, D., <u>Pressure Sensors: Selection and Application</u>, Dekker, New York, 1991.

EXERCISES

7.1 Write an engineering brief describing:
    (a) A force transducer
    (b) A torque transducer
    (c) A pressure transducer

7.2 List the different types of sensors used in fabricating the transducers listed in Exercise 7.1.

7.3 Prepare a graph showing the sensitivity of a steel link type load cell-bridge combination. (E = 29,000 ksi and $v = 0.29$) Use $S_g = 2$ and $V_s = 10$ V. Let the cross-sectional area A of the link vary from 0.02 in.^{2} to 20 in.^{2}

7.4 The sensitivity of the transducer of Exercise 7.3 can be increased if the input voltage V_s is increased. If each gage in the bridge can dissipate 0.5 W of power, determine the maximum sensitivity that can be achieved without endangering the strain-gage ($R_g = 350 \, \Omega$) sensors.

7.5 Determine the voltage ratio V_0/V_s for the load cell of Exercise 7.3 if the fatigue strength S_f of the elastic member is 90,000 psi.

7.6 If the load cell of Exercise 7.3 is used in a static load application, what maximum load could be placed on the transducer? What voltage ratio V_0/V_s would result?

7.7 The calibration constant of a transducer procured from a commercial supplier is listed as 2.0 mV/V. Determine the sensitivity S of the transducer if P_{max} = 100,000 lb and V_s = 10 V.

7.8 Design a beam-type load cell with variable range and sensitivity. Use aluminum (E = 10,000,000 psi, v = 0.33, and S_f = 20,000 psi) as the beam material and four electrical resistance strain gages (S_g = 2.00 and R_g = 350 Ω) as the sensors. Design the load cell to give the following sensitivities and corresponding range:

(V_0/V_s) in (mV/V)	Range (lb)
2	1,000
3	500
4	200

7.9 Show that the torque cell shown in Fig. 7.5 is insensitive to both axial load P and moments M_x and M_y.

7.10 Determine the sensitivity of a torque cell if E = 30,000,000 psi, v = 0.30, V_s = 8 V, D = 1.0 in., S_g = 2.00, and R_g = 350 Ω.

7.11 The sensitivity of the torque cell described in Exercise 7.10 can be increased if the input voltage V_s is increased. If each gage in the bridge can dissipate 0.5 W of power, determine the maximum sensitivity that can be achieved without endangering the strain-gage sensors.

7.12 Determine the sensitivity of the torque cell of Exercise 7.11 if strain gages having R_g = 1000 Ω are used in place of the 350-Ω gages.

7.13 A torque cell with a capacity of 500 ft-lb is supplied with a calibration constant of (V_0/V_s) = 4 mV/V and a recommendation that the input voltage V_s = 10 V. If the cell is used with V_s = 8 V and a measurement of V_0 yields 18 mV, determine the torque T.

7.14 Determine the sensitivity of the torque cell described in Exercise 7.13.

7.15 Why are at least four slip rings used to transmit the voltages associated with a torque cell on a rotating shaft?

7.16 Outline the advantages associated with the use of telemetry for data transmission from a rotating shaft.

7.17 A solid circular shaft having a diameter of 3.0 in. is rotating at 800 RPM and is transmitting 200 hp. Show how four strain gages can be used to convert the shaft itself into a torque cell. Determine the sensitivity of this shaft-torque transducer if the shaft is made of steel having E = 30,000,000 psi and v = 0.30.

7.18 Design a static pressure transducer having a 1.5-in.-diameter diaphragm fabricated using steel with a fatigue strength of 75,000 psi. Select a linear variable-differential transformer (LVDT) to use as a sensor to convert the center point deflection of the diaphragm to an output voltage V_0. The capacity of the transducer is to be 2,000 psi and linearity must be maintained within 0.3 percent. Determine the sensitivity of your transducer.

7.19 Repeat Exercise 7.18 by using a special-purpose four-element diaphragm strain gage as the sensor in place of the LVDT. Assume that for each element of the strain gage p_g = 1 W, R_g = 350 Ω and S_g = 2.00.

7.20 Determine the natural frequency of the pressure transducer of Exercise 7.18.

7.21 A cylindrical elastic element for a very-high-pressure transducer is shown in Fig. E7.21. If the capacity of the pressure transducer is to be 60,000 psi and if the fatigue strength of the steel used in fabricating the cylindrical elastic element is 80,000 psi, determine the diameters D_i and D_o.

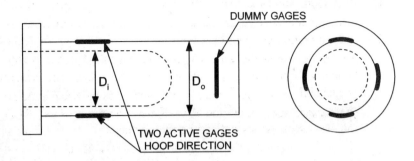

Fig. E7.21

7.22 Determine the sensitivity of the pressure transducer described in Exercise 7.21 if the strain gages used as sensors have $p_g = 0.5$ W, $S_g = 2.00$, and $R_g = 350\ \Omega$.

7.23 Explain why dummy gages are mounted at the positions shown in Fig. E7.21.

7.24 The load cell shown in Fig. 7.11 was shown to be insensitive to moments M_x and M_y. Show, in addition, that it is not sensitive to torque M_z.

7.25 A load cell with a natural frequency $f_n = 10$ kHz is to be used to measure a terminated ramp function that exhibits a rise time of 1 ms. Determine the maximum error due to the response characteristics of the transducer.

7.26 Prepare a graph showing the maximum error of a load cell with a natural frequency of 20 kHz as a function of rise time if the loading function is a terminated ramp.

7.27 A transducer having a natural frequency ω_n will be used to monitor a sinusoidal forcing function having a frequency ω. Determine the error if ω/ω_n equals:

      (a) 0.05   (b) 0.10   (c) 0.20   (d) 0.50

    Plot a curve showing error as a function of frequency ratio ω/ω_n.

7.28 Derive the response equation for a transducer with $d = 0$ if the input function is a ramp that can be expressed as $F(t) = \dot{F}_0\, t$.

7.29 Interpret the results of Exercise 7.28 and determine the magnitude of any error that may result.

7.30 Derive the response equation for a transducer with damping ($d \neq 0$) if the input is an impulse I_0 as shown in Fig. E7.30.

7.31 Use the results of Exercise 7.30 to show the response of the transducer if:

      (a) 0.01   (b) 0.10   (c) 0.20   (d) 0.50   (e) 0.70

7.32 Write an engineering brief outlining the factors producing errors in transducers.

7.33 Write a specification describing a calibration procedure for static application of:

    (a) Pressure transducers
    (b) Load cells
    (c) Torque cells.

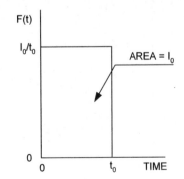

Fig. E7.30

EXERCISES AND SOLUTIONS

Exercise 7.4

$$p_g = v_g i_g = (v_s/2)(v_s/2R_g)$$

Therefore: $\quad v_s = 2\sqrt{p_g R_g} = 2\sqrt{0.5(350)} \doteq 26.5 \text{ V}$

From Eq. (7.4):

$$S = \frac{S_g(1 + \nu)v_s}{2AE} = \frac{2(1 + 0.29)(26.5)}{2(A)(29,000,000)} = \frac{1.179(10^{-6})}{A}$$

A (in.^{2})	S (μV/lb)
0.02	58.939
0.05	23.576
0.10	11.790
0.50	2.358
1.00	1.179
5.00	0.236
10.00	0.118
20.00	0.059

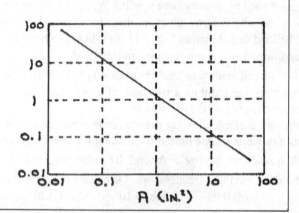

Exercise 7.10

From Eq. (7.19):

$$S = \frac{16(1 + \nu)S_g v_s}{\pi D^3 E} = \frac{16(1 + 0.30)(2.00)(8)}{\pi(1)^3(30,000,000)}$$

$$= 3.53(10^{-6}) \text{ V/(in.-lb)} = 3.53 \ \mu\text{V/(in-lb)}$$

Exercise 7.14

From Eq. (7.19):

$$S = \frac{16(1 + \nu)S_g v_s}{\pi D^3 E} = Kv_s = = \frac{v_o}{T}$$

$$\left(\frac{v_o}{v_s}\right)^* = KT_{max}$$

Therefore, $\quad K = \dfrac{(v_o/v_s)^*}{T_{max}} = \dfrac{4(10^{-3})}{500} = 8.0(10^{-6}) \ \text{(V/V)/(ft-lb)}$

$$S = Kv_s = 8.0(10^{-6})(10) = 80(10^{-6}) \text{ V/(ft-lb)} = 80 \ \mu\text{V/(ft-lb)}$$

Exercise 7.17

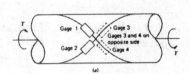 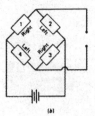

Mount four gages on the shaft and connect them into a Wheatstone bridge as shown above.

$$T = \frac{33000 \text{ hp}}{2\pi N} = \frac{33000(200)}{2\pi(800)} = 1313 \text{ ft-lb}$$

$$\tau = \frac{T\,R}{J} = \frac{1313(12)(1.5)}{(\pi/2)(1.5)^4} = 2972 \text{ psi (elastic)}$$

With $S_g = 2.00$, $R_g = 120$ Ω, and $v_s = 10$ V:

From Eq. (7.19):

$$S = \frac{16(1 + \nu)S_g v_s}{\pi D^3 E} = \frac{16(1 + 0.30)(2.00)(10)}{\pi(3)^3(30,000,000)}$$

$$= 0.163(10^{-6}) \text{ V/(in.-lb)}$$

$$= 0.163 \text{ }\mu\text{V/(in-lb)}$$

Exercise 7.21

For a thick-walled cylinder under internal pressure:

$$\sigma_r = \frac{R_i^2\, p}{R_o^2 - R_i^2}\left(1 - \frac{R_o^2}{r^2}\right) \qquad \sigma_\theta = \frac{R_i^2\, p}{R_o^2 - R_i^2}\left(1 + \frac{R_o^2}{r^2}\right) \qquad \sigma_a = \frac{R_i^2\, p}{R_o^2 - R_i^2}$$

For $\sigma_{max} = 80,000$ psi and $p = 60,000$ psi:

At $r = R_i$:

$$\sigma_{max} = \sigma_\theta = \frac{R_i^2\, p}{R_o^2 - R_i^2}\left(1 + \frac{R_o^2}{R_i^2}\right) = \frac{R_o^2 + R_i^2}{R_o^2 - R_i^2}\, p = \frac{(R_o/R_i)^2 + 1}{(R_o/R_i)^2 - 1}\, p$$

Thus:

$$\frac{(R_o/R_i)^2 + 1}{(R_o/R_i)^2 - 1} = \frac{\sigma_{max}}{p} = \frac{80000}{60000} = 1.3333$$

which yields $\quad (R_o/R_i)^2 = 7.00 \qquad$ or $\qquad R_o/R_i = D_o/D_i = 2.646$

Therefore, use: $\qquad D_o = 2.646$ in. $\qquad$ and $\qquad D_i = 1.000$ in.

Exercise 7.26

From Eq. (7.40):

With f = 20 kHz:

$$\varepsilon_{max} = \frac{2.0}{\omega_n t_o} = \frac{2.0}{2\pi f_n t_o} = \frac{2.0}{2\pi (20)(10^3) t_0} = \frac{15.92(10^{-6})}{t_0}$$

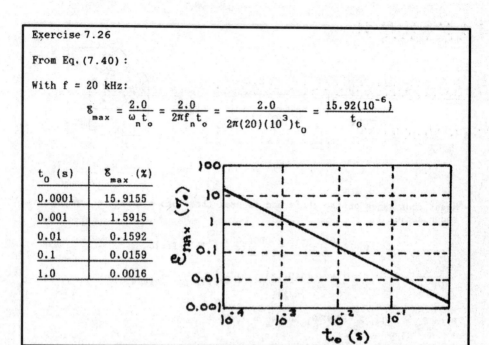

t_0 (s)	ε_{max} (%)
0.0001	15.9155
0.001	1.5915
0.01	0.1592
0.1	0.0159
1.0	0.0016

Exercise 7.31

From Exercise 7.30:

$$x = \frac{F_o}{k}\left[1 - \frac{e^{-d\omega_n t}}{\sqrt{1-d^2}}\cos\left(\omega_n\sqrt{1-d^2} - \phi\right)\right]$$

where

$$\tan\phi = \frac{d}{\sqrt{1-d^2}}$$

d	$\sqrt{1-d^2}$	$1/\sqrt{1-d^2}$	$\phi°$	ϕ rad
0	1	1	0	1
0.01	0.9999	1.0001	0.57	0.0032π
0.10	0.9950	1.0050	5.74	0.0319π
0.20	0.9798	1.0206	11.5	0.0639π
0.50	0.8660	1.1547	30.0	0.1667π
0.70	0.7141	1.4003	44.4	0.2467π

CHAPTER 8

TEMPERATURE MEASUREMENTS

8.1 INTRODUCTION

Temperature, unlike other quantities such as length, time or mass, is an abstract quantity that must be defined in terms of the behavior of materials as the temperature changes. Some examples of material behavior used in the measurement of temperature include change: in volume of a liquid, in length of a bar, in electrical resistance of a wire, in pressure of a gas at constant volume and in color of a lamp filament.

Several temperature scales have been developed over time to provide a suitable reference for the level of thermodynamic activity associated with temperature changes. Gabriel D. Fahrenheit in 1715 introduced the Fahrenheit scale with 180 divisions (degrees) between the freezing point ($32°$ F) and the boiling point ($212°$ F) of water. Anders Celsius in 1742 divided the same interval, between the freezing and boiling points of water, into 100 divisions and later Linnaeus set the zero value of this scale at the freezing point of water. This scale was initially known as Centigrade (reflecting the 100 divisions) but the name was changed in 1948 to Celsius in honor of Anders Celsius. Two other temperature scales are used to describe absolute temperatures where the zero value is set equal to the thermodynamic minimum. These scales are the Kelvin and Rankine scales defined by:

$$\theta_K = T_C + 273.15 \tag{8.1a}$$

$$\theta_R = T_F + 459.67 \tag{8.1b}$$

where θ_K and θ_R are absolute temperature in Kelvin and Rankine respectively.

T_C and T_F are temperatures in Celsius and Fahrenheit respectively.

Using absolute temperatures, the ideal gas law is written as:

$$p\boldsymbol{V} = R\theta \tag{8.2}$$

where p is the absolute pressure; $\boldsymbol{V}$ is the specific volume; R is the universal gas constant; θ is the absolute temperature.

Temperature is related to the kinetic energy of molecules at a localized region in a body; however, this energy cannot be measured directly and temperature is inferred. To circumvent this difficulty, the International Temperature Scale was established using the behavior of a number of materials at thermodynamic fixed points.

The International Temperature Scale is based on 17 fixed points that cover the temperature range from -270.15 °C to 1084.62 °C. Most of the 17 points correspond to an equilibrium state during a phase transformation of a specified material (see Table 8.1).

Table 8.1
Fixed Points on the International Temperature Scale

Fixed Point No.	Material	State	Temperature
1	He	Vapor	-270.15 to -268.15
2	e-H_2[a]	Triple Point[b]	-259.3467
3	e-H_2	Vapor	≈ -256.16
4	e-H_2	Vapor	≈ -252.85
5	Ne	Triple Point	-248.5939
6	O_2	Triple Point	-218.7916
7	Ar	Triple Point	-189.3442
8	Hg	Triple Point	-38.8344
9	H_2O	Triple Point	0.01
10	Ga	Melting	27.7646
11	In	Freezing	156.5985
12	Sn	Freezing	231.928
13	Zn	Freezing	419.527
14	Al	Freezing	660.323
15	Ag	Freezing	961.78
16	Au	Freezing	1064.18
17	Cu	Freezing	1084.62

a: e-H_2 Hydrogen at the equilibrium concentrations of ortho-molecular and para-molecular forms.

b: Triple point— Temperature at which the solid, liquid, and vapor phases are in equilibrium.

The fixed points associated with either melting or freezing of a material are determined at a pressure of one standard atmosphere. Between selected fixed points, the temperature is defined by the response of specified sensors with empirical equations providing for the required interpolation. Several different definitions are provided in the International Temperature Scale for very low temperatures (approaching absolute zero). At these temperatures, a helium gas thermometer is employed to measure pressure, and the temperature is determined from temperature-pressure relations. Between the triple point of e-H_2 (13.8033 K) and the freezing point of Ag (961.78 °C), the temperature is defined with a platinum resistance thermometer. The platinum resistance thermometers are calibrated at specified fixed points with carefully defined interpolation equations. Above the freezing point of Ag, the temperature is defined using optical pyrometers to measure radiation and Planck's law to convert radiation to temperature.

8.2 EXPANSION METHODS FOR MEASURING TEMPERATURE

When materials are subjected to temperature changes ($\Delta T = T - T_0$), they expand or contract according to:

$$\Delta L = \alpha(L \, \Delta T) \tag{8.3}$$

where ΔL is the change in length; L_0 is the length at the reference temperature T_0 and α is the temperature coefficient of expansion.

The temperature coefficient of expansion α, of the order of 20×10^{-6} °C, is too small to permit an easy measurement of ΔL for most materials. This fact usually precludes the use of Eq. (8.3) to determine the temperature T directly from length change ΔL measurements.

Expansion methods are employed to measure temperature, but the approach is less direct than that indicated by Eq. (8.3). The liquid-in-glass thermometer consists of a glass capillary tube with a bulb containing a volume of liquid (usually Hg). When the temperature changes, the volume of the liquid increases more than the volume of the glass capillary and its bulb. This differential change in volume causes the liquid to extend in the capillary tube. A scale marked on the capillary is used to convert the extension of the fluid in the tube to the temperature measurement.

The liquid-in-glass thermometer is an accurate device ($\pm 0.2°$ C to $2°$ C) depending on the design of the thermometer and the procedures used to measure the temperature. However, it suffers from two severe disadvantages. First, the output requires an operator for read-out and the thermometer cannot be used in a closed-loop control system. Second, the time required to reach the equilibrium temperature is excessive for many practical applications. For this reason, the common thermometer used by a physician to measure a patient's temperature has been replaced with a resistance detector that responds immediately with a digital readout.

A second temperature measurement technique, based on differential expansion, is the bimetallic-strip thermometer. The principle of operation of the bimetallic-strip thermometer is illustrated in Fig. 8.1. Strips of two different metals are welded together to form a laminated-beam. The beam is straight when its temperature T is the same as the welding temperature T_W. When the temperature of the beam changes, the two metals expand (or contract) by different amounts, because the expansion coefficients of the two metals are different ($\alpha_1 \neq \alpha_2$). This differential expansion between the two layers causes the beam to deform into a segment of a circular arc. The radius of curvature ρ of the circular arc is:

$$\rho = \frac{\left[3\left(1+r_h\right)^2 + \left(1+r_h r_E\right)\left(r_E^2 - \frac{1}{r_h r_E} \right) \right] h}{6(\alpha_1 - \alpha_2)(1+r_h)^2 \Delta T}$$

(8.4)

where $r_h = h_2/h_1$ is the thickness ratio and $r_E = E_2/E_1$ is the modulus ratio

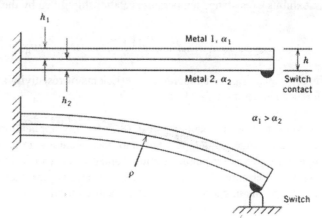

Fig. 8.1 Deflection of a bimetallic-strip thermometer.
(a) Straight beam when $T = T_W$.
(b) Curved beam when $T > T_W$.

The sensitivity of the bimetallic strip thermometer is maximized by minimizing the radius of curvature ρ for a given temperature change ΔT. Minimization is accomplished by reducing the thickness h and maximizing ($\alpha_1 - \alpha_2$). Two common materials used in constructing the strips are stainless steel with $\alpha_1 = 16 \times 10^{-6}$/°C, and Invar with $\alpha_2 = 0.02 \times 10^{-6}$/°C

The bimetallic strip is very useful in constructing thermostats used in controlling temperatures. In this application, the bimetallic strip carries one of the contacts for a switch as shown in Fig. 8.1b. When $(T - T_W)$ is sufficient, the beam element rotates and closes the switch, which activates either a heating or cooling system so as to bring the temperature T in close correspondence with T_W.

In many instances, the throw of a straight beam element is not sufficient to activate switches subjected to small ΔT_S. To enhance the sensitivity of the switch, the metallic difference strips are often formed into larger spiral or helical structures, where the increased length of the bimetallic element increases the distance moved by the active switch contact.

8.3 RESISTANCE THERMOMETERS

Resistance thermometers consist of a sensor element that exhibits a change in resistance with a change in temperature, a signal conditioning circuit that converts the resistance change to an output voltage, and appropriate instrumentation to record and display the output voltage. Two different types of sensors are normally employed: resistance temperature detectors (RTDs) and thermistors.

Resistance temperature detectors are resistive grids formed of materials such as platinum, nickel, or a nickel-copper alloy known commercially as Balco[1]. These materials exhibit a positive coefficient of resistivity. They are used in RTDs because they are stable and provide reproducible responses to temperature over long periods of time.

Thermistors are fabricated from semiconducting materials such as oxides of manganese, nickel or cobalt. These semiconducting materials, formed into the shape of small beads by sintering, exhibit a high negative coefficient of resistivity. In some special applications, where very-high accuracy is required, doped silicon or germanium is used as the thermistor material.

The equations governing the response of RTDs and thermistors to a temperature change and the circuits used to condition their outputs are different; therefore, they will be treated separately in the following subsections.

8.3.1 Resistance Temperature Detectors (RTDs)

One design of a RTD consists of a wire coil sensor with a framework for support, a sheath for protection, a linearizing circuit, a Wheatstone bridge and a VDM. The sensor is a resistive element that exhibits a resistance-temperature relationship given by the expression:

$$R = R_0\left(1 + \gamma_1 T + \gamma_2 T^2 + \ldots\ldots \gamma_n\right) \tag{8.5}$$

Where $\gamma_1, \gamma_2, \ldots \gamma_n$, are temperature coefficients of resistivity and R_0 is the resistance of the sensor at a reference temperature $T_0 = 0$ °C.

The number of terms retained in Eq. (8.5) for any application depends upon the material used in the sensor, the range of temperature and the accuracy required in the measurement. Resistance-temperature curves for platinum, nickel and copper, which illustrate typical nonlinearities in resistance R with temperature T for each of these materials, are shown in Fig. 8.2. For a limited range of temperature, the linear form of Eq. (8.5) is often used.

$$\frac{\Delta R}{R_0} = \gamma_1\left(T - T_0\right) \tag{8.6}$$

---

[1] Balco is a trade name for a product of the W.B. Driver Co.

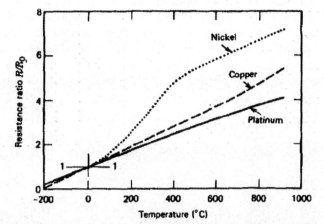

Fig. 8.2 Resistance-temperature curves for nickel, copper and platinum.

When the error due to neglecting nonlinear terms becomes excessive, either linearizing circuits can be used to compensate for the nonlinearities or additional terms can be retained from Eq. (8.5) to relate the measured ΔR to the unknown temperature T. Retaining the temperature coefficients γ_1 and γ_2 from Eq. (8.5) yields the second-order relationship.

$$\frac{\Delta R}{R_0} = \gamma_1(T - T_0) + \gamma_2(T - T_0)^2 \qquad (8.7)$$

Equation (8.7) is more cumbersome to employ, but it provides more accurate results over a wider temperature range.

Fig. 8.3 Wire wound and thin film RTD temperature sensors.

Sensing elements are available in a wide variety of forms. Two different types of RTD sensors are shown in Fig. 8.3. The illustration on the left is a thin film sensor sandwiched between plastic films, which serves to support the thin metallic film. The sensor on the right is fabricated from a high- purity (99.99%) platinum wire, which is wound about a ceramic core and hermetically sealed in a ceramic capsule.

Platinum is the superior material for precision thermometry. It resists contamination and corrosion and its mechanical and electrical properties are stable over long periods of time. The platinum wire coils are stress relieved after winding, immobilized against strain and artificially aged during fabrication to provide for long-term stability. Drift is usually less than 0.1 °C when the sensor is used at its upper temperature limit. The sensing element is usually protected by a sheath fabricated from stainless steel, glass or a ceramic. These sheaths are pressure tight to protect the sensing element from the corrosive effects of both moisture and the process medium. Lead wires from the sensor exit from the sheath through a specially designed seal. The method of sealing between the sheath and the lead wires depends on the upper temperature limit of the sensor. Epoxy cements are used for the low-temperature range (< 260 °C), while glass and ceramic cements are used for the high-temperature range (> 260 °C). Because the temperature at the sheath exit is usually much lower than the process temperature being monitored, lead wires insulated with Teflon or impregnated fiberglass are often suitable for use with process temperatures as high as 750 °C.

Immersion type transducers are inserted in a media to measure fluid temperatures. The response time in this application is relatively long (between 1 and 5 s is required to approach 100% response), as shown in Fig. 8.4. This relatively long response time for immersion thermometers is not usually a serious concern, because the rate of change of liquid temperatures in most processes is small.

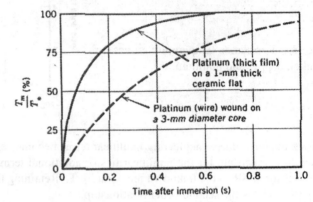

Fig. 8.4 Response time for wire-wound and thick-film platinum RTDs immersed in fluid at a temperature T_*.

Platinum RTDs are also constructed using either thick- or thin-film technologies. With both of these approaches, a film of platinum is placed on a thin, flat, ceramic substrate and encapsulated with a glass or ceramic coating. Both the thick- and thin-film methods of fabrication permit the resistance (typically 100 Ω) of the sensor to be developed on a substrate with significantly smaller volume and mass. As a result, the response time of film-type RTDs is reduced appreciably as indicated in Fig. 8.4.

A distinction must be made between the sensing element and the probe. In previous paragraphs, wire-wound and film-type sensing elements (Fig. 8.3) were described. The probe (see Fig. 8.5) is an assembly consisting of the sensing element, a sheath, a seal, lead wires and a connector. The sheath is usually a closed end tube that protects the sensing element from the corrosive effects of the media being measured. The sheath also protects the junction between rugged lead wires and the fragile wires from the sensing element.

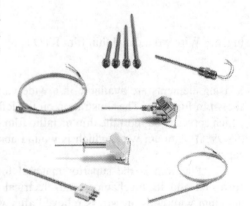

Fig. 8.5 Probes assemblies for different applications and instruments.

The probes are designed to accommodate specific applications. The probes protect the sensing element; however, they add a large mass to the sensor and markedly degrade the sensor's response time. When response time must be minimized, the probe assembly is eliminated and the sensor is exposed directly to the media.

Rapid temperature changes are common on specimen surfaces; therefore, modifications have been made in film-type RTDs to improve their response time. These modified RTD surface sensors incorporate a photoetched grid fabricated from Balco foil and they resemble strain gages. These foil sensors are available on either polyimide or glass-fiber-reinforced epoxy carriers. Similar wire grid sensors are available with either Teflon or phenolic-glass carriers or as free filaments. The sensors with carriers are bonded to the surface with an adhesive suitable for the temperature range to be encountered. The free filament sensors are normally mounted by flame spraying. The response time of a thin-film sensor compares favorably with a small thermocouple; therefore, the measurement of rapidly changing surface temperatures with a suitable RTD is possible.

An example of a foil-type, dual-grid resistance temperature detector is shown in Fig. 8.6. This construction detail shows two, thin-foil, sensing elements connected in series and laminated in a glass-fiber-reinforced, epoxy-resin matrix. One of the two sensing elements is fabricated from nickel and the other from manganin. The nickel and maganin exhibit equal but opposite nonlinearities in their resistance-temperature characteristics over a wide temperature range. By connecting the nickel and manganin in series, the nonlinear effects cancel and the composite sensor provides a linear response with temperature over the range from $-269°$ to $24°$ C. The bondable RTD is fabricated with integral printed-circuit terminals to provide for easy attachment of the lead wires.

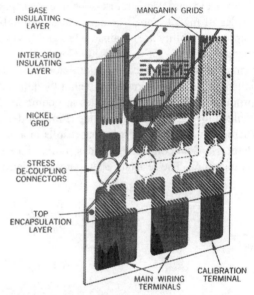

Fig. 8.6 Cryogenic temperature sensor. Courtesy of Micro-Measurements, Vishay Precision Group

8.3.2 Common Errors

Four common errors encountered when RTDs are used to measure temperature result from lead-wire effects, stability, self-heating and the sensitivity of the RTD to strain. Lead-wire errors can be minimized by making the lead wires as short as possible. The total resistance of the leads should always be less than 1% of the sensor resistance. The effect of lead-wire resistance is to increase the apparent resistance of the sensor and thus cause a zero shift (offset) and a reduction in sensitivity. The error due to temperature-induced resistance changes in the lead wires can be eliminated by using the three-lead-wire systems described in Fig. 6.12.

Stability of the sensors is usually assured by aging of the elements during the manufacturing process. Stability may become a source of error when the upper temperature limit of a sensor is exceeded either by design or accident. Anytime the upper temperature limit of a sensor is exceeded, new temperature measurements should be repeated until stable and reproducible readings are obtained. Stability can also be affected by the polymeric carrier used with bondable RTDs. These carriers have a finite life and lose their strength at temperatures in excess of 120 °C (250 °F).

Self-heating errors are produced when excitation voltages or currents are used in the signal conditioning circuits. Usually there is no reason for large excitation signals, because an RTD is a high-output sensor [a typical output is about 1 mV/(V-°C) for a platinum RTD]. Self-heating errors can be minimized by limiting the power dissipation in the RTD to less than 2 mW. In those applications, where small temperature changes are to be measured and high sensitivity is required, sensors with large surface areas are employed. Sensors with large surface areas can dissipate larger amounts of heat; therefore, higher excitation voltages are used without introducing self-heating errors.

Bonded RTD sensors resemble strain gages and, in fact, they respond to strain. Fortunately, the strain sensitivity of the sensor is small in comparison to its temperature sensitivity. A bonded RTD with a nickel sensor exhibits an apparent temperature change of 1.7 °C (3 °F) when subjected to an axial tensile strain of 1,000 μm/m. The magnitude of the strain effect is such that it usually is neglected in most applications.

8.3.3 Thermistors

Thermistors are temperature-sensitive resistors fabricated from semiconducting materials, such as oxides of nickel, cobalt or manganese and sulfides of iron, aluminum or copper. Thermistors with improved stability are obtained when oxide systems of manganese-nickel, manganese-nickel-cobalt, or manganese-nickel-iron are used. Conduction is controlled by the concentration of oxygen in the oxide semiconductors. An excess or deficiency of oxygen from exact stoichiometric requirements results in lattice imperfections known as Schottky defects and Frankel defects. N-type oxide semiconductors are produced when the metal oxides are compounded with a deficiency of oxygen that results in excess ionized metal atoms in the lattice (Frankel defects). P-type oxide semiconductors are produced when there is an excess of oxygen that results in a deficiency of ionized metal atoms in the lattice (Schottky defects). Semiconducting oxides, unlike metals, exhibit a decrease in resistance with an increase in temperature. The resistance-temperature relationship for a thermistor can be expressed as:

$$\ln \frac{R}{R_0} = \beta\left(\frac{1}{\theta} - \frac{1}{\theta_0}\right)$$

or

$$R = R_0 e^{\beta(1/\theta - 1/\theta_0)}$$

(8.8)

where R is the resistance of the thermistor at temperature θ; R_0 is the resistance of the thermistor at reference temperature θ_0; β is a material constant that ranges from 3,000 K to 5,000 K; θ and θ_0 are absolute temperatures, K.

The sensitivity S of a thermistor is obtained from Eq. (8.8) as:

$$S = \frac{\Delta R/R}{\Delta T} = -\frac{\beta}{\theta^2}$$

(8.9)

For β = 4,000 °K and θ = 298 °K, the sensitivity S equals −0.045/ °K, which is more than an order of magnitude higher than the sensitivity of a platinum resistance thermometer (S = + 0.0035/ °K). The very-high sensitivity of thermistors results in a large output signal, good accuracy and resolution. For example, a typical thermistor with R_0 = 2,000 Ω and S = − 0.04/ °K exhibits a response $\Delta R/\Delta T$ = 80 Ω/ °K. This very large resistance change can be converted to a voltage with a simple two wire potentiometric circuit. The voltage change associated with a temperature change as small as 0.0005 °K can be easily and accurately monitored.

Equation (8.8) indicates that the resistance R of a thermistor decreases exponentially with an increase in temperature. Typical response curves for a family of thermistors are shown in Fig. 8.7. Because the output from the thermistor is nonlinear, precise determinations of temperature must be made by measuring the resistance R and using a calibration table.

Thermistors are produced by mixing two or more semiconducting oxide powders with a binder to form a slurry. Small drops (beads) of the slurry are formed over the lead wires, dried and fired in a sintering furnace. During sintering, the metallic oxides shrink and bond to the lead wires, forming an excellent electrical connection. The beads are then hermetically sealed by encapsulating the beads with glass. The glass coating improves stability of the thermistor by eliminating water absorption into the metallic oxide. Thermistor beads, such as those shown in Fig. 8.8, are available in diameters that range from 0.005 in. (0.125 mm) to 0.060 in. (1.5 mm). Thermistors are also produced in the form of disks, wafers, flakes, rods and washers to provide sensors of the size and shape required for a wide variety of applications.

A large variety of thermistors are commercially available with resistances (at the reference temperature T_0) that vary from a few ohms to several meg-ohms. When a thermistor is selected for a particular application, the minimum resistance at high temperature must be sufficient to avoid overloading of the readout device. Similarly, the maximum resistance at low temperature must not be so high that noise becomes a serious problem. Thermistors having a resistance $R_0 = 3,000$ Ω that varies from a low of about 2,000 Ω to a high of 5,000 Ω over the temperature range are commonly employed.

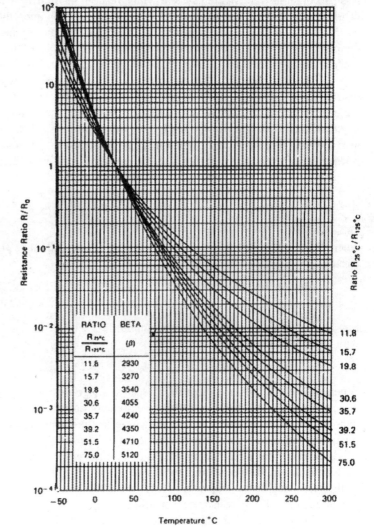

Fig. 8.7 Resistance as a function of temperature for different thermistors.

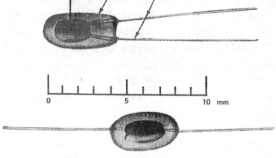

Fig. 8.8 Bead type thermistors encapsulated in glass for stability.

Thermistors can be used to measure temperatures from a few degrees above absolute zero to about 315 °C (600 °F). Thermistors are used at higher temperatures; however, their stability begins to degrade above this limit. The range of a thermistor is usually limited to about 100 °C (180 °F), particularly, if it is part of an instrumentation system with a readout instrument that has been compensated to provide nearly linear output. The accuracy of thermistors depends upon the techniques employed to measure ΔR/R and to calibrate the sensor. With proper techniques and glass encapsulated thermistors, temperatures of 125 °C can be measured with an accuracy of 0.01 °C. Long-term drift data indicate that stabilities better than 0.003 °C/year, when cycled between 20 and 125 °C, can be achieved.

The accuracy of the measurement of temperature with a thermistor depends on the instrumentation system employed and the method used to account for the nonlinear response. Because the change in resistance is so large (ΔR/ΔT = 80 Ω/°K), a common multimeter (4 or 4 1/2 digits) can be employed to measure R within ±1 Ω, as indicated in Fig. 8.9. No bridge or potentiometer circuits are required. If the readings of resistance are processed in a data acquisition system with a computing microprocessor, the temperature can be approximated very closely by using the Steinhart-Hart relation:

$$\frac{1}{\theta} = A + B \ln R_T + C\left(\ln R_T\right)^3 \tag{8.10}$$

where θ is the absolute temperature in (°K); A, B and C are coefficients determined from calibration curves similar to those shown in Fig. 8.7.

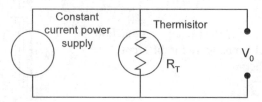

Fig. 8.9 Constant current potentiometer circuit with DVM used to measure R_T directly.

When the data points are selected to span a range near the center of the operating range of the transistor (about 100 °C), Eq. (8.10) is extremely accurate. When thermistors are used to measure temperature, errors resulting from lead-wire effect are usually small enough to be neglected even for relatively long lead wires. The sensitivity of a thermistor is high; therefore, the change in resistance ΔR_T resulting from a temperature change is much greater than the small change in resistance of the lead wires due to the temperature variation. Also, the resistance of the thermistor is very large relative to the resistance of the lead wires ($R_T/R_L \approx 1,000$); consequently, any reduction in sensitivity of the sensor due to lead-wire resistance is negligible.

Errors may occur as a result of self-heating because the power ($P = I^2 R_T$) dissipated in the thermistor will heat it above its ambient temperature. Recommended practice limits the current flow through the thermistor to a value such that the temperature rise due to the power dissipation is smaller than the precision to which the temperature is to be measured. A typical thermistor with $R_T = 5,000\ \Omega$ is capable of dissipating 1 mW with an increase in temperature of 1 °C. This corresponds to a self heating factor $F_{sh} = 1$ °C/mW. Thus, if the temperature is to be determined with an accuracy of 0.5 °C, the power to be dissipated should be limited to less than 0.5 mW. This limitation establishes a minimum value for the current I at:

$$I = \sqrt{\frac{P}{R_T}} = \sqrt{\frac{0.0005}{5000}} = 316\ \mu A$$

In this example, it is prudent to limit the current I to approximately 100 μA. Adequate response can be obtained, even at these low currents, because the sensitivity of a thermistor is so very high. Precise measurements of ΔV_0 can be made easily with a DMV.

8.4 THERMOCOUPLES

A thermocouple is a very simple temperature sensor that consists of two dissimilar materials in thermal contact. The thermal contact, called a junction, may be made by twisting wires together or by welding, soldering or brazing the two wires together. The junctions may also be formed by pressing the two materials together with sufficient pressure. An example of a single thermocouple junction is shown in Fig. 8.10a.

The operation of a thermocouple is based on a combination of thermo-electric effects that produce a small open circuit voltage when two thermocouple junctions are maintained at different temperatures. A diagram of the dual junction thermocouple circuit is shown in Fig. 8.10b where junctions J_1 and J_2 are maintained at temperatures T_1 and T_2 respectively. The thermoelectric voltage V_0 is a non-linear function of temperature which can be represented by an empirical equation having the form:

$$V_0 = C_1(T_1 - T_2) + C_2(T_1^2 - T_2^2) \tag{8.11}$$

where C_1 and C_2 are thermoelectric constants that depend on the materials and T_1 and T_2 are junction temperatures.

Fig. 8.10 Thermocouple sensor and circuit for measuring the temperature difference $T_1 - T_2$.
   (a) Single junction; (b) Dual junction

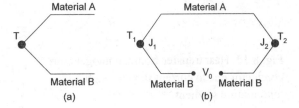

The generation of the open circuit voltage indicated by Eq. (8.11) is due to the Seebeck effect. The Seebeck effect is produced by diffusion of electrons across the interface between the two materials. The electric potential of the material accepting electrons becomes negative at the interface zone, while the potential of the material providing the electrons becomes positive. Thus, an electric field is established by the flow of electrons across this interface. When this electric field becomes sufficient to balance the diffusion forces, a state of equilibrium with respect to electron migration is established. Because the magnitude of the diffusion force is controlled by the temperature of the thermocouple junction, the electric potential developed at the junction provides a measure of the temperature.

In addition to the Seebeck effect, two other basic thermoelectric effects occur in a thermocouple circuit. These are the Peltier and the Thompson effects after the scientists that first observed and explained the thermoelectric phenomena.

The Peltier effect occurs when a current flows in the thermocouple circuit. The presence of the current I in the thermocouple circuit produces the well known self-heating effect, where the Joule heat transfer is $q = I^2R$. However, the Peltier heat transfer is in addition to the Joule heating effect. The Peltier heating is given by:

$$q_P = \pi_{AB} I \qquad (8.12)$$

where q_P is the heat transfer in watts (W) and π_{AB} is the Peltier coefficient for the A to B couple.

It should be noted that $\pi_{AB} = -\pi_{BA}$ and the Peltier coefficient depends on the direction of current flow through the junction. This fact implies that heat will transfer from the junction to the environment at junction J_1 and from the environment to the junction at junction J_2. This dual junction heat transfer, illustrated in Fig. 8.11, is the basis of a Peltier refrigerator which is a cooling device without moving parts.

Fig. 8.11 Heat transfer in and out of a pair of thermoelectric junctions due to the Peltier effect.

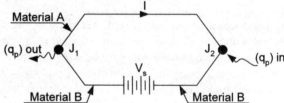

The Thompson effect is another thermoelectric interaction that affects the behavior of a thermocouple circuit. This effect is the generation or absorption of heat q_T, whenever a temperature gradient and a current exist in a conductor. The Thompson effect, illustrated in Fig. 8.12, results in a quantity of heat q_T being transferred which is given by:

$$Q_T = \sigma I(T_1 - T_2) \qquad (8.13)$$

where σ is the Thompson coefficient which depends on the conductor material.

Fig. 8.12 Heat transfer from a homogeneous conductor due to current flow through a temperature gradient.

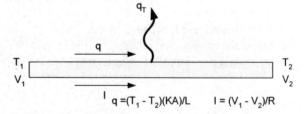

Both the Peltier and Thompson effects produce voltages that contribute to the output of a thermocouple circuit and affect the accuracy of the measurement of temperature. Both effects can be minimized by severely limiting the current I which flows through the thermocouple circuit (Fig. 8.10b) during the measurement of V_0.

The thermocouple circuit of Fig. 8.10b is used to sense an unknown temperature T_1, while junction 2 is maintained at a known reference temperature T_2. Because the reference temperature T_2 is known, it is possible to determine the unknown temperature T_1 by measuring the voltage V_0. It is clear from Eq. (8.11) that the response of a thermocouple is a nonlinear function of the temperature.

Also, experience has shown that Eq. (8.11) is not a sufficiently accurate representation of the voltage-temperature relationship to be used with confidence, when precise measurements of temperature are required. Accurate conversion of the output voltage V_0 to $(T_1 - T_2)$ is achieved either by using calibration (look up) tables or a higher order polynomial instead of Eq. (8.11). Examples of look-up tables are presented in Appendix A. It is important to note that the reference temperature is $T_2 = 0$ °C (32 °F) in these tables.

The higher order polynomials used for temperature determinations are of the form:

$$T_1 - T_2 = a_0 + a_1 V_0 + a_2 V_0^2 + \ldots\ldots + a_n V_0^n \tag{8.14}$$

where a_0, a_1, ...a_n are coefficients specified for each pair of thermocouple materials and $(T_1 - T_2)$ is the difference in junction temperature in °C. The polynomial coefficients for six different types of thermocouples are given in Appendix A.

8.4.1 Principles of Thermocouple Behavior

The practical use of thermocouples is based on six operating principles that are stated below and illustrated in Fig. 8.13.

1. A thermocouple circuit must contain at least two dissimilar materials and at least two junctions (see Fig. 8.13a).
2. The output voltage V_0 of a thermocouple circuit depends only on the difference between junction temperatures $(T_1 - T_2)$ and is independent of the temperatures elsewhere in the circuit (see Fig. 8.13b) if no current flows in the circuit.
3. If a third metal C is inserted into either leg (A or B) of a thermocouple circuit (see Fig. 8.13c), the output voltage V_0 is not affected provided the two new junctions (A/C and C/A) are maintained at the same temperature (for example, $T_i = T_j = T_3$).
4. The insertion of an intermediate metal C into junction 1 (see Fig. 8.13d) does not affect the output voltage V_0 provided the two junctions formed by insertion of the intermediate metal (A/C and C/B) are maintained at the same temperature T_1.
5. A thermocouple circuit with temperatures T_1 and T_2 produces an output voltage $(V_0)_{1-2} = f(T_1 - T_2)$, and one exposed to temperatures T_2 and T_3 produces an output voltage $(V_0)_{2-3} = f(T_2 - T_3)$. If the same circuit (see Fig. 8.13e) is exposed to temperatures T_1 and T_3, the output voltage $(V_0)_{1-3} = f(T_1 - T_3) = (V_0)_{1-2} + (V_0)_{2-3}$.
6. A thermocouple circuit fabricated from materials A and C generates an output voltage $(V_0)_{A/C}$ when exposed to temperatures T_1 and T_2, while a similar circuit fabricated from materials C and B generates an output voltage $(V_0)_{C/B}$. Furthermore, a thermocouple fabricated from materials A and B generates an output voltage $(V_0)_{A/B} = (V_0)_{A/C} + (V_0)_{C/B}$ (see Fig. 8.13f).

The six principles of thermoelectric behavior are important because they provide the basis for the design, circuitry and application of thermocouples to temperature measurements. The first principle formalizes the experimental observation that a thermocouple circuit must be fabricated with two different materials so that two junctions are formed. The output voltage V_0 (see Fig. 8.13a) has been observed to be a nonlinear function of the difference in temperature $(T_1 - T_2)$ at these two junctions. For clockwise current flow, as illustrated in Fig. 8.13a, the output voltage V_0 can be expressed as:

$$V_0 = e_{B/A} T_1 + e_{A/B} T_2 \tag{a}$$

where $e_{B/A}$ is the junction potential per unit temperature at a junction as the current flows from material B to material A; $e_{A/B}$ is the junction potential per unit temperature at a junction as the current flows from material A to material B.

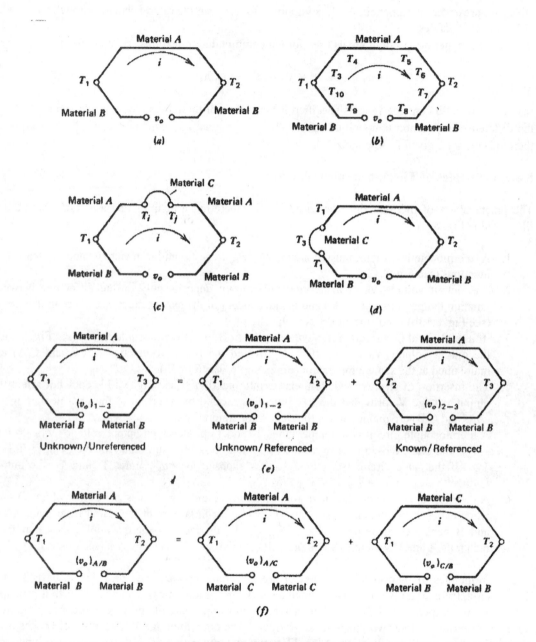

Fig. 8.13 Typical situations encountered during the use of thermocouples. (a) Basic thermocouple circuit. (b) Output depends on $(T_1 - T_2)$ only. (c) Intermediate metal in circuit. (d) Intermediate metal in junction. (e) Voltage addition from identical thermocouples at different temperatures. (f) Voltage addition from different thermocouples at identical temperatures.

Because $e_{B/A} = -e_{A/B}$, Eq. (a) can be written in its more familiar form as:

$$V_0 = e_{B/A} (T_1 - T_2) \tag{b}$$

Experiments indicate that the relationship between V_0 and the temperature difference $(T_1 - T_2)$, as expressed by Eq. (b), depends upon the two materials used to fabricate the thermocouple and is nonlinear. Because Eq. (b) is non-linear, the junction potential $e_{B/A}$ is not a constant with respect to temperature.

Thermocouple calibration tables such as those presented in Appendix A are used to relate temperature difference $(T_1 - T_2)$ to a measured output voltage V_0. Because an unknown temperature T_1 is being measured, the reference temperature T_2 must be known. The information presented in Appendix A is based on a reference temperature $T_2 = 0$ °C (32 °F). If the reference temperature T_2 is not 0 °C, but rather some other known value, such as 100 °C, it is still possible to determine T_1. However, the procedure involves application of the fifth principle of thermoelectric behavior.

The second principle indicates that the voltage output V_0 from a thermocouple circuit is not influenced by the temperature distribution along the conductors, except at points where connections are made to form junctions (see Fig. 8.13b). This principle provides assurance that the output voltage V_0 of the thermocouple circuit is independent of the length of the lead wires and the temperature distribution along their length. The output voltage V_0 is determined only by the junction temperatures.

The third principle deals with insertion of an intermediate conductor (such as copper lead wires or a voltage measuring instrument) into one of the legs of a thermocouple circuit (see Fig. 8.13c). The effect of inserting material C into the A-B-type thermocouple can be determined by writing the equation for the output voltage V_0 as:

$$V_0 = e_{B/A} T_1 + e_{A/C} T_i + e_{C/A} T_j + e_{A/B} T_2 \tag{c}$$

Because $e_{B/A} = -e_{A/B}$ and $e_{A/C} = -e_{C/A}$, Eq. (c) can be written as:

$$V_0 = e_{B/A} (T_1 - T_2) + e_{A/C} (T_i - T_j) \tag{d}$$

It should be noted, however, that temperature gradients along the length of the lead wires results in heat transfer and affects the junction temperature. Equation (d) indicates that the effect of the A/C junctions is eliminated if $T_i = T_j$. A similar analysis with the third metal C inserted in leg B of the thermocouple shows that the effect of B/C junctions is eliminated if $T_i = T_j$. This principle verifies that insertion of a third material C into the circuit will have no effect on the output voltage V_0, if the junctions formed in either leg A or leg B are maintained at the same temperature $T_i = T_j = T_3$, a junction which is formed during fabrication of a thermocouple. Such a situation occurs when junctions are formed by twisting the two thermocouple materials A and B together and soldering or brazing the connection with an intermediate metal C (see Fig. 8.13d). The influence of the presence of the intermediate metal in the junction can be evaluated by considering the expression for output voltage V_0 which can be written as:

$$V_0 = e_{B/C} T_1 + e_{C/A} T_1 + e_{A/B} T_2 \tag{e}$$

Because $e_{A/C} = e_{C/B} + e_{B/A}$ Eq. (e) reduces to:

$$V_0 = e_{B/A} (T_1 - T_2) \tag{f}$$

Equation (f) verifies that the output voltage V_0 is not affected by the presence of a third material C, which may be inserted during fabrication of the thermocouple, if the two junctions B/C and C/A are at the same temperature.

The fifth principle deals with the relationship between output voltage V_0 and the reference junction temperature. As mentioned previously, data in Appendix A are based on a reference temperature of 0 °C (32 °F). In some instances, it may be more convenient to use a different reference temperature (say boiling water at 100 °C). The effect of this different reference temperature can be accounted for by using the equivalent thermocouple system illustrated in Fig. 8.13e. The output from the equivalent system that incorporates two thermocouple circuits is:

$$(V_0)_{1-3} = f(T_1 - T_3) = (V_0)_{1-2} + (V_0)_{2-3} \qquad (8.15)$$

Use of Eq. (8.15) for the case of an arbitrary reference temperature T_3 can be illustrated by considering the example of a copper-constantan thermocouple exposed to an unknown temperature T_1. Assume that the arbitrary reference temperature T_3 is maintained at 100 °C. Also assume that an output voltage $(V_0)_{1-3} = 8.388$ mV is recorded under these conditions. The voltage $(V_0)_{2-3}$ of Eq. (8.15) can be determined from Appendix A, because it is known that $T_2 = 0$ °C and $T_3 = 100$ °C. Thus, $(V_0)_{2-3} = -(V_0)_{3-2} = -4.277$ mV. Solving Eq. (8.15) for $(V_0)_{1-2}$ yields:

$$(V_0)_{1-2} = (V_0)_{1-3} - (V_0)_{2-3} = 8.388 - (-4.277) = 12.665 \text{ mV}$$

Appendix A indicates that an output voltage $(V_0)_{1-2} = 12.665$ mV would be produced by a temperature $T_1 = 261.7$ °C. The same procedure can be used to correct for any arbitrary (but known) reference temperature.

The sixth principle illustrates the use of voltage addition (super- position) to analyze thermocouple circuits fabricated from different materials, as shown in Fig. 8.15f. The output voltage for the equivalent circuit is:

$$(V_0)_{A/B} = (V_0)_{A/C} + (V_0)_{C/B}$$

or $\qquad\qquad\qquad\qquad\qquad\qquad\qquad\qquad\qquad\qquad\qquad\qquad (8.16)$

$$(V_0)_{A/B} = (V_0)_{A/C} - (V_0)_{B/C}$$

By employing this principle, calibration tables can be developed for any pair of materials if the calibrations for the individual materials are paired with a standard thermocouple material such as platinum. For example, materials A and B, when paired with the standard material C, would provide $(V_0)_{A/C}$ and $(V_0)_{C/B} = -(V_0)_{B/C}$. The calibration for a junction formed by using materials A and B could then be determined by using Eq. (8.16). Use of this principle eliminates the need to calibrate all possible combinations of materials [for n thermoelectric materials n(n-1) calibrations are necessary]. Instead, by calibrating all n materials against the standard reference material platinum only (n-1) calibrations are required.

8.4.2 Thermoelectric Materials

The thermoelectric effect occurs whenever a thermocouple circuit is fabricated from any two dissimilar metals; therefore, the number of materials suitable for use in thermocouples is very large. In most cases, materials are selected to:

1. Provide long-term stability at the upper temperature levels.
2. Ensure compatibility with available instrumentation.
3. Minimize cost.
4. Maximize sensitivity over the range of operation.

The sensitivity of a number of materials in combination with platinum is presented in Table 8.2. The results from Table 8.2 can be used to determine the sensitivity S at 0 °C (32 °F) of a thermocouple fabricated from any two materials listed in the table. For instance, the sensitivity of a Chromel-Alumel thermocouple is determined from Eq. (8.20) as:

$$S_{Chromel/Alumel} = 25.8 - (-13.6) = 39.4 \ \mu V/°C$$

It is important to recall that the sensitivity S of a thermocouple is not constant; the output voltage V_0 is a nonlinear function of the difference in junction temperatures $(T_1 - T_2)$. Sensitivity S as a function of temperature for the seven most frequently used material pairs is listed in Table 8.3. The letters E, J, K, N, R, S and T are designated by the ANSI standards. The material pairs used in these thermocouple junctions are defined in Table 8.4.

The voltage output V_0 as a function of temperature for several popular types of thermocouples is shown in Fig. 8.14. This graphical display shows that E-type (Chromel-Constantan) thermocouples generate the largest output voltage at a given temperature; unfortunately, they have an upper temperature limit of only 1,000 °C (1832 °F). The upper limit of the temperature range is increased (but the sensitivity is decreased) to 1,260 °C (2,300 °F) with K-type (Chromel-Alumel) thermocouples, to 1,538 °C (2,800 °F) with S-type (platinum 10% rhodium-platinum) thermocouples, and to 2,800 °C (5,072 °F) with G-type (tungsten-tungsten 26% rhenium) thermocouples. The operating range of temperature, together with the span of output voltages for most of the popular types of thermocouples, is listed in Table 8.5.

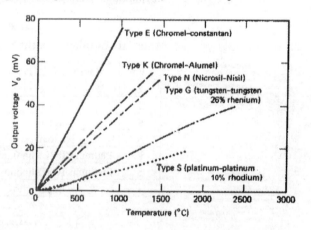

Fig. 8.14 Output voltage as a function of temperature T_1 with a reference temperature of T = 0 °C for several different typed of thermocouples.

Table 8.2
Thermoelectric Sensitivity S of Several Materials in Combination with Platinum at 0 °C (32 °F)

Material	Sensitivity μV/°C	Sensitivity μV/°F	Material	Sensitivity μV/°C	Sensitivity μV/°F
Bismuth	−72	−40	Copper	+6.5	+36.
Constantan	−35	−19.4	Gold	+6.5	+3.6
Nickel	−15	−8.3	Tungsten	+7.5	+4.2
Alumel	−13.6	−7.6	Nicrosil	+15.4	+8.6
Nisil	−10.7	−5.9	Iron	+18.5	+10.3
Platinum	0	0	Chromel	+25.8	+14.3
Mercury	+0.6	+0.3	Germanium	+300	+167
Carbon	+3	+1.7	Silicon	+440	+244
Aluminum	+3.5	+1.9	Tellurium	+500	+278
Lead	+4	+2.2	Selenium	+900	+500
Silver	+6.5	+3.6			

TABLE 8.3
Sensitivity as a Function of Temperature for Seven Different Types of Thermocouples (mV/°C)

Temperature °C	E	J	K	N	R	S	T
−200	25.1	21.9	15.3	9.9	--	--	15.7
−100	45.2	41.1	30.5	20.9	--	--	28.4
0	58.7	50.4	39.5	26.1	5.3	5.4	38.7
100	67.5	54.3	41.4	29.7	7.5	7.3	46.8
200	74.0	55.5	40.0	33.0	8.8	8.5	53.1
300	77.9	55.4	41.4	35.4	9.7	9.1	58.1
400	80.0	55.1	42.2	37.0	10.4	9.6	61.8
500	80.9	56.0	42.6	--	10.9	9.9	--
600	80.7	58.5	42.5	--	11.3	10.2	--
700	79.8	62.2	41.9	--	11.8	10.5	--
800	78.4	--	41.0	--	12.3	10.9	--
900	76.7	--	40.0	--	12.8	11.2	--
1000	74.9	--	38.9	--	13.2	11.5	--

From NBS Monographs 125 (1974) and 161 (1978).

TABLE 8.4
Materials Employed in the Standard Thermocouples

Type	Positive Material	Negative Material
E	Chromel	Constantan
J	Iron	Constantan
K	Chromel	Alumel
N	Nicrosil	Nisil
R	Platinum 13% Rhodium	Platinum
S	Platinum 10% Rhodium	Platinum
T	Copper	Constantan

TABLE 8.5
Operating Range and Voltage Span for Several Different Types of Thermocouples

Thermocouple Materials	Temperature Range		Voltage Span (mV)
	°C	°F	
Copper-Constantan	-185 to 400	-300 to 750	-5.284 to 20.850
Iron-Constantan	-185 to 870	-300 to 1,600	-7.52 to 50.05
Chromel-Alumel	-185 to 1260	-300 to 2,300	-5.51 to 51.05
Chromel-Constantan	0 to 980	32 to 1,800	0 to 75.12
Nicrosil-Nisil	-270 to 1,300	-450 to 2,372	-4.345 to 47.502
Platinum 10% Rhodium-Platinum	0 to 1,535	32 to 2,800	0 to 15.979
Platinum 13% Rhodium-Platinum	0 to 1,590	32 to 2,900	0 to 18.6366
Platinum 30% Rhodium-Platinum	38 to 1,800	100 to 3,270	0.007 to 13.499
Platinel 1813-Platinel 1503	0 to 1,300	32 to 2,372	0 to 51.1
Iridium-60% Rhodium 40% Iridium	1,400 to 1,830	2552 to 3,326	7.30 to 9.55
Tungsten 3% Rhenium-Tungsten 25% Rhenium	10 to 2,200	50 to 4,000	0.064 to 29.47
Tungsten-Tungsten 26% Rhenium	16 to 2,800	60 to 5,072	0.042 to 43.25
Tungsten 5% Rhenium-Tungsten 26% Rhenium	0 to 2,760	32 to 5,000	0 to 38.45

Long term thermal stability is an important property of a thermocouple installation if temperature is to be monitored over very long periods of time. A relatively new thermocouple, type N—nicrosil against nisil, exhibits a very high thermoelectric stability. Thermal instabilities in several of the other standard thermocouples such as the E, J, K and T occur after 100 to 1,000 hrs exposure to temperature.

The most important negative effect of thermal instabilities is the gradual and cumulative drift in the output voltage V_0 during long exposure of the thermocouple to elevated temperatures. This effect is largely due to compositional changes caused by oxidation (particularly internal oxidation). Both the nisil and nicrosil alloys have been formulated to eliminate internal oxidation and substantially reduce external oxidation.

The long term drift in the output from N, E, J, and K type thermocouples is shown as a function of time in Fig. 8.15, at a constant aging temperature of 777 °C. The thermal drift of the J thermocouple fabricated from AWG #14 wire is excessive after only 100 to 200 hrs. Increasing the wire size to AWG #8 improves the time stability of the J thermocouple, but it remains inadequate for extended applications. The type E thermocouple, while superior to the J thermocouple, also shows excessive voltage drift. Only the K and N thermocouples exhibit the stability required for measurement of temperatures up to 777 °C for at least 1,500 hrs.

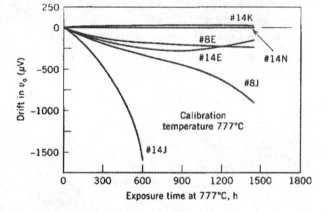

Fig. 8.15 Drift in output voltage for different types of thermocouples as a function of exposure time at a constant aging temperature of 777 °C.

The stability with exposure time of the K and N type thermocouples at higher temperatures is shown in Fig. 8.16. It is evident that the performance of the K type thermocouple degrades rapidly at temperatures exceeding 1,050 °C. However, the drift in voltage with exposure time for the N type thermocouple is less than 100 µV (about 2 °C) after 1,000 hrs at temperatures up to 1,200 °C.

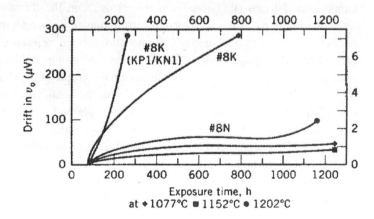

Fig. 8.16 Drift in output voltage for K and N thermocouples as a function of time at different aging temperatures.

8.4.3 Reference Junction Temperature

Because a thermocouple circuit responds to a temperature difference $(T_1 - T_2)$, it is essential that the reference junction be maintained at a constant and accurately known temperature T_2. Four common methods are used to maintain the reference temperature.

The simplest technique utilizes an ice and water bath, as illustrated in Fig. 8.17. The reference junction is immersed in a mixture of ice and water in a thermos bottle that is capped to prevent heat loss and temperature gradients. Water (sufficient only to fill the voids) must be removed and ice must be replaced periodically to maintain a constant reference temperature. Such an ice bath can maintain the water temperature (and thus the reference temperature) to within 0.1 °C (0.2 F) of the freezing point of water.

A very-high-quality reference temperature source is available that employs thermoelectric refrigeration (Peltier cooling effect). Thermocouple wells in this unit contain distilled and deionized water that is maintained at precisely 0 °C (32 °F). The outer walls of the wells are cooled by the thermoelectric refrigeration elements until freezing of the water in the wells begins. The increase in volume of the water as it begins to freeze on the walls of the wells expands a bellows that contacts a microswitch and deactivates the refrigeration elements. The cyclic freezing and thawing of the ice on the walls of the wells accurately maintains the temperature of the wells at 0 °C (32 °F). This automatic precise control of temperature can be maintained over extended periods of time.

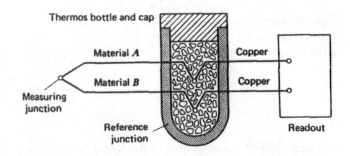

Fig. 8.17 An ice-bath methods for maintaining a reference temperature of 0 °C (32 °F)

The electrical-bridge method, illustrated in Fig. 8.18, is usually used with potentiometric, strip-chart, recording devices to provide automatic compensation for reference junctions that are free to follow ambient temperature conditions. This method incorporates a Wheatstone bridge, with a resistance temperature detector (RTD) as the active element, in the thermocouple circuit. The RTD and the reference junctions of the thermocouple are mounted on a reference block that follows the ambient temperature. When the ambient temperature of the reference block varies, the RTD changes resistance. The bridge is designed to produce an output voltage that is equal but opposite to the voltage developed in the thermocouple circuit as a result of the changes in temperature T_2 from 32 °F (0 °C). Thus, the electrical-bridge method automatically compensates for changing ambient conditions. This method is widely used with potentiometric recording devices that are used to display one or more temperatures over long periods of time, when it is not practical to maintain an ice bath.

A different type of reference temperature control is obtained by using an oven that maintains a fixed temperature higher than any expected ambient temperature. The system is practical because heating is more easily obtained than cooling; however, the thermoelectric voltage-temperature tables must be corrected for the higher reference junction temperature.

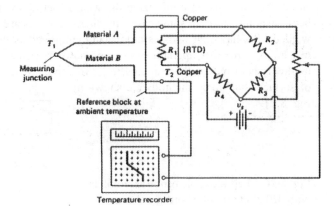

Fig. 8.18 The electrical bridge method of compensation for changes in the reference temperature.

8.4.4 Fabrication and Installation Procedures

Proper installation of a thermocouple may involve fabrication of the junction, selection of the lead wires (diameter and insulation) and placement of the thermocouple on the surface of the component or in the fluid at the point, where the temperature is to be measured. The recommended procedure for forming a thermocouple junction, illustrated in Fig. 8.19, consists of butting the two wires together and fastening by welding, brazing or soldering to form a small bead of material around the junction. The wire diameter used in the fabrication of the thermocouple depends upon the dynamic response required of the thermocouple and the hostility of the environment in which the thermocouple must operate. When temperature fluctuations are rapid, the wire diameter must be small and any protective sheathing must be eliminated to minimize thermal lag. Wire diameter as small as 0.0125 mm (0.0005 in.) is routinely employed when response time becomes an important factor in the temperature measurement. On the other hand, thermocouples are often required to operate over long periods of time at high temperatures in either reducing or oxidizing atmospheres. In these applications, heavy-gage wires are used with relatively large-diameter junctions so that part of the junction can be sacrificed to extend the period of stable operation.

Thermocouples are widely used to measure fluid temperatures in tanks, pipes, boilers, reactors, etc. The thermocouple is usually protected from the fluid by metal wells or by mounting the thermocouple in a metal probe that is insulated with swaged and compacted ceramic powders as indicated in Fig. 8.20. The exposed thermocouple junction (Fig. 8.20a) is used to measure the temperature of non-corrosive gases where rapid response of the sensor is necessary. The ungrounded junction (Fig. 8.20b) is used in corrosive fluids, where the temperature is changing slowly with time. The thermocouple is totally insulated from the probe tube with ceramic powder (usually Mg0). The grounded junction (Fig. 8.20c) is used in corrosive fluids and gases where moderate response time is required.

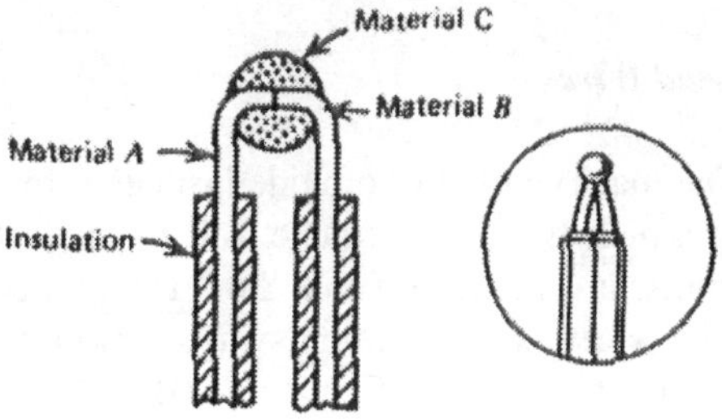

Fig. 8.19 Fabrication details for a thermocouple junction.

Surface installations are usually made by welding or brazing the thermocouple to the surface. When possible, the thermocouple is embedded in a shallow, small-diameter hole prior to welding. Care should be exercised in minimizing the weld material and in maintaining the geometry of the surface being instrumented. In some cases, the thermocouples are adhesively bonded to the surface instead of welded. Special filler epoxies are usually employed as the adhesive because they can be cured in a few hours at room temperature. Ceramic powders (usually Al_2O_3) are used as fillers for the epoxy to markedly improve the thermal coefficient of conductivity $k = 8$ (Btu-in.)/(hr-ft^2-°F). Some examples of surface attachment methods are shown in Fig. 8.21.

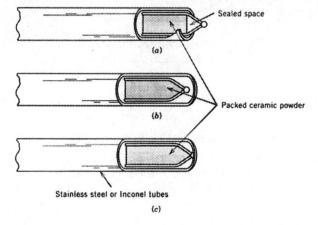

Fig. 8.20 Thermocouple probe assemblies with different junction configurations.
(a) Exposed junction.
(b) Ungrounded junction.
(c) Grounded junction.

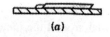

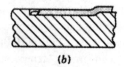

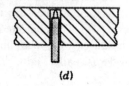

Fig. 8.21 Examples of surface attachment techniques for thermocouples.
    a. Directly on the surface
    b. In a groove
    c. In a chordal hole in a tube wall.
    d. From the rear of a plate.

Lead Wires

The material used to provide insulation for the lead wires is determined by the maximum temperature to which the thermocouple will be subjected. Types of insulation, together with their temperature limits, are listed in Table 8.6. For higher-temperature applications, thermocouple wire is available with a ceramic insulation swaged into a metal sheath. For extremely high temperature applications (2,315 °C or 4,200 °F), ceramic (Beryllia) tubes are often used to insulate the wires.

      In some installations, it is necessary to separate the measuring and the reference junction by an appreciable distance. In these instances, extension wires are inserted between the measuring junction and the reference junction. The extension wires are fabricated from the same materials as the thermocouple junctions and hence they will exhibit approximately the same thermoelectric properties. The primary advantage of using extension wires is improvement in the properties of the wire. For example, stranded wire of smaller diameter with PVC insulation can be used for the extension wires to provide a lower cost sensing system that is easier to install. The changes in diameter and insulation are possible because the extension wire is removed from the temperature T_1 and is at or near room temperature.

TABLE 8.6
Characteristics of Thermocouple-Wire Insulation

Material	Abrasion Resistance	Flexibility	Temperature (°C) Max.	Temperature (°C) Min.
Polyvinyl chloride	Good	Excellent	105	−40
Polyethylene	Good	Excellent	75	−75
Nylon	Excellent	Good	150	−55
Teflon-FEP	Excellent	Good	200	−200
Teflon-PFA	Excellent	Good	260	−267
Silicon Rubber	Fair	Excellent	200	−75
Nextel braid	Fair	Good	1204	−17
Glass braid	Poor	Good	482	−75
Refrasil braid	Poor	Good	871	−75
Kapton	Excellent	Good	316	−267

Ordinary copper lead wire is used to connect the voltage recording instrument to the sensing system as shown in Fig. 8.22. A convenient technique that is often employed involves the use of an isothermal block that provides the reference temperature and eliminates the effect of the voltage produced by the Cu/A and B/Cu junction.

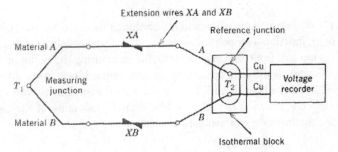

Fig. 8.22 Schematic illustration of the use of extension wires and copper lead wires in a thermocouple circuit.

8.4.5 Recording Instruments for Thermocouples

Previously it was shown that thermocouples are voltage generators; however, the voltage generated by a thermocouple (see Table 8.3) is small; therefore, small voltage losses due to current flow in the circuit ($\Delta V_0 = IR$) can produce significant errors in the temperature measurements. Also, when a temperature gradient and or a current flow exists in the circuit both Peltier and Thompson effects act to produce parasitic heating which can also produce significant errors in temperature measurements. Thus, the output voltage V_0 from a thermocouple circuit must be measured and recorded with an instrument having a high input impedance so that current flow in the circuit is minimized. The most common instruments used to measure and record the output voltage V_0 from a thermocouple circuit are the digital voltmeter (DVM), the strip-chart recorder and the oscilloscope. Each of these high-input-impedance instruments exhibit $R_M = 10^6 \, \Omega$ or higher.

The digital voltmeter is ideal for static and quasi-static measurements where it can be used in the manual mode of operation or as the voltage measuring component of a data-logging system for automatic recording at high sampling rates. A digital voltmeter with an input impedance of 10 MΩ will limit current flow in the thermocouple circuit to 10^{-10} A with a thermocouple voltage of 1 mV. Under such conditions, the IR losses and junction heating and cooling due to the Peltier and Thompson effects are negligible. A commercial DVM which has been adapted to provide readout directly in terms of degrees (°F or °C) for five different types of thermocouples is shown in Fig. 8.23. This meter has a resolution of 0.1 degree with a LCD digital display. Depending on the type of thermocouple connected to the meter, the temperature extremes that can be recorded range from $- 210$ °C to $+ 1,000$ °C. The instrument is portable, hand-held and battery powered. A microprocessor is incorporated in the DVM circuit to process the analog voltage output. The processing involves measuring the analog voltage output with an integrating type ADC. The digital code corresponding to this voltage is used as input to the microprocessor to determine the temperature by using the polynomial expression given in Eq. (8.14). The digital output from the microprocessor is displayed to give a direct reading of the temperature. With instruments like this one, where microprocessors are incorporated, the look-up tables given in Appendix A are not required.

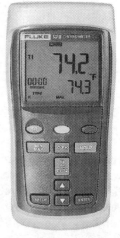

Fig. 8.23 A hand-held, battery powered thermocouple meter capable of direct recording the temperature from J, K, T, E and N type thermocouples.
Courtesy of Fluke inc .

These direct reading instruments eliminate the need for the reference junction by using the method of cold junction compensation where the thermoelectric voltages due to the reference junction are subtracted from the signal from the measuring junction in accordance with Eq. (8.11). This is accomplished by incorporating an isothermal block in the instrument and measuring its temperature with a thermistor or an RTD. In the digital instruments with microprocessors, the subtraction process and compensation is performed by digital processing of the signals from the measuring junction and the thermistor on the isothermal block.

Fig. 8.24 Strip chart recorder for making permanent records of temperature-time for long periods of time.

A strip-chart recorder, with its servomotor-driven pen, displays the temperature directly on a circular chart, as shown in Fig. 8.24. A clock motor drives the paper to provide a continuous time-temperature record that can be saved for inspection at a later date. A relatively large LCD display provides an easy to read output. The recorder is powered from line voltage, but a battery back-up is provided to maintain its operation in the event of a power failure.

High-frequency variations in temperature can be recorded with an oscilloscope. The use of an oscilloscope is straightforward, because its input impedance and voltage sensitivities are well matched to the thermocouple circuit.

8.4.6 Noise Suppression in Thermocouple Circuits

Because the voltage signals from thermocouple circuits are usually low (1 to 10 mV), the noise voltages imposed on the signal must be minimized to maintain the accuracy of the measurement. The noise voltages are generated by capacitive coupling of the thermocouple extension wires with nearby power lines that run parallel to the extension wires. The concept of capacitive coupling is illustrated in Fig. 8.25a.

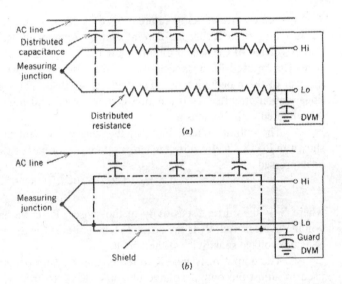

Fig. 8.25 Shielding technique to suppress noise in a thermocouple circuit.
(a) Capacitive coupling generates noise voltage.
(b) Shielding on the wire and the guard on a DVM.

There are two techniques that are effective in minimizing the noise signal. The first technique, shown in Fig. 8.25b, involves shielding the thermocouple wires so that the noise voltage is generated in the shield and not the thermocouple leads. The shield is connected to the guard[2] on the DVM. The noise voltage is eliminated by capacitive coupling the guard to the system ground. Properly shielded extension wires and guarded DVM circuits reduce the electrical noise appreciably.

Low pass filters can also be employed to eliminate the noise voltages. The frequency of noise generated by capacitive coupled power lines is 60 Hz. In most temperature measurements, the frequency associated with temperature fluctuations is much lower than 60 Hz. For this reason, low pass filters which pass signals with f < 10 Hz and severely attenuate signals with f ≥ 60 Hz are very effective in reducing the magnitude of the noise voltages.

---

[2] The guard is a metal box which surrounds the circuitry in the DVM. The guard acts to shield the enclosed circuits from capacitive coupled noise voltages.

8.5 INTEGRATED-CIRCUIT TEMPERATURE SENSORS

The integrated-circuit temperature sensor is a semi-conductor device that provides an output current I proportional to absolute temperature θ_A when an input voltage V_s (between 4 and 30 V) is applied across its two terminals. This type of temperature sensor is a high-impedance, constant-current regulator over the temperature range from −55 °C (−70 °F) to 150 °C (300 °F). It exhibits a nominal current sensitivity S_I of 1 µA/°K. The current sensitivity is controlled by an internal resistance that is laser trimmed during production to give an output of 298.2 µA at a 298.2 °K (26 °C). Input voltage-current-temperature characteristics of a typical sensor are shown in Fig. 8.26.

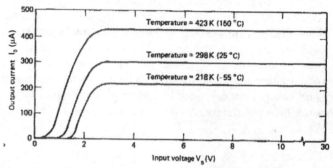

Fig. 8.26 Input-voltage-current-temperature characteristics of a two-terminal integrated-circuit temperature transducer.

The integrated-circuit temperature sensor is ideally suited for remote temperature measurements because it acts like a constant-current source. As a result, lead wire resistance R_L has no effect on the output voltage of the sensor circuit at the recording instrument. A well-insulated pair of twisted lead wires can be used for distances of several hundred feet. Also, many of the problems associated with the use of thermocouples or RTD devices, small output signals, need for precision amplifiers and linearization circuitry, cold junction compensation and thermoelectric effects at connections are not encountered with this sensor.

The output voltage V_0 from this sensor's circuit is controlled by a series resistance R_s, as shown in Fig. 8.27. Because the temperature sensor serves as a current source, this output voltage can be expressed as:

$$V_0 = I\,R_s = S_I\,\theta_A\,R_s = S_T\,\theta_A \qquad (8.17)$$

where S_I is the current sensitivity of the sensor; R_s is the series resistance across which the output voltage is measured; θ_A is the absolute temperature; I is the current output at absolute temperature θ_A; S_T is the voltage sensitivity of the circuit.

The output resistance R_s often contains a trim potentiometer, as shown in Fig.8.27, which is used to adjust the output voltage to 1 mV/°K or 10 mV/°K. This trim adjustment also permits the calibration error at a given temperature to be adjusted so as to improve accuracy over a given range of temperatures.

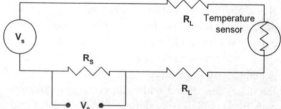

Fig. 8.27 Integrated circuit temperature sensor in a circuit with lead wire resistance and a series output resistance, with a trip potentiometer for standardizing sensitivity.

Unfortunately, the integrated-circuit temperature sensor is limited to a range of temperatures from −55 °C to 150 °C. Over this temperature range, it is an excellent temperature sensor.

8.6 DYNAMIC RESPONSE OF TEMPERATURE SENSORS

In previous sections we have introduced several different temperature sensors such as bimetallic strips, RTDs, thermistors and thermocouples. These sensors are all intended to measure temperature over a small region of a much larger body. The sensors have different operating principles, but exhibit several common characteristics, which include dynamic response and sources of error. Also, they are calibrated using similar techniques. We consider all of these sensors in the following descriptions of dynamic response, sources of error and calibration.

Temperature sensors are classified as first-order systems, because their dynamic response is controlled by a first-order differential equation, which describes the rate of heat transfer between the sensor and the surrounding medium. Consider the sensor at a time t in a media with a temperature T_m as shown in Fig. 8.28. A heat balance leads to the transient differential equation:

$$q = hA(T_m - T) = mc\frac{dT}{dt} \tag{8.18}$$

where q is the rate of heat transfer to the sensor by convection; h is the convective heat-transfer coefficient; A is the surface area of the sensor through which heat passes; m is the mass of the sensor; c is the specific heat capacity of the sensor.

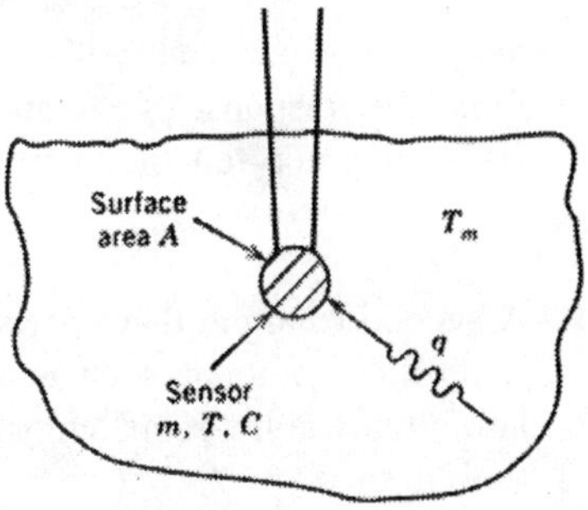

Fig. 8.28 Model of temperature sensor leading to Eq. (8.18)

Equation (8.18) can also be expressed as:

$$\frac{dT}{dt} + \frac{hA}{mc}T = \frac{hA}{mc}T_m \tag{8.19}$$

Solving Eq. (8.19) for its homogeneous part yields:

$$T = C_1 e^{-t/\beta} \tag{8.20}$$

where C_1 is a constant of integration; β is the time constant for the sensor given by:

$$\beta = \frac{mc}{hA} \tag{8.21}$$

A complete solution of Eq. (8.19) requires specification of the temperature T_m as a function of time and the initial conditions. Two examples provide valuable insight into the dynamic behavior of temperature sensors; namely, the response to step-function inputs and to ramp-function inputs.

Consider first the response of a temperature sensor to a step-function input (sensor is suddenly immersed in a fluid medium maintained at constant temperature T_m. In this example, the particular solution of Eq. (8.19) is $T = T_m$; therefore, the general solution is:

$$T = C_1 e^{-t/\beta} + T_m \tag{8.22}$$

For the initial condition $T(0) = 0$, the integration constant $C_1 = -T_m$ in Eq. (8.22); thus, the final expression for temperature T as a function of time t for the step-function input is:

$$\frac{T}{T_m} = \left(1 - e^{-t/\beta}\right) \tag{8.23}$$

Results of this relationship, shown in Fig. 8.29, indicate that a temperature sensor requires considerable time before it begins to approach the temperature of the surrounding medium T_m. The temperature of the sensor is within 5% of T_m at $t = 3\beta$ and within 2% of T_m at $t = 3.91\beta$. The response time can be shortened by reducing the time constant β. Smaller values of β are obtained by designing a sensor with a small mass, a large surface area and a low specific heat capacity. An example of a rapid-response thermocouple is shown in Fig. 8.30. This type of thermocouple is fabricated from thin foil with a thickness of approximately 0.012 mm (0.0005 in.). The foil elements are mounted on a thin polymeric carrier to facilitate bonding to a surface. The time constant β for foil thermocouples with large surface area and small mass ranges from 2 to 5 ms, depending primarily on the convective heat-transfer coefficient h existing between the sensor and the medium.

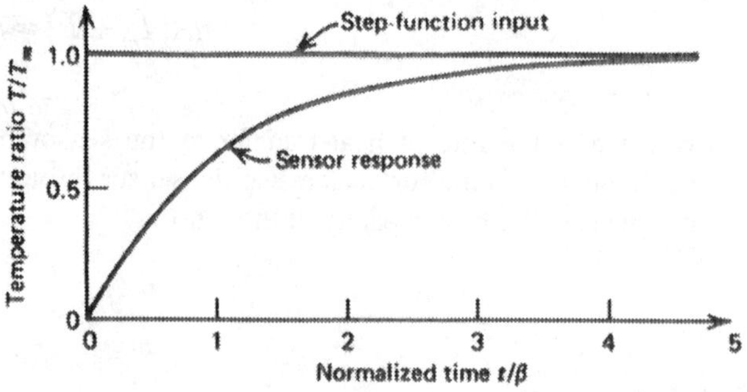

Fig. 8.29 Response of a temperature sensor to a step-function input.

A second example that shows dynamic behavior involves the response of a temperature sensor to a ramp-function input, such as the one illustrated in Fig. 8.30. The sensor and the surrounding medium are initially at the same temperature; thereafter, the temperature of the medium increases linearly with time so that:

$$T_m = bt \tag{a}$$

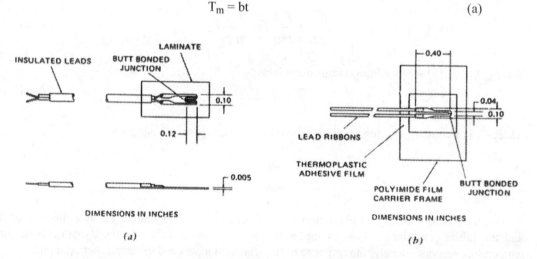

(a) Encapsulated foil element. (b) Free-filament foil element.

Fig. 8.30 Rapid response foil-type thermocouples.

Solving Eq. (8.23) for the particular solution gives:

$$T = b(t - \beta) \tag{b}$$

where b is the slope of the temperature-time ramp function, as illustrated in Fig. 8.31. The general solution of Eq. (8.23) for the ramp-function input is:

$$T = C_1 e^{-t/\beta} + b(t - \beta) \tag{8.24}$$

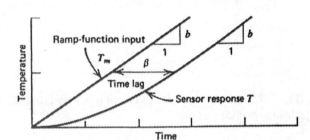

Fig. 8.31 Response of a temperature sensor to a ramp-function input.

For the initial condition $T(0) = T_m(0) = 0$, the integration constant C_1 in Eq. (8.24) equals β; therefore, the response of a temperature sensor to a ramp-function input can be expressed as:

$$\begin{aligned} T &= b\beta e^{-t/\beta} + b(t - \beta) \\ &= bt - b\beta(1 - e^{-t/\beta}) \end{aligned} \tag{8.25}$$

The results of Eq. (8.25), shown in Fig. 8.31, indicate that the initial response of the sensor is sluggish; however, after a short initial interval, the sensor tracks the rise in temperature of the medium surrounding the sensor with the correct slope, but with a time lag equal to β. The exponential term in Eq. (8.25) is important during the initial response and the linear term dominates the long-term response, because the exponential term decreases rapidly with time and becomes negligible when $t > 3\beta$. Because the lag time β can be determined from a simple experiment, accurate temperature measurements can be made for times greater than 3β by correcting for this time lag. Sensors with small time constants should be used to reduce the time lag and the transient period, so that the errors in the dynamic response are small enough to be acceptable.

8.7 SOURCES OF ERROR IN TEMPERATURE MEASUREMENTS

There are many different errors that arise in measuring temperature with sensors such as thermocouples or RTDs, etc. Many of these sources such as loading by the voltage recorder, precision of the read out, effects of noise and dynamic response have been discussed previously. In this section, a source of error unique to temperature sensors, namely insertion errors, will be introduced. Insertion errors are the result of heating or cooling of the junction that change the junction temperature T from the medium temperature T_m. Insertion errors are classified as conduction errors, recovery errors and radiation errors. Conduction and recovery errors are described in this section. Radiation errors are discussed in Section 8.9.

To illustrate the error due to conduction of heat, consider measurement of the surface temperature at a point on a massive solid body, as shown in Fig. 8.32. Assume that the sensor is bonded to the surface so that the thermal contact resistance can be neglected. The lead wires from the sensor pass through a fluid (usually air) with a temperature T_f. Assume that the fluid temperature T_f is lower than that of the solid: hence, the sensor and its lead wires conduct heat away from the solid. The heat transfer (per unit time and area) by the sensor and lead wires is usually much greater than the convective heat loss from the surface to the fluid (air). As a result, temperature gradients occur in the solid that cause heat to flow toward the sensor. This fact implies that the temperature of the sensor T is depressed below that of the surface; therefore, the sensor will provide a low reading of T_f.

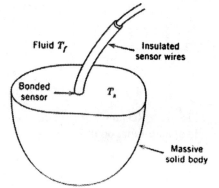

Fig. 8.32 Temperature measurement of a massive solid with a surface bonded sensor.

Hennecke and Sparrow have determined the errors due to conduction of the sensor and the lead wires. The results of this analysis are formulated neatly into three dimensionless groups:

$$\frac{T_s - T}{T_s - T_f} \tag{8.26a}$$

$$\frac{\sqrt{(kA)_e / R}\ \tanh\left[L / \sqrt{(kA)_e R} \right]}{\pi r_1 k_s} \tag{8.26b}$$

$$\frac{h_s r_1}{k_s} \tag{8.26c}$$

where T, T_s, T_f are the sensor, surface, and fluid temperatures respectively; k_s is the coefficient of thermal conductivity of the solid; h_s is the convective heat transfer between the solid and fluid; R is the radial thermal resistance of the lead wires given by:

$$R = \frac{(1/2\pi r_1 h) + \ln_e(r_i / r_w)}{2\pi k_i} \tag{8.26d}$$

r_i is the outer radius of the insulated lead wire; r_w is the radius of the conductor in the lead wire; $r_1 = \sqrt{2}\ r_w$ is an equivalent radius of the lead wires; L is the length of the lead wires; $(kA)_e$ is an effective conductivity-area product defined by:

$$(kA)_e = k_w A_w + k_i A_i \tag{8.26e}$$

A_w, and A_i are the cross sectional areas of the wire and insulation; k_w, and k_i are the coefficients of thermal conductivity of the wire and insulation.

The first dimensionless number, defined by Eq. (8.26a), gives the difference between T and T_s and is used for the ordinate of the graphs shown in Fig. 8.33. The second dimensionless number, defined by Eq. (8.26b), is used for the abscissa of the graphs shown in Fig. 8.33. The Biot number, defined by Eq. (8.26c), is used as a parameter in the graphs of Fig. 8.33.

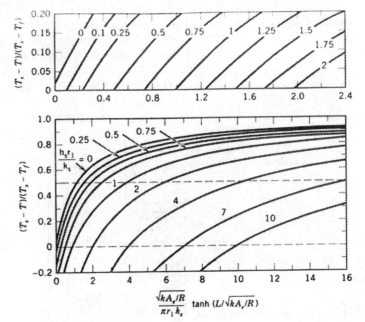

Fig. 8.33 Non-dimensional graph providing measurement errors for a surface mounted thermocouple.

The magnitude of the abscissa is an indication of the thermal resistance of the sensor compared to that of the solid body. For a fixed Biot number, the error is accentuated when the thermal resistance of the sensor-lead wires is low compared to that of the solid body. Note also that temperature errors are minimized by increasing the Biot number.

A second error occurs when temperature sensors are inserted in a gas that is moving at a high velocity. This measurement produces a recovery error due to stagnation of the flow when the temperature probe is inserted in the flow field. In this application, the total temperature T_t is sensed by an adiabatic or stagnation probe, as illustrated in Fig. 8.34. The total temperature is given by:

$$T_t = +\frac{v}{2Jgc_p} = T + T_v \qquad (8.27)$$

where T is the static or free stream temperature; v is the velocity of the gas; J is the mechanical equivalent of heat and c_p is the specific heat of the gas at constant pressure.

The term $v^2/2Jgc_p$ in Eq. (8.27) is defined as the dynamic temperature. In real fluids, the stagnation recovery factor is introduced to account for differences between the total temperature and the stagnation temperature T_{st} that is observed in experiments with stagnation probes. Accordingly, we modify Eq. (8.27) to read:

$$T_{st} = T + ST_v \qquad (8.28)$$

where S is the stagnation recovery factor which is given for air, water, and steam in Fig. 8.35. Thus, it is possible to establish the free stream temperature T by using Eq. (8.28) after employing stagnation probes to measure T_{st}, determining T_v from velocity measurements, and establishing S from Fig. 8.35.

Fig. 8.34 Schematic drawing of an adiabatic temperature probe.

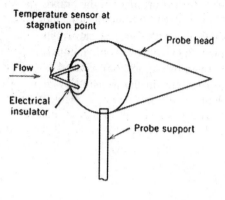

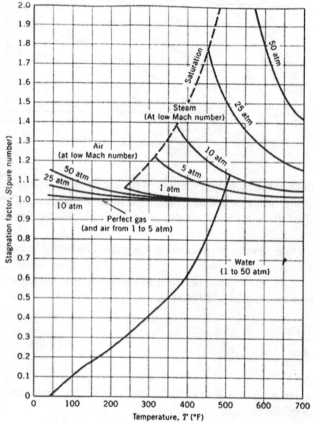

Fig. 8.35 Stagnation recovery factor for air, water and steam.

8.8 CALIBRATION METHODS

Calibration of temperature sensors is usually accomplished by using the freezing-point (or boiling-point), the melting-wire or the comparison method. The freezing-point method is the easiest and most frequently employed calibration technique. With this approach, the temperature sensor is immersed in a melt of pure metal that has been heated in a furnace to a temperature above its melting point. The temperature of the melt is slowly reduced while a temperature-time record, similar to the one shown in Fig. 8.36, is recorded. As the metal changes state from liquid to solid, the temperature remains constant at the freezing-point temperature T_F providing an accurate reference temperature for calibration. The particular metal selected for the bath is determined by the temperature required for the calibration. Usually, a sensor should be calibrated at three points within its temperature range (preferably the minimum, midpoint and maximum). The freezing points of a number of metals are listed in Table 8.2. These data indicate that the freezing-point approach can be used to provide calibration temperatures in the range from 232 °C (450 °F) with tin to 1084.6 °C (1984.3 °F) with copper. The metals must be pure because small quantities of an impurity can significantly affect the freezing point and thus affect the calibration. Metals used as freezing point standards are commercially available for temperatures ranging from 125 °F to 600 °F in 125 °F increments. These standards are accurate to ± 1 °F.

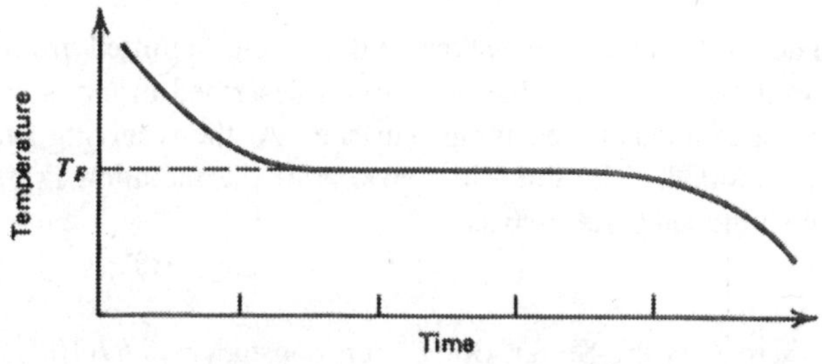

Fig. 8.36 Typical temperature-time curve for a metal during solidification.

The lower range of the temperature scale is often calibrated by using the boiling phenomenon. The temperature sensor is immersed in a liquid bath and heated until the fluid begins to boil and a stable calibration temperature is achieved. Atmospheric pressure must be considered in ascertaining the boiling point of any liquid, because pressure variations can significantly affect the calibration results. For example, reducing the atmospheric pressure from 29.922 to 26.531 in. of Hg, results in a decrease in the saturation (boiling) temperature of water from 212 °F to 206 °F.

The melting-wire method of calibration is used with thermocouples. With this approach, the hot junction of the thermocouple is made by connecting the two dissimilar wires with a pure third metal, such as silver or tin. When the hot junction is heated, the output voltage V_0 drops to zero. The output voltage V_0 immediately prior to the voltage drop is the melting point (calibration temperature T_M) of the specific material used for the joint.

The comparison method utilizes two temperature sensors: one of unknown quality and one of reference or standard quality. Both sensors are immersed in a liquid bath that is temperature cycled over the range of interest. The response of the "standard" sensor gives the temperature of the bath at any time and is used as the calibration temperature for the unknown sensor. The "standard" temperature sensor must be calibrated periodically to ensure its accuracy. Also, the standard sensor should not be used for any purpose other than calibration.

8.9 RADIATION METHODS (PYROMETRY)

As the temperature of a body increases, it becomes increasingly difficult to measure the temperature with resistance temperature detectors, thermistors or thermocouples. The problems associated with measurement of high temperatures by means of these conventional methods (lack of stability, breakdown of insulation, etc.) provided the motivation for developments in **pyrometry** (inferring temperature from a measurement of the radiation emitted by the body). By employing the principles of radiation, methods have been developed to measure surface temperatures without contacting the body. These non-contact methods have eliminated the stability and insulation failure problems, which plagued the sensor methods of measurement of very high temperatures.

Two different radiation methods are widely employed. The first, which is described as optical pyrometry, compares the brightness of light radiating from a body with a known standard. The second method uses a photon detector to measure the photon flux density that varies with the temperature of the surface. Instruments are commercially available that permit temperature to be measured at a point or over an entire field by using photon detectors with suitable optical arrangements and electronic systems.

First, consider the basic principles of radiation upon which pyrometric measurements are based. The classical method of optical pyrometry is then introduced to show a very direct method of measurement and an approach to correct for the effect of emissivity.

8.9.1 Principles of Radiation

The electromagnetic waves and particles emitted from the surface of a body are referred to as "radiation". This radiation is often described in terms of photons that propagate from each emission point to another (receiving) surface. At the receiving surface, the photons are absorbed, reflected or transmitted. The intensity (power) of the radiation E_b from a black (ideal) surface is related to the absolute temperature θ as:

$$E_b = \sigma\theta^4 \tag{8.29}$$

where σ is the Stefan-Boltzmann constant = $5.67(10^{-8})$ W/(m^2 - °K) and E_b is the power radiated (W/m^2).

The radiation from a heated surface is emitted with many different wave lengths. The electromagnetic spectrum, as shown in Fig. 8.37, covers a wide range in wave lengths; however, the light spectrum associated with thermal radiation exhibits wave lengths from about 300 nm to 20 μm.

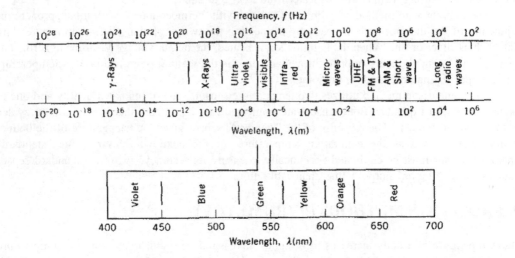

Fig. 8.37 Electromagnetic spectrum with the light spectrum enlarged.

Max Planck developed a relationship that describes the radiation power E_λ in terms of the absolute temperature θ and the wave length λ of the radiation.

$$E_\lambda = \frac{2\pi c^2 h}{\lambda^5 \left(e^{hc/k\lambda\theta} - 1\right)} = \frac{C_1}{\lambda^5 \left(e^{C_2/\lambda\theta} - 1\right)} \tag{8.30}$$

where h is Planck's constant = $6.626 (10^{-34})$ J-s; c is the velocity of light = $299.8(10^6)$(m/s); k is Boltzmann's constant = $1.381(10^{-23})$(J/°K); C_1 is a constant = $2\pi c^2 h = 3.75(10^{-16})$ W-m²; C_2 is a constant = hc/k = $1.44(10^{-2})$ m-°K.

The spectral radiation intensity E_λ is the amount of power emitted by radiation of wavelength λ from a flat surface at temperature θ into a hemisphere. It is evident from Eq. (8.30) that the spectral radiation intensity E_λ depends upon both wavelength λ and temperature θ. A graph of E_λ versus λ for several different temperatures is shown in Fig. 8.38. Note that E_λ exhibits maxima at a specific wavelength, which depends on temperature. Observe that the wavelength associated with the peak E_λ increases as the temperature decreases. The wavelength λ_p with the peak in E_λ can be expressed as:

$$\lambda_p = \frac{2898(10^{-6})}{\theta} \tag{8.31}$$

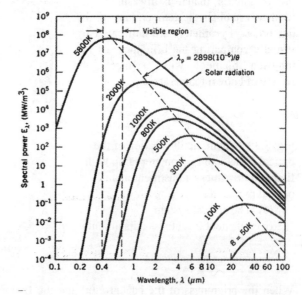

Fig. 8.38 Spectral power emission from a black surface at different temperatures.

The area under each of the curves in Fig. 8.38 is the total power E_t emitted at the particular temperature θ. Thus:

$$E_t = \int_\lambda E_\lambda d\lambda = 5.67(10^{-8})\theta^4 \ \text{W} / \text{m}^2 \tag{8.32}$$

Equation (8.32) is the Stefan-Boltzmann Law with the emissivity ε equal to unity ($\varepsilon = 1$). From the previous discussion, it is evident that:

1. The total power E_t increases as a function of θ^4.
2. The maximum value of spectral radiation intensity E_λ occurs at shorter wavelengths as the temperature increases.

Both of these physical principles are used as the basis for a measurement of temperature.

8.9.2 The Optical Pyrometer

The optical pyrometer, illustrated schematically in Fig. 8.39a, is used to measure temperature over the range from 700 °C to 4,000 °C (1,300 °F to 7,200 °F). The radiant energy emitted by the body is collected with an objective lens and focused onto a calibrated pyrometer lamp. An absorption filter is inserted in the optical system between the objective lens and the pyrometer lamp, when the temperature of the body exceeds 1,300 °C (2,370 °F). The radiant energy from both the hot body and the filament of the pyrometer amp is then passed through a red filter with a sharp cutoff below λ = 0.63 μm. The light transmitted through this filter is collected by an objective lens and focused for viewing with an ocular lens. The image observed through the eyepiece of the pyrometer is that of the lamp filament superimposed on a background intensity due to the hot body. The current to the filament of the pyrometer lamp is adjusted until the brightness of the filament matches that of the background. Under a matched condition, the filament disappears (hence the commonly used name, disappearing-filament optical pyrometer), as illustrated in Fig. 8.39b. The current required to produce the brightness match is measured and used to establish the temperature of the hot body. Pyrometers are calibrated by visually comparing the brightness of the tungsten filament with a blackbody source of known temperature (ε = 1).

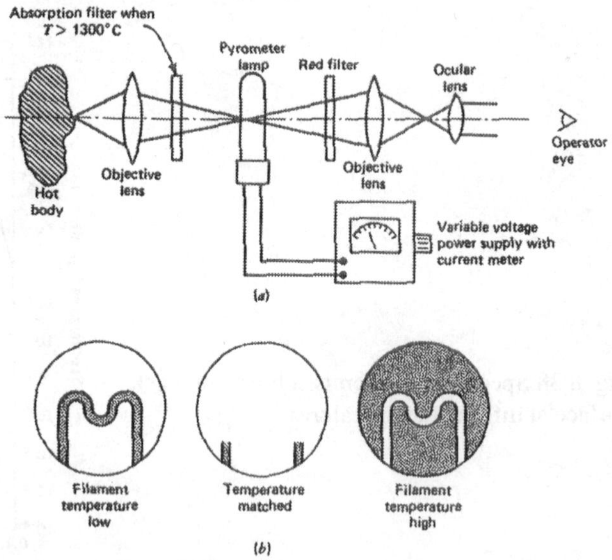

Fig. 8.39 Schematic illustration of the optical system and pyrometer lamp with filament brightness adjustment in an optical pyrometer.
   (a) The optical system.
   (b) Filament brightness adjustment.

When the brightness of the background and the filament are matched, it is evident that E_λ for these two objects are the same. Thus, Eq. gives:

$$\frac{\varepsilon}{\left(e^{C_2/\lambda_r \theta} - 1\right)} = \frac{1}{\left(e^{C_2/\lambda_r \theta_f} - 1\right)} \tag{8.33}$$

where λ_r is the wavelength of the red filter (λ = 0.63 μm); ε is the emissivity of the surface of the hot body at λ = 0.63 μm; θ_f is the temperature of the filament and θ is the unknown surface temperature.

When θ < 4,000 °C (7,200 °F), the term $e^{C_2/\lambda_r \theta} \gg 1$ and Eq. (8.33) reduces to:

$$\theta = \frac{1}{\lambda_r (\ln \varepsilon) / C_2 + 1/\theta_f} \tag{8.34}$$

It is obvious from Eq. (8.34) that $\theta = \theta_f$ only when $\varepsilon = 1$. If $\varepsilon \neq 1$, then $\theta \neq \theta_f$, and Eq. (8.34) must be used to determine the temperature θ from the temperature θ_f indicated by the pyrometer. The emissivity of a number of materials, with oxidation-free surfaces, are listed in Table 8.7.

TABLE 8.7
Emissivity ε of Engineering Materials at $\lambda = 0.65$ μm

Material	Solid	Liquid	Material	Solid	Liquid
Beryllium	0.61	0.61	Tantalum	0.49	---
Carbon	0.80-0.93	---	Thorium	0.36	0.40
Chromium	0.34	0.39	Titanium	0.63	0.65
Cobalt	0.36	0.37	Tungsten	0.43	---
Columbian	0.37	0.40	Uranium,	0.54	0.34
Copper	0.10	0.15	Vanadium	0.35	0.32
Iron	0.35	0.37	Zirconium	0.32	0.30
Manganese	0.59	0.59	Steel	0.35	0.37
Molybdenum	0.37	0.40	Cast iron	0.37	0.40
0.40Nickle	0.36	0.37	Constantan	0.35	---
Platinum	0.30	0.38	Monel	0.37	---
Rhodium	0.24	0.30	90 Ni – 10 Cr	0.35	---
Silver	0.07	0.07	80 Ni 20 Cr	0.35	---
			60 Ni 24 Fe 16 Cr	0.36	---

If the emissivity of a surface is not known precisely, then an error will occur when Eq. (8.34) is used to determine the temperature θ. The change in temperature as a function of change in emissivity is obtained from Eq. (8.34) as:

$$\frac{d\theta}{\theta} = -\frac{\lambda\theta}{C_2}\frac{d\varepsilon}{\varepsilon}$$

(8.35)

Because $\lambda\theta/C_2 < 0.1$ for $\theta < 2{,}000$ °C (3,630 °F), errors in temperature measurements are mitigated considerably with respect to errors in emissivity. For example, at a temperature of 1,500 °K, a 20% error in emissivity produces only 1.3% error in temperature.

For relatively low to intermediate temperature measurements, a portion of the surface is coated with either a black paint or a black ceramic providing an emissivity ε approaching one. For very high temperatures, a hole can be drilled in the body, with a depth to diameter ratio of six or more. This hole acts as a blackbody with $\varepsilon \approx 1$ and the temperature measured by focusing the optical pyrometer on the hole represents the correct temperature of the object.

The disappearing-filament optical pyrometer is an accurate instrument. If the emissivity of the hot body is known, the error in a temperature measurement is usually less than 1%.

8.9.3 Infrared Pyrometers

There are many applications, regardless of the temperature, where the measurement must be made without contacting the body. The optical pyrometer described previously is effective for temperatures above 700 °C (1,290 °F), where a significant amount of radiant power is emitted in the visible light region of the spectrum. At lower temperatures, the radiation emissions are concentrated in the infrared regions and are not visible to the human eye.

Infrared pyrometers employ the infrared portion of the spectrum by using thermal detectors to measure the surface temperature of the body emitting infrared waves. A schematic illustration of a thermal detector, sometimes called a radiometer, is shown in Fig. 8.40. The lens collects the infrared radiation emitted from the area included in the focused spot and collimates the radiation as shown. The radiation is reflected from the end mirror and focused on a temperature sensor. Thermocouples or thermistors are usually employed as temperature sensors. The equilibrium temperature of the sensor is a direct measurement of the magnitude of the radiation absorbed. The magnitude of the radiation gives the temperature of the emitting surface as indicated by Eq. (8.32).

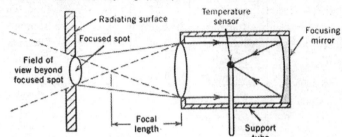

Fig. 8.40 Schematic illustration of a radiometer.

Target size and distance from the lens to the object are critical in the operation of infrared pyrometers. The field of view of an infrared pyrometer depends upon the focal length and diameter of the collecting lens. The optical system of the instrument collects all of the radiation from the objects in the field of view and the reading represents an average of these temperatures. To show the importance of this averaging effect on accuracy of an infrared pyrometer, consider the objects arranged in the field of view of the pyrometer in Fig. 8.41. In this illustration, object A covers the entire field of view and the reading represents the average surface temperature of object A. However, if object A is removed from the field, then object B and the wall are both included in the field of view. The indicated temperature will be between the temperature of the wall and that of object B, and will depend on the relative area of each object in the circular field of view.

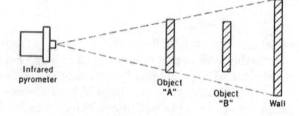

Fig. 8.41 Example showing the effect of several objects in the field of view of an infrared pyrometer.

Most infrared pyrometers have a fixed-focal-length collecting lens, which defines the field of view. This field of view is usually expressed in terms of a d/D ratio where d is the distance from the lens to the object and D is the diameter of the field at the position d. Note that the diameter of the field is equal to the diameter of the collecting lens, when d is twice the focal length of the lens. General purpose infrared pyrometers use lenses with focal lengths between 500 and 1,500 mm, although close-focus instruments use lenses with focal lengths between 10 and 100 mm and long-range instruments use 10 m focal length lenses. It is even possible to employ fiber optics to transmit the radiation from the source to the sensor.

Emissivity affects the reading of an infrared pyrometer in the same manner that it affects the reading from an optical pyrometer. When the emissivity is less than 1, the radiation power actually emitted from the surface of the body is less than expected and the instrument gives a reading lower than the true surface temperature. The manufacturers of infrared pyrometers accommodate the emissivity error by installing an emissivity compensator on the instrument. The emissivity compensator is a calibrated gain adjustment, which increases the amplification of the sensor signal to compensate for the power lost due to an emissivity of less than one. This gain adjustment can also be used to correct for transmission losses that occur when viewing the object through glass or plastic port holes, smoke, dust or vapors.

A commercial infrared pyrometer is shown in Fig. 8.42. This instrument covers the temperature range from − 10 to 1,600 °F or − 20 to 1,000 °C. Emissivity is adjustable from 0.1 to 1.0 in increments of 0.01. The temperature, which is continuously updated, is displayed on a four digit LCD. Accuracies are specified as ± 1.0% of the full scale reading. An analog output of 1 mV per degree enables connection to data acquisition equipment, including chart recorders and computers.

Fig. 8.42 Commercial infrared pyrometer. Courtesy of Omega Engineering, Inc.

8.9.4 Photon Detector Temperature Instruments

A second approach that uses radiation to measure temperature employs a photon detector. The instruments equipped with photon detectors differ from those with temperature detectors in two ways. First, the response time of the photon detector is several orders of magnitude faster than the thermal detector. This advantage is used to develop instruments capable of scanning a field and producing images depicting the temperature distributions over an area of a surface. Second, the photon detectors must be maintained at a very low temperature during operation and it is necessary to have a source of liquid nitrogen.

The sensor in a photon detector responds by generating a voltage proportional to the photon flux density φ impinging on the sensor. A schematic diagram of a photon detector system for measuring temperature is shown in Fig. 8.43. The photons emitted from a small area A_s of a surface (not necessarily hot) are collected by a lens and focused on a photon detector of area A_d. The photon flux density φ at the detector, when the optical system is focused, can be expressed as:

$$\phi = \frac{kD^2 \varepsilon}{4f^2} g(T) \qquad (8.36)$$

where k is the transmission coefficient of the lens and filter; D is the diameter of the lens; f is the focal length of the lens; g(T) is a known function of the temperature of the surface; ε is the emissivity of the surface.

The output voltage V_0 from the detector, as a result of the flux density φ, is:

$$V_0 = k_t \frac{D^2}{4f^2} \varepsilon g(T) \qquad (8.37)$$

where k_t is the system sensitivity, which includes the transmission coefficient of the lens, the amplifier voltage gain, and the detector sensitivity.

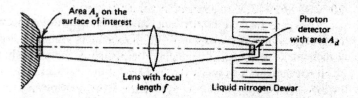

Fig. 8.43 Schematic illustration of a temperature measuring instrument with a photon detecting sensor.

The system sensitivity k_t is essentially a constant; however, a zoom lens is employed in a typical instrument to provide for different fields of view where the solid angle may range from 3.5 to 40 degrees. The term $\varepsilon g(T)$ depends only on the temperature of the surface and its emissivity. A typical response curve, shown in Fig. 8.44, indicates that the output voltage varies as a function of the cube of the temperature. Thus, Eq. (8.37) can be simplified to:

$$V_0 = K\varepsilon T^3 \qquad (8.38)$$

where K is a calibration constant for the instrument.

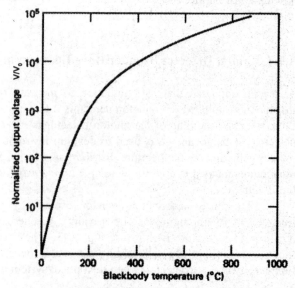

Fig. 8.44 Typical response curve for an indium-antimonide photo detector.

In practice, K is determined by calibrating the instrument with a blackbody source ($\varepsilon = 1$) over an appropriate range of temperatures. When the instrument is used for temperature measurements, the emissivity ε of the surface must be considered, because it may differ significantly from the value shown in Table 8.7. Any correction is easily made by substituting the correct value of the emissivity into Eq. (8.37) and solving for the required temperature T. Thus:

$$T = \left(\frac{V_0}{k\varepsilon}\right)^{1/3} \qquad (8.39)$$

Errors in temperature due to inaccuracies in emissivity are mitigated by 1/3 because differentiation of Eq. (8.37) gives $dT/T = -(1/3)(d\varepsilon/\varepsilon)$.

Many different commercial instruments employ different types of photon detectors; therefore, it is difficult to list specifications that cover the full range of products. Typical specifications for scanners like the one shown in Fig. 8.44 indicate that they are used to measure temperatures in the range from − 20 °C to 1,600 °C, with a sensitivity of 0.1 °C at 30 °C.

There are several different ways of cooling the detector to the required temperature. In the early days of thermal imaging, liquid nitrogen was poured into imagers to cool the detector. Although satisfactory, the logistical and safety implications led to the development of other cooling methods. High pressure gas can be used to cool a detector to the required temperatures. The gas is allowed to rapidly expand in the cooling systems and this expansion results in the significant reduction in the temperature of a gas. Mechanical cooling systems are the standard for portable imaging systems. These have the logistical advantage of freeing the detection system from the requirements of carrying high pressure gases or liquid nitrogen.

A full field IR camera is illustrated in Fig. 8.48. This instrument has a cooled focal-plane-array of photon detectors that provide a 640 × 512-pixel format that enables full field measurements while working in snapshot mode. The camera can also function at frame rates up to 4,500 frames/s enabling measurement of rapidly changing temperatures. A number of interchangeable infrared lenses including telephoto, standard, wide-angle, macroscope and microscope types permit the field of view to be adjusted according to the application. The microscope lenses capture detailed images of electrical assemblies and components, even from large measuring distances, with a pixel size of 5 μm.

Fig. 8.45 A high speed IR recording system for full field temperature measurements at high speed. Courtesy of InfraTec GmbH, Infrarotsensorik und Messtechnik.

8.10 SUMMARY

Temperature is an abstract quantity and as such must be defined in terms of the behavior of materials as the temperature changes. This is accomplished by defining the temperature associated with phase transformations in several different materials over the temperature range from − 259 °C to 1,084 °C.

The different sensors available for temperature measurement include resistance temperature detectors (RTDs), thermistors, expansion thermometers, integrated-circuit sensors, thermocouples and pyrometers. Each type of sensor or instrument has advantages and disadvantages; selection of the proper sensor for a particular application is usually based on considerations of temperature range, accuracy requirements, environment, dynamic response requirements and available instrumentation.

The most frequently used temperature measuring sensor is the thermocouple, because it is a low-cost transducer that is easy to fabricate and install. The signal output is relatively low and must be measured and recorded with an instrument having a high input impedance so that current flow in the circuit is minimized; otherwise, significant errors can be introduced. The nonlinear output of the thermocouple was previously considered a disadvantage; however, modern instruments used to record the output voltage incorporate a microprocessor to linearize the output and give readout in terms of temperature directly. The range of temperatures that can be measured with thermocouples is very large, from − 185 °C to 2,800 °C.

Resistance-based temperature sensors (RTDs and thermistors) are usually employed when a high sensitivity is required. Because of the high voltage output, higher accuracies can be achieved.

The RTD-type sensor is available in coil form for fluid temperature measurements and in a bondable grid form for surface temperature measurements. These sensors are easy to install and the instrumentation used to monitor the output signal is inexpensive and easy to employ. Thermistors are used in many commercial temperature recorders because their high voltage output permits a reduction in complexity and cost of the readout system. The range of thermistors is limited and the output is extremely nonlinear.

A comparison of the four most popular point sensors for measuring temperature that lists advantages and disadvantages is given in Fig. 8.46.

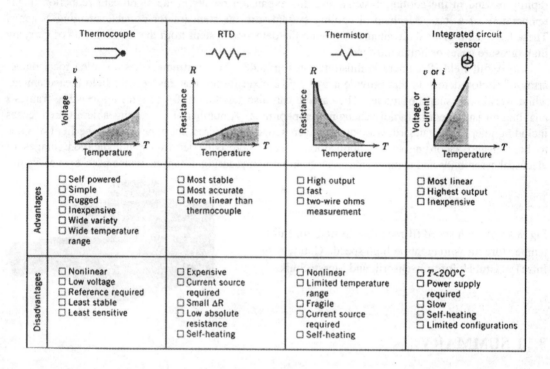

Fig. 8.46 Advantages and disadvantage of the most common temperature sensors.
Courtesy of Omega Engineering, Inc.

Bimetallic thermometers are used primarily in control applications where long-term stability and low cost are important considerations. They are often used to activate switches in on-off (bang-bang) temperature control situations, where precise control is not required.

Pyrometers are used primarily to monitor the extremely high temperatures associated with metallurgical processes. The disappearing-filament optical pyrometer has been a reliable instrument in many industrial applications for several decades. In more recent years, with the development of thermal and photon detectors, radiation methods of temperature measurement have been extended into the lower temperature range. A significant advantage of instruments, that use either thermal or photon detectors as sensors, is their ability to measure temperature without contacting the specimen in applications involving thin films, paper or moving bodies.

An advantage of photon detector instruments, with the rapid response time of the detector, is their ability to scan the field of view and to establish temperature distributions over extended areas. The disadvantages of photon-detector-based instruments are their relatively high cost and the need for liquid nitrogen to cool the photon detector.

Temperature sensors are first-order systems that respond to a step change in temperature in a manner that is described by the equation:

$$T = T_m (1 - e^{-t/\beta})$$ (8.23)

Errors due to the time required for heat transfer can be minimized by reducing the time constant β for the sensor.

REFERENCES

1. American National Standards Institute (ANSI), Standard MC 96.1 - 1975, Instrument Society of America, 1976.
2. American Society of Mechanical Engineers, Temperature Measurement, Supplement to ASME Performance Test Codes, PTC 19.3, 1974.
   - (a) Chapter 4, Resistance Thermometers.
   - (b) Chapter 5, Liquid-in-Glass Thermometers.
   - (c) Chapter 7, Optical Pyrometers.
3. Benedict, R. P.: Fundamentals of Temperature, Pressure, and Flow Measurement, 3rd Ed., Wiley, New York, 1984.
4. Benedict, R. P. and R. J. Russo: "Calibration and Application Techniques for Platinum Resistance Thermometers," Transactions of the American Society of Mechanical Engineers, Journal of Basic Engineering, June, 1972, pp. 381-386.
5. Curtis, D. J. and G. J. Thomas: "Long Term Stability and Performance of Platinum Resistance Thermometers for Use to 1063 C," Metrologia, vol. 4, no. 4, October, 1968, pp. 184-190.
6. Harrison, T. R.: Radiation Pyrometry and its Underlying Principles of Radiant Heat Transfer, Wiley, New York, 1960.
7. Hennecke, D.K. and E. M. Sparrow: "Local Heat Sink on a Convectively Cooled Surface - Application to Temperature Measurement Error", Int. J. Heat Mass Transfer, vol. 13, 1970, pp. 287-304.
8. Kinzie, P. A.: Thermocouple Temperature Measurement, Wiley, New York, 1973.
9. Magison, E. C.: Temperature Measurement in Industry, Instrument Society of America, Research Triangle Park, NC, 1990.
10. McGee, T. D.: Principles and Methods of Temperature Measurement, Wiley, New York, 1988.
11. Omega Engineering: Temperature Measurement Handbook, Omega Engineering, Stamford, Connecticut, 2011.
12. Peltier, J. C. A.: "Investigation of the Heat Developed by Electric Currents in Homogeneous Materials and at the Junction of Two Different Conductors," Annales de Chimie et Physique, vol. 56 (2nd Ser.) 1834, p. 371.
13. Powell, R. L., W. J. Hall, C. H. Hyink, Jr., L. L. Sparks, G. W. Burns, M. G. Scroger, and H. H. Plumb: "Thermocouple Reference Tables Based on IPTS-68," **NBS Monograph** 125, March, 1974.
14. Preston-Thomas, H.: "The International Temperature Scale of 1990 (ITS-90)", Metrologia, vol. 27, 1990, pp. 3-10.
15. Seebeck, T. J.: "Evidence of the Thermal Current of the Combination Bi-Cu by its Action on Magnetic Needle," Royal Academy of Science, Berlin, 1822-1823, p. 265.
16. Thompson, W.: "On the Thermal Effects of Electric Currents in Unequal Heated Conductors," Proceedings of the Royal Society, vol. 7, May, 1854.

EXERCISES

8.1 Why are the fixed points on the International Temperature Scale important?

8.2 Describe how you would calibrate a temperature sensor using the triple point of water and the freezing point of tin.

8.3 How is a temperature sensor calibrated if it is to operate over the temperature range from 1,200 °C to 1,600 °C?

8.4 A bimetallic strip is fabricated from stainless steel and invar with thicknesses of 0.5 and 1.0 mm respectively. Determine the radius of curvature of the strip if it undergoes a temperature change of :

  (a) 120 °C   (b) 70 °F   (c) 230 °C   (d) – 80 °F

The mechanical and thermal properties of stainless steel and invar are as follows; steel: E = $28(10^6)$ psi or 193 GPa; Invar: E = $21(10^6)$ psi or 145 GPa.

8.5 From the results shown in Fig. 8.2, determine the temperature coefficients of resistivity γ_1, γ_2 and γ_3 in Eq. (8.5) for a resistance temperature detector (RTD) fabricated from platinum for the temperature range from – 200 °C to 1,000 °C.

8.6 From the results shown in Fig. 8.2, determine the temperature coefficients of resistivity γ_1, γ_2, and γ_3 in Eq. (8.5) for a resistance temperature detector (RTD) fabricated from copper for the temperature range from –200 °C to 1,000 °C.

8.7 From the results shown in Fig. 8.2, determine the temperature coefficients of resistivity γ_1, γ_2, and γ_3 in Eq. (8.5) for a resistance temperature detector (RTD) fabricated from nickel for the temperature range from 0 °C to 1,000 °C.

8.8 Repeat Exercise 8.5 for a temperature range from 0 °C to 700 °C.

8.9 Repeat Exercise 8.6 for a temperature range from 0 °C to 500 °C.

8.10 Repeat Exercise 8.7 for a temperature range from 0 °C to 400 °C.

8.11 From the results shown in Fig. 8.2, determine the temperature coefficients of resistivity γ_1, and γ_2, in Eq. (8.7) for a resistance temperature detector (RTD) fabricated from platinum for the temperature range from 100 °C to 400 °C.

8.12 A resistance temperature detector (RTD) fabricated from platinum exhibits a temperature coefficient of resistivity γ_1 = 0.003902/ °C. Assume γ_2 is negligible. If the resistance of the sensor is 100 Ω at 0 °C, find the resistance at:

  (a) – 240 °C (b) – 120 °C   (c) 90 °C   (d) 260 °C   (e) 600 °C   (f) 900 °C

8.13 Show that lead-wire effects are completely eliminated by using a three-wire system to connect a resistance temperature detector (RTD) into a Wheatstone bridge.

8.14 Show that lead-wire effects are completely eliminated by using a four-wire system to connect a resistance temperature detector (RTD) into a constant-current potentiometer circuit.

8.15 Using the data for temperature as a function of time shown in Fig. 8.4, determine the response time constant for: (a) a platinum thick-film RTD   (b) a platinum wire-wound RTD.

8.16 A platinum RTD with a resistance of 100 Ω at 0 °C is used in a constant-current potentiometer circuit. If the current I equals 5 mA, determine the output voltage V_0 at the following temperatures:

  (a) – 240 °C (b) – 120 °C   (c) 90 °C   (d) 260 °C   (e) 600 °C   (f) 900 °C

8.17 Determine the error due to self heating of an RTD if its self heating factor is F_{sh} = 0.35 °C/mW. The sensor (R_T = 100 Ω) is placed in an equal arm bridge with a supply voltage of 5 V.

8.18 Using the Callendar-Van Dusen equation prepare a graph showing the nonlinearities in $\Delta R/R_0$ with temperature. Cover the range from:

  (a) –200 °C to +200 °C   (b) 0 °C to 600 °C
  (c) +400 °C to +900 °C   (d) – 200 °C to +800 °C

8.19 Describe four common errors encountered in measuring temperature with an RTD. Indicate procedures that can be taken to minimize each of these errors.

8.20 Verify Eq. (8.9).

8.21 If $\beta = 4,350$ °K and $R_0 = 3,000$ Ω at $T_0 = 298$ °K, determine the resistance of a thermistor at:
   (a) – 80 °C   (b) –40 °C   (c) 0 °C   (d) 50°C   (e) 75 °C   (f) 150 °C

8.22 Write an engineering brief describing the relative merits of the RTD and thermistor as temperature sensors. Also indicate the disadvantages of each sensor.

8.23 Recommend a sensor, either an RTD or a thermistor, to be used to control a process where the temperature is:
   (a) 400 °C   (b) 90 °C   (c) – 200 °C

8.24 The thermistor described in Exercise 8.21 is connected in a constant current potentiometer circuit. If the current is 10 mA, prepare a graph showing the output voltage V_0 as the temperature increases from –50 to +300 °C. Use $R_T = 100$ Ω at $T_0 = 25$ °C.

8.25 Determine the constants A, B, and C in Eq. (8.14) by using the data given in Fig. 8.7 for a thermistor with:
   (a) $\beta = 3,270$ (b) $\beta = 4,240$ (c) $\beta = 4,710$

8.26 If the self heating error is to be limited to 0.5 °C for a thermistor with $R_T = 5,000$ Ω, determine the maximum current that can be used with the constant current potentiometer circuit. Let (a) 0.5 °C/mW   (b) 1.0 °C/mW   (c) 2.0 °C/mW

8.27 List the primary advantages and disadvantages of:
   Liquid-in-glass thermometers   (b) Bimetallic thermometers   (c) Pressure thermometers

8.28 Prepare a graph showing $T_1 - T_2$ as a function of output voltage using Eq. (8.16) and the coefficients given in Table A-5 for:
   (a) Chromel-alumel (type K)   (b) Chromel-constantan (type E)
   (c) Copper-constantan (type T)

8.29 Compare the results of Exercise 8.28 with the results listed in Tables A.2, A.3, and A.4.

8.30 A digital voltmeter (DVM) is being used to measure the output voltage V_0 from a copper-constantan thermocouple, as shown in Fig. E8.30.
   (a) Determine the output voltage V_0 indicated by the DVM.
   (b) If the DVM reading changes to 2.078 mV, what is the new temperature T_1?
   (c) Does temperatures T_2 or T_3 influence the measurement? Why?

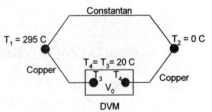

Fig. E8.30

8.31 A digital voltmeter (DVM) is being used to measure the output voltage V_0 from a copper-constantan thermocouple, as shown in Fig. E8.31. Determine the output voltage V_0 indicated by the DVM.

Fig. E8.31

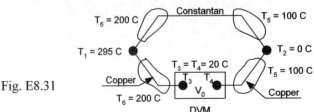

8.32 A digital voltmeter (DVM) is being used to measure the output voltage V_0 from a Chromel-Alumel thermocouple, as shown in Fig. E8.32.

(a) Determine the output voltage V_0 indicated by the DVM.
(b) If the DVM reading changes to 20.470 mV, what is the new temperature T_1?
(c) Does the copper-alumel junction at the DVM influence the reading on either (a) or (b)?

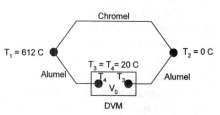

Fig. E8.32

8.33 A digital voltmeter (DVM) is being used to measure the output voltage V_0 from an iron-constantan thermocouple, as shown in Fig. E8.33.
(a) Determine the temperature T_1 associated with a DVM reading of 14.123 mV.
(b) Does the separation at junction 1 influence the measurement of T_1? List any assumptions made in reaching your answer.
(c) How far can the junctions be separated before errors will develop? Explain.

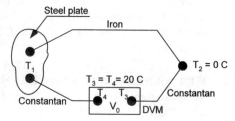

Fig. E8.33

8.34 A digital voltmeter (DVM) is being used to measure the output voltage V_0 from an iron-constantan thermocouple, as shown in Fig. E8.34.
(a) Determine the output voltage V_0 indicated by the DVM.
(b) If the DVM reading changes to 21.333 mV, what is the new temperature T_1?

Fig. E8.34

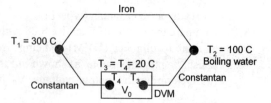

8.35 A digital voltmeter (DVM) having an input impedance of 10 MΩ is being used to measure the output voltage V_0 of the iron-constantan thermocouple shown in Fig. E8.35. The thermocouple is fabricated from AWG No. 20 wire having a resistance of 0.357 Ω per double foot (1 ft of iron plus 1 ft of constantan). The distance between junctions 1 and 2 is 40 ft. Determine:
(a) The IR drop due to the long lead wires.
(b) The output voltage V_0 indicated by the DVM.
(c) The temperature associated with the output voltage indicated by the DVM.

Fig. E8.35

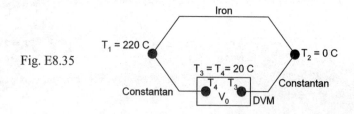

8.36 A chromel-constantan thermocouple is accidentally grounded at both the active and reference junctions, as shown in Fig. E8.36. If the resistance of the thermocouple is 3 Ω and the resistance of the ground loop is 0.2 Ω, determine the error introduced into the measurement of temperature T_1.

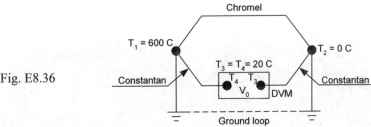

Fig. E8.36

8.37 The extension wires of an iron-constantan thermocouple were improperly wired to produce the situation illustrated in Fig. E8.37. Determine the error introduced into the measurement of temperature T_1.

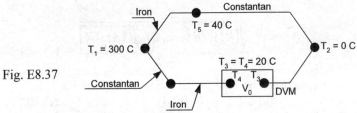

Fig. E8.37

8.38 Write an engineering brief describing the seven different material combinations employed in standard thermocouples.

8.39 A thermocouple installation made with AWG No. 14 wire is to be used to measure a temperature of 777 °C. Determine the error, due to drift, after an exposure of 500 hours if the thermocouples are:
    (a) Type J   (b) Type E   (c) Type K   (d) Type N

8.40 Stability improvement occurs with larger diameter wire. At an exposure of 1,100 hours, indicate the error in a measurement of a temperature of 1,202 °C with an N-type thermocouple fabricated from AWG No. 8 wire.

8.41 Write an engineering brief describing three methods for controlling reference junction temperature.

8.42 Write an engineering brief describing the modern instruments used to measure the voltage V_0 from a thermocouple.

8.43 Continue the engineering brief of Exercise 8.42. Describe cold junction compensation methods and linearization techniques.

8.44 Write a set of instructions to be used by laboratory technicians to minimize noise in thermocouple circuits.

8.45 Write an engineering brief comparing an integrated-circuit temperature sensor to:
    (a) a thermocouple   (b) a thermistor   (c) a RTD

8.46 Verify Eqs.(8.20) and (8.21).

8.47 Verify Eqs.(8.24) and (8.25).

8.48 Develop an expression for the response of a temperature sensor to the truncated-ramp type of input function shown in Fig. E8.48 for:
    (a) $0 < t \leq t_0$ (b) $t > t_0$

8.49 Outline the procedure you would follow to determine the lag time associated with thermocouple response to a ramp-function type of input.

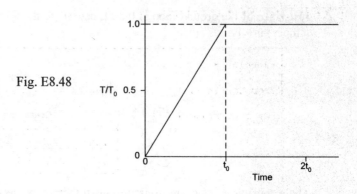

Fig. E8.48

8.50 Determine the error in measuring surface temperature T_s due to conduction of the sensor and lead wires if $T_f = 0.9 T_s$ and:

$$\frac{\sqrt{(kA)_{\dot{e}}/R} \tanh\left[L/\sqrt{(kA)_{\dot{e}}/R}\right]}{\pi r_1 k_{\dot{s}}} = 8 \quad \text{and} \quad \frac{h_s r_1}{k_s} = 1$$

8.51 Repeat Exercise 8.50 for the following values of $h_s r_1/k_s$:
      (a) 2   (b) 4   (c) 10

8.52 Evaluate the dynamic temperature $T_v = V^2/2Jgc_p$ for air as v varies from 0 to 1,000 miles per hour.

8.53 Write an engineering brief to be used by a laboratory technician in calibrating thermocouples for use at temperatures ranging from 125 °F to 600 °F.

8.54 Graph the results of Planck's Law [Eq. (8.30)] for temperatures of 1,100 °C, 200 °C, 500 °C, 1,000 °C, and 2,000 °C.

8.55 Use the results of Exercise 8.54 to verify Eq. (8.31).

8.56 Use the results of Exercise 8.54 for T = 1,000 °C to verify Eq. (8.32).

8.57 Use Eq. (8.34) to prepare a graph showing the relationship between θ and θ_f if the emissivity ε is: (a) 0.1   (b) 0.2   (c) 0.3   (d) 0.4   e) 0.6   (f) 0.8

8.58 Verify Eq. (8.35).

8.59 Use Eq. (8.35) to prepare a graph of error dT/T versus temperature T over the range from 1,000 °C to 4,000 °C for an optical pyrometer if the emissivity ε of the surface is in error by $d\varepsilon/\varepsilon$ equal to: (a) 0.05   (b) 0.10   (c) 0.20   (d) 0.50

8.60 Write an engineering brief describing the operation of an infrared pyrometer for a laboratory technician.

8.61 Determine k in Eq. (8.37b) by using the response curve for an indium antimonide photon detector shown in Fig. 8.44.

8.62 Write an engineering brief comparing the optical pyrometer with an instrument employing a photon detector.

EXERCISE SOLUTIONS

Exercise 8.5

From Eq. (8.5) :

$$R = R_0(1 + \gamma_1 T + \gamma_2 T^2 + \gamma_3 T^3)$$

For a platinum RTD:

Temp	-200	400	1000
R/R$_0$	0.25	2.42	4.33

$$\gamma_1(-200) + \gamma_2(-200)^2 + \gamma_3(-200)^3 = -0.75$$

$$\gamma_1(400) + \gamma_2(400)^2 + \gamma_3(400)^3 = 1.42$$

$$\gamma_1(1000) + \gamma_2(1000)^2 + \gamma_3(1000)^3 = 3.33$$

Solving yields:

$$\gamma_1 = 3.686(10^{-3})/(^\circ C)$$

$$\gamma_2 = -0.329(10^{-6})/(^\circ C)^2$$

$$\gamma_3 = -0.027(10^{-9})/(^\circ C)^3$$

Exercise 8.15

$$\frac{T}{T_m} = 1 - e^{-t/\beta}$$

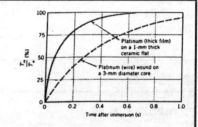

Type	T/T$_m$	t(s)	$e^{-t/\beta}$	t/β	$\beta = \dfrac{t}{1.609}$
thick film	0.8	0.20	0.2	1.609	0.124 s
wire	0.8	0.63	0.2	1.609	0.391 s

Exercise 8.26

$$R_T = 5000\ \Omega \qquad \mathcal{E} = 0.5\ ^\circ C \qquad P = \mathcal{E}/F_{sh}$$

$$i = \sqrt{P/R_T} = \sqrt{\mathcal{E}/F_{sh}R_T}$$

(a) For $F_{sh} = 0.5\ ^\circ C/mW$: $\quad i = \sqrt{\mathcal{E}/F_{sh}R_T} = \sqrt{0.5/(500)(5000)} = 0.447\ mA$

(b) For $F_{sh} = 1.0\ ^\circ C/mW$: $\quad i = \sqrt{\mathcal{E}/F_{sh}R_T} = \sqrt{0.5/(1000)(5000)} = 0.316\ mA$

(c) For $F_{sh} = 2.0\ ^\circ C/mW$: $\quad i = \sqrt{\mathcal{E}/F_{sh}R_T} = \sqrt{0.5/(2000)(5000)} = 0.224\ mA$

Exercise 8.34

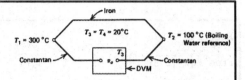

(a) From Table A.5:

$$v_o = v_{300} - v_{100}$$

$$= 16.325 - 5.268 = 11.057 \text{ mV}$$

(b) $v_T = v_o + v_{100} = 21.333 + 6.268 = 26.801 \text{ mV}$

$v_o = 26.801 \text{ mV}$ corresponds to $T_1 = 489.5 \,^\circ\text{C}$.

Exercise 8.46

From Eq. (8.19) :
$$\frac{dT}{dt} + \frac{1}{\beta} T = \frac{1}{\beta} T_m \qquad \text{where } \frac{1}{\beta} = \frac{hA}{mc}$$

The homogeneous solution is:
$$T = C_1 e^{-t/\beta}$$

The particular solution is:
$$T = T_m$$

The general solution is:
$$T = C_1 e^{-t/\beta} + T_m$$

Since $T = 0$ at $t = 0$:
$$C_1 = -T_m$$

Thus:
$$T = T_m \left[1 - e^{-t/\beta}\right]$$

Exercise 8.55

From Eq. (8.31) :
$$\lambda_p = \frac{2898}{\theta} \ \mu\text{m}$$

$T(^\circ\text{C})$	$\theta(^\circ\text{K})$	Equation $\lambda_p \ (\mu\text{m})$	Graph $\lambda_p \ (\mu\text{m})$
100	373	7.77	8
200	473	6.13	6
500	773	3.75	4
1000	1273	2.28	2
2000	2273	1.27	1

CHAPTER 9

FLUID FLOW MEASUREMENTS

9.1 INTRODUCTION

Fluid flow measurements, expressed in terms of either volume flow rate or mass flow rate, are used in many applications, such as industrial process control, city water systems, petroleum or natural-gas pipeline systems, irrigation systems, etc. The fluid involved in the measurement may be a liquid, a gas, or a mixture of the two (mixed-phase flow). The flow can be confined or closed (as in a pipe or conduit), semi-confined (as in a river or open channel), or unconfined (as in the wake behind a jet). In each situation, several methods of flow measurement can be used to determine the required flow rates. Several of the more common measurement techniques are discussed in this chapter.

The concept of mass flow rate can be visualized by considering confined flow in a circular pipe as shown in Fig. 9.1. The local mass flow rate dm/dt through area dA surrounding point P (see Fig. 9.1a) can be expressed as:

$$\frac{dm}{dt} = \rho v \, dA \qquad (9.1a)$$

where ρ is the mass density of the fluid at point P; v is the velocity of the fluid at point P in a direction normal to area dA.

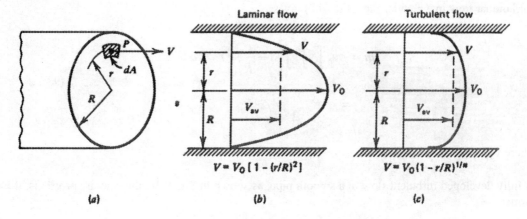

Fig. 9.1 Mass flow rate in a closed conduit. (a) General concept.
(b) Velocity profile. (c) Velocity profile.

The total mass flow rate $\dot{m}$ through the cross section of a pipe containing point P is:

$$\dot{m} = \int \frac{dm}{dt} = \int_A \rho v \, dA \qquad (9.1b)$$

Equation (9.1b) is valid for any plane area and both fluid density and fluid velocity can vary over this cross section. When the fluid is either a liquid or a gas, with small changes in pressure, the density is treated as a constant; therefore, it can be factored out of the second integral in Eq. (9.1b) to give:

$$\dot{m} = \rho \int_A v \, dA = \rho Q \tag{9.1c}$$

where $Q = \rho \int_A v \, dA$ is the volume flow rate.

For laminar flow, a parabolic velocity profile exists, as shown in Fig. 9.1b, which can be expressed as:

$$v = v_0 \left(1 - \frac{r^2}{R^2} \right) \tag{9.2}$$

where v is the centerline velocity; R is the inside radius of the pipe; r is a position parameter.

In those instances when the density of the fluid is a constant, Eq. (9.1b) can be used to define an "average" velocity v_{av}. Thus:

$$\dot{m} = \rho \int_A v \, dA = \rho v_{av} A \tag{9.3}$$

For laminar flow in a circular pipe, Eq. (9.3) gives:

$$\dot{m} = \rho v_0 \int_0^{2\pi} \int_0^R \int_A \left(1 - \frac{r^2}{R^2} \right) r \, dr \, d\theta \tag{9.4}$$

$$= \rho \pi R^2 \frac{v_0}{2} = \rho A v_{av}$$

where $v_{av} = v_0/2$ for laminar flow.

In fully developed turbulent flow in a smooth pipe, as shown in Fig. 9.1c, the velocity profile is of the form:

$$v = v_0 \left(1 - \frac{r}{R} \right)^{1/n} \tag{9.5a}$$

where the exponent n depends upon Reynolds number Re. For a circular pipe Re is:

$$\text{Re} = \frac{\rho v_{av} D}{\mu} \tag{9.5b}$$

where μ is the absolute viscosity of the fluid and D is the diameter of the pipe.

For the case of the circular pipe, it can be shown that the average velocity v_{av} is related to the centerline velocity v_0 by the expression:

$$v_{av} = \frac{2n^2}{(n+1)(2n+1)} v_0 \tag{9.6}$$

Values of the exponent n as a function of Reynolds number Re are shown in Fig. 9.2 together with the corresponding velocity ratios v_{av}/v_0. From the laminar-flow results of Eq. (9.4) and the turbulent-flow results of Eq. (9.6), it is evident that mass flow rates are established from velocity measurements at a point only if the velocity profile is known.

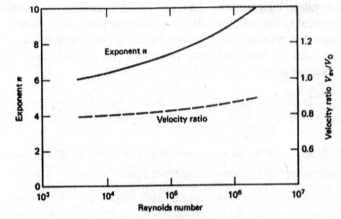

Fig. 9.2 Exponent n and velocity ration v_{av}/v_0 as a function of Reynolds number.

An approximation for the integral of Eq. (9.3), which can be applied for any flow measurement, is the finite sum representation:

$$\dot{m} = \sum_{i=1}^{n} \rho_i A_i v_i = \rho v_{av} A \tag{9.7}$$

As an example, consider the open-channel-flow problem illustrated in Fig. 9.3. Here, the mass flow rate through each area A_i is summed to obtain the total mass flow rate.

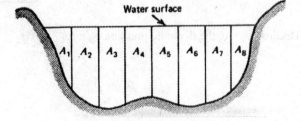

Fig. 9.3 Measurement of mass flow rate in an open channel.

In the following sections, different flow measurement methods are described that determine either velocity measurements at a point or average velocity over some cross section. Usually, instruments inserted into the flow (insertion-type transducers) provide velocity information at a point. Other devices (or obstructions), such as orifices, nozzles and weirs, alter the basic flow in such a way that changes in pressure are related to the average flow rate.

9.2 FLOW VELOCITY (Insertion-Type Transducers)

Transducers designed to measure velocity at a point in the flow field are discussed in this section. The types of transducers considered are pitot tubes, hot-wire and hot-film anemometers, drag-force transducers, turbine meters and vortex shedding devices.

9.2.1 Pitot Tube (Incompressible Flow)

The use of a pitot tube to measure velocity at a point in a fluid is illustrated in Fig. 9.4. The velocity of the fluid at point O is measured by inserting an open-ended pitot tube downstream from this point. As the fluid particles move from point O to point S (the stagnation point at the center of the pitot-tube opening), their velocity decreases to zero resulting in an increased pressure at point S. A second vertical section of pipe called a piezometer tube above point O measures the static pressure, while the pitot tube measures the total pressure at the stagnation point S. The dynamic pressure is the difference between the total and static pressures. For the streamline from point O to point S, the Bernoulli equation gives:

$$\frac{p_0}{\gamma} + \frac{v_0^2}{2g} = \frac{p_s}{\gamma} + \frac{v_s^2}{2g} \tag{9.8}$$

where v_0 and v_s are velocities at points 0 and S; g is the local acceleration due to gravity; γ is the weight per unit volume of the fluid; p_0 and p_s are the static and stagnation pressures, respectively.

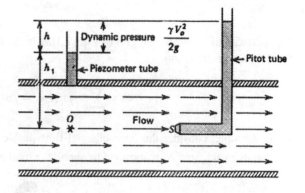

Fig. 9.4 Velocity measurements with a pitot tube.

Because $v_s = 0$, the dynamic pressure $p_d = (p_s - p_0)$ is:

$$p_d = p_s - p_0 = \frac{\gamma v_0^2}{2g} = \gamma h \tag{9.9}$$

where h is the dynamic head defined in Fig. 9.4. The velocity at point O, obtained from Eq. (9.9), is:

$$v_0 = \sqrt{2g\left(\frac{p_s - p_0}{\gamma}\right)} = \sqrt{2gh} \tag{9.10}$$

Velocity measurements made with a pitot tube require accurate static pressure measurements. Slight geometric errors in the pressure tap, such as a rounded corner or a machining burr, lead to significant errors in the static pressure measurement. To minimize such errors, static pressure measurements are often made with a piezometer ring, as illustrated in Fig. 9.5. The use of multiple holes around the periphery of the tube minimizes the static pressure errors.

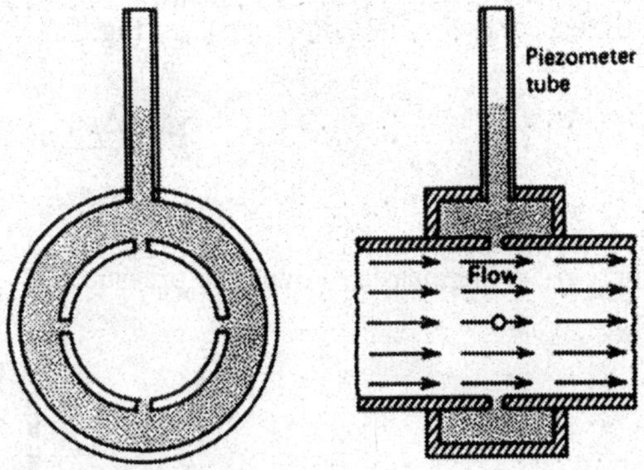

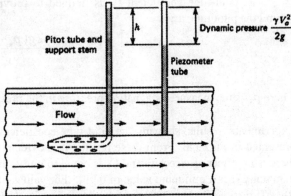

Fig. 9.5 Piezometer ring for making static-pressure measurement.

Pitot-static tubes are compact and efficient transducers that combine static-pressure measurements and stagnation-pressure measurements into a single unit, as illustrated schematically in Fig. 9.6. The static pressure recorded by a pitot-static tube is usually lower than the true static pressure because of the increase in velocity of the fluid near the tube. However, this difference between the indicated and true static pressure can be accounted for by employing a calibration coefficient C_I in Eq. (9.10). Thus:

$$v_0 = C_I \sqrt{2g \left(\frac{p_s - p_0'}{\gamma} \right)} \qquad (9.11)$$

where C_I is an experimentally determined calibration constant for the tube; p_0' is the indicated static pressure.

Fig. 9.6 Velocity measurement with a pitot-static tube.

In the pitot-static tube, designed by Prandtl, the static pressure tap is located at the point where the drop in static pressure due to the increase in velocity of the fluid near the tube is exactly equal to the increase in static pressure due to fluid stagnation along the leading edge of the support stem. Thus, for the Prandtl pitot-static tube, the instrument coefficient C_I is unity. For other pitot-static tube designs, the instrument coefficient C_I must be determined by calibration.

The stagnation pressure p_s is easy to measure accurately for most flow conditions. Four factors that affect the accuracy of this measurement are geometry of the pitot tube, misalignment (yaw) of the pitot tube with the flow direction, viscous effects at low Reynolds number and transverse-pressure gradients in flows with high-velocity gradients.

Geometric and misalignment effects are illustrated in Fig. 9.7, where dynamic pressure measurement error $\mathcal{E}$ is plotted as a function of pitot-tube orientation (angle of attack of the pitot tube with respect to the flow direction). In Fig. 9.7,

$$\mathcal{E} = \frac{\Delta p_d}{p_d} = \frac{p_d - p_d'}{p_d} \tag{a}$$

where p_d' is the measured dynamic pressure.

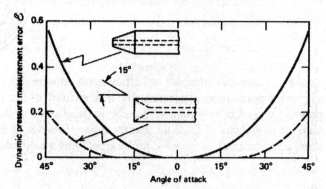

Fig. 9.7 Dynamic pressure measurement error as a function of pitot tube orientation.

It is evident from Fig. 9.7 that a square-end pitot tube with a 15-degree internal bevel angle is capable of providing dynamic pressure data with errors of less than 1%, provided the yaw angle is less than 25 degrees. Thus, with reasonable care and normal flow conditions, small errors in pitot-tube orientation do not produce serious error in dynamic pressure measurements.

A pitot-tube coefficient C_P is defined to provide a measure of viscous effects due to flow around the pitot tube as:

$$C_P = \frac{p_s' - p_0'}{p_d} = \frac{2g(p_s - p_0)}{\gamma v_0^2} \tag{b}$$

where p_s' is the measured stagnation pressure in the presence of viscous effects.

Experimental results, showing the pitot-tube coefficient C_P as a function of Reynolds number Re are presented in Fig. 9.8. From these results, it is evident that for Reynolds numbers greater than 1,000 there is no effect of viscosity and C_P is equal to unity. In the range $50 \leq \text{Re} \leq 1,000$, C_P is slightly less than unity (has a minimum value of 0.99). For values of $\text{Re} < 50$, C_P is always greater than unity. For $\text{Re} < 1$, the coefficient C_P is given by the approximate expression $C_P \approx 5.6/\text{Re}$. It is clear that viscous effects are important only for Reynolds numbers less than 50.

When a pitot tube is placed in a flow field with a large velocity gradient, the conditions around the tip of the tube can be significantly altered with respect to a uniform flow field. This flow gradient causes the total pressure measured to be greater than the true pressure, because the effective center of the pitot tube is shifted from the geometric center toward a region of higher velocity. Because the amount of this shift is limited to approximately 0.2D for square-end pitot tubes (where D is the diameter of the pitot tube), small diameter tubes are required to measure flows with high-velocity gradients.

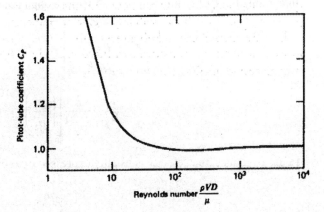

Fig. 9.8 Pitot tube coefficient C_P as a function of Reynolds number.

In Figs. 9.4 to 9.6, the pressures p_s and p_0 are measured with manometers. In practice, these pressures can be measured with manometers or pressure gages. Differential pressure transducers are also commercially available for measuring the pressure difference $(p_s - p_0)$, directly. A popular differential pressure transducer utilizes a thin diaphragm as the elastic element. Electrical resistance strain gages used in conjunction with a Wheatstone bridge provide for continuous monitoring of the pressure difference $(p_s - p_0)$. The velocity v_0 and mass flow rate $\dot{m}$ are determined by using Eqs. (9.7) and (9.10).

9.2.2 Pitot Tube (Compressible Flow)

In the previous discussion, the fluid was assumed to be incompressible. Measurements of compressible flow are more complicated and require the use of the equation of motion for a compressible fluid, energy considerations and a description of the flow process.

The equation of motion (Euler equation) for one-dimensional flow of a compressible ideal (nonviscous or frictionless) fluid can be expressed as:

$$\frac{dp}{\rho} + v \, dv = 0 \qquad (9.12)$$

where $\rho = \gamma/g$ is the mass density of the fluid.

This equation is based on the assumption that compressible-flow measurements are usually concerned with light gases and with flows where changes of pressure and velocity dominate and changes of elevation are negligible. When there is no heat transfer and no work done by pumps or turbines in the flow of an ideal fluid, the flow is isentropic and the energy equation for steady flow along a streamline reduces to Eq. (9.12). Thus, the energy and Euler equations are identical for isentropic flow of an ideal fluid. Along a streamline for a perfect gas:

$$\frac{p_1}{\rho_1^k} = \frac{p_2}{\rho_2^k} \qquad (9.13)$$

where k is the adiabatic exponent (ratio of specific heat at constant pressure to specific heat at constant volume for gas) $k = c_p/c_v$.

Integrating Eq. (9.12) and using Eq. (9.13), we obtain the velocity-pressure relations given by:

$$\frac{v_2^2 - v_1^2}{2} = \frac{p_1}{\rho_1} \frac{k}{k-1} \left[1 - \left(\frac{p_2}{p_1} \right)^{(k-1)/k} \right]$$

$$= \frac{p_2}{\rho_2} \frac{k}{k-1} \left[\left(\frac{p_1}{p_2} \right)^{(k-1)/k} - 1 \right] \tag{9.14}$$

In gas dynamics, the velocity is usually expressed in terms of the Mach Number:

$$M = v/c \tag{9.15a}$$

where the sonic velocity c is given by the expression:

$$c = \sqrt{\frac{kp}{\rho}} \tag{9.15b}$$

Substituting Eqs. (9.15) into Eq. (9.14) gives:

$$\frac{v_2^2}{c_1^2} = M_1^2 = \frac{2}{k-1} \left[1 - \left(\frac{p_2}{p_1} \right)^{(k-1)/k} \right] \tag{9.16}$$

Applying Eq. (9.16) to a stagnation point in a compressible flow ($v_2 = 0$ and $p_2 = p_s$) together with the free-stream conditions ($p_1 = p_0$ and $M_1 = M_0$) yields:

$$\frac{p_s}{p_0} = \left[1 + \frac{k-1}{2} M_0^2 \right]^{k/(k-1)} \tag{9.17}$$

This result indicates that measurements of stagnation pressure p_s and static pressure p_0 provide sufficient data to determine the free-stream Mach number. Determining the velocity v_0, however, requires measuring a temperature in addition to the static and stagnation pressures. In practice, the stagnation temperature T_s is measured with a thermocouple placed near the stagnation point. When T_s, p_s and p_0 are known, the velocity v_0 can be determined by using the expression:

$$\frac{v_0^2}{2} = c_p T_s \left[1 - \left(\frac{p_0}{p_s} \right)^{(k-1)/k} \right] \tag{9.18}$$

A comparison of velocities predicted by Eq. (9.10) with those given by Eq. (9.18) shows an agreement within 1% for pressure differences ($p_s - p_0$) less that 0.83 psi or Mach numbers less than 0.28. For larger pressure differences or Mach numbers, the agreement becomes less satisfactory and Eq. (9.18) should be used for velocity determinations. The comparison above was based on air where c = 343 m/s = 1,226 ft/s at 68 °F. For supersonic flow ($M_0 > 1$), a shock wave forms in front of the pitot tube upstream from the stagnation point. Velocity measurements for this complicated case are beyond the scope of this text.

9.2.3 Hot-Wire and Hot-Film Anemometers

Hot-wire and hot-film anemometers are devices that can be used to measure either velocity or velocity fluctuations (at frequencies up to 500 kHz) at a point in the flow field. Typical sensing elements (hot-wire and hot-film and their supports are shown in Fig. 9.9. Hot-wire sensors are fabricated from platinum, platinum-coated tungsten or a platinum-iridium alloy. Because the wire sensor is extremely fragile, hot-wire anemometers are usually used only for clean air or gas applications. Hot-film sensors, on the other hand, are extremely rugged; therefore, they can be used in both liquids and contaminated gas environments. The hot-film sensor incorporates high-purity platinum film bonded to a high-strength, fused-quartz rod. After the platinum film is bonded to the rod, the thin film is protected by using a thin coating of alumina if the sensor will be used in a gas or a thin coating of quartz if the sensor will be used in a liquid. The alumina coatings have a high abrasion resistance and a high thermal conductivity. Quartz coatings are less porous and can be used in heavier layers for electrical insulation. Other hot-film anemometer shapes for special-purpose applications include conical, wedge, and hemispheric probes.

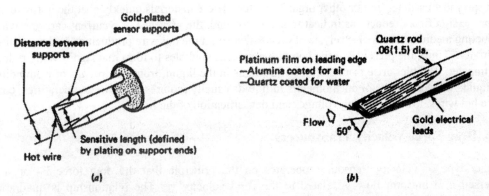

Fig. 9.9 Detail design of hot wire and hot film anemometers.

Hot-wire and hot-film anemometers measure velocity indirectly by relating power supplied to the sensor (rate of heat transfer from the sensor to the surrounding cooled fluid) to the velocity of the fluid in a direction normal to the sensor. Heat transfer from a heated wire placed in a flow field was studied by King, who noted that the heat transfer rate q is given by the expression:

$$q = \left(A + B\sqrt{\rho v}\right)\left(\theta_a - \theta_f\right) = I_a^2 R_a \qquad (9.19)$$

where A and B are calibration constants; θ_a and θ_f are the absolute temperatures of the anemometer (hot wire or hot film) and the fluid, respectively; I is the current passing through the wire (or film) sensor; R_a is the resistance of the wire (or foil) sensor.

The quantity ($\theta_a - \theta_f$) is typically maintained at approximately 450 °F (232 °C) in air and 80 °F (27 °C) in water.

Materials used for hot-wire and hot-film sensors exhibit a change in resistance with temperature. The resistance-temperature effect can be represented with sufficient accuracy for thermal anemometer applications by the linear expression:

$$R_a = R_r [1 + \gamma(T_a - T_r)] \tag{9.20}$$

where R_r is the resistance of the sensor at reference temperature T_r ; γ is the temperature coefficient of resistance of the wire or foil.

From Eq. (9.19) it is evident that the fluid velocity v can be determined by measuring either the current I_a or the resistance R_r. In practice, the velocity is determined by using a hot-wire or a hot-film anemometer as the active element in a Wheatstone bridge. With a constant-current bridge, the sensor current I_a is maintained as the sensor resistance R_a changes with the fluid flow to produce an output voltage V_0 that is related to the velocity of the fluid. With a constant-temperature bridge, the sensor resistance R_a (and thus the sensor temperature T_a) is held at a constant value by varying the current passing through the sensor as the fluid velocity changes. In this circuit, the current I_a is used to provide a measure of the velocity. A description of each of these systems follows.

When hot-wire or hot-film sensors are used in liquids, several problems arise. First, liquids often carry dirt particles, lint or other organic matter. These materials quickly coat the hot wire or film and cause significant reductions in heat transfer. Second, the presence of a current-carrying wire in a conducting medium causes electrolysis of metals that shunt the hot wire producing spurious changes in sensitivity. Third, the presence of the hot wire may cause bubbles to form that significantly reduce the heat transfer. Bubbles arise from entrained air or gas in the liquid, from electrolysis or from boiling of the liquid. Successful use of anemometers in liquids usually requires low wire temperatures, coatings on the hot wires, lower operating voltages and degasification of the liquid.

9.2.4 Drag Force Velocity Transducers

Another type of velocity transducer operates on the principle that the drag force F_D on a body immersed in a uniform flow is related to the fluid velocity v. The relationship is quadratic and depends on the fluid density ρ and the frontal area A of the body normal to the flow direction.

$$F_D = C_D \frac{\rho v^2 A}{2} \tag{9.21}$$

where C_D is a nondimensional number known as the drag coefficient.

The drag coefficient depends upon Reynolds number Re and the shape of the body. Drag coefficients for a sphere and for a circular disk as a function of Re are shown in Fig. 9.10. Because the drag coefficient for the circular disk is constant over a wide range of velocities ($C_D \approx 1.05$ for Re $\geq 3,000$) and because the magnitude of the drag coefficient for the disk is much more than that for the sphere, the circular disk is the preferred body used in a drag-force transducer.

4A. Rotameter

The rotameter is a popular flow measurement device based on drag principles. The rotameter, shown schematically in Fig. 9.11, consists of a transparent tapered tube and a solid float (bob) that is free to move vertically in the tube. At any flow rate within the range of the meter, fluid entering the bottom of the tube lifts the float (thereby increasing the area between the float and the tube) until the drag and buoyancy forces are balanced by the weight of the float. This balance condition can be expressed by the equation:

$$C_D \frac{\rho_f v^2 A_b}{2} + \rho_f \mathcal{V}_b g = \rho_b \mathcal{V}_b g \tag{9.22}$$

where A_b is the frontal area of the float, $\mathcal{V}$ the volume of the float, ρ is the density of the float, and v is the mean velocity of the fluid in the annular space between the float and the tube.

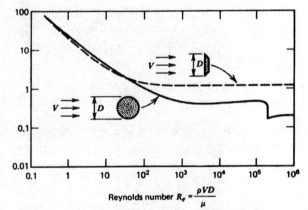

Fig. 9.10 Drag coefficients for a sphere and a circular disk as a function of Reynolds number.

The first term in Eq. (9.22) is the drag, the second term is the buoyancy force and the third term is the weight of the float. The annular area A for the flow is expressed as:

$$A = \frac{\pi}{4}\left[(D+ay)^2 - d^2\right]$$

where D is the inside diameter at the bottom of the tube; y is a position coordinate with an origin at the bottom of the tube; a is a constant that describes the taper of the tube; d is the diameter of the float.

The tubes are constructed so that $D^2 + a^2y^2 \approx d^2$. Hence, the annular area is:

$$A \approx \frac{\pi}{2} Day \tag{9.23}$$

The mass flow rate m is obtained from Eqs. (9.22) and (9.23) as:

$$\dot{m} = \rho_f Av = \frac{\pi}{2} Day \sqrt{\frac{2g\mathcal{V}_b}{C_D A_b}(\rho_b - \rho_f)\rho_f} \tag{9.24a}$$

$$= K\sqrt{(\rho_b - \rho_f)\rho_f}\; y$$

where $K = 2\pi Da \sqrt{\dfrac{g\mathcal{V}_b}{C_D A_b}}$ is an instrument constant depending on the geometry of the tube and float.

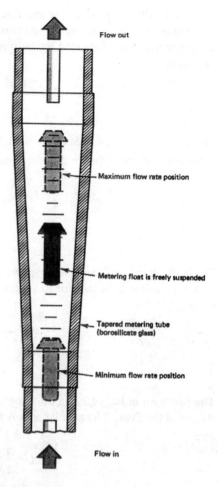

Flow out

Maximum flow rate position

Metering float is freely suspended

Tapered metering tube
(borosilicate glass)

Minimum flow rate position

Flow in

Fig. 9.11 Schematic illustration of a glass tube industrial rotameter flow meter.

The drag coefficient can be made nearly independent of viscosity by using sharp edges on the float and the influence of fluid density is eliminated by selecting $\rho_b = 2\rho_f$. Equation (9.24) reduces to:

$$\dot{m} = \frac{K\rho_b}{2} y \tag{9.24b}$$

The flow rate is indicated by the position of the float, which can be measured on a graduated scale or detected magnetically and transmitted to a remote location for recording.

9.2.5 Current Meters

Current meters are mechanical devices that are widely used to measure water velocities in open rivers, channels and streams. The rotational speed of its rotor is proportional to fluid velocity. A direct-reading, propeller-type current meter with sensing unit, rod suspension, torpedo-shaped package and propeller is shown in Fig. 9.12. As the propeller rotates, a magnetically activated reed switch in the sensing unit produces a train of electrical pulses at a frequency proportional to the speed of the propeller. A circuit in the readout meter, which incorporates a battery power supply and a pulse rate integrator, converts the train of pulses to a direct display of the fluid velocity. Typically, the range of such instruments is 0.025 to 10 m/s. Linearity of the unit shown in Fig. 9.12 is within ±5 % over the full range of the unit. Error caused by temperature change is approximately 0.05% per °F referenced to 75 °F.

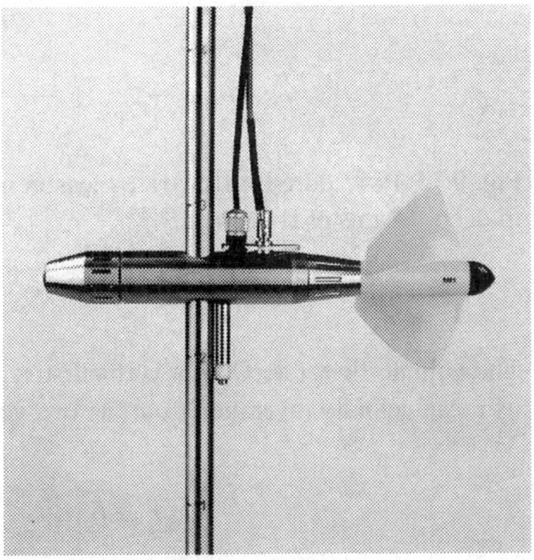

Fig. 9.12 Propeller type current meter with sensing unit, rod suspension and alignment fins.

The U.S. Geological Survey (USGS) has established a typical velocity profile (by using data from thousands of measurements) for use in measuring flow rates (discharge rates) in large rivers, canals and streams. This profile, shown in Fig. 9.13 shows that the velocity distribution in a typical large stream is parabolic with the maximum velocity occurring some distance (from 0.05h to 0.25h, where h is the depth of the stream) below the free surface. The free-surface velocity is typically 1.18 times the average velocity. The USGS profile indicates that the mean velocity often occurs at 0.6h. An accurate estimate of the mean velocity can usually be obtained by averaging the velocities v_2 and v_8 measured at points 0.2h and 0.8h, as indicated in Fig. 9.13.

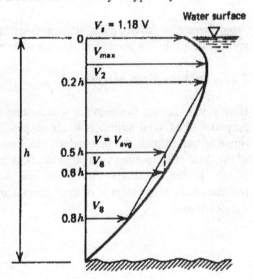

Fig. 9.13 Typical profile for a deep river.

The flow rate in a stream is measured by using the procedure illustrated in Fig. 9.14. First, a segment of the river with a fairly regular cross section is selected as the site for the measurement. The cross section of the river is then divided into vertical strips, as shown in Fig. 9.14. The mean velocity along each vertical line is determined by averaging velocity measurements made at points 0.2h and 0.8h below the free surface. Thus:

$$v_i = \frac{v_{2i} + v_{8i}}{2}$$

$$(9.25)$$

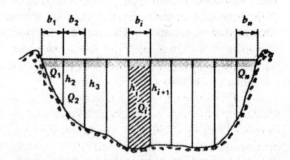

Fig. 9.14 Procedure for flow-rate measurements
in deep streams or rivers.

The volume flow rate Q_i in a vertical strip is calculated by using the height of the strip, its width and
its mean velocity (averaged from the two vertical lines bounding the strip). Thus:

$$Q_i = b_i \left(\frac{h_i + h_{i+1}}{2} \right) \left(\frac{v_i + v_{i+1}}{2} \right) \qquad (9.26a)$$

The total volume flow rate for the stream is the sum of the flow rates for all of the strips:

$$Q = \sum_{i=1}^{N} Q_i \qquad (9.26b)$$

From the above development, it is obvious that many flow-rate data points are needed to establish
volume flow rates for rivers and streams with sufficient accuracy.

9.2.6 Turbine Flow Meters

Basically, a turbine flowmeter is a miniature propeller supported on the center line of a pipe. The
propeller of its axial turbine is freely suspended (see Fig. 9.15) and rotates as the fluid flows (either
liquid or gas) through the flowmeter. The rotational speed of the turbine is proportional to the velocity
of the fluid. Because the volume of the flow passage
is fixed, the rotational speed is an accurate
representation of the volume of fluid flowing through
the flowmeter.

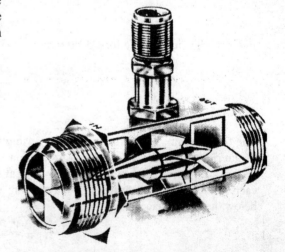

Fig. 9.15 Cutaway view of a turbine flow meter.

The only physical connection between the turbine and its housing is the turbine bearings. The rotation of the turbine is sensed by a magnetic coil in the flowmeter body that responds to the passage of each turbine blade past a coil. The output from this coil is a train of voltage pulses with a frequency proportional to the volume flow rate. The pulses are transmitted to an appropriate data processing system near the flowmeter where they are amplified, counted and interfaced with a microprocessor, to either measure or control the fluid flow.

Flowmeters have been developed with outstanding levels of accuracy, linearity, durability and reliability. Flowmeters are commercially available to measure fluid flow within the temperature range from − 430 °F to + 750 °F. Accuracy within ± 0.05% in liquids and ± 0.5 percent in gases is easily obtained at flow rates from 0.03 to 20,000 gal/min. Turbine flowmeters are currently used to monitor and control critical flow rates in a number of different industrial processes.

9.3 FLOW RATES IN CLOSED SYSTEMS BY PRESSURE MEASUREMENTS

Several devices that measure average velocity or flow rate, by inserting a constriction in the stream tube, are considered in this section. These devices are the venturi meter, flow nozzle and orifice meter. The operation of each of these devices is based on the fact that a change in cross-sectional area of a steam tube causes a corresponding change in velocity and pressure of the fluid within that tube.

The Bernoulli equation applied to an ideal incompressible fluid ($\rho_1 = \rho_2$), flowing through the tube shown in Fig. 9.16 gives:

$$\frac{p_1}{\gamma} + \frac{v_1^2}{2g} + z_1 = \frac{p_2}{\gamma} + \frac{v_2^2}{2g} + z_2 \tag{9.27}$$

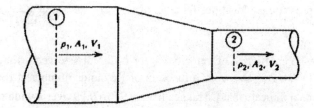

Fig. 9.16 Illustration of conservation of mass at two locations in a closed system.

The velocity v_1 can be eliminated from Eq. (9.27) by using the continuity equation that requires that:

$$Q = A_1 v_1 = A_2 v_2 \tag{9.28}$$

Thus, the ideal volume flow rate Q_1 (for an ideal frictionless fluid) is

$$Q_1 = \frac{A_2}{\sqrt{1-(A_2/A_1)^2}} \sqrt{2g\left(\frac{p_1}{\gamma} + z_1 - \frac{p_2}{\gamma} - z_2\right)} \tag{9.29}$$

For real fluid flow and the same head loss [$(p_1 - p_2)/\gamma + (z_1 - z_2)$], the flow rate is less than that predicted by Eq. (9.29) due to friction that acts at the walls between the two pressure measuring points. This energy loss is usually accounted for by introducing an experimentally determined coefficient C_v (coefficient of velocity) into Eq. (9.29). Actual flow rate Q_a is then expressed as:

$$Q_a = \frac{C_v A_2}{\sqrt{1-(A_2/A_1)^2}} \sqrt{2g\left(\frac{p_1}{\gamma}+z_1-\frac{p_2}{\gamma}-z_2\right)} \qquad (9.30)$$

The head loss difference term $[(p_1 - p_2)/\gamma + (z_1 - z_2)]$, in Eq. (9.30) can be measured with any of the standard pressure gages, such as a differential manometer or a differential pressure transducer. Specific details for different constriction devices are presented in the following subsections.

9.3.1 Venturi Meter

A typical venturi meter consists of a cylindrical inlet section, a smooth entrance cone (acceleration cone) with an angle of approximately 21 degrees, a short cylindrical throat section and a diffuser cone (deceleration cone) with an angle between 5 and 15 degrees. Recommended proportions and pressure tap locations for a venturi meter, as specified by the American Society of Mechanical Engineers (ASME) code, are shown in Fig. 9.17. Small diffuser angles tend to minimize the head loss from pipe friction, flow separation and turbulence. In order for the venturi meter to function properly, the flow must be fully developed as it enters the inlet pressure ring area (1). This developed flow is accomplished by installing the meter downstream from a section of straight and uniform pipe that is about 50 pipe diameters long. Straightening vanes may also be installed upstream of the venturi meter to reduce any rotational motion in the fluid. The pressures at the inlet section (1) and at the throat section (2) are measured with piezometer rings, as indicated in Fig. 9.17.

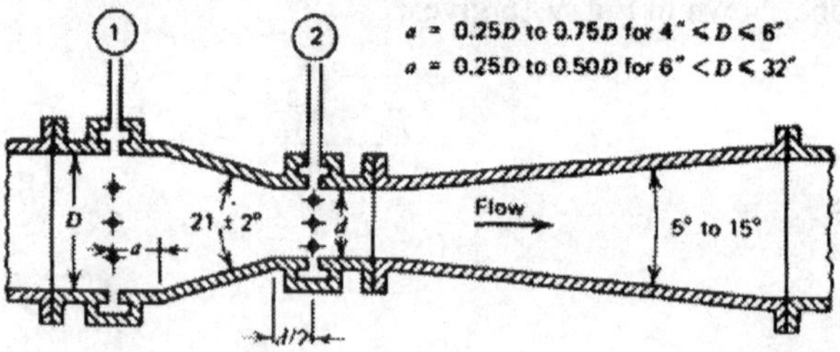

Fig. 9.17 Recommended proportions and pressure tap locations for a venturi meter.

The coefficient of velocity C_v for different size venturi meters having a pipe-to-throat diameter ratio $D/d = 2$ is shown as a function of Reynolds number at the throat ($Re = \rho v_2 d/\mu$) in Fig. 9.18. These data indicate that C_v ranges from 0.97 to 0.99 over a wide range of size for $Re > 10^5$. For $Re < 10^4$, C_v decreases sharply with decreasing Re and C_v becomes a very important correction factor. Experimental evidence at other diameter ratios indicates that C_v decreases with increasing D/d.

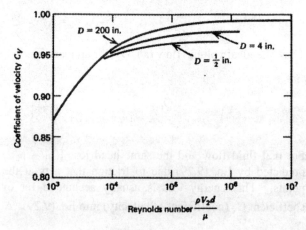

Fig. 9.18 Coefficient of velocity C_v as a function of Reynolds number for venturi meters with a diameter ratio of $D/d = 2$.

9.3.2 Flow Nozzle

A flow nozzle is essentially a venturi meter with the diffuser cone removed. Because the diffuser cone is used to minimize head loss caused by the presence of the meter in the system, it is clear that larger head losses will occur in flow nozzles than in venturi meters. The flow nozzle is preferred over the venturi meter in many applications, because of its lower initial cost and because it can be easily installed between two flanges in any piping system. The geometry recommended by ASME for a long-radius flow nozzle is shown in Fig. 9.19.

The upstream pressure is measured with a piezometer ring located one pipe diameter upstream from the inlet face of the nozzle, while the throat pressure is measured with a piezometer ring located one-half pipe diameter downstream from the inlet face of the nozzle. Errors associated with the measurement of throat pressure at location (2) are adjusted, by using either a velocity coefficient C_V for the flow nozzle or a discharge coefficient C_D for the meter where $(C_D = Q_a/Q_i)$.

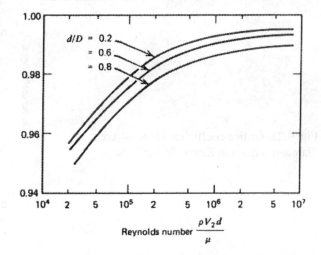

Fig. 9.19 Geometry recommended for a long-radius flow nozzle.

Extensive research on flow nozzles has produced a significant body of reliable data on flow nozzle installation procedures and velocity coefficients. Flow coefficients for the long radius ASME flow nozzle are shown in Fig. 9.20.

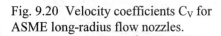

Fig. 9.20 Velocity coefficients C_V for ASME long-radius flow nozzles.

9.3.3 Orifice Meter

An orifice meter consists of a plate with a sharp-edged circular hole (see Fig. 9.21) that is inserted between two flanges of a piping system. Its purpose is to determine the flow rate from pressure-difference measurements across the orifice. The flow pattern developed by flow through a sharp-edged orifice plate is also shown in Fig. 9.21. This flow pattern indicates that the streamlines tend to converge a short distance downstream from the plane of the orifice; therefore, the minimum-flow area is smaller than the area of the opening in the orifice plate. This minimum-flow area is known as the "vena contracta." The area at the vena contracta is accounted for in Eq. (9.30) by defining a contraction coefficient C_C as:

$$A_2 = C_C A_0 \tag{9.31}$$

where A_0 is the area of the hole in the orifice plate. When Eq. (9.31) is substituted into Eq. (9.30), the flow rate through the orifice becomes:

$$Q_a = CA_0 \sqrt{2g\left(\frac{p_1}{\gamma}+z_1-\frac{p_2}{\gamma}-z_2\right)} \tag{9.32a}$$

where the orifice coefficient C is defined as:

$$C = \frac{C_v C_C}{\sqrt{1-(C_C A_0 / A_1)^2}} \tag{9.32b}$$

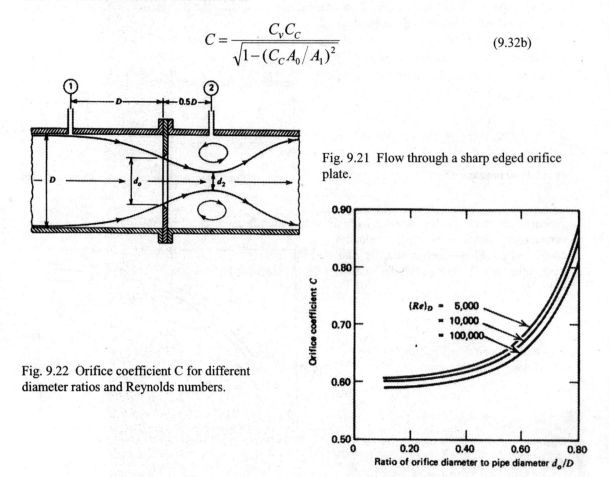

Fig. 9.21 Flow through a sharp edged orifice plate.

Fig. 9.22 Orifice coefficient C for different diameter ratios and Reynolds numbers.

The value of the orifice coefficient C depends upon the velocity coefficient C_v, the contraction coefficient C_C and the area ratio A_0/A_1 of the installation. The orifice coefficient C is also affected by the location of the pressure taps. Ideally, the pressure p_2 should be measured at the vena contracta; however, this is difficult to implement in practice, because for $Re > 10^5$ the location of the vena contracta changes with Reynolds number and area ratio. As a result, pressure taps are usually placed one pipe diameter upstream and one-half pipe diameter downstream from the inlet face of the orifice plate. Variations of orifice coefficient C as a function of the ratio of orifice diameter to pipe diameter are shown in Fig. 9.22 for different Reynolds numbers $(Re)_D$ for these locations of the pressure taps. For $(Re)_D > 100,000$, the value of C remains essentially constant.

9.4 FLOW RATES IN PARTIALLY CLOSED SYSTEMS

Many variations of the orifice meter are used in practice. For example, consider either the submerged orifice (a) or the free discharging orifice (b) of Fig. 9.23 that are used to control fluid flow from one large reservoir to another. In these two cases, the area of the orifice is so small compared to the face area of the reservoir that ratio $A_0/A_1 \approx 0$; therefore, Eq. (9.32) becomes:

$$Q_a = CA_0 \sqrt{2g(h_1 - h_2)} \qquad (9.33)$$

where $C = C_V C_C$ is the orifice or discharge coefficient, and h_1 and h_2 are the static heads. Orifice coefficient C depends on the design of the orifice and its entrance and exit configuration, as shown in Table 9.1.

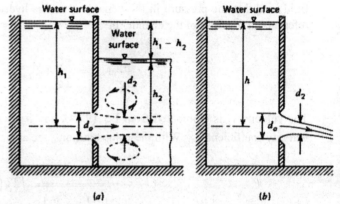

Fig. 9.23 Flow through an orifice between reservoirs.
(a) Submerged orifice.
(b) Free discharging orifice.

The coefficients in Table 9.1 are nominal values for large-diameter (d > 1 in. or 25 mm) orifices operating under static heads ($h_1 - h_2$) in excess of 50 in. (1.25 m) of water. Above these limits of diameter and static head, the coefficients are essentially constant. For smaller diameter orifices and lower static heads, both viscous effects and surface tension effects begin to influence the discharge coefficient and the results in Table 9.1 are not valid.

Table 9.1
Orifices and Their Nominal Coefficients

	Sharp edged	Rounded	Short tube[a]	Borda
C	0.61	0.98	0.80	0.51
C_C	0.62	1.00	1.00	0.52
C_V	0.98	0.98	0.80	0.98

9.5 MEASURING FLOW RATES IN OPEN CHANNELS

Accurate measurement of flow rates in open channels is important for navigation, flood control, irrigation, etc. The two broad classes of devices used for this type of measurement and control are the sluice gate and the weir. Both of these devices require placement of an obstruction (dam) in the flow channel and thus the flow is altered. Pressures are usually obtained by measuring free-surface elevations to give the heads used in computing flow rates.

9.5.1 Sluice Gate

The sluice gate is an open-channel version of the orifice meter. As shown in Fig. 9.24, the flow through a gate exhibits jet contraction on the top surface, which produces a reduced area of flow or vena contracta just downstream from the gate. If it is assumed that there are no energy losses (ideal fluid) and that the pressure in the vena contracta is hydrostatic, Bernoulli equation with respect to a reference at the floor of the channel gives:

$$\frac{v_1^2}{2g} + y_1 = \frac{v_2^2}{2g} + y_2 \tag{9.34}$$

The velocity v_1 is eliminated from Eq. (9.34), and friction losses are accounted for by introducing a velocity coefficient C_V. With these substitutions, the actual flow rate Q_a is:

$$Q_a = \frac{C_v C_C A}{\sqrt{1 - \left(y_2/y_1\right)^2}} \sqrt{2g\left(y_1 - y_2\right)} \tag{9.35}$$

where A is the area of the sluice gate opening; C_C is a contraction coefficient that accounts for the reduced area at the vena contracta.

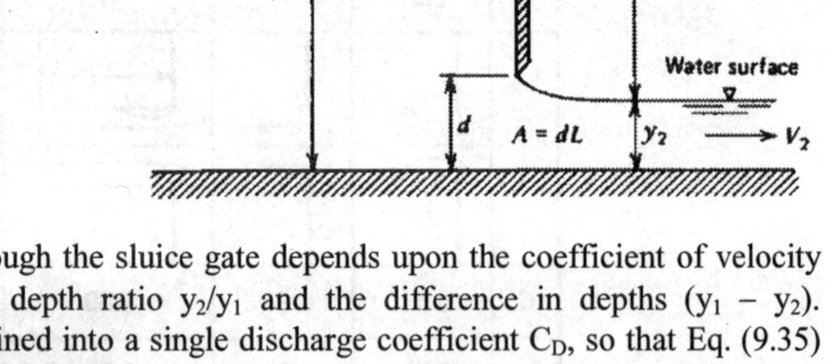

Fig. 9.24 Flow through a sluice gate.

Note that the flow rate or discharge through the sluice gate depends upon the coefficient of velocity C_V, the contraction coefficient C_C, the depth ratio y_2/y_1 and the difference in depths ($y_1 - y_2$). Frequently, all of these effects are combined into a single discharge coefficient C_D, so that Eq. (9.35) is written as:

$$Q_a = C_D A \sqrt{2gy_1} \tag{9.36}$$

Values for the discharge coefficient C_D usually range between 0.55 and 0.60 providing free flow is maintained downstream from the gate. When flow conditions downstream produce submerged flow, the value of the discharge coefficient is reduced significantly.

With a constant upstream head y_1, it is clear from Eq. (9.36) that the flow rate is controlled by the area of the sluice gate opening. Because the width L of the gate is fixed, the height of the gate opening controls the flow rate. The position of the gate is easily monitored with any displacement transducer and the flow rate is easily measured and/or controlled.

9.5.2 Weirs

A weir is an obstruction in an open channel over which fluid flows. The flow rate or discharge over a weir is a function of the weir geometry and of the weir head H (vertical distance between the weir crest and the liquid surface in the undisturbed region upstream from the weir). The discharge equation for a weir is derived by considering a sharp-crested rectangular weir, illustrated in Fig. 9.25, and applying the Bernoulli equation to a typical streamline. Using the weir crest as the reference we write:

$$H + \frac{v_1^2}{2g} = (H - h) + \frac{v_2^2}{2g}$$

(9.37)

where h is a distance below the free surface where v_2 exists in the weir plane.

Solving Eq. (9.37) for v_2 yields:

$$v_2 = \sqrt{2g\left(h + \frac{v_1^2}{2g}\right)}$$

(9.38)

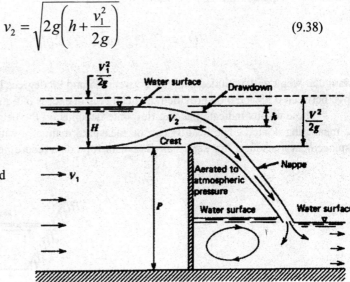

Fig. 9.25 Flow over a sharp-crested rectangular weir.

In those instances when v_1 is small (usually the case), the velocity distribution in the flow plane above the crest of the weir is:

$$v_2 = \sqrt{2gh}$$

(9.39)

The ideal flow rate Q over the weir is obtained by integrating the flow (v_2 dA) over the area of the flow plane above the weir to obtain:

$$Q = \int_A v_2 \, dA = \int_0^H \sqrt{2gh} \, L \, dh = \frac{2}{3}\sqrt{2g} \, LH^{3/2} \qquad (9.40)$$

where L is the width of the weir.

The actual flow rate Q_a over a weir is less than the ideal flow rate Q due to the vertical drawdown contraction from the top, friction losses in the flow and non-horizontal velocities in the flow plane above the weir. These effects are accounted for by introducing a weir discharge coefficient C_D.

$$Q_a = C_D Q = \frac{2}{3}\sqrt{2g} \, C_D LH^{3/2} \qquad (9.41)$$

Values of C_D range from 0.62 to 0.75 as the ratio of weir head H to weir height P ranges from 0.1 to 2.0. The weir must be sharp for these coefficients to be valid. When the rectangular weir does not extend across the full width of the channel, additional contractions occur due to the ends so that the effective width of the weir is (L − 0.1nH), where n is the number of end contractions. Corrosion and algae often cause the weir edges to appear rough and rounded. This rounding produces an increase in the weir coefficient due to a reduction in the edge contraction.

When flow rates are small, a triangular (V-notch) weir, as illustrated in Fig. 9.26, is often used. This type of weir exhibits a higher degree of accuracy over a wider range of flow rates than the rectangular weir. The V-notch weir also has the advantage that the average width of the flow section increases as the head increases. The discharge equation for the triangular weir is derived in the same manner as the equation for the rectangular weir. The results are:

$$Q_a = \frac{8}{15}\sqrt{2g} \, \tan(\theta/2) \, C_D H^{5/2} \qquad (9.42)$$

Triangular weirs with included angles θ between 45 and 90 degrees have discharge coefficients C_D that range between 0.58 and 0.60 provided the head H is in excess of 5 in. of water.

These results indicate that the flow rate depends on the head H when weirs are being used as the measuring device. The head H can be measured manually with a scale or with a float-activated displacement transducer that serves as the sensor for a data recording system.

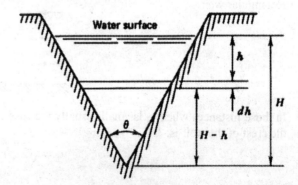

Fig. 9.26 A triangular or V-notched weir.

9.6 COMPRESSIBLE FLOW EFFECTS IN CLOSED SYSTEMS

When a gas flows through a gradual contraction in a piping system or through a venturi type of flowmeter, compressibility effects occur that must be considered at Mach numbers greater than 0.3 for accurate measurements. By using the energy equation, the equation of state for a perfect gas, the continuity relationship for one-dimensional flow, and assuming the process to be isentropic, it can be shown that the mass flow rate $\dot{m}_c$ through a venturi-type contraction is:

$$\dot{m}_c \frac{A_2}{\sqrt{1-\left(p_2/p_1\right)^{2/k}\left(A_2/A_1\right)^2}} \sqrt{\frac{2k}{k-1}p_1\rho_1\left[\left(\frac{p_2}{p_1}\right)^{2/k}-\left(\frac{p_2}{p_1}\right)^{(k+1)/k}\right]} \tag{9.43}$$

The corresponding relation (Bernoulli's equation) for an incompressible flow is:

$$\dot{m}_B = \frac{A_2\rho_1}{\sqrt{1-\left(A_1/A_2\right)^2}}\sqrt{2g\left(\frac{p_1-p_2}{\gamma_1}\right)} \tag{9.44}$$

A comparison of Eqs. (9.43) and (9.44) indicates that an expansion factor C_E can be incorporated into Eq. (9.44) to account for the differences between compressible and incompressible flow. Energy losses are accounted for by introducing a velocity coefficient C_V, in the same manner as in Eq. (9.25), to correlate ideal and actual flow rates. With the introduction of these coefficients, the expression for mass flow rate for both compressible and incompressible flow becomes:

$$\dot{m} = \frac{C_v C_E A_2\rho_1}{\sqrt{1-\left(A_1/A_2\right)^2}}\sqrt{2g\left(\frac{p_1-p_2}{\gamma}\right)} \tag{9.45}$$

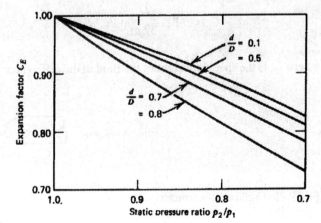

Fig. 9.27 Expansion factor C_E as a function of static pressure ratio for a venturi type contraction.

Values of the expansion factor C_E for different pressure ratios p_2/p_1 are shown in Fig. 9.27. This relation is limited to subsonic flow (M < 1) at the throat. The critical pressure ratio for a gas, above which the flow will be subsonic, is given by:

$$\left(\frac{p_2}{p_1}\right)_{Critical} = \left(\frac{2}{k+1}\right)^{k/(k-1)} \tag{9.46}$$

For air ($k = 1.4$), the critical pressure ratio is 0.528.

9.7 OTHER FLOW MEASUREMENT METHODS FOR CLOSED SYSTEMS

Several widely used, but markedly different, flow-measurement methods for closed systems are discussed in this section. Included is a capillary flow meter for very small flow rates, positive-displacement flowmeters that are used when high accuracy is needed under steady-flow conditions, hot-film mass flow transducers that are insensitive to temperature and pressure variations and laser-Doppler anemometers for non-contracting flow measurements.

9.7.1 Capillary Flow Meter

When very small flow rates must be measured, the capillary flow meter, shown schematically in Fig. 9.28, is very useful. The operation of this meter is based on the well-understood and experimentally verified conditions associated with laminar flow in a circular pipe. The Hagen-Poiseuille law, that governs laminar flow is written as:

$$\frac{p_1 - p_2}{\gamma} = \frac{32\mu L}{\gamma D^2} v = \frac{\gamma_m - \gamma}{\gamma} h \tag{9.47}$$

This relation is valid for $(Re)_D < 2{,}000$. The velocity v is expressed in terms of the pressure difference $(p_1 - p_2)$ or a differential manometer head h, as shown in Fig. 9.28, as:

$$v = \frac{D^2}{32\mu L}(p_1 - p_2) = \frac{D^2}{32\mu L}(\gamma_m - \gamma)h \tag{9.48}$$

where γ_m is the specific weight of the fluid in the differential manometer.

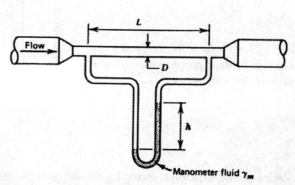

Fig. 9.28 Capillary flow meter.

The volume flow rate, obtained from Eq. (9.48), is:

$$Q = \frac{\pi D^4}{128 \mu L} (\gamma_m - \gamma) h = Kh \qquad (9.49)$$

Because the viscosity μ and the specific weight γ of the fluid are temperature dependent, the calibration constant K is a function of temperature. When the constants have been established for the appropriate temperature, the flow rate Q is determined from a visual inspection or optical measurement of the differential manometer head h or through a measurement of the pressure difference ($p_1 - p_2$) with a differential pressure transducer and an appropriate recording instrument.

9.7.2 Positive-Displacement Flowmeters

Positive-displacement flowmeters are normally used where high accuracy is needed (examples are home water and gasoline pump meters). Two common types of positive-displacement flowmeters are the nutating-disk meter (wobble meter) and the rotary-vane meter.

The nutating-disk meter, shown schematically in Fig. 9.29, is widely used as the flow sensing unit in home water meters. In this type of meter, an inlet chamber is formed by the housing, a disk and a partition between the inlet and outlet ports. Water is prevented from leaving the chamber by the disk that maintains line contact with the upper and lower conical surfaces of the housing. When the pressure is reduced on the outlet side by a demand for water, the pressure difference causes the disk to wobble (but not rotate) about the vertical axis (axis of symmetry of the housing) and thus provides a passage for the flow around the partition. The wobble of the disk causes a small pin attached to the spherical mount for the disk to trace out a circular path about the vertical axis of the device. This motion of the pin is used to drive the recording mechanism. Because a fixed volume of water moves through the device during each revolution of the drive shaft, a simple mechanical or electronic counter can be used to monitor the flow rate. The nutating-disk flowmeter is accurate to within 1% when it is in good condition. When it is worn, the accuracy will be considerably less, especially for very small flow rates (such as a leaky faucet).

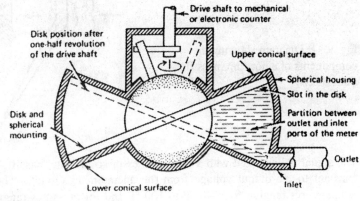

Fig. 9.29 Nutating disk positive displacement flow meter.

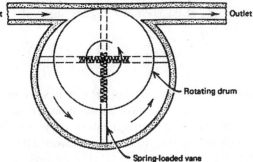

Fig. 9.30 Rotary-vane positive displacement flow meter.

A second positive-displacement flowmeter, illustrated in Fig. 9.30, is the rotary-vane. This type of flowmeter consists of a cylindrical housing in which an eccentrically mounted drum, with several spring-mounted vanes, rotates. A fixed volume of fluid is transferred from the inlet port to the outlet port during each rotation of the drum. Thus, a counter is used to monitor the flow rate. The rotary-vane flowmeter is generally more rugged and accurate (about ½%) than the nutating-disk flowmeter.

9.7.3 Hot-Film Mass Flow Transducers

The hot-film sensor, discussed in Section 9.2, provides the basis for a mass flow transducer that is relatively insensitive to gas temperature and gas pressure variations. The mass flow rate in a closed channel depends on the cross-sectional area A of the channel, the density ρ of the fluid and the flow velocity v. With a fixed channel area A, the momentum per unit area ρv provides a measure of the mass flow rate. Equation (9.19) applied to mass flow transducer design is written as:

$$q = \left[A + B(\rho v)^{1/n} \right]\left(\theta_a - \theta_f \right) = I_a^2 R_a \qquad (9.50)$$

Note that the momentum per unit area (ρv) appear as a product term in Eq. (9.50). A transducer developed to measure ρv directly is shown in Fig. 9.31. The hot-film probe in the center of the venturi throat responds to ρv, while the temperature sensor measures the fluid temperature. Inlet screens align the flow field. The hot-film sensor is heated by current from an anemometer control circuit to a temperature above that of the fluid. The fluid then transports heat away from the sensor in proportion to the flow rate.

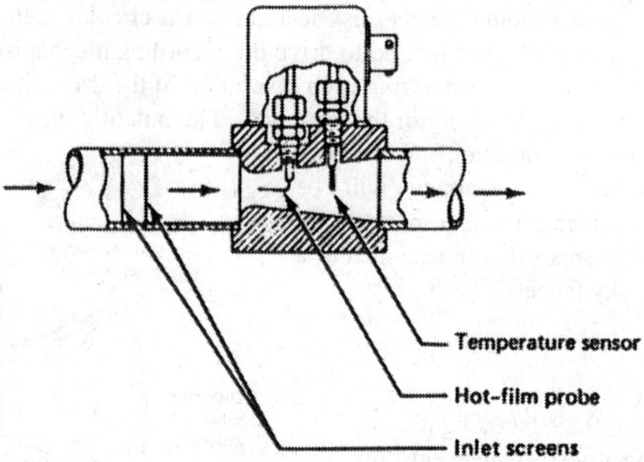

Fig. 9.31 Diagram showing the components of a hot film mass flow transducer.

Temperature sensor

Hot–film probe

Inlet screens

The signal is linearized with a microprocessor so that the mass flow rate is related with a calibration constant to the output voltage from the anemometer circuit. The calibration constant is valid for temperatures ranging from 40 °F to 100 °F and for pressures ranging from 15 psia to 30 psia. Flow ranges of 1,000 to 1 with an accuracy of 0.5%, a repeatability of 0.05% and a response time of 1 ms are possible.

9.7.4 Laser Velocimetry Systems

The coherence of laser light has lead to the development of an optical method of velocity measurement known as laser-Doppler anemometry or laser- Doppler velocimetry. In wave propagation, frequency changes occur as a result of movement of the source, receiver, propagating medium or intervening reflector or scatterer. Such frequency changes arc known as Doppler shifts and are named after the Austrian mathematician and physicist Christian Doppler (1803-1853).

An example of the Doppler effect in the field of acoustics is the increase of the pitch of a train whistle as the train approaches an observer, followed by a decrease in pitch as the train moves away. The effect, illustrated in Fig. 9.32, is based on the perception that the number of sound waves arriving per unit time at the observer's position represents the frequency of the whistle.

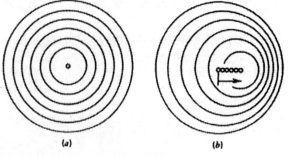

Fig. 9.32 Illustration of the Doppler effect.
    (a) Wave nodes from a stationary source.
    (b) Wave nodes from a moving source.

(a)   *(b)*

In laser-Doppler anemometry there is no relative movement between the source and the receiver. Instead, the Doppler shift is produced by the movement of particles (either natural or seeded) in the flow. These particles scatter light from the source and permit the light to reach the receiver. This same principle provides the basis for radar; however, in the case of radar, a much lower frequency part of the electromagnetic spectrum is used. The velocities commonly measured by using laser-Doppler anemometry are very small when compared to the velocity of light; therefore, the corresponding Doppler shifts in the frequency are very small. With red light from a helium-neon laser ($\lambda = 632.8$ nm, $f = 4.7(10^{14})$ Hz and a supersonic flow of 500 m/s, the Doppler shift in frequency is approximately 790 MHz. To confirm this result, note that the Doppler frequency shift f_D is:

$$\Delta f = f_D = \frac{fv}{c} \tag{9.51}$$

where f is the frequency of the light source; c is the propagation velocity of light 2.98×10^8 m/s; v is the particle velocity.

Because the resolution of a good-quality optical spectrometer is about 5 MHz, only velocities associated with high velocity flows can be measured with reasonable accuracy by using direct Doppler-shift measurements indicated in Eq. (9.51).

An optical beating technique for determining small Doppler shifts, which is equivalent to heterodyning in radio (signal mixing to obtain alternating constructive and destructive interference or beating), may be employed for lower velocity measurements. Light scattered from particles seeded in flowing water was mixed (heterodyned) with an unshifted reference beam of light from the laser to produce a beat frequency that is equal to the Doppler-shift frequency. The result of adding two signals with slightly different frequencies to obtain a beat frequency is illustrated in Fig. 9.33.

A schematic illustration of a simple reference beam anemometer, shown in Fig. 9.34, shows the light from the laser divided with a beam splitter into an illuminating beam and a reference beam. Some of the light from the illuminating beam is scattered in the direction of the reference beam by the particles in the flow. The light from the two beams is combined (added) by the photodetector. The output signal contains a beat frequency equal to the Doppler-shift frequency that is produced by the movement (velocity) of the particles. This frequency is determined using a spectrum analyzer. Optimum results are obtained when the intensity of the reference beam is approximately equal to that of the scattered beam. An attenuator is placed in the path of the reference beam to adjust its intensity. The reference beam anemometer is simple in principle; however, high signal-to-noise ratios are difficult to obtain in practice. The relationship between Doppler-shift frequency f_D and particle velocity v is:

$$f_D = \frac{2v\cos\alpha}{\lambda}\sin\frac{\theta}{2} \qquad (9.52)$$

where λ is the wavelength of the light; θ is the angle between the illuminating and reference beams; α is the angle between the particle velocity vector and a normal to the bisector of the angle between the illuminating and reference beams.

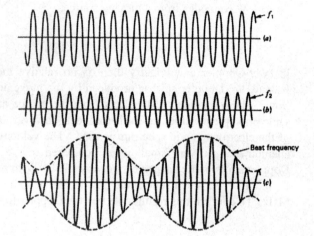

Fig. 9.33 Signal addition (heterodyning) yields a combined signal with a beat frequency f = (f – f)/2.
  (a) Signal No. 1
  (b) Signal No. 2
  (c) Combined signal.

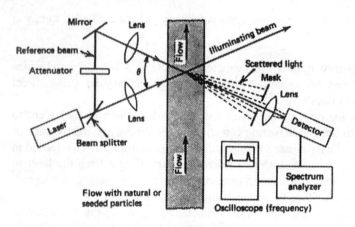

Fig. 9.34 Reference beam anemometer.

Typical frequency f_D versus velocity v curves for a reference beam anemometer are shown in Fig. 9.35. Because the wavelength of the helium-neon laser is known to an accuracy of 0.01% and because modern signal processing electronics provide very accurate determinations of the Doppler-shift frequency f_D, the accuracy of velocity determinations is controlled by the accuracy in determining the angle θ. The useful range of θ between 0.28 and 28° for gas, liquid and two-phase flow are shown within the crosshatched area in Fig. 9.35.

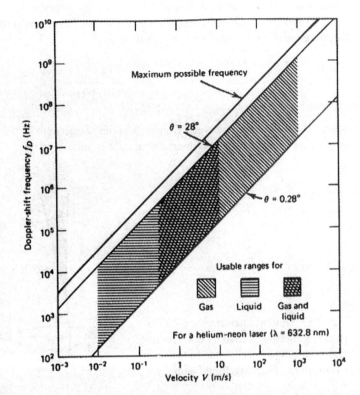

Fig. 9.35 Doppler shift frequency versus velocity for a reference beam anemometer.

A second type of velocity measuring instrument, known as a differential-Doppler anemometer, is shown in Fig. 9.36. In this instrument, scattered light from two equal-intensity beams are combined to produce the beat signal. The frequency of this beat signal is equal to the difference between the Doppler shifts for the two angles of scattering. The primary advantage of this mode of operation is that the beat frequency is independent of the receiving direction. The light is collected with a large aperture lens that is focused on the photodetector. All of this light contributes to the output signal enhancing the signal to noise ratio. When the particle concentration is low, the differential-Doppler anemometer is preferred to the reference beam anemometer because of its sensitivity to low intensity signals.

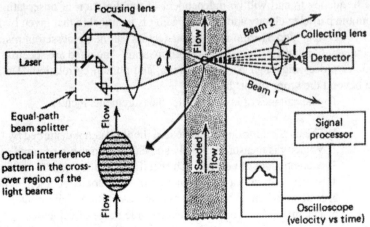

Fig. 9.36 Differential Doppler anemometer.

Operation of the differential-Doppler anemometer is based on the optical interference pattern (fringe pattern) formed in the crossover region of the two beams, as shown in Fig. 9.37. The spacing of the interference fringes is given by the expression:

$$s = \frac{\lambda}{2\sin(\theta/2)} \qquad (9.53)$$

where s is the spacing between fringes; λ is the wavelength of the light that is producing the fringes; θ is the angle between the two intersecting light beams.

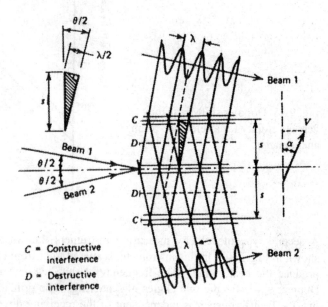

Fig. 9.37 Optical interference patterns (fringe patterns) formed by constructive and destructive interference in the cross over region of the two light beams.

A particle in the flow moving with a velocity v in a direction that makes an angle α, as defined in Fig. 9.36, produces a modulation of light intensity as it moves through the fringes. Because the light scattered from the particle depends on the intensity associated with the fringes, it is also modulated at the frequency f_D and will be independent of the direction of observation. The frequency f_D obtained from the particle velocity and fringe spacing is identical to that given by Eq. (9.52).

Output signals from the photodetectors can be processed in many ways to obtain the Doppler frequency f_D required for velocity determinations. Included are spectrum analysis, frequency tracking, counter processing, filter bank processing, and photon correlation. Details of all of these procedures are beyond the scope of this book.

The advantages of laser-Doppler measurements include:

1. The method is non-obtrusive and the flow is not disturbed by the presence of a probe.
2. Velocity is measured directly and calibration is not required.
3. A component of velocity in a specified direction can be measured.
4. System output is a linear function of the velocity component being measured.
5. Velocities can be measured in flows exhibiting high turbulence.
6. The method is suitable for a very wide range of velocities.

9.8 SUMMARY

The methods employed to measure flow depend primarily on five factors:

1. Is the fluid incompressible or is it necessary to account for compressibility?
2. Is the system closed, partially closed, or is a body moving through a boundless medium?
3. To what degree is it permissible to disturb the flow field in making the measurement?
4. How important are the energy losses due to the insertion of flow meters?
5. What are the requirements for frequency response and accuracy?

Clearly, it is relatively easy to measure steady state flow of an incompressible fluid that is transported in a closed system. One simply inserts a calibrated flowmeter (Section 9.3) that has been standardized and measures differential pressure.

When the fluid is compressible it is necessary to measure temperature in addition to pressure differences across the obstruction to predict mass flow rates. In this situation, the flowmeter calibration combines the effects of energy losses and expansion with coefficients C_V and C_E.

Often disturbances to the flow are not important and it is a simple matter, say to build a sluice gate, to measure flow in an irrigation ditch. However, in other instances, even a minor disturbance can alter the flow field. Probes and obstructions cannot be employed and non-contact Doppler velocimetry is required.

For high-frequency phenomena, where small probes are possible, hot-wire or hot-film anemometers provide high accuracy to frequencies of 500 kHz. These probes are also widely employed in the study of turbulence either to determine the mean velocity of the turbulence or the spectrum of the turbulence.

For low velocity air flow (probably the most common application), the pitot tube remains the preferred approach with simple manometers to measure the differential pressures.

Accuracy in the measurement of flow and/or mass rates depends very strongly on calibration. The calibration process includes the flow sensing device, usually one or two pressure sensors, and a voltage record. When possible, system calibration techniques should be employed. However, when system calibration is not feasible, serious attention must be given to establish each of the individual calibration constants.

REFERENCES

1. Benedict, R. P.: Fundamentals of Temperature, Pressure, and Flow Measurement, 3rd ed., Wiley, New York, 1984.
2. Benedict, R. P.: "Most Probable Discharge Coefficients for ASME Flow Nozzles," Transactions of the American Society of Mechanical Engineers, Journal of Basic Engineering, December, 1966, p. 734.
3. Daugherty, R. L. and J. R. Franzini: Fluid Mechanics with Engineering Applications, 8th Ed., McGraw-Hill, New York, 1985.
4. Dean, R. C.: "On the Necessity of Unsteady Flow in Fluid Mechanics," ASME Journal of Basic Engineering 81D; March, 1959, pp. 24-28.
5. Drain, L. E.: The Laser-Doppler Technique, Wiley, New York, 1980.
6. Durrani, T. S. and C. A. Greated: Laser Systems in Flow Measurement, Plenum Press, New York, 1977.
7. Durst, F., A. Melling, and J. H. Whitelaw: Principles and Practice of Laser-Doppler Anemometry, 2nd ed., Academic Press, New York, 1981.
8. French, R. H.: Open Channel Hydraulics, McGraw-Hill, New York, 1985.

9.   Goldstein, R. J., (Ed.): Fluid Mechanics Measurements, Hemisphere, New York, 1983.
10.   Holman, J. P.: Experimental Methods for Engineers, 4th ed., McGraw-Hill, New York, 1984.
11.   John J. E. and W. L. Haberman: Introduction to Fluid Mechanics, 3rd ed., Prentice-Hall, Englewood Cliffs, NJ, 1988.
12.   Lenz, A. T.: "Viscosity and Surface-Tension Effects on V-Notch Weir Coefficients," Transactions of the American Society of Civil Engineers, vol. 108, 1943, pp. 759-802.
13.   Miller, R. W.: Flow Measurement Engineering Handbook, 2nd ed., McGraw-Hill, New York, 1989.
14.   Munson, B.R., D.F. Young, and T.H. Okiishi: Fundamentals of Fluid Mechanics, Wiley, New York, 1990.
15.   Panton, R. L.: Incompressible Flow, Wiley, New York, 1984.
16.   Perry, A. E.: Hot-Wire Anemometry, Clarendon Press, Oxford, 1982.
17.   Spitzer, David W.: Industrial Flow Measurement, Instrument Society of America, Research Triangle Park, NC, 1990.
18.   The U.S. Standard Atmosphere, U.S. Government Printing Office, Washington, DC, 1976.
19.   Vennard, J. K. and R. L. Street: Elementary Fluid Mechanics, 6th ed., Wiley, New York, 1982.
20.   White, F. M.: Viscous Fluid Flow, 2nd Ed., McGraw-Hill, New York, 1991.

EXERCISES

9.1 For laminar flow in a circular pipe, show that the average velocity v_{av} is one-half of the centerline velocity v_0.

9.2 The velocity profile for fully developed flow in circular pipes is given by Eq. (9.5). Show that the average velocity V_{av} is related to the centerline velocity V_0 by Eq. (9.6).

9.3 Water at 60 °F flows through a 10-inch-diameter pipe with an average velocity of 20 ft/s. Determine the weight flow rate, the mass flow rate, the energy per second being transmitted through the pipe in the form of kinetic energy $(\gamma Q v^2/2g)$, the velocity profile exponent n, and the centerline velocity.

9.4 For the rectangular duct shown in Fig. E9.4, the velocity profile can be approximated by the expression:

$$v = v_C\left[1-(x/a)^2\right]\left[1-(y/b)\right]^2$$

Determine v_{av} in terms of v_C for this case.

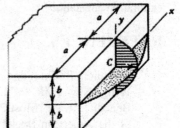

Fig. E9.4

9.5 A pitot tube is connected to a manometer filled with fluid of specific weight γ_m as shown in Fig. E9.5. When the manometer connection pipes are filled with the flowing fluid of specific weight γ, the pressure differential is independent of dimension a. Show that the free-stream velocity is given by the expression:

$$v_0 = C_1\sqrt{2g\frac{\gamma_m - \gamma}{\gamma}h} = K\sqrt{h}$$

Show that K = 1.087 when the manometer fluid is mercury, $C_1 = 0.98$, v_0 is expressed in meters per second, and h is measured in centimeters. How would these results be altered if the pipe were inclined at an angle of 60 degrees from the horizontal?

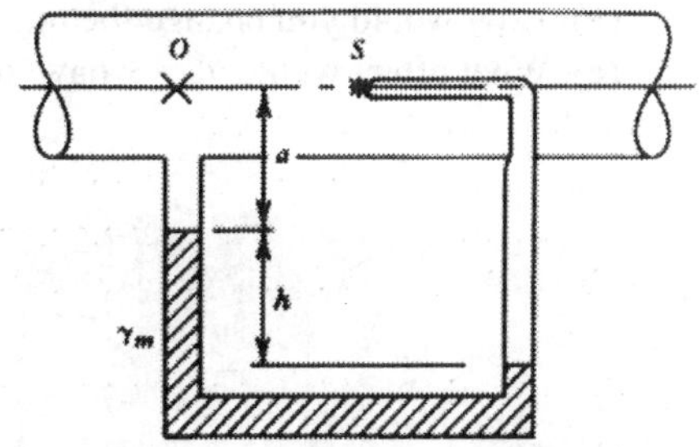

Fig. E9.5

9.6 Compare the velocity measurement error associated with a 40-degree misalignment for the two types of pitot tubes shown in Fig. 9.7 when the true dynamic pressure is 4 in. of water for carbon dioxide flowing.

9.7 A 0.125-in.-diameter pitot tube is to be used to measure the velocity of two liquids (water and glycerin). What is the minimum velocity for each liquid below which viscous effects must be considered? Assume both liquids are at room temperature.

9.8 A pitot-static tube is used to measure the speed of an aircraft. The air temperature and pressure are 30 °F and 12.3 psia, respectively. What is the aircraft speed in miles per hour if the differential pressure is 35 in. of water? Solve by using both Eq. (9.10) and Eq. (9.18). Compare the results.

9.9 A circular plate having a diameter of 25 mm is to be used as a drag force velocity transducer to measure the velocity of water at 68 °F. Determine the velocity sensitivity of the plate and the minimum velocity for which this sensitivity is valid.

9.10 Current meter data were collected at 13 vertical locations similar to those shown in Fig. 9.14 on a river that is 144 ft wide. The calibration constant for the current meter can be expressed as v = 2.45 N, where v is the flow velocity in feet per second and N is the speed of the rotating element in revolutions per second. Determine the river flow rates if the data collected at the 13 locations are as follows:

Station No.	River Depth (ft)	Rotating Element (RPM) At 0.2h	At 0.8h
1	0.0	----	----
2	3.0	40.1	31.2
3	3.5	51.1	41.5
4	4.2	59.0	43.0
5	3.7	62.1	48.2
6	5.1	68.3	50.2
7	4.6	65.6	48.2
8	3.8	60.2	45.8
9	4.0	56.5	48.0
10	3.2	57.3	39.8
11	3.1	48.8	38.0
12	2.0	41.2	29.8
13	0.0	----	----

9.11 Show that the ideal and actual volume flow rates for the closed system show in Fig. E9.11 are:

$$Q_a = C_V Q_i = \frac{C_V A_2}{\sqrt{1-(A_2/A_1)^2}} \sqrt{\frac{2g(\gamma_m - \gamma)h}{\gamma}}$$

where γ_m is the specific weight of the manometer fluid ($\gamma_m > \gamma$).

(a) Why aren't dimensions a and b in the above equation?
(b) How would you change the manometer connection if $(\gamma_m < \gamma)$?
(c) What effect would $\gamma_m < \gamma$ have on the above equation?

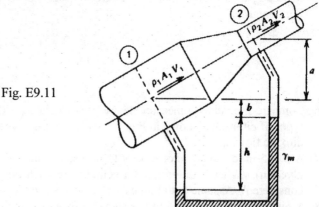

Fig. E9.11

9.12 A 3.0-in. by 1.5-in.-diameter venturi meter is used to measure the volume flow rate of turpentine in a chemical processing plant. Pressure differences are measured with a manometer having water as the manometer fluid.
   (a) Determine the ideal flow-rate sensitivity when the pressure drop is measured in inches of water.
   (b) How can the actual flow-rate sensitivity be estimated by using Fig. 9.18?
   (c) For a manometer reading of 18 in. of water and a fluid temperature of 68 °F, determine the actual flow rate.

9.13 The flow of water at 150 °F in an existing 10-in.-diameter pipe line is to be measured by using a 6-in.-diameter ASME long-radius flow nozzle. The flow rate will vary from 0.05 to 3.0 ft³/s.
   (a) What range of pressure drops should the differential pressure transducer be able to measure?
   (b) If a manometer is to be used to measure these pressure drops, select a reasonable manometer fluid for use in this application if it is assumed that a manometer can be easily read to ± 0.05 in.

9.14 A mercury manometer is connected to a standard orifice meter with a 30-mm-diameter hole that has been placed in a 100-mm-diameter pipe. What is the flow rate of crude oil at 20 °C if the manometer reading across the orifice plate is 240 mm of Hg.

9.15 Compare flow rates through 50-mm-diameter openings under 1.50-m static heads if the openings have been constructed as sharp-edged, rounded, short-tube, or Borda orifices. Ancient Rome's famous water system used sharp-edged orifices to meter water to Roman citizens. The clever citizens found that they could obtain 30 percent more water by inserting a short tube into the orifice and thus cheat Caesar out of significant water revenues.

9.16 An 8-in.-diameter opening is to be located in the side of a large tank. Water flows from the tank into a large reservoir. Estimate the flow between the tank and the reservoir when the difference in free-surface elevations is 20 ft. Assume:
   (a) That the most efficient orifice construction from Table 9.1 is used.
   (b) That the most inefficient orifice construction from Table 9.1 is used.
   (c) What assumptions are made when the terms "large tank" and "large reservoir" are used?

9.17 A 3.0-m-wide by 0.40-m-deep sluice gate is used to control the overflow of water from a small reservoir with a surface area of 100,000 m². When the water surface in the reservoir is 3.0 m above the bottom of the spillway (see Fig. 9.24), estimate the flow rate through the sluice gate and the rate at which the reservoir surface is falling. Assume $C_C = 0.61$ and $C_V = 0.96$.

9.18 Derive Eq. (9.41) for the flow rate over a rectangular weir and carefully list any assumptions required for the derivation. If C_D is assumed to be equal to 0.623 and if end contraction effects are neglected, show that:

(a) $Q_a = 3.33\ LH^{3/2}$ for the US Customary System of units.

(b) $Q_a = 1.83\ LH^3$ for the SI System of units.

9.19 T. Rehbock of the Karlsruhe Laboratory in Germany developed the following empirical expression for the weir discharge coefficient C_D, which yields good results for rectangular weirs with good ventilation, sharp edges, smooth weir faces, and adequate water stilling.

$$C_D = 0.605 + 0.08\ H/P + 1/305\ H$$

Plot values of C_D as a function of H (0.08 ft < H < 2.0 ft) for P equal to 0.2, 0.5, 1.0, 2.0 and 5.0 ft. Note: H/P must be less than 2 for the Rehbock equation to retain an accuracy of 1%.

9.20 A rectangular weir is to be placed in a 5-m-wide channel to measure a nominal flow rate of 6.0 m^3/s while maintaining a minimal channel depth of 4.0 m. Determine a suitable rectangular weir (width L and height P) if H/P must be less than 0.4 to ensure that $v_1^2/2g$ is negligible. What would the height P be for a 90-degree V-notch weir? If the flow rate doubles, which weir would experience the smaller change in weir head H?

9.21 The flow rate in a rectangular open channel of width L must be measured while a nearly constant fluid depth y is maintained. A floating sluice gate and a weir have been proposed as methods to achieve these goals. The two methods are shown in Fig. E9.21.

(a) Show that the flow rate under the sluice gate as given by the following linear equation between Q and H is accurate within 5%, provided C_{Ds} is constant and $H_s/P_s < 0.1$.

$$Q = C_D \sqrt{2gP_s}\ LH_s$$

(b) Compare the sluice gage and weir discharge equations and show that the sluice gate and weir readings are related by the expression:

$$H_s = \frac{2C_{Dw}}{3C_{Ds}} \frac{H_w^{3/2}}{\sqrt{P_s}}$$

(c) Based on the information of Part (b), which method will give the least variation of H with flow rate?

(d) Which unit is least expensive to install and maintain?

(e) Which proposal would you select and why?

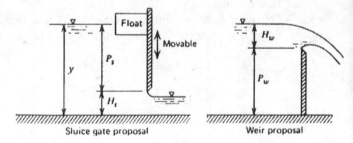

Fig. E9.21

9.22 Air stored in a tank at 300 psia and 150 °F flows into a second tank at 250 psia through a 1.0-in.-diameter flow nozzle. Determine:

(a) The mass flow rate of the air moving from one tank to the other.

(b) The minimum pressure in the second tank for subsonic flow.

9.23 Oxygen at 70 °F and 150 psia is flowing in a 3-in.-diameter line at a rate of 6 lb/s. Estimate the pressure drop across a 1.5-in.-diameter venturi meter that would be available for measuring the flow rate.

9.24 A capillary-tube flowmeter is being constructed to measure the flow rate of water. The glass tubing has an inside diameter of 1.00 mm and the pressure taps are located 0.1 m apart.

    (a) Estimate the flow rate if the manometer reading is 200 mm of mercury and the water temperature is 20 °C.

    (b) How much error results if the water temperature increases to 25 °C? Neglect any effects resulting from the expansion of the glass with temperature change.

9.25 Calibration of flowmeters is often performed with an experimental facility consisting of a pump, valve to regulate the flow from the pump, test meter and manometer, weight tank and scale, stopwatch, and reservoir as shown in Fig. E9.25.

    (a) What minimum length L of pipe should be used on the inlet side of the test meter?

    (b) What is the maximum flow rate that can be measured if errors are to be limited to ± 1%, if water caught in the weigh tank is limited to 200 lb, and if the stop watch can be started and stopped within 0.05 s of the correct time?

    (c) What additional information must be collected in order to properly calibrate the flowmeter?

    (d) How should flow rate Q versus manometer reading h be plotted in order to obtain the meter calibration relationship?

    (e) Find a standard relating to calibration of flowmeters in the library and study the calibration procedures recommended.

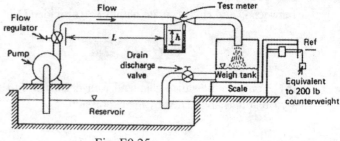

Fig. E9.25

9.26 Write an engineering brief for a laboratory technician describing the operation of a hot-film mass flow transducer.

9.27 Prepare a graph showing particle velocity in a flow field as a function of the Doppler shift in frequency. Assume that a helium-neon laser is used as the light source.

EXERCISE SOLUTIONS

Exercise 9.2

For fully developed flow:

From Eq. (9.5):

$$V = V_0 \left(1 - \frac{r}{R}\right)^{1/n}$$

From Eq. (9.3):

$$\dot{m} = \rho \int_A V \, dA = \rho V_{av} A$$

$$\dot{m} = \rho V_0 \int_0^{2\pi} \int_0^R \left(1 - \frac{r}{R}\right)^{1/n} r \, dr \, d\theta = 2\pi \rho V_0 \int_0^R \left(1 - \frac{r}{R}\right)^{1/n} r \, dr$$

$$= 2\pi \rho V_0 R^2 \int_0^1 \left(1 - \frac{r}{R}\right)^{1/n} \left(\frac{r}{R}\right) d\left(\frac{r}{R}\right)$$

Let $x = \frac{r}{R}$:

$$= 2\pi \rho V_0 R^2 \int_0^1 \left(1 - x\right)^{1/n} x \, dx$$

$$= 2\pi \rho V_0 R^2 \frac{n^2}{(1 + 2n)(n + 1)}$$

Since the cross-sectional area of a circular pipe is πR^2,

$$\dot{m} = 2\rho A V_0 \frac{n^2}{(1 + 2n)(n + 1)} = \rho V_{avg} A$$

Therefore:

$$V_{avg} = \frac{2n^2}{(n + 1)(1 + 2n)} V_0$$

Exercise 9.7

From Table B-2:

For Glycerin: $\qquad \rho = 2.439$ slugs/ft^3 $\qquad \mu = 3120(10^{-5})$ lb·s/ft^2

For Water: $\qquad \rho = 1.936$ slugs/ft^3 $\qquad \mu = 2.10(10^{-5})$ lb·s/ft^2

From Fig. 9.8: $\qquad C_p > 1$ if Re < 100

For Re $= \frac{\rho V D}{\mu} = 100$: $\qquad V_{min} = \frac{100 \, \mu}{\rho D}$

For glycerin: $\qquad V_{min} = \frac{100 \, \mu}{\rho D} = \frac{100(3120)(10^{-5})}{2.439 \,(0.125/12)} = 122.8$ ft/s.

For water: $\qquad V_{min} = \frac{100 \, \mu}{\rho D} = \frac{100(2.10)(10^{-5})}{1.936 \,(0.125/12)} = 0.104$ ft/s.

Exercise 9.10

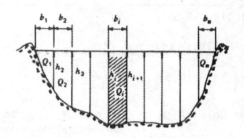

From Eq. (9.25) :

$$V_i = \frac{1}{2}\left(V_{2i} + V_{8i}\right)$$

$$= \frac{2.45}{2(60)}\left[N_{0.2h} + N_{0.8h}\right]$$

From Eq. (9.26) :

$$Q_i = \frac{1}{4}b_i(h_i + h_{i+1})(V_i + V_{i+1})$$

Exercise 9.25

(a) Use L > 10 to 30 pipe diameters to straighten the flow.

(b)

$$W = \gamma Q t$$

Therefore

$$Qt = \frac{W}{\gamma} = \frac{200}{62.4} = 3.205 \text{ ft}^3$$

For less than 1% error:

$$t_{min} = 100(0.05) = 5 \text{ s}$$

$$Q_{max} = \frac{3.205}{5} = 0.641 \text{ ft}^3/\text{s}$$

(c) The time t to collect a certain volume of water (to calculate Q).

The manometer reading h.

The inlet and throat diameters (to check the coefficients).

(d) Plot Q versus h on log log paper.

$$Q_a = CA_0\sqrt{\frac{2g(\gamma_m - \gamma)}{\gamma}} = K\sqrt{h}$$

Thus,

$$\log Q_a = \log K + \frac{1}{2}\log h$$

which is a straight line with a slope of $\frac{1}{2}$.

CHAPTER 10

ACCELERATION MEASUREMENTS, SEISMIC MODEL AND PIEZO SENSORS

10.1 INTRODUCTION

Many methods have been developed to measure linear and angular displacements (s and θ), velocities (v and ω) and accelerations (a and α). Displacements and accelerations are usually measured directly, while velocities are often obtained by integrating acceleration signals. The definitions of velocity (v = ds/dt or ω = dθ/dt) and acceleration (a = dv/dt = d^2s/dt^2 or α = dω/dt = $d^2\theta/dt^2$) suggest that any convenient quantity can be measured and the others can be obtained by integrating or differentiating the recorded signal. Because the differentiation process amplifies errors due to noise and other signal disturbances, differentiation is rarely used to determine either velocity or acceleration. The integration process reduces error and can be employed to determine velocity by integrating acceleration or to determine s by integrating velocity. However, it is important to account for the initial conditions (the lower limit in the integration process) to avoid errors. Displacement measurements are most frequently made in process-control applications, while acceleration measurements are made in vibration, shock or motion-measurement investigations.

Measurements of kinematic quantities, such as displacement, velocity and acceleration, must be made with respect to a system of reference axes. The basic frame of reference in mechanics is the primary inertial system that consists of an imaginary set of rectangular axes fixed in space. Measurements made with respect to this **primary inertial system** are absolute and the laws of Newtonian mechanics are valid as long as velocities are small compared to the speed of light (300,000 km/s or 186,000 mi/s).

A reference frame attached to the surface of the earth exhibits motion in the primary inertial system; therefore, corrections to the basic equations of mechanics may be required when measurements are made relative to an earth-based reference frame. For example, the absolute motion of the earth must be considered in calculations related to rocket-flight trajectories. However, for engineering measurements involving machines and structures that remain on the surface of the earth, corrections are extremely small and are usually neglected. Thus, measurements made relative to the earth on earth-bound engineering applications are considered absolute.

Measurements of quantities that describe motion (displacement, velocity and acceleration) are made using two significantly different approaches. One approach incorporates a fixed reference plane to which the base of the transducer is attached. The other approach involves seismic transducers that are employed when the use of a fixed reference plane is not possible. The principles of seismic transducers are described in this chapter and motion measurements relative to a fixed reference were described in Chapter 5.

10.2 THE SEISMIC TRANSDUCER MODEL

The mechanical behavior of seismic transducers is characterized by considering the one-degree-of-freedom dynamic model shown in Fig. 10.1a. It is assumed that y > x and $\dot{y} > \dot{x}$ in constructing the free-body diagram of the seismic mass shown in Fig. 10.1b. The equation of motion of the seismic mass, obtained from Newton's second law, is:

$$m\ddot{y} + C(\dot{y} - \dot{x}) + k(y - x) = F(t) \qquad (10.1)$$

where m is the seismic mass; k is the spring constant; C is the viscous damping constant.

x, $\dot{x}$ and $\ddot{x}$ are the displacement, velocity and acceleration of the base plane.

y, $\dot{y}$, and $\ddot{y}$ are the displacement, velocity and acceleration of the seismic mass.

F(t) is a time-dependent forcing function due to either a force or a pressure [F(t) = A p(t)].

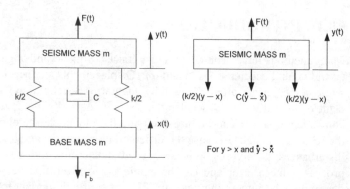

Fig. 10.1 (a) Single-degree-of-freedom model of a seismic instrument. (b) Free body diagram of the seismic mass.

The force required to attach the transducer base to the support structure is F_b. Note that this force does not affect the transducer.

To design a transducer using the seismic model, a sensor is placed between the base and the seismic mass. For the coordinates shown in Fig. 10.1a, the relative displacement of the sensor and its derivatives are:

$$z = y - x \qquad \dot{z} = \dot{y} - \dot{x} \qquad \ddot{z} = \ddot{y} - \ddot{x} \qquad (10.2)$$

Substituting Eqs. (10.2) into Eq. (10.1) gives the differential equation of motion:

$$m\ddot{z} + C\dot{z} + kz = F(t) - m\ddot{x} = R(t) \qquad (10.3)$$

where R(t) = F(t) − m$\ddot{x}$ represents the transducer excitation due to the external force and the inertia force produced by the base acceleration. Equation (10.3) shows that the relative motion z depends on the excitation, the damping C and the frequency of the excitation R(t) relative to the natural frequency $\left(\omega_n = \sqrt{k/m}\right)$ of the transducer.

The seismic transducer model, illustrated in Fig. 10.1, is employed as a frame to support accelerometers and dynamic force transducers. In the design of motion or force transducers, a sensor is placed between the base and the seismic mass to measure the relative displacement z or its derivatives $\dot{z}$ and $\ddot{z}$. Because z, $\dot{z}$ and $\ddot{z}$ are related to R(t) by Eq. (10.3), the unknown quantities $\ddot{x}$ or F(t) can be determined.

10.3 DYNAMIC RESPONSE OF THE SEISMIC MODEL

The dynamic response of the seismic model is given by Eq. (10.3). A general solution of this second-order differential equation is important because its solution enables one to characterize the response of specific transducers to different transient excitations.

Before beginning the solution of Eq. (10.3), we note that the transducer excitation R(t) is:

$$R(t) = F(t) - m\ddot{x} \qquad (10.4)$$

When the seismic frame is used to measure x, $\dot{x}$ or $\ddot{x}$, the applied force $F(t) = 0$ and $R(t) = -m\ddot{x}$. When it is used as a dynamic force transducer, the base of the transducer is fixed to a reference plane and $x = 0$ and $R(t) = F(t)$. When the seismic frame of a force transducer is attached to an accelerating base, the output is due to both $F(t)$ and $\ddot{x}$ as indicated in Eq. (10.4). Under these conditions, significant force measurement errors can occur when $F(t)$ is small and $\ddot{x}$ is large. This condition occurs when the structure under test is in a resonating condition. Also, there are situations where the gravity force mg causes acceleration measurement errors (see Exercise 10.4).

10.3.1 Sinusoidal Excitation

The method of analysis employed to obtain the steady-state response of the model involves the use of exponential functions. Using this approach the excitation has magnitude R_0, frequency ω and is written as:

$$R(t) = R_0\, e^{j\omega t} \qquad (a)$$

The corresponding relative motion and its derivatives are written as:

$$z = z_0 e^{j\omega t} \qquad \dot{z} = j\omega z_0 e^{j\omega t} \qquad \ddot{z} = -\omega^2 z_0 e^{j\omega t} \qquad (b)$$

where z_0 is the complex amplitude (magnitude and phase) of the response relative to the excitation R_0. Substituting Eqs. (a) and (b) into Eq. (10.3) yields:

$$\left(k - m\omega^2 + jC\omega\right) z_0 e^{j\omega t} = R_0 e^{j\omega t} \qquad (10.5)$$

The frequency response function $H(\omega)$ of the output z_0 relative to the input excitation R_0 is:

$$H(\omega) = \frac{z_0}{R_0} = \frac{1}{k - m\omega^2 + jC\omega} = \frac{1}{[(k - m\omega^2)^2 + (C\omega)^2]^{1/2}} e^{-j\phi} \qquad (10.6)$$

Both magnitude and phase information are given by Eq. (10.6). The magnitude $|H(\omega)|$ is:

$$|H(\omega)| = \frac{1}{k\left[(1 - r^2)^2 + (2rd)^2\right]^{1/2}} \qquad (10.7)$$

and the phase angle ϕ is:

$$\phi = \tan^{-1} \frac{C\omega}{k - m\omega^2} = \tan^{-1} \frac{2rd}{1 - r^2} \qquad (10.8)$$

where $d = \dfrac{C}{2\sqrt{km}}$ is the dimensionless damping ratio and $r = \omega/\omega_n = f/f_n$ is the dimensionless frequency ratio.

The particular solution of Eq. (10.3) for sinusoidal excitation is given by:

$$z = \frac{R_0}{\left[(k-m\omega^2)^2+(C\omega)^2\right]^{1/2}}e^{j(\omega t-\phi)}$$

$$= \frac{R_0}{\left[(1-r^2)^2+(2dr)^2\right]^{1/2}}e^{j(\omega t-\phi)} \tag{10.9}$$

$$= H(\omega)R_0 e^{j\omega t}$$

The angle between the rotating quantities R_0 and z_0 on the complex plane is illustrated in Fig. 10.2. Phase angle is considered to be negative when the response z_0 lags the excitation R_0 as indicated in Fig. 10.2

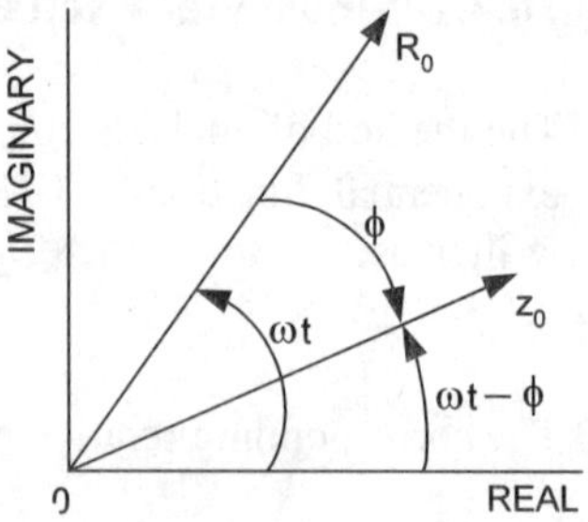

Fig. 10.2 Representation of the phase relation between the input excitation R_0 and the response z_0.

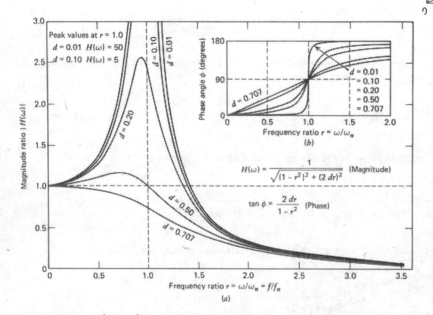

Figure 10.3 Frequency response curves for transducers for force and acceleration measurements.

The magnitude $\left|H(\omega)\right|$ and phase ϕ for the seismic model are shown in Fig. 10.3 as a function of the dimensionless frequency ratio r for various damping ratios d. The magnitude and phase vary considerably with input frequency. We note that d = 0.64 gives a phase shift that is nearly linear with frequency ω. A linear phase shift is essential to avoid signal distortion for frequency components below the transducers natural frequency. A damping ratio of 0.64 is sought because signals of different frequencies are shifted the same amount in time. Unfortunately, transducers usually exhibit low damping ratios (0.1 to about 4%) and the nearly linear phase shift with excitation frequency cannot be achieved. To avoid signal distortion due to non-linear phase shift, the frequency range of seismic transducers is limited to $0.2\,f_n$. The phase shift is nearly zero in this low-frequency range for such low damping ratios. Also, an examination of Fig. 10.3 shows the dynamic response to be the same as that for static loads when $(f/f_n) < 0.2$ because $\left|H(\omega)\right|$ and $kz \approx R_0$.

10.3.2 Transient Excitations

A basic concern, when seismic transducers are used, is the response of the mechanical sensing structure to transient events. A transient input involves rapid changes that occur over a short period of time. The rapid change is preceded and followed by a constant input for long periods of time compared to system response times. Step, ramp-hold, half-sine and triangular inputs are classic transient signals used to study transducer response characteristics.

A. Step Excitation

The characteristic response of a second-order system to a step input depends on its degree of damping. While three different cases are possible—overdamped, critically damped and underdamped, only the underdamped case is applicable to transducers because their degree of damping is nearly zero. The response of an underdamped transducer to a step function input is given by:

$$\frac{z}{z_0} = 1 - \frac{e^{-d\omega_n t}}{\sqrt{1-d^2}} \cos(\omega_n t - \phi) \tag{10.10}$$

where

$$\phi = \tan^{-1}\left(\frac{d}{\sqrt{1-d^2}}\right) \tag{10.10a}$$

For lightly damped transducers ($d < 2\%$), Eq. (10.10) indicates that the initial cycle of response is approximated by $[1 - \cos(\omega_n t)]$. A graph of this response, shown in Fig. 10.4, shows that it bears little resemblance to a step input. This example is indicative of the type of measurement error that occurs when the transducer is forced to "ring" at its natural frequency. The step input produces changes, which are much too rapid for a mechanical system to follow with fidelity.

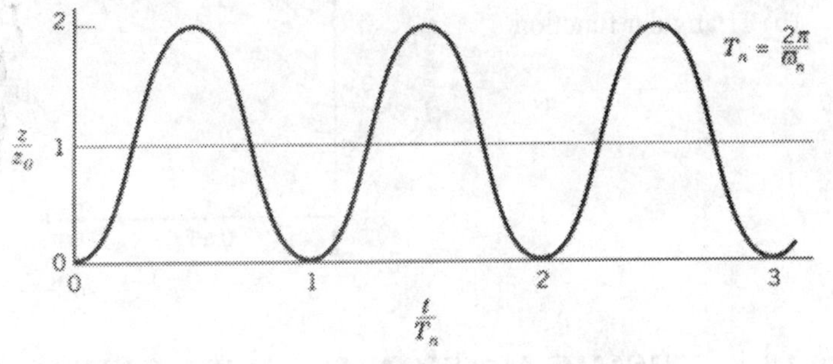

Fig. 10.4 Transducer ringing at its natural frequency ω_n when subjected to a step pulse.

B. Ramp-Hold Excitation

The terminated ramp-hold function described in Section 7.7.1 applies to seismic transducers as well because the governing differential equations are identical in form. Thus, the deviation of $1/\omega_n t_0$ for the ramp portion and the maximum error of $(2/\omega_n t_0)$ for the hold portion of the signal apply. Generally, $\omega_n t_0 > 10\pi$ is required in order to obtain satisfactory measurements.

C. Half-Sine and Triangle Pulses

Two common transients for impact loading are the half-sine and triangle pulses shown in Fig. 10.5. In this figure, the response of the transducer for pulse durations of T_n and $5T_n$ are shown where T_n is the natural period of the transducer. It is evident from these graphs that a reasonable response from the transducer requires a pulse duration that is at least five times the natural period of the transducer and preferably larger. For pulse durations equal to the natural period of the transducer T_n, the output is severely distorted as shown in Fig. 10.5. The conclusion drawn from this transient analysis is that either the transient rise time (or fall time) or the duration time must be greater than five times the period of the transducer. Transducer "ringing" at its natural frequency, which severely distorts the input signal, is a clear indication that this rule is being violated.

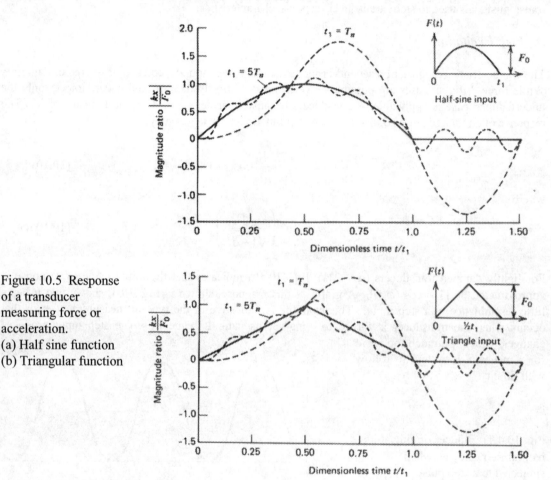

Figure 10.5 Response of a transducer measuring force or acceleration.
(a) Half sine function
(b) Triangular function

10.4 SEISMIC MOTION TRANSDUCERS

The theoretical basis for seismic motion instruments is a mechanical model, which leads to the equation of motion given by Eq. (10.3). The external force F(t), which acts on the seismic mass m, is zero in motion measurement applications, because the seismic mass is isolated in a protective case. The transducer is excited by an inertia force $m\ddot{x}$ applied through the base motion. In this treatment, the base motion is considered to be sinusoidal so that:

$$x = x_0 e^{j\omega t} \qquad \dot{x} = j\omega x_0 e^{j\omega t} \qquad \ddot{x} = -\omega^2 x_0 e^{j\omega t} \tag{10.11}$$

Thus, the excitation force R(t) in Eq. (10.3) becomes:

$$R(t) = R_0\, e^{j\omega t} = m\omega^2\, x_0{}^{j\omega t} \tag{10.12}$$

These equations are essential in describing seismic displacement, velocity and acceleration transducers.

10.4.1 Seismic Displacement Transducers

The characteristic behavior of a seismic displacement transducer is obtained by substituting Eq. (10.12) into the steady-state solution of Eq. (10.3) as given by Eq. (10.9). The result for the relative displacement z is:

$$z = \frac{r^2 x_0}{\left[\left(1-r^2\right)^2 + \left(2rd\right)^2\right]^{1/2}}\, e^{j(\omega t - \phi)} = H(\omega)x_0 e^{j\omega t} \tag{10.13}$$

The frequency response function $H(\omega)$ is shown in Fig. 10.6 in the form of a magnitude ratio z/x_0 and a phase angle ϕ versus frequency ratio $r = \omega/\omega_n$ for specific damping ratios. It is evident from these curves that ratio z/x_0 approaches unity and phase angle ϕ approaches 180 degrees for frequency ratios greater than 4, irrespective of the amount of damping. The peak of the response curve decreases and the peaks occur at higher frequency ratios as the damping ratio is increased from $d = 0.01$ to 0.707.

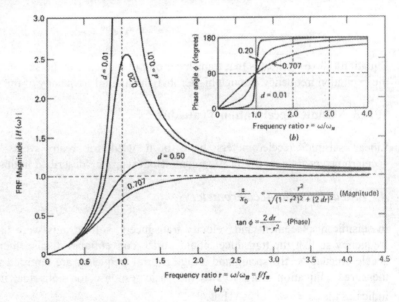

Fig. 10.6 The frequency response function $H(\omega)$ for a displacement transducer.

The results of Fig. 10.6 indicate that seismic displacement transducers must have a very low natural frequency so that their frequency ratio ω/ω_n is large. With the constraints $r \gg 1$ and $\phi \approx \pi$, Eq. (10.13) reduces to:

$$z = \frac{r^2 x_0}{\left[\left(-r^2\right)\right]^{1/2}}\, e^{j(\omega t - \pi)} \approx -x_0 e^{j(\omega t - \pi)} = -x_0 \tag{10.14}$$

Equation (10.14) indicates that the seismic mass does not move; therefore, the transducer output response z is equal in magnitude to the input base motion x. The amount of damping used is not critical because the response curves for both $|H(\omega)|$ and ϕ converge for $r > 4$.

Seismic displacement transducers are designed with soft springs and a relatively large seismic mass to give an instrument with a very low natural frequency. As a result, the common sensors used to measure the relative displacement z are linear variable differential transformers (LVDTs) or electrical resistance strain gages mounted on elastic supports that also serve as the soft springs.

10.4.2 Seismic Velocity Transducers

A seismic displacement transducer becomes a seismic velocity transducer when a magnetic core velocity sensor is used to measure the relative velocity z between the seismic mass and the instrument base. The governing equation that describes this type of instrument is obtained by differentiating Eq. (10.14) with respect to time. Thus,

$$\dot{z} = \frac{r^2 (j\omega x_0)}{\left[\left(1-r^2\right)^2 + (2rd)^2\right]^{1/2}} e^{j(\omega t - \phi)} = H(\omega)(j\omega x_0) e^{j\omega t} \tag{10.15}$$

The frequency response function $H(\omega)$ is the same as that of a displacement transducer. Thus, for the conditions that $r \gg 1.0$ and $\phi \approx \pi$, Eq. (10.14) reduces to:

$$\dot{z} \approx -j\omega x_0 e^{j\omega t} = -\dot{x} \tag{10.16}$$

Equation (10.16) indicates that transducer output motion z is the same as base input velocity $\dot{x}$ when the excitation frequency is much higher than the natural frequency of the transducer.

10.4.3 Seismic Acceleration Transducers

Linear seismic accelerometers have been used for many years; however, angular seismic accelerometers are a recent development. Both types are described in this subsection.

A. Linear Seismic Accelerometers

In seismic displacement and velocity transducers, soft springs were used to achieve a low natural frequency so that the transducer could utilize conventional displacement and velocity sensors. For accelerometers, a stiff spring and a high natural frequency are required when the inertia force $m\ddot{x}$ is measured. Equation (10.13) gives the basic response for sinusoidal input motion and Eq. (10.11) indicates that $\ddot{x} = -\omega x_0 e^{j\omega t}$. Thus,

$$z = -\frac{e^{-j\phi}}{\omega_n^2 \left[\left(1-r^2\right)^2 + (2rd)^2\right]^{1/2}} \ddot{x} = -H(\omega) \frac{1}{\omega_n^2} \ddot{x} \tag{10.17}$$

The frequency response function $H(\omega)$ in Eq. (10.17) is the same as that given in Eq. (10.6) and illustrated in Fig. 10.3. It is evident from these curves that the magnitude of $H(\omega)$ approaches unity and the phase angle ϕ approaches 0 when r is very small, irrespective of the amount of damping. Under the condition that $r \ll 1$, Eq. (10.17) reduces to:

$$z = -\frac{1}{\omega_n^2}\ddot{x} = -\frac{m\ddot{x}}{k} \qquad (10.18)$$

Equation (10.18) shows that in a seismic acceleration transducer the inertia force $m\ddot{x}$ is resisted by the spring force kz. This type of instrument requires a stiff spring and a small seismic mass so that it has a high natural frequency. Both piezoelectric and piezoresistive sensors are ideal for this application because they serves as a very stiff spring while providing an electrical output with a high sensitivity. Consequently, seismic transducers are small and light so that their presence has an insignificant effect on most vibrating structures.

Two common accelerometer designs, where the piezoelectric element is subjected to either compression or shear, are shown in Fig. 10.7. The single-ended compression type consists of a base, a threaded center post, a flat washer shaped piezoelectric element, a seismic mass and a nut. The piezo-electric element is prestressed by tightening the nut onto the center post. This unit has two spring elements, a center post k_1 and a piezoelectric element k_2 that act in series. The seismic mass is protected from the environment by a cover. This design is somewhat susceptible to base bending. The shear design consists of a base with a center post, a cylindrical shaped piezoelectric element and a seismic mass. The piezoelectric element is bonded to both the center post and the seismic mass. The entire assembly is sealed in a protective case. This design is less sensitive to base bending than the single-ended compression type described previously. If the center post is hollow and extends through the case at the top and bottom, the transducer can be mounted by using a bolt, which passes through the hole. This design is used in many of the smaller transducers.

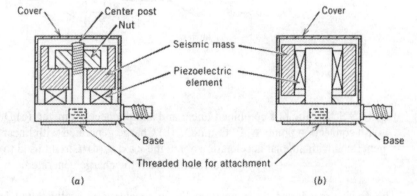

Figure 10.7 Section views of accelerometers designed with piezoelectric sensors.

B. Angular Seismic Accelerometers

Angular seismic accelerometers are difficult to design with high sensitivity for angular acceleration and low sensitivity to linear acceleration. However, recent developments in micromachining and fabrication of synthetic piezoelectric materials have resulted in a new transducer which allows both linear and angular acceleration to be measured simultaneously.

The design features of this accelerometer, shown in Fig. 10.8a, include a base, a center post and two cantilever beams fabricated from a piezoelectric ceramic. The piezo-beams labeled 1 and 2 are supported by a center post and the entire assembly is enclosed in a case. The x-y axes describe the orientation of the piezo-beams relative to the transducer base. Linear motion is sensed in the y-direction and angular motion by the counter clockwise angle α. The symbols A, B, C, and D indicate locations of the lead wire connections. The entire top and bottom surface on each piezo-beam is an electrode.

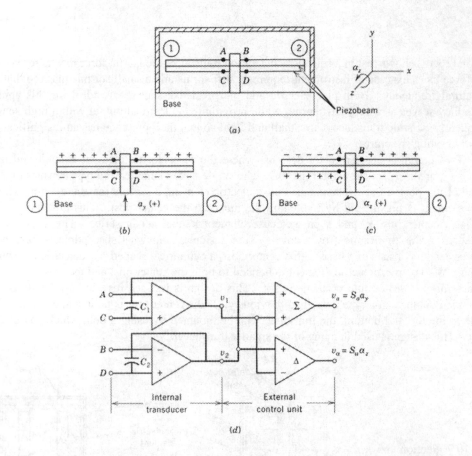

Fig. 10.8 Schematic of a combined linear and angular accelerometer. (a) Dual piezo-beam construction with connection points A, B, C and D. (b) Charge generated with linear acceleration. (c) Charge generated with angular acceleration about the z axis. (d) Circuit used to extract linear and angular acceleration from the charge generated.

The charge developed for a positive linear acceleration is illustrated in Fig. 10.8b. With proper polarity in the piezo-beam, the entire top surface of each beam becomes positively charged, while the entire bottom surface is negatively charged due to the acceleration induced stresses in the beams. Similarly, when the beam accelerates downward, the polarity of the electrical charge is reversed.

The charge condition for a positive angular acceleration is shown in Fig. 10.8c. With this inertia loading, the top of piezo-beam 1 is negative while its bottom is positive and the top of piezo-beam 2 is positive while the bottom is negative. The electrical connections from points A, B, C and D are used as input for the dual voltage follower/amplifier circuit shown in Fig. 10.8d.

10.5 PIEZOELECTRIC FORCE TRANSDUCERS

The seismic frame can also be used to support a piezoelectric crystal that senses the applied force F(t). If the base is attached to a fixed point, $m\ddot{x} = 0$ and Eq. (10.4) shows that R(t) = F(t). The analysis for the ramp-hold excitation presented in Section 7.7.1 clearly showed the importance of having an extremely high natural frequency for a force transducer.

The cross-section of a typical piezoelectric load cell is shown in Fig. 10.9. The seismic mass and base are separated by a two-piece piezoelectric sensor. The two-piece sensor permits the outer case to be the circuit ground while the interface at the center provides the circuit signal. The sensor is preloaded by tightening the seismic mass onto the central stud. Then, the outer case and seismic mass are welded together. The advantages of piezoelectric load cells are high output signal, high natural frequency and large stiffness for its size. Unfortunately, the transducer's high natural frequency is degraded when it is attached to another mass, because the transducer's effective seismic mass is relatively small.

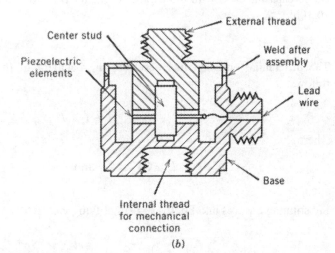

Fig. 10.9 Cross section showing construction details of a piezoelectric force sensor.

10.6 PIEZOELECTRIC SENSOR CIRCUITS

Piezoelectric sensors are often employed in accelerometers and in force and pressure transducers to obtain high natural frequencies, low weight and excellent sensitivity. Piezoelectric sensing elements are charge-generating devices that exhibit a high-output impedance; therefore, extremely high-input-impedance, signal-conditioning instruments, such as voltage followers and charge amplifiers must be employed to convert the charge to an output voltage, which is measured and recorded. The operational and performance characteristics of these circuits are discussed in detail in this section.

10.6.1 Charge Sensitivity Model

The charge is generated by a piezoelectric element when it is subjected to pressure. This charge is directly proportional to the electrode area A and pressure p exerted on the piezoelectric element. The charge generated is related to the measured quantity by a linear relationship of the form:

$$q = S_q * a \qquad\qquad (10.19)$$

where q is the charge generated by the piezoelectric element (pC); S_q* is the charge sensitivity of the transducer (pC/g, pC/lb, pC/N, pC/psi or pC/Pa) and a is the quantity being measured (acceleration, force or pressure in g's, lbs, N, psi or Pa).

This linear charge model expressed in Eq. (10.19) is used in developing circuit sensitivities in all subsequent developments.

10.6.2 Voltage Follower Circuit

A schematic diagram of a circuit containing a piezoelectric sensor and a voltage follower (unity-gain buffer amplifier) is shown in Fig. 10.10a. The piezoelectric sensor is denoted by the charge generator symbol. The circuit includes capacitances C_t of the transducer, C_c of the cable, C_s of the standardizing section in the amplifier end of the circuit and C_b of the blocking capacitor used to protect the amplifier. The resistance R represents the combined effect of amplifier input impedance and a load resistor in parallel with the amplifier. Combining the transducer, cable and standardizing capacitances into a single capacitance C with the parallel capacitor law, we obtain the equivalent circuit, shown in Fig. 10.10b:

$$C = C_t + C_c + C_s \tag{a}$$

The differential equation that describes the behavior of the circuit in Fig. 10.10b is obtained as follows:

$$I = I_1 + I_2 = \dot{q} = S_q^* \dot{a} \tag{b}$$

where

$$I_1 = C\dot{V_1} \qquad \text{and} \qquad I_2 = C_b(\dot{V_1} - \dot{V}) = \frac{V_0}{R} \tag{c}$$

Substituting Eqs. (c) into Eq. (b) and simplifying yields:

$$\dot{V_0} + \frac{V_0}{RC_{eq}} = \frac{S_q^*}{C}\dot{a} \tag{10.20}$$

where

$$\frac{1}{C_{eq}} = \frac{1}{C} + \frac{1}{C_b} \tag{d}$$

Typical values of C range from 300 pF to 10,000 pF, while values of C_b are usually of the order of 100,000 pF. For practical purposes, the equivalent capacitance C_{eq} of Eq. (d) is essentially the same as the combined source capacitance C given by Eq. (a).

The frequency response function for this circuit is obtained by using $a = a_0\, e^{j\omega t}$ for the quantity being measured and $V = V_0\, e^{j\omega t}$ for the response voltage. Substituting these equations into Eq. (10.20) gives the output voltage as:

$$V_0 = \left(\frac{jRC_{eq}\omega}{1 + jRC_{eq}\omega}\right)\left(\frac{S_q^* a_0}{C}\right) \tag{10.21}$$

The basic voltage sensitivity of the instrument is obtained from Eq. (10.22) as:

$$S_v = \frac{V_0}{a_0} = \frac{S_q^*}{C} \tag{10.22}$$

Equation (10.22) shows that voltage sensitivity of the measurement system of Fig. 10.10a depends on all source capacitances that contribute to C. The specific cable used during the measurement, environmental factors such as temperature and humidity, and dirt (including grease, or sprays), which play no role in a clean laboratory but may be significant in an industrial setting, can produce a change in the circuit voltage sensitivity.

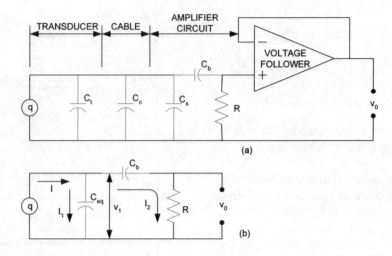

Fig. 10.10 (a) Voltage-follower circuit with a piezoelectric sensor. (b) The equivalent circuit.

The frequency response function H(ω) for the circuit in Fig 10.10a is obtained from the first bracket on the right-hand side of Eq. (10.21). Thus,

$$H(\omega) = \frac{CV_0}{S_q a_0} = \frac{jRC_{eq}\omega}{1 + jRC_{eq}\omega} = \frac{\omega\tau}{\left[1 + (\omega\tau)^2\right]^{1/2}} e^{j\phi}$$

(10.23)

$$\tau = RC_{eq} \qquad \phi = \frac{\pi}{2} - \tan(\omega\tau)$$

where τ is the circuit time constant (seconds) and ϕ is the phase angle of the output voltage relative to the input signal (radians).

The low-frequency characteristics of this circuit are given in Fig. 10.11a where $|H(\omega)|$ is shown as a function of ωτ. The non-linearity of $|H(\omega)|$ with ωτ is evident in this figure. The response curve of Fig. 10.11a is linearized by expressing $|H(\omega)|$ in decibels and by plotting it as a function log ωτ, as shown in Fig. 10.11b. This form of representation of the frequency response function is known as a Bode diagram. The phase angle, given as a function of ωτ, is shown in Fig. 10.11c. Because the attenuation is 30% and the phase shift is 45° when ωτ = 1, it is clear that a minimum value must be established for ωτ that is much higher. Signal attenuation and phase angle as a function of ωτ are presented in Table 10.1.

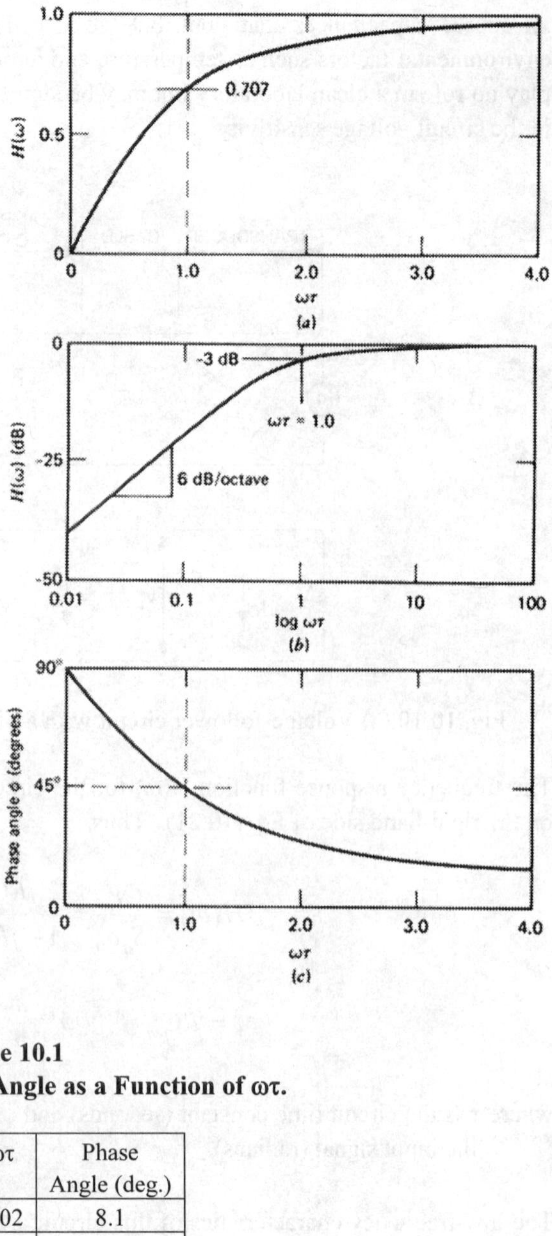

Figure 10.11 Frequency response function H(ω) for piezoelectric sensors at low frequencies.
(a) Magnitude of H(ω) versus $\omega\tau$.
(b) Magnitude of H(ω) in decibels versus log $\omega\tau$.
(c) Phase angle ϕ versus $\omega\tau$.

Table 10.1
Attenuation and Phase Angle as a Function of $\omega\tau$.

Percent Attenuation	$\omega\tau$	Phase Angle (deg.)
1	7.02	8.1
2	4.93	11.5
5	3.04	18.2
10	2.06	25.8
20	1.33	36.9
30	1.00	45.0

It is evident from the values listed in Table 10.1 that $\omega\tau$ should be greater than 2π to limit the attenuation to 1%. This limit is equivalent to requiring that $f\tau > 1$ where f is the frequency of the input signal in Hz.

Miniaturization of electronic components has enabled the placement of voltage-follower circuits in transducer housings. A unity-gain amplifier (voltage-follower) is used in commercially available transducers that incorporate piezoelectric sensors. Additional components required with these transducers include a power supply, a cable to connecting the transducer to the power supply and a recording instrument.

Placing the voltage follower circuit inside the transducer housing where it is adjacent to the piezoelectric crystal effectively removes the cable capacitance C_c from the charge generating side of the circuit. A connecting cable is still required but it is on the output side of the circuit where its effect on the transmitted signal is small. Moreover, the sensor capacitance C and the input resistance R are not significantly affected by environmental conditions because these components are protected inside the transducer housing. The resistance and capacitance are adjusted during assembly to give adequate voltage sensitivity and a reasonable time constant τ.

10.6.3 Charge Amplifier Circuit

The circuit diagram for a piezoelectric sensor and a charge amplifier is shown in Fig. 10.12. Two op-amps are connected in series to provide the required input impedance and gain. The first op-amp is the charge amplifier that converts the charge q into the voltage V_2. It employs both capacitive C_f and resistive R_f feedback. The second op-amp is an inverting amplifier that standardizes the system voltage sensitivity. It has a variable input resistance $R_1 = bR_{f1}$ ($0 \leq b \leq 1.0$) and a fixed feedback resistance R_{f1}. The circuit can be reduced to the form shown in Fig. 10.13 combining the input (source) capacitances of the transducer C_t, the cable C_c and the op-amp C_a into an effective source capacitance C. The unit calibration capacitance C_{cal} has no effect on circuit performance if its input is not grounded.

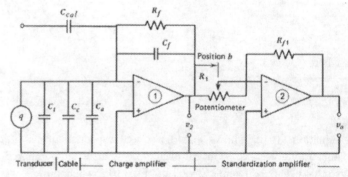

Fig. 10.12 Charge amplifier circuit for use with piezoelectric sensors.

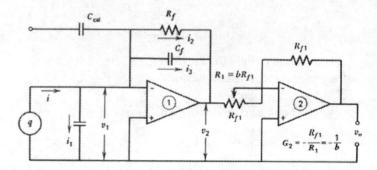

Fig. 10.13 The equivalent circuit for the charge amplifier and piezoelectric sensor.

The differential equation for the circuit in Fig. 10.13 is obtained by writing:

$$I = I_1 + I_2 + I_3 = \dot{q} = S_q * \dot{a}$$

$$= C\dot{V}_1 + \frac{V_1 - V_2}{R_f} + C(\dot{V}_1 - \dot{V}_2) = S_q * \dot{a} \tag{10.24}$$

Equation (10.24) can be expressed in terms of the output voltage v_0 by observing that:

$$V_2 - G_1 V_1 \qquad v_0 = -G_{C2} V_2 = -\frac{1}{b} V_2 \tag{a}$$

where G_1 is the open-loop gain of the first op-amp; G_{C2} is the circuit gain of the second op-amp (= 1/b)
and b is the potentiometer setting.

These equations combine to yield:

$$\frac{1}{G_{C2}}\left[\frac{C}{G_1} + C_f\left(1 + \frac{1}{G_1}\right)\right]\dot{v}_0 + \frac{1}{G_{C2}}\left(1 + \frac{1}{G_1}\right)\frac{v_0}{R_f} = S_q * \dot{a} \tag{b}$$

Because G_1 is very large ($> 10^5$) for a typical op-amp, Eq. (b) reduces to:

$$\dot{V}_0 + \frac{V_0}{R_f C_{eq}} = \left(\frac{G_{C2} S_q *}{C_{eq}}\right)\dot{a} \tag{10.25}$$

where

$$C_{eq} = \frac{C}{G_1} + C_f = C_f\left(1 + \frac{C}{C_f G_1}\right) \tag{10.26}$$

Equation (10.25) shows that the source capacitance has little effect on this measurement system because the term $C/C_f G_1$ will usually be small when compared to unity. With reasonable limits on C so that $C/C_f G_1 \approx 0$, and $C_{eq} = C_f$ and Eq. (10.25) becomes:

$$\dot{V}_0 + \frac{V_0}{R_f C_f} = \left(\frac{G_{C2} S_q *}{C_f}\right)\dot{a} \tag{10.27}$$

A comparison of Eq. (10.27) with Eq. (10.20) shows that they are identical. This fact implies that the frequency response characteristics given in Fig. 10.11 are the same for the voltage-follower and the charge-amplifier circuits.

The voltage sensitivity of the charge-amplifier circuit is given by:

$$S_v = \left(\frac{G_{C2} S_q *}{C_f}\right) = \frac{1}{b}\frac{S_q *}{C_f} = \frac{S_q **}{C_f} \tag{10.28}$$

This equation indicates that a charge amplifier has two parameters (b and C_f) that can be adjusted to control voltage sensitivity. The charge sensitivity S_q* of a particular transducer can be set to a standard value of 1, 10 or 100 pC/unit. The standardized value is obtained by adjusting the potentiometer so that $S_q*/b = S_q**$ for the particular piezoelectric transducer in use.

When the charge sensitivity is standardized, the instrument range is established by selecting the feedback capacitance. Typical instruments provide feedback capacitances ranging from 10 to 50,000 pF in a 1-2-5-10 sequence.

The time constant for the charge amplifier is given by Eq. (10.26) as $\tau = R_f C_f$. It is important to note that both R_f and C_f are contained in the charge amplifier. On the other hand, the time constant for the voltage follower is given by Eq. (10.23) as $\tau = R C_{eq}$. The important distinction for the voltage follower is that the equivalent capacitance C_{eq} is due to the combined capacitances of the transducer, the cable and the amplifier. It is much more difficult to control C_{eq} in the voltage follower, because the cable and transducer capacitances are external to the signal conditioning circuit.

In commercial charge amplifiers, different time constants can be selected for each of the three ranges (short, medium and long). For the high reciprocal sensitivities, with the charge amplifier adjusted to long, the time constant is 5,000,000 s (nearly two months). On the other hand, for very-low reciprocal sensitivities, with the charge amplifier adjusted to short, the time constant is only 10 ms.

In comparing the relative merits of the charge-amplifier and voltage-follower circuits it is clear that the charge amplifier is preferred because of the following advantages.

1. The time-constant is controlled by the feedback resistance and the feedback capacitance and is independent of the transducer and cable capacitance.
2. System performance is independent of transducer and cable capacitance if the source capacitance is less than the maximum allowed for a given amount of error.
3. Charge sensitivity can be standardized by controlling the gain of the standardization amplifier.
4. A wide range of voltage sensitivities and time constants are available by changing the feedback capacitance.

10.6.4 Built-in Voltage Followers

Microelectronic developments have enabled the design of miniature voltage-follower circuits that are incorporated in the transducer housing. A P-channel MOSFET (Metal-Oxide-Semiconductor Field-Effect Transistor) unity-gain amplifier (voltage-follower) is used for this application. The additional components required for this circuit are a power supply, a cable to connect the transducer to the power supply, and a recording instrument as shown in Fig. 10.14.

The power supply shown in Fig. 10.14, which consists of a dc supply voltage V_s and a current regulating diode (CRD), provides a nominal +11 V at the transistor (S), when there is no input signal. The capacitance C_1 shields the recording instrument from this dc voltage. The meter (M) monitors the transducer cable connection. If the meter shows zero, a short exists in the connection, but if the meter shows V_s the circuit is open.

The equivalent circuit for this built-in voltage follower is illustrated in Fig. 10.15. Considering the input to the voltage follower, we write:

$$\dot{V}_1 + \frac{V_1}{RC} = \left(\frac{S_q^*}{C}\right)\dot{a} = S_v\dot{a} \tag{10.29}$$

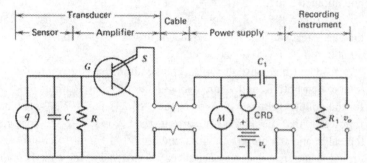

Fig. 10.14 Diagram of a measurement circuit with a piezoelectric transducer and a built-in amplifier.

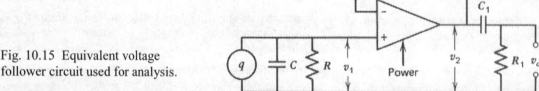

Fig. 10.15 Equivalent voltage follower circuit used for analysis.

The MOSFET amplifier exhibits a unity-gain; therefore, the output side is:

$$\dot{V}_0 + \frac{V_0}{R_1C_1} = \dot{V}_2 = \dot{V}_1 \tag{10.30}$$

The steady-state frequency response function obtained from Eqs. (10.29) and (10.30) is:

$$H(\omega) = \frac{CV_0}{S_q^*} = \left(\frac{jRC_1\omega}{1 + jRC_1\omega}\right)\left(\frac{jRC\omega}{1 + jRC\omega}\right) \tag{10.31}$$

The presence of two time constants is evident by the form of Eq. (10.31).

$$\tau = RC \qquad \text{and} \qquad \tau_1 = R_1C_1$$

The internal time constant $\tau = RC$ is fixed at the time of instrument assembly. Ideally, this value of τ should be very large; however, typical values range from 0.5 to 2,000 s. The value of τ is limited due to constraints on R for amplifier current and constraints on C for voltage sensitivity. The external time constant $\tau_1 = R_1C_1$ is controlled by the blocking capacitor C_1 (limited by the power supply) and by the input resistance R_1 of the readout instrument (selected by transducer user). Because these instruments have input resistances ranging from 0.01 MΩ to over 1 MΩ, the external time constant usually becomes the controlling time constant. Magnitude and phase-angle response characteristics of this dual time constant instrument are described by Eq. (10.31) and are shown in Fig. 10.16.

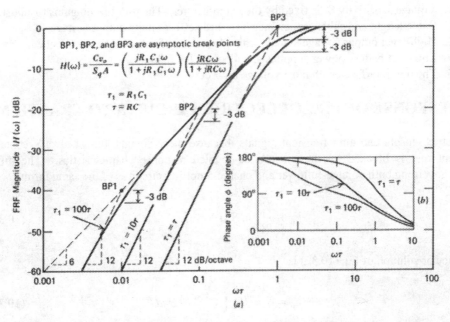

Fig. 10.16 Frequency response function H(ω) for a piezoelectric transducer with a built-in amplifier. (a) Magnitude of H(ω) versus log (ωτ). (b) Phase angle φ versus log ωτ.

The Bode diagrams in Fig. 10.16 show the effect of external time constant on instrument response for three time constant ratios of 1, 10, and 100. When $\tau_1 = \tau$, the low-frequency response drops off at a rate of 12 dB/octave and the phase-angle rapidly approaches 180°. At $\omega\tau = 1$ (break point BP3), the amplitude is attenuated 6 dB (down 50%) and a 90° phase shift occurs. When $\tau_1 > \tau$, signal attenuation occurs at even lower values of $\omega\tau$. To minimize error due to attenuation and phase shift, a low frequency minimum on $\omega\tau$ must be maintained. The minimum values of $\omega\tau$ for errors of 2 and 5% for time constant ratios τ_1/τ of 1, 10, and 100 are given in Table 10.2.

Table 10.2
Minimum Values of ωτ for Errors of 2 and 5% for the built-in voltage-follower circuit.

$\dfrac{\tau_1}{\tau}$	2%	5%
1	7.00	4.36
10	4.93	3.06
100	4.90	3.04

Errors can be limited to 2% when τ_1/τ is greater than 10 if $\omega\tau$ is greater than 5. Similarly, errors can be limited to 5% when τ_1/τ is greater than 10 if $\omega\tau$ is greater than 3. The values of $\omega\tau$ listed in Table 10.1 for τ_1/τ equal to 100 are the same as those obtained for the single time constant systems described in Table 10.2.

The concept of placing a miniaturized voltage follower in the transducer housing yields the following advantages:

1. Voltage sensitivity S_v is fixed by the manufacturer. The user has no gains to adjust.
2. Cable length and cable capacitance have little effect on the output voltage.
3. High-level output voltage signals with a low-level of cable noise are obtained.
4. Low-cost battery power supplies are adequate for field use.
5. The unit interfaces with most voltage recorders.

10.7 RESPONSE OF PIEZOELECTRIC CIRCUITS TO TRANSIENTS

Piezoelectric sensors can alter transient signals, because these signals almost always contain a dc-component that is blocked by the sensor's ac-coupled response characteristics. The differential equation governing both voltage-follower and charge-amplifier circuit is of the same form:

$$\dot{V}_0 + \frac{V_0}{RC} = S_v \dot{a} \tag{10.32}$$

The particular solution of Eq. (10.32) is:

$$V_0 = S_v e^{-t/RC} \int_0^t e^{\vartheta/RC} \dot{a}(\vartheta) d\vartheta \tag{10.33}$$

where ϑ is a dummy variable of integration. This solution can be applied to a transient signal if a(ϑ) is defined.

As an example consider the case where a (ϑ) is defined by the rectangular pulse illustrated in Fig. 10.17a. While this pulse cannot be generated mechanically, it nevertheless provides a limiting case for judging the adequacy of the electronic circuit's low-frequency response.

The derivative a, shown in Fig. 10.17b, is expressed as:

$$\dot{a} = a_0 \delta(\vartheta) - a_0 \delta(\vartheta - t_1) \tag{a}$$

where $\delta(\vartheta)$ is the Dirac delta function.

This function has properties such that it is zero except when the argument is zero and the area under the function is unity when integrated over the zero argument. Substituting Eq. (a) into Eq. (10.33) and integrating yields:

$$V_0 = S_v a_0 \left[u(t) e^{-t/RC} - u(t - t_1) e^{-(t-t_1)/RC} \right] \tag{10.34}$$

where $u(t - t_1)$ is the unit-step function obtained by integrating $\delta(\vartheta)$.

The output signal V_0, shown in Fig. 10.12c, has two significant characteristics. First, the output signal decays exponentially during the pulse duration and an error of $(1 - e^{-t/RC})$ develops with time. Second, an undershoot occurs at $t = t_1$, that is equal to the maximum error associated with the rectangular pulse. The maximum error is estimated using a series expansion of the function $(1 - e^{-t_1/RC})$ to give:

$$\varepsilon = \frac{t_1}{RC} \left[1 - \frac{1}{2} \frac{t_1}{RC} + \frac{1}{6} \left(\frac{t_1}{RC} \right)^2 - \dots \right] \tag{b}$$

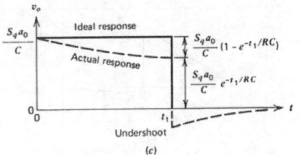

Figure 10.17 Response of a
piezoelectric sensor.
    (a) A rectangular pulse
(transient) input.
    (b) Time derivative of the
input pulse.
    (c) The output voltage with
time.

When t_1/RC is small compared to unity, Eq. (b) reduces to:

$$\mathcal{E}_{max} = \frac{t_1}{RC} \qquad \text{or} \qquad \tau = RC = \frac{t_1}{\mathcal{E}_{max}} \qquad (10.35)$$

The time constant $\tau = RC$ clearly controls the error which develops during the duration of the pulse. The error can be minimized by making τ/t_1 very large. The time constant necessary to limit the error in measuring a rectangular pulse is given in Table 10.3.

    Triangular and half-sine pulse shapes are good examples of transient pulses. The minimum time constants required to limit specified measurement errors for these pulse shapes are also listed in Table 10.3. It is evident from this analysis that the rectangular pulse requires the largest time constant for a given level of error. The potential error occurring in a given measurement can be estimated by comparing the transient shape of the output signal with the pulses listed in Table 10.3. Also, undershoot with its exponential decay is clear evidence of an inadequate time constant.

    Transducer systems utilizing the built-in voltage-follower present a special problem because they exhibit two time constants. An analysis of this circuit (Fig. 10.14) with a rectangular pulse for a(t) indicates that the two time constants can be combined into an effective time constant τ_e given by:

$$\tau_e = \frac{\tau_1 \tau}{\tau_1 + \tau} \qquad (10.36)$$

This effective time constant can be used with Table 10.3 to estimate the maximum errors associated with typical transient measurements by comparing the output pulse with the shapes listed.

Table 10.3
Time Constant Requirements to Limit Error

Pulse Shape	Time Constants		
	2% Error	5% Error	10% error
Rectangular pulse	$50t_1$	$20t_1$	$10t_1$
Triangular pulse	$25t_1$	$10t_1$	$5t_1$
Half-sine pulse	A $16t_1$	A $6t_1$	A $3t_1$
	B $31t_1$	B $12t_1$	B $6t_1$

Overview

A typical frequency response function for a piezoelectric transducer is shown in Fig. 10.18. At the low-frequency end of the frequency spectrum [below (ω_1), the system exhibits a rapid drop in amplitude (6 dB/octave)]. Also, periodic signals undergo serious phase distortion and transient signals exhibit exponential decay. Signal fidelity at this end of the frequency spectrum is controlled by the electrical RC time constant. Between ω_1 and ω_2, the system exhibits essentially zero phase shift and nearly constant output per unit input. Measurements should be limited to this range of the spectrum if possible. For frequencies higher than (ω_2), mechanical resonance becomes important and causes amplitude magnification and phase distortion of signals with a periodic input. For transient signals, a serious ringing occurs if the rise (or fall) time of the transient input is less than 5 times the natural period of the transducer.

In every experimental measurement, it is the engineer's responsibility to select transducers and recording instruments that provides data with a minimum of error regardless of input type or shape of the input signal; therefore, it is important that all of the effects illustrated in Fig. 10.18 be understood and given careful consideration.

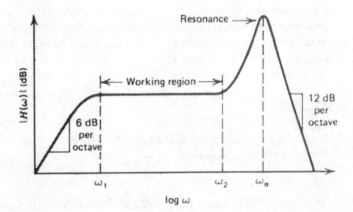

Figure 10.18 Typical response function $H(\omega)$ for a piezoelectric transducer.

10.8 PIEZORESISTIVE TRANSDUCERS

Piezoelectric force, pressure and accelerometers with their higher resonant frequencies, signal levels and amplitude ranges have displaced classical strain gage technology in transducers used for measurements of dynamic events. However, piezoelectric transducers exhibited zero-shift at high stress levels associated with high-amplitude, high-frequency mechanical shock. Ralph Plumlee at Sandia National Labs found that a dipole switching mechanism was responsible for zero-shift in the ferroelectric ceramics used as sensors in piezoelectric transducers. Later in the 1970s, semiconductor (piezoresistive) strain gages were introduced as the sensor for accelerometers, because they would respond to low frequency (static) excitation. The success of piezoresistive strain gages in accelerometers lead to the development of the first all silicon, miniature electro-mechanical systems (MEMS) accelerometer in the 1980s. These accelerometers, exhibited amplitude ranges in excess of 100,000 Gs and resonant frequencies of the order of 100,000 to 400,000 Hz. The piezoresistive MEMs accelerometer became the transducer of choice to measure very high G levels in dynamic experiments.

One problem that occurred when using the MEMS accelerometers in high G environments (impact and explosive generated shock waves) was the seismic mass vibrating at resonant frequency. When vibrating at resonance, the amplitude of the seismic mass became excessive and the accelerometers fail. The damping ratio of single crystal silicon used to fabricate these sensors approaches zero. The low damping ratio leads to extremely high stresses induced in the sensing element of the accelerometer when it is in resonance. Recently the design of the seismic mass and the assembly of the transducer have been modified to introduce a small amount of aerodynamic damping (d = 0.02 to 0.10). While this is a modest amount of damping the reduction in peak amplitude of the vibration when the seismic mass is resonating is dramatic. In addition, a mechanical stop has been added to the design to limit the over ranging to 100%. The aerodynamic damping is due to the energy dissipation by the vibration of the seismic mass within closely controlled clearances between the seismic mass and the mechanical stop.

10.8.1 Design of a MEMs Piezoresistive Accelerometer

A schematic illustration of a MEMs piezoresistive accelerometer is presented in Fig. 10.19. The accelerometer is made from three main components all fabricated by etching silicon with MEMs processes. The parts are the base, the lid and the center element. The center element is complex and requires careful processing. It includes seismic mass with integral beams that extend from the frame to the seismic mass. The silicon beams are implanted by diffusion with p or n type doping, to provide four strain sensing elements. These four elements are connected into a Wheatstone bridge and conductors are brought out through the case. Metalized pads are provided in some designs, which are used to connect a power supply and a recorder. In other designs, the assembly is encased in a metal package with lead wires attached. The metal case has two small holes for screw attachment to the component.

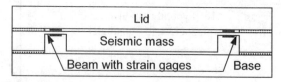

Figure 10.19 A schematic illustration of a MEMs piezoresistive accelerometer

The Meggitt (Endevco) model 7270A high-g accelerometer has been used successfully in many cannon, sled and flight tests under high g impact conditions. This model of the accelerometer is available with acceleration ranging from 6,000 g's to 200,000 g's. However, one of the disadvantages of the packaging of the model 7270A, shown in Fig. 10.20, is its relatively large size. The sensing element is packaged inside a metal case with two clearance holes for no. 2 screws used to mount the gage to a component. Lead wires extend from this case to make the required electrical connections.

Figure 10.20 Meggitt (Endevco) model 7270A accelerometer showing its packaging in a metal case.

If the metal case is removed, the sensing element in the accelerometer can be packaged more efficiently giving an accelerometer with a much smaller size as shown in Fig. 10.21. In this design, the silicon is encased in an alumina overcoat, the mounting holes are eliminated and the silicon base is bonded to the component with a structural epoxy. Electrical connections are made by soldering pads on the alumina casing to surface mounting pads on the specimen being investigated.

Fig. 10.21 PCB model 3501A accelerometer without metal case. Its size is 2.16 by 3.5 by 6 mm and it weighs 0.15 grams.

Often acceleration measurements are required in the x, y and z directions. For this measurement, triaxial transducers are employed. Triaxial transducers utilize three single axis accelerometers mounted on either a small block or a wedge as shown in Fig. 10.22.

PCB Model 3503A with a
wedge mounting block and wire
for electrical connections.

Meggitt (Endevco) Model 73 with square
mounting block and bonding pads for electrical
connections.

Fig. 10.22 Triaxial accelerometers.

The characteristics of an accelerometer depend on its manufacturer and its maximum g level. Typical characteristics for two single axis accelerometers manufactured by PCB are given in Table 10.4.

Table 10.4 Characteristics of the PCB model # 3501A accelerometers

Characteristic	3501A2020kg	3501A2060kg
Sensitivity	0.010 mV/g	0.003 mV/g
Range	± 0 to 20 kg	± 0 to 60 kg
Bandwidth (± 1Db)	10 kHz	20 kHz
Resonance frequency	>60 kHz	>120 kHz
Overload stops	≥ 30 kg	≥ 80 kg
Temperature range	− 54 to + 121 C	− 54 to + 121 C
Supply voltage	10 V	10 V
Bridge resistance	6 kΩ	6 kΩ
Size	2.16 x 3.5 x 6 mm	2.16 x 3.5 x 6 mm
Weight	0.15 gram	0.15 gram
Mounting	Adhesive	Adhesive
Electrical connection	Surface mount	Surface mount

10.9 PIEZORESITIVE PRESSURE GAGES

Piezoresistive pressure sensors are one of the early sensors to employ MEMS technology. The pressure sensors developed are widely used in biomedical applications, automotive industry and household appliances. The sensing material in a piezoresistive pressure sensor is a diaphragm formed on a silicon substrate, which deforms with applied pressure. This deformation changes the spacing of crystal lattice of the silicon, which in turn causes a change in the band structure of the piezo-resistors that are implanted in the gage's diaphragm. As a result the piezo-resistors exhibit either an increase or decrease in their resistance which is linear with the applied pressure.

There are several advantages associated with piezo-resistive pressure sensors which include:

- Low-cost fabrication with large silicon wafers.
- Mature MEMs processing technology.
- Different pressure ranges possible with MEMs processing.
- Wide differences in sensitivities possible with MEMs processing.
- Read-out circuitry can be either on-chip or discrete.

10.9.1 MEMS Processing Methods

The process begins with a wafer of silicon that is coated with photoresist and then a pattern of holes and lines (traces) are created in the photoresist. N and P type elements are diffused into the surface of silicon as shown in Fig. 10.23 to produce piezoresistive strain gages. The traces in the photoresist are filled with metal, usually aluminum, to connect the strain gages into a Wheatstone bridge and to provide the conductors for the output signals. Finally the back side of the wafer is etched away to create a thin diaphragm, which deflects under pressure.

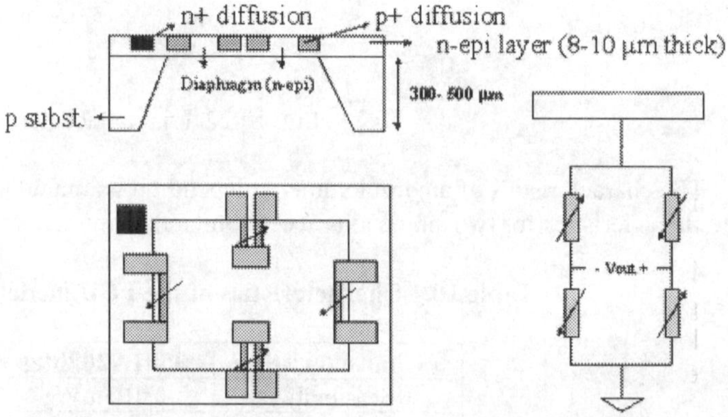

Fig. 10.23 Processing of a piezoresistive pressure gage using MEMs methods.

For a typical piezoresistive pressure gage, the piezoresistive elements are located on an n-type epitaxial layer of typical thickness 2-10 μm, which is formed on a p-type silicon substrate. The pressure sensitive diaphragm is formed by silicon back-end bulk micromachining. For this etching process, anisotropic an etchants KOH is employed. The sensor is packaged by mounting the die on an alumina substrate, as shown in Fig. 10.24. Wire bonding is used to connect the electrodes on the die to the metallic traces on the alumina substrate.

Fig. 10.24 Bonding the pressure sensing die to the alumina substrate.

A hole is formed at the center of the alumina substrate to enable the pressure to act on the diaphragm. Finally a cap is attached to the back, shown in Fig. 10.25, which is designed to accept a hose used to convey the pressure from its source to the pressure gage. Pins are soldered onto the alumina substrate that carries the electrical connections. In an application, these pins are inserted into the through holes in a printed circuit board to make connections to the power supply and readout instrumentation.

Fig. 10.25 A packaged pressure sensor that uses a cap as a cover and pressure port.

10.10 ACCELEROMETER CALIBRATION

The voltage sensitivity or calibration constant of a transducer is a very important quantity. Transducer manufacturers provide calibration information, traceable to the National Institute of Standards and Technology (NIST), when the instrument is shipped to the customer. Users must recalibrate the instrument to ensure that the original calibration has not changed with use and/or abuse. Users generally employ comparison methods to recalibrate instruments. Calibration is a process where a known input is generated and instrument response is recorded so that a ratio of output/input can be established over the ranges of interest (frequency and magnitude).

The most widely used calibration method (constant-acceleration method) requires only the simple act of rotating the accelerometer's sensitive axis in the earth's gravitational field. This produces a nominal change in acceleration of two g's (– one g to + one g). The primary disadvantages of this simple method are limited range, local gravity variations and absence of any verification of its frequency response characteristics. The method provides a quick means to ensure that an accelerometer is at least functional. Centrifuges are required to achieve higher levels of constant acceleration, but these facilities are costly and are not readily available in most laboratories.

A sinusoidal input, such as that produced by a vibration generator, provides calibration signals at different frequencies and different levels of acceleration. This sinusoidal input is widely used for both comparison and absolute calibration. In the comparison method, two accelerometers (test and standard) are mounted as close as possible to one another on the head of a vibration table. Some calibration accelerometers are constructed so that the test accelerometer is mounted directly on the back of the calibration standard. This procedure is often referred to as "the back-to-back calibration method". The standard accelerometer should be used only for calibration and never for testing. The calibration of this "standard" is traceable to NIST. Standard accelerometers, which are adjusted to give a constant sensitivity (usually 10.0 mV/g) over a broad range of frequencies, are available.

Linearity of the test accelerometer at a specified frequency is obtained from a graph of the output signal from the test accelerometer versus the output signal from the standard accelerometer as the level of acceleration is increased over a wide range. The sensitivity of the test accelerometer as a function of frequency is determined by varying the frequency of the vibration table and adjusting its acceleration level to maintain the signal from the standard accelerometer at a constant value. Accuracies of ± 0.2% for the calibration constants of the test accelerometer are attainable with the comparison technique.

Portable calibrating systems are available for field use. One such unit, shown in Fig. 10.26, uses a dual magnet system with two mechanically coupled moving coils. One coil operates as the driver and the other serves as a velocity sensor. The coils can be connected to external instrumentation for performing reciprocity calibration.

The local acceleration of gravity can be accurately measured by aligning the calibrator vertically, mounting the test accelerometer on the calibrator, and placing a small (less than 1 gm) nonmagnetic object on the accelerometers free surface. At an acceleration level of ± 1 g, the object will begin to "rattle". The onset of "rattle" can be detected accurately (±1%) in the accelerometer signal.

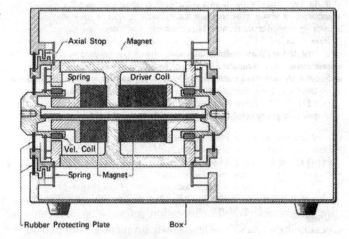

Fig. 10.26 Construction details of a portable accelerometer calibrator.

Absolute accelerometer calibration methods require precise measurement of frequency ω and amplitude x because peak acceleration magnitude is given by the equation:

$$a_{max} = -\omega^2 \, x_{max} \qquad (10.37)$$

As an example of the amplitude involved, a sinusoidal displacement of 0.001 in. at a frequency of 100 Hz gives a peak acceleration of 1.02 g's. Thus, the peak-to-peak amplitudes that must be accurately measured are extremely small. For frequencies below 100 Hz to 200 Hz, reasonable results can be obtained with a microscope. For frequencies above 200 Hz, it is necessary to use proximity gages and interferometric methods to measure the amplitudes with sufficient accuracy to employ Eq. (10.37) for absolute calibration of the test accelerometer.

An impulse method of accelerometer calibration, based on Newton's Second Law, is written as:

$$F = ma = mg\left(\frac{a}{g}\right) \qquad (10.38)$$

A schematic diagram of the fixture used for impulse calibration is shown in Fig. 10.27. The system consists of a solid steel cylinder on which the test accelerometer is mounted, a guide tube to control cylinder motion, a force transducer and a "rigid" support base. The calibration is performed in two steps and requires measuring three voltages.

First, the test mass (cylinder and accelerometer) is positioned on the force transducer and voltage V_{mg} is measured when the test mass is quickly removed (see Fig. 10.28a). Second, the test mass is dropped onto the force transducer, while the transient impulse voltage V_f (force transducer) and V_a (accelerometer) are simultaneously measured (see Fig. 10.28b). Because the force and acceleration acting on these transducers are determined by their output voltage divided by their sensitivity, we write:

$$F_{mg} = mg = \frac{V_{mg}}{S_f} \qquad F = \frac{V_f}{S_f} \qquad \frac{a}{g} = \frac{V_a}{S_a} \qquad (10.39)$$

where S_f and S_a are the voltage sensitivities of the force transducer and accelerometer, respectively.

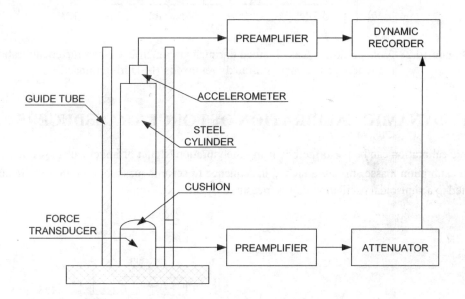

Fig. 10.27 Schematic illustration of a gravimetric calibration system for accelerometers.

Substitution of Eqs. (10.39) into Newton's second law gives S_a:

$$S_a = \left(\frac{V_a}{V_f}\right) V_{mg} \qquad (10.40)$$

Equation (10.40) shows that the unknown accelerometer sensitivity S_a is the impact voltage ratio (V_a/V_f) times the static voltage V_{mg}. Note, that the force transducer sensitivity S_f does not enter into this accelerometer calibration technique.

The cushion material and the size of the mass in Fig. 10.27 control the duration time of the impact pulse, and the drop height controls the amplitude. A typical calibration is performed over a range of amplitudes and pulse durations by using a combination of different drop heights and cushion materials. The preamplifiers shown in Fig. 10.27 can be any one of the three standard types (voltage follower, charge amplifier or built-in voltage follower). The attenuator is a voltage divider used to decrease the signal amplitude from the force transducer. If the attenuator is adjusted to give $V_f = V_a$ during impact, the voltage V_{mg} obtained after the attenuator is set becomes a direct measure of accelerometer voltage sensitivity S_a.

The major advantages of this calibration method are its portability and low cost.

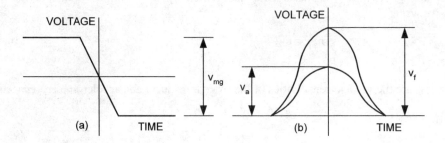

Figure 10.28 Voltage-time traces obtained during a gravimetric accelerometer calibration.
(a) When the test mass is quickly removed. (b) During impact.

10.11   DYNAMIC CALIBRATION OF FORCE TRANSDUCERS

Dynamic calibration can be performed by using the vibration exciter arrangement shown in Fig. 10.29. Known calibration masses m_c are attached in sequence to seismic mass m, then the transducer base is subjected to a sinusoidal oscillation that is measured by the accelerometer.

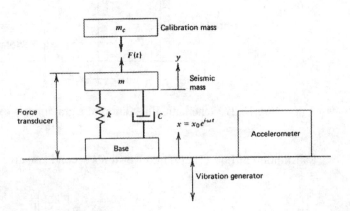

Figure 10.29 Calibration of a force transducer with a vibration generator.

With this arrangement, the external force F(t) applied to the force transducer by the calibration mass is:

$$F(t) = m_c \ddot{y} = -m_c (\ddot{x} + \ddot{z})$$ (10.41)

The differential equation which describes the motion of the force transducer during calibration is obtained by substituting Eq. (10.41) into Eq. (10.3) to give:

$$(m + m_c)\ddot{z} + C\dot{z} + kz = -(m + m_c)\ddot{x}$$ (10.42)

The output signals V_f and V_a from the force transducer and the accelerometer, respectively, are:

$$V_f = S_f (m + m_c)\ddot{x} \quad \text{and} \quad V_a = S_a \left(\frac{\ddot{x}}{g} \right)$$ (a)

From Eqs. (a), it is obvious that the voltage ratio (V_f/V_a) is related to the sensitivity ratio (S_f/S_a) by:

$$\frac{V_f}{V_a} = \frac{S_f}{S_a}(m+m_c)g = \frac{S_f}{S_a}(W+W_c) \qquad (10.43)$$

where W is the weight of the seismic mass and W_c is the weight of the calibration mass.

A graph of voltage ratio V_f/V_a as a function of weight W_c for a typical calibration is shown in Fig. 10.30. It is evident from Eq. (10.43) that the slope s is the sensitivity ratio S_f/S_a and that the horizontal axis intercept is the seismic weight W. During calibration, several graphs of V_f/V_a are obtained over a wide range of input amplitudes (to check linearity) and frequencies (to check for resonance effects) for each value of W_c. When the slope s is established, the voltage sensitivity S_f is given by:

$$S_f = s\, S_a \qquad (10.44)$$

The accelerometer sensitivity S_a is accurately known because it comes from a standard accelerometer.

Calibration accuracies of $\pm\, 0.5\,\%$ are possible with the sinusoidal method; however, care must be exercised to avoid the natural frequency of the force transducer when adding calibration mass. The addition of the mass m_c decreases the natural frequency of the force transducer and Eq. (10.44) is not valid near the resonance condition because the force voltage becomes too large.

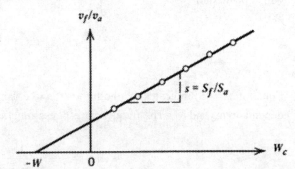

Fig. 10.30 Voltage ratio V_f/V_a versus calibration weight W_c from a sinusoidal calibration of a force transducer.

10.11.1 Force-Transducer Calibration by Impact

In structural testing, a half-sine input force is applied at a specified point by striking the structure with a hammer. Force transducers, installed on the hammerhead, measure these impact forces. A typical impact hammer with an impact head and an attached force transducer is shown in Fig. 10.31. The time duration of the impact force is controlled by the stiffness of the structure, the mass of the hammer's impact head and the mass of the hammer's body. It is common practice to change the masses of the hammer body and impact head to achieve different impact time durations. It will be shown that these changes affect the calibration and performance of the force transducer.

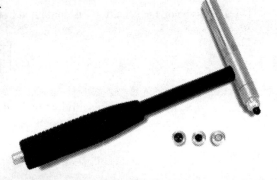

Fig. 10.31 Impulse hammer with a force transducer incorporated into its head.

A schematic model of the impact-hammer force-transducer combination is shown in Fig. 10.32 where m_h is the mass of the impact head and m_b is the mass of the hammer body. The mass m_p of the pendulum and accelerometer is also used in the calibration. The differential equation for the force transducer is:

$$m_e\ddot{z} + c\dot{z} + kz = -\left(\frac{1}{1+M}\right)F(t) \qquad (10.45)$$

where M is a mass ratio and m_e is an effective transducer mass given by:

$$M = \frac{m_h}{m_b} \quad \text{and} \quad m_e = \frac{m_b m_h}{m_b + m_h} = \frac{m_h}{1+M} \qquad (a)$$

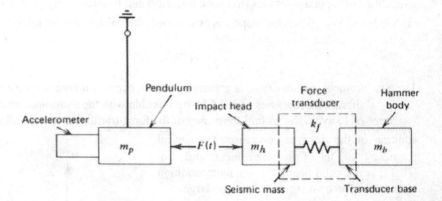

Fig. 10.32 Calibration of an impact hammer with a pendulum system.

Equation (10.45) indicates that both the effective damping and the natural frequency of the transducer depend on m_e and M. The frequency response function obtained from Eq. (10.45) is:

$$H(\omega) = \frac{1}{k - m_e\omega^2 + jC\omega} = \frac{1}{k(1 - r^2 + 2jdr)} \qquad (10.46)$$

Transducer output as a function of frequency is obtained from Eqs. (10.45) and (10.46) as:

$$V_f(\omega) = S_z z = \left[\frac{S_z}{k}\left(\frac{1}{1+M}\right)\right]\frac{F(\omega)}{(1 - r^2 + 2jdr)} \qquad (b)$$

The effective voltage sensitivity is contained in the first bracketed term of Eq. (b). Thus,

$$S_f^* = \left[\frac{S_z}{k}\left(\frac{1}{1+M}\right)\right] = S_f\left(\frac{1}{1+M}\right) \qquad (10.47)$$

where $S_f = S_z/k$ is the static sensitivity obtained from a static calibration of the transducer.

It is evident that the effective sensitivity is changed when either the base (hammer body) or impact tip masses are changed. It is possible to predict the new transducer sensitivity when one or both masses are changed because S_f is not altered by changing system masses and m_b and m_h are known.

When a calibration is performed using the system shown in Fig. 10.32, the force F(t) applied by the pendulum is:

$$F(t) = m_p a = W_p \left(\frac{a}{g} \right) \qquad (10.48)$$

where a is the acceleration of the pendulum during impact.

The accelerometer output voltage during impact is given by:

$$V_a = S_a (a/g) \qquad (10.49)$$

Combining Eqs. (b), (10.47), (10.48), and (10.49) gives:

$$\frac{V_f}{V_a} = \frac{S_f^*}{S_a} W_p \qquad (10.50)$$

The results of Eq. (10.50) are similar to Eq. (10.44) except that the term for the seismic mass is absent from Eq. (10.50). If the voltage ratio V_f / V_a is measured on a suitable recorder, the calibration constant S_f^* is:

$$S_f^* = \left(\frac{V_f}{V_a} \right) \left(\frac{S_a}{W_p} \right) \qquad (10.51)$$

Again, if standard accelerometers are used and care is exercised during the measurements, accurate calibration (better than $\pm 1\%$) can be achieved. This calibration procedure for impact hammers is adequate for operating frequencies that are much lower than the natural frequency of the force transducer. At higher frequencies, stress wave effects become important and force measurements made with such hammer devices exhibit considerable error.

10.12 OVERALL SYSTEM CALIBRATION

Electronic measurement systems contain a number of components, such as power supplies, transducers, amplifiers, signal conditioning circuits and recording instruments. It is possible to calibrate each component; however, this is a time consuming procedure and is subject to calibration errors for each component. A more precise and direct procedure establishes a single calibration constant for the complete system that relates the recording instrument reading to the quantity being measured.

System calibration involves not only voltage sensitivity determinations, but also determinations of the dynamic response characteristics of the system such as rise time, overshoot and its time constant. An ideal method for system calibration does not require the transducer to be disconnected from either the measurement system or the structure to which it is mounted. This approach employs a known voltage input at the transducer end of the system. For piezoelectric transducers, a voltage generator is connected to the system through a calibration capacitor C_{cal}, as shown in Fig. 10.13.

The calibration voltage $V_{cal}*$ needed to simulate a charge q_{cal}, is related to a_{cal} by Eq. (10.19). Thus,

$$V_{cal}^* = \frac{q_{cal}}{C_{cal}} = \frac{S_q^* a_{cal}}{C_{cal}} \qquad (10.52)$$

The charge amplifier voltage sensitivity is given by Eq. (10.28) as:

$$S_v \frac{S_q^*}{bC_f} \qquad (10.53)$$

The charge amplifier output voltage V_{cal}, due to the calibration voltage $V_{cal}*$ is:

$$V_{cal} = S_v a_{cal} = \frac{S_q^* a_{cal}}{bC_f} = \frac{C_{cal} v_{cal}^*}{bC_f} \qquad (10.54)$$

Equation (10.54) indicates that potentiometer can be adjusted to provide a standardized output voltage that includes any circuit loading effects. The specified range is then established by selecting the feedback capacitance C_f.

The voltages used in calibration may be sinusoidal, periodic, or transient. Precision voltage sources are available that provide either a 0 to 10 volt full-scale step pulse or a 0 to 10 volt full-scale 100 Hz square wave. The voltage level is adjustable over the full range with a resolution of 0.02% of full-scale and a linearity of ± 0.25% of full-scale. Precision calibration capacitors are available for use in calibrating charge amplifiers that do not have built-in calibration capacitors. It is important to avoid connecting a voltage source to the input of a charge amplifier without a series connected calibration capacitance.

A step input voltage is commonly used to test the total system because this signal thoroughly checks system fidelity. A typical response signal is shown in Fig. 10.33. This signal establishes the system rise time, overshoot and exponential decay characteristics. Each of these quantities is important because they imply measurement limitations. Unfortunately, the transducer's natural frequency is not excited by this calibration technique. Also, the natural frequency of the instrument system is difficult to interpret from the signal oscillations about the exponential decay trace.

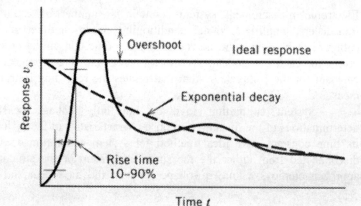

Fig. 10.33 Typical response of a measurement system to a step input.

Calibration of transducers and complete instrument systems must be performed periodically to ensure satisfactory performance. As the number of channels in a system increases, the need for accurate and efficient calibration procedures becomes more important. Calibration must always be regarded as a vital step in the experimental process for the data collected is never better than the calibration accuracy.

10.13 SOURCES OF ERROR WITH ACCELEROMETERS

Many factors affect the performance of accelerometers and the accuracies achieved when they are used in field or laboratory applications. These factors include transducer mass, sensitivity and mounting methods.

The mass of an accelerometer affects the accuracy of the measurement by changing the dynamic response characteristics of a light-weight structure. The magnitude of the error can be estimated from:

$$a_s = a_m\left(1 + m_a/m_s\right) \qquad \text{and} \qquad f_s = f_m\sqrt{\left(1 + m_a/m_s\right)} \qquad (10.55)$$

where a and f are acceleration and frequency and subscripts s and m indicate structure and measured, respectively. To minimize the effect of the transducer on the process (in this case vibration) it is essential that the mass ratio m_a/m_s be minimized (5% or less).

The upper limit on the range (5,000 to 10,000 g's) of a piezoelectric accelerometer is controlled by the strength of the piezoelectric material. The lower limit is established by the noise imposed on the output signal by the amplifiers and the connecting cables. Usually, this noise level is equivalent to an acceleration signal of 0.0001 g's. Accelerometers are also sensitive to motions perpendicular to the sensing axis. Maximum transverse sensitivity is less than ± 5% for most commercially available accelerometers.

The upper limit on the range of piezoresistive accelerometers is much higher and g levels of up to 100,000 g are possible. The difficulty with piezoresistive accelerometers at these high g levels is the probability of exciting resonance with very high amplitude vibration of the seismic mass. Under these resonance conditions the accelerometers frequently fail. Recently piezoresistive accelerometers that exhibit a small amount of aerodynamic damping have been developed that prevent failure due to high amplitude vibrations at resonance.

The output of both piezoelectric and piezoresistive accelerometers vary with temperature. The charge sensitivity S_q of a piezoelectric material depends on temperature, as shown in Fig. 10.34. These results indicate that corrections are needed when an accelerometer is used at temperatures other than the 20 °C (68 °F) reference temperature. Most general purpose accelerometers function at temperatures up to 250 °C (482 °F). Depolarization of the piezoelectric material occurs at the Curie temperature.

Fig. 10.34 Charge sensitivity of piezoelectric accelerometers with temperature.

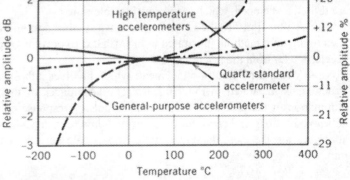

Piezoresistive gages exhibit output with variations in temperature. To minimize error the output from the Wheatstone bridge is zeroed out at the test temperature and the test is conducted at constant temperature. If the temperature changes during the test period, the signal output is due to the combined effect of acceleration and ΔT and the results are in error.

One of the most critical factors in acceleration measurements is the method used to attach the accelerometer to the structure because improper mounting can compromise the usable frequency range of the accelerometer. The preferred mounting method is illustrated in Fig. 10.35a. The accelerometer is attached to the structure with a steel stud. A thin layer of grease, applied before attachment, significantly improves contact between the accelerometer base and the structure by filling all of the interface voids.

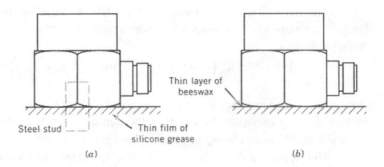

Fig. 10.35 Attachment methods for accelerometers.

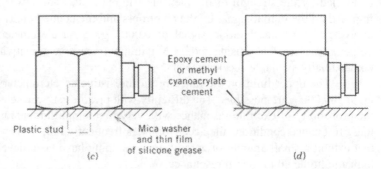

A second mounting method is shown in Fig. 10.35b where sealing wax is used to bond the accelerometer to a structure. This mounting method gives nearly as effective a response as attaching the accelerometer with a stud; however, the wax is limited to a maximum temperature of 40 °C (104 °F). The strength of the bond, which depends on accelerometer mass and contact area, limits maximum accelerations to about 10 g's. The advantage of this method is low cost because no holes are drilled and tapped, which saves considerable time.

A thin film of silicone grease, a mica washer and an electrically insulating plastic stud are used in the third method, illustrated in Fig. 10.35c, to prevent ground loops by electrically isolating the accelerometer from the test item.

A fourth method of attachment, which involves adhesively bonding the accelerometer to the structure, is illustrated in Fig. 10.35d. The advantages of this method are electrical isolation and elimination of the mounting holes. The frequency response of the transducer is not affected, if the adhesive is strong and rigid; however, using a low modulus adhesive leads to erratic behavior. Epoxy adhesives are the most durable while cyanoacrylate cement is easiest to apply as it polymerizes in minutes.

10.14 SUMMARY

A broad range of topics associated with motion measurement and dynamic force measurement were considered in this chapter. A single-degree-of- freedom vibration model, using relative motion between a seismic mass and a transducer base as a motion coordinate, describes the basic dynamic characteristics common to all seismic instruments. These instruments include seismic displacement, velocity and acceleration transducers as well as dynamic force transducers. The steady state frequency response function describing the output from these transducers is a forced single-degree-of-freedom mechanical system. For transient signals, it is shown that input signal rise time must be greater than five times a transducer's natural period. A similar rule of thumb is required for measuring transient half-sine or triangular inputs, where pulse durations must be greater than five times the natural period of the transducer.

Motion measurement without a fixed reference requires a seismic transducer frame. Seismic theory was applied to displacement, velocity and acceleration measurements. It was shown that displacement and velocity transducers are effective above their natural frequency because the seismic mass essentially remains motionless while the base moves. For this reason, these instruments have soft springs and large masses. Commonly used sensing elements for displacement transducers include linear variable- differential transformers (LVDTs) and resistance strain gages mounted on soft elastic springs. On the other hand, accelerometers require stiff springs and a small seismic mass to provide high natural frequencies. Accelerometers are very lightly damped so their usable frequency range is limited to 20% of their natural frequency. Either piezoelectric elements or piezoresistive gages are used as sensing elements in accelerometers.

A piezoelectric sensor is used to generate a charge proportional to acceleration, force or pressure. The electrical characteristics of this sensor when used with voltage-follower, charge-amplifier and built-in voltage-follower interface devices are described. The charge amplifier is extremely versatile, but costly, while the built-in voltage follower is less expensive and easier to use. It is shown that voltage followers and charge amplifiers have a single RC time constant that controls the sensor's low-frequency response. The built-in voltage follower has dual time constants, one set by the manufacturer during assembly and the other by the user. The dynamic response of these circuits to sinusoidal and transient signals was developed. It was noted that sinusoidal signals attenuate at 6 dB/octave for frequencies below the low-frequency cutoff. Also, small RC time constants produce signal undershoot when measuring transient signals.

REFERENCES

1. Stein, Peter K. "The Unified Approach to Engineering Measurement Systems," Stein Engineering Services, Phoenix, AZ, 1992.
2. Dally, J. W., Riley W. F. and K. G. McConnell: Instrumentation for Engineering Measurements, Wiley, New York, 1993.
3. Walter, P. L. and H. D. Nelson: "Limitations and Corrections in Measuring Structural Dynamics," Experimental Mechanics, Vol. 12, No. 9 1979, pp. 309-316..
4. Han, S. B. and K. G. McConnell: "Effect of Mass on Force Transducer Sensitivity," Experimental Techniques, Vol. 10, no. 7, 1986, pp. 19-22.
5. Maini, A. K., Digital Electronics: Principles, Devices and Applications, John Wiley, New York, 2007.
6. Figliola, R. S. and D. E. Beasley, Theory and Design for Mechanical Measurements, 5th Ed., Wiley, New York, 2010.
7. Beckwith, T. G., R. D. Marangoni and J. H. Lienhard V: Mechanical Measurements, 6th ed., Prentice Hall, Englewood Cliffs, NJ, 2007.

8. Shukla, A. and J. W. Dally: Experimental Solid Mechanics, College House Enterprises, Knoxville, TN 2010.

9. Doebelin, E. O.: Measurement Systems Application and Design, International Edition, Tata McGraw-Hill, New York, 2004.

10. Holman, J. P.: Experimental Methods for Engineers, 8th ed., McGraw-Hill, 2011.

11. Klaassen, K. B. and S Gee, Electronic Measurement and Instrumentation, Cambridge University Press, New York, 1996.

12. Wheeler, A. J., A. R. Ganji, Introduction to Engineering Experimentation, Prentice Hall, Englewood Cliffs, NJ, 2009.

13. Walter, Patrick L., "Fifty Years Plus of Accelerometer History for Shock and Vibration (1940-1996)," Shock and Vibration 6, ISSN 1070-9622, 197-207.

14. Plumlee, Ralph H., "Zero-Shift in Piezoelectric Accelerometers," Sandia National Laboratories Research Report, SC-RR-70-755, March 1971.

15. Sill, Robert D., "Test Results and Alternate Packaging of a Damped Piezoresistive MEMS Accelerometer", 52nd Annual NDIA Fuze Conference, Sparks, NV, May 13-15, 2008.

16. Walter, Patrick L., "Lessons Learned in Applying Accelerometers to Nuclear Effects Testing", Shock and Vibration, Volume 15, Number 6, pp. 619-630, November 2008.

EXERCISES

10.1 The expression x = 8 cos (12t) + 6 sin (12t) is a harmonic function with a frequency of 12 rad/s. Show that x can be written as either x = 10 cos (12t + θ_1) or x = 10 sin (12t + θ_2). Determine the phase angles θ_1 and θ_2. Which angle is leading and which angle is lagging the reference phase? What is the reference phase for each expression of x?

10.2 If a simple harmonic motion has an amplitude of 0.001 in. and a frequency of 100 Hz, determine the maximum velocity (in inches per second) and the maximum acceleration (in g's) associated with the motion. If the amplitude of the motion doubles and the frequency remains the same, what is the effect on the maximum velocity and the maximum acceleration? If the frequency doubles and the amplitude of motion remains the same, what is the effect on the maximum velocity and the maximum acceleration?

10.3 Graph the real and imaginary parts of H(ω) [see Eq. (10.6)] over the frequency range 0 < r < 2 if k = 1.0×10^6 lb/in. and d = 0.02. Compare these graphs to Fig. 10.3. Explain the differences.

10.4 A uniform rigid bar of mass m_b and length L rotates in the vertical plane about the pin at O as shown in Fig. E10.4. An accelerometer is mounted at point B at a distance b from pin O. Show that the tangential acceleration at point B is given by:

$$a_B = -\left[\frac{3b}{2L}\right]g\sin(\omega_n t)$$

where $\omega_n = \sqrt{3g/2L}$ is the bar's pendulous natural frequency. Show that the acceleration indicated by the accelerometer is given by:

$$a_{acc} = -\left[1 - \frac{3b}{2L}\right]g\sin(\omega_n t)$$

Why does the accelerometer indicate an incorrect acceleration? Hint: See Eq. (10.4) and evaluate the forces acting on the seismic mass m of the accelerometer.

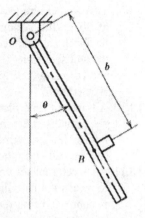

Fig. E10.4

10.5 Show that the mechanical response of an underdamped seismic instrument to a step input is given by:

$$\frac{x}{x_0} = 1 - \frac{e^{-d\omega_n t}}{\sqrt{1-d^2}} \cos(\omega_n - \phi) \quad \text{where} \quad \phi = \tan^{-1}\left(\frac{d}{\sqrt{1-d^2}}\right)$$

Sketch a typical response and compare to Fig. 10.4.

10.6 A velocity meter is being designed with a natural frequency of 5 Hz, damping of 5%, and a sensitivity of 8.3 mV/(in./s). The magnetic core weight is 0.20 lb and is mounted on soft springs. Determine the required spring constant for supporting the core. The velocity meter is mounted on a surface that is vibrating with a maximum velocity of 8.0 in./s. Determine the peak output voltage and phase angle if the frequency of vibration is (a) 8.0 Hz and (b) 20 Hz. Which measurement has the greatest error? Why? Would performance be improved by increasing the damping by a factor of 2? How could you increase the damping electrically?

10.7 An accelerometer is used to measure a periodic signal that can be expressed as:

$$a(t) = a \sin(0.2\omega_n t) - 0.4a \sin(0.6\omega_n t)$$

where ω_n is the natural frequency of the accelerometer. The relative motion of the transducer can be expressed as:

$$z(t) = b_1 \sin(0.2\omega_n t - \phi_1) + b_3 \sin(0.6\omega_n t - \phi_3)$$

Determine the coefficients b_1 and b_3 and phase angles ϕ_1 and ϕ_3 when the transducer damping is (a) 5% and (b) 60%. Which damping condition gives the best modeling? Why?

10.8 An accelerometer with a charge sensitivity of 83 pC/g and a capacitance of 1,000 pF is connected to a voltage follower with an input connector capacitance of 15 pF (in parallel with the cable capacitance), a 10,000 pF blocking capacitor, and a 100-MΩ resistance. A 10 ft long cable with a capacitance of 312 pF connects the accelerometer and the voltage follower. Determine:

    (a) the instrument's voltage sensitivity in mV/g.
    (b) the time constant error between $\tau = RC$ and $\tau = RC_{eq}$.
    (c) the – 3 dB low cutoff frequency in Hz. ,

10.9 An accelerometer with a charge sensitivity S_q = 170 pC/g and a capacitance C_t = 10,000 pF is used to measure low level accelerations. The transducer cable is 30 ft long with a capacitance of 30 pF/ft. Assume that the op-amp has a minimum gain G_1 > 20,000. What minimum feedback capacitance can be used if source capacitance error is to be less than 0.5%? What is the unit sensitivity (g's/volt) if C_f = 200 pF and the transducer dial setting is (a) 0.085, (b) 0.170, and (c) 0.340? Which transducer setting gives the largest voltage signal for a given level of acceleration?

10.10 A transient time history increases in a near linear fashion from 0 to the maximum value in 1.0 ms, remains at the maximum value for 3 ms, and then, returns to zero in 0.50 ms. Based on this information, determine the minimum transducer natural frequency and time constant so that ringing and undershoot errors are bounded by 5%.

10.11 An accelerometer with an internal time constant of 0.5 s, a sensitivity of 10 mV/g is to be used to measure a half-sine shock loading with a time duration of 0.1 seconds. If the accelerometer is connected to a recording device with a 1.0 MΩ input resistance through a 1.0 µF coupling capacitor C_1. Estimate the peak reading error and the amount of undershoot.

10.12 A traveling microscope with a least count of 0.0001 in. is used to measure the peak-to-peak displacement during a sinusoidal calibration of an accelerometer. The microscope is focused on an object having a diameter of 0.0011 in., as shown in Fig. E10.12. For the readings shown, determine the acceleration (in g's) if the frequency of oscillation is:

        (a) 50 Hz   (c) 500 Hz

        (b) 100 Hz   (d) 1000 Hz

        (e) What is your estimate of the percent error in
           these measurements?

        (f) Would any of these acceleration levels be
           difficult to obtain if the moving mass
           weighs 0.35 lb and the vibration exciter can
           deliver a maximum force of 100 lb?

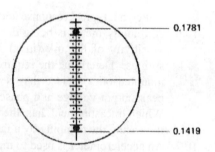

Fig. E10.12

10.13 Several calibration methods require accurate knowledge of the local acceleration of gravity. A common method for obtaining this quantity utilizes a simple pendulum (see Fig. E10.13). If a pendulum having a length of 25 in. is used with a stopwatch that can be started and stopped consistently within 0.15 s, which variable—pendulum length or period of oscillation—must be measured most accurately? How can the 0.15-s uncertainty in the period measurement be overcome? What shape should the pendulum mass have so that its center of mass can most easily be located accurately? Would increasing the pendulum length or using multiple period measurements increase the accuracy of the measurement of g?

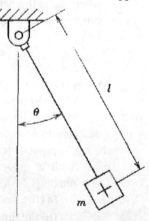

Fig. E10.13

10.14 Data obtained from four gravimetric calibration tests are listed below:

(mV)	Test Number			
	1	2	3	4
V_{mg}	46.6	46.5	46.7	46.5
V_f	19.48	78.1	302	1162
V_a	4.23	16.83	64.5	254.0

Determine the sensitivity S_a of the accelerometer. After the tests were conducted it was determined that the local acceleration of gravity was 31.30 ft/s instead of the nominal 32.17 ft/s. What effect will this change have on the previously determined values of S_a?

10.15 The RMS voltage ratio V_f/V_a versus calibration weight W_c curve from a typical sinusoidal calibration of a dynamic force gage is shown in Fig. 10.17. If a similar curve for a dynamic force gage being calibrated has a slope of 8.06 g's/lb and intersects the vertical axis at a value of 0.403 V/V, determine:

    (a) The sensitivity of the force gage if the sensitivity of the accelerometer is 6.20 mV/g.

    (b) The weight of the seismic mass.

10.16 In a dynamic force gage calibration, the transducer sensitivity dial of the charge amplifier being used with the accelerometer was set at b = 0.276 and the transducer sensitivity dial of the charge amplifier being used with the force gage was set at b = 1.00. The charge sensitivity of the accelerometer is 2.76 pC/g. The feedback capacitor of the charge amplifier being used with the accelerometer was set at 100 pF, while that of the force transducer was set at 2,000 pF. The slope of the V_f/V_a versus W_c curve is 7.82 g/lb. Determine the charge sensitivity of the force gage.

10.17 Explain how Eq. (10.43) is changed, if any, when the accelerometer in Fig. 10.29 is part of the calibration mass m_c so that the acceleration being measured is $\ddot{y}$ instead of $\ddot{x}$.

10.18 An impact hammer with attached force transducer is to be calibrated by impacting a mass suspended as a pendulum, as shown in Fig. 10.32. The sensitivity of the accelerometer is 7.30 mV/g. The peak voltage ratio V_f/V_a versus pendulum weight W_p curve has a slope of 7.19 g/lb. The hammer head weighed 0.165 lb and the hammer body weighed 0.769 lb during the calibration tests. Show that the voltage sensitivity of the force gage as installed is 52.5 mV/lb. At a later date, the weight of the hammer head was increased to 0.611 lb and the weight of the body was increased to 1.278 lb in order to obtain some desired impact force characteristics. Show that the voltage sensitivity of the force gage changes to 43.2 mV/lb.

10.19 A pressure transducer having a charge sensitivity of 1.46 pC/psi is to be used with a charge amplifier to measure hydraulic pump pressures that range from 100 to 1000 psi. The charge amplifier has a calibration capacitor (C_{cal} = 1000 pF), as shown in Fig. 10.13. The required voltage sensitivity for this application is 5 mV/psi. Specify:

    (a)   The transducer sensitivity setting b.

    (b)   The feedback capacitor setting C_f.

    (c)   The peak calibration charges to simulate 100 psi and 1000 psi.

    (d)   The peak calibration voltages required to simulate 100 psi and 1000 psi.

    (e)   The anticipated calibration output voltages corresponding to the two pressures.

    (f)   How would this problem be changed if acceleration in g were specified instead of psi for the measurement variable?

10.20 A force transducer with a sensitivity of 1.0 mV/lb is mounted on a lightweight hammer as shown in Fig. 10.31. Using the impact hammer calibration method shown in Fig. 10.32 and

Eq. (10.47), devise a method to determine both the force transducer sensitivity S_f and the effective hammer masses (m_h and m_b) so that the mass ratio M can be calculated for various hammer body and impact tip mass combinations and new values for transducer sensitivity S_f^* can be predicted.

10.21　The "pop test" illustrated in Fig. E10.21 provides a convenient means for testing the overall performance of a pressure transducer. The pressure variation resulting from rupture of the diaphragm approaches a step input; therefore, typical step input-damped response occurs. During a specific test, the first three peaks were 9.01, 7.59, and 6.67 mV, while the first three valleys were 0, 1.778, and 2.92 mV for an initial chamber pressure of 3.0 psig. The final steady-state response was 5.0 mV. The three peaks occurred at 0.375, 1.125, and 1.875 ms, while the valleys occurred at 0, 0.750, and 1.50 ms. Determine:

　　　(a) The natural frequency of the transducer in Hertz.
　　　(b) The damping in percent.
　　　(c) The transducer sensitivity in mV/psi.

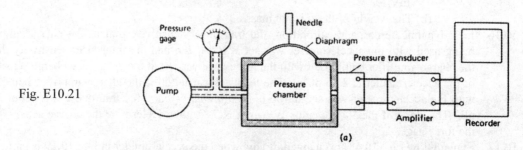

Fig. E10.21

(a)

10.22　A charge amplifier has a 1,000 pF calibration capacitance and is to be used with an accelerometer that has a charge sensitivity of 41.8 pC/g. A maximum acceleration of 80 g's is to be measured. Select appropriate values for b, C_f, and V_{cal}^* if the recorder has a ± 10.0 volt full scale voltage range. What is the system's overall voltage sensitivity?

10.23　When a step input voltage is applied to the calibration capacitor in a charge amplifier, the output voltage may look like that shown in Fig. 10.33. What terms in a typical measurement system contribute to the exponential decay? What is the source of the damped oscillation and rise time? Is the damped oscillation due to the mechanical response of the transducer?

10.24　Describe the difference between piezoelectric and piezoresistive accelerometers citing advantages and disadvantages in your discussion?

10.25　Piezoresistive pressure transducers are fabricated with metallic strain gages and diffusion implanted piezoresistive gage elements. Describe the differences between the two types of transducers citing advantages and disadvantages of each type.

EXERCISE SOLUTIONS

Exercise 10.2

$$\omega = 2\pi f = 2\pi(100) = 628 \text{ rad/s}$$

$$V = \delta\omega = 0.001(628) = 0.628 \text{ in./s} = V_{max}$$

$$a = \delta\omega^2/g = 0.001(628)^2/386 = 1.02 \text{ g's} = a_{max}$$

With $\qquad \delta_1 = 2\delta$ and $f_1 = f$ $\qquad$ Both V and a are doubled.

With $\qquad \delta_2 = \delta$ and $f_2 = 2f$ $\qquad$ V is doubled and a is quadrupled.

Exercise 10.7

$$a(t) = a \sin(0.2\omega_n t) - 0.4a \sin(0.6\omega_n t)$$

$$z(t) = b_1 \sin(0.2\omega_n t - \Phi_1) + b_3 \sin(0.6\omega_n t - \Phi_3)$$

$$b_i = \frac{a_i}{\sqrt{(1 - r_i^2)^2 + (2r_i d)^2}} \qquad \text{and} \qquad \Phi_i = \tan^{-1} = \frac{2r_i d}{1 - r_i^2}$$

For d = 0.05:

Freq Comp	r	$1 - r^2$	2rd	H	b	$\tan \phi$	ϕ	ϕ_{lin}
1	0.2	0.96	0.020	1.041	1.041a	0.0208	1.19	18.0
3	0.6	0.64	0.060	1.556	-0.622a	0.0938	5.36	54.0

For d = 0.60:

Freq Comp	r	$1 - r^2$	2rd	H	b	$\tan \phi$	ϕ	ϕ_{lin}
1	0.2	0.96	0.240	1.011	1.011a	0.250	14.0	18.0
3	0.6	0.64	0.720	1.038	-0.415a	1.125	48.4	54.0

The 60 % damping gives the best results with amplitude distortion under 4 % and phase distortions of 22 % and 10 %.

Exercise 10.10

From Table 10.3 for a rectangular pulse with t_1 = 4 ms and 5% error:

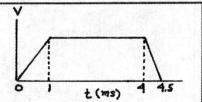

$$\tau = RC = 20t_1 = 20(4.0) = 80 \text{ ms (minimum)}$$
$$= 20(4.5) = 90 \text{ ms (preferred)}$$

For a ramp-hold response:

$$\mathcal{E}_{max} = \frac{2}{\omega_n t_0} = \frac{2}{2\pi f_n t_0}$$

$$f_n = \frac{2}{2\pi \mathcal{E}_{max} t_0} = \frac{2}{2\pi(0.050)(1)(10^{-3})}$$

$$= 6.37(10^3) \text{ Hz} = 6.37 \text{ kHz}$$

Exercise 10.15

$s = 8.06$ g/lb

$S_a = 6.20$ mV/g

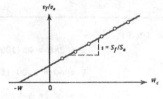

(a) From Eq. 10.44 :

$$S_f = sS_a = 8.06(6.20) = 49.97 \text{ mV/lb} \cong 50.0 \text{ mV/lb}$$

(b) From the graph above:

$$s\, W_s = 0.403$$

$$W_s = \frac{0.403}{s} = \frac{0.403}{8.06} = 0.050 \text{ lb}$$

Exercise 10.18

$$S_a = 7.30 \text{ mV/g} \qquad W_h = 0.165 \text{ lb}$$

$$s = 7.19 \text{ g/lb} \qquad W_b = 0.769 \text{ lb}$$

From Eq. 10.50 :

$$\frac{v_f}{v_a} = \frac{S_f^*}{S_a} W_p$$

Therefore:

$$S_f^* = sS_a = 7.19(7.30) = 52.5 \text{ mV/lb}$$

With $W_h = 0.611$ lb and $W_b = 1.278$ lb:

$$M = \frac{m_h}{m_b} = \frac{0.611/32.2}{1.278/32.2} = 0.478$$

Therefore:

$$S_f^* = \frac{S_f}{1 + M} = \frac{63.8}{1.478} = 43.2 \text{ mV/lb}$$

Exercise 10.21

$$T = 0.75 \text{ ms}$$

(a)

$$f_n = \frac{1}{T} = \frac{1}{0.75(10^{-3})} = 1333 \text{ Hz}$$

$$\omega_n = 2\pi f_n = 2\pi(1333) = 8378 \text{ rad/s}$$

(b) For the first peak:

$$1 + e^{-d\omega_n t_1} = \frac{9.01}{5} = 1.802 \qquad e^{d\omega_n t_1} = 1.247$$

$$d = \frac{\ln 1.247}{\omega_n t_p} = \frac{\ln 1.247}{8378(0.375)(10^{-3})} = 0.070 = 7 \text{ \%}$$

For the second peak:

$$1 + e^{-d\omega_n t_2} = \frac{7.59}{5} = 1.518 \qquad e^{d\omega_n t_2} = 1.931$$

$$d = \frac{\ln 1.931}{\omega_n t_p} = \frac{\ln 1.247}{8378(1.125)(10^{-3})} = 0.070 = 7 \text{ \%}$$

(c)

$$S_p = \frac{\Delta V}{\Delta p} = \frac{0.005}{3.0} = 1.667(10^{-3}) \text{ V/psi} = 1.667 \text{ mv/psi}$$

CHAPTER 11

STATISTICAL ANALYSIS OF EXPERIMENTAL DATA

11.1 INTRODUCTION

Experimental measurements of quantities such as pressure, temperature, length, force, stress or strain will always exhibit some variation if the measurements are repeated a number of times with precise instruments. This variability, which is fundamental to all measuring systems, is due to two different causes. First, the quantity being measured may exhibit significant variation. For example, in a materials study to determine fatigue life at a specified stress level, large differences in the number of cycles to failure are noted when a number of specimens are tested. This variation is inherent in the fatigue process and is observed in all fatigue life measurements. Second, the measuring system, which includes the transducer, signal conditioning equipment, A/D converter, recording instrument, and an operator may introduce error in the measurement. This error may be systematic or random, depending upon its source. An instrument operated out of calibration produces a systematic error, whereas, reading errors due to interpolation on a chart are random. The accumulation of random errors in a measuring system produces a variation that must be examined in relation to the magnitude of the quantity being measured.

The data obtained from repeated measurements represent an array of readings, not an exact result. Maximum information can be extracted from such an array of readings by employing statistical methods. The first step in the statistical treatment of data is to establish the distribution. A graphical representation of the distribution is usually the most useful form for initial evaluation. Next, the statistical distribution is characterized with a measure of its central value, such as the mean, the median, or the mode. Finally, the spread or dispersion of the distribution is determined in terms of the variance or the standard deviation.

With elementary statistical methods, the experimentalist can reduce a large amount of data to a very compact and useful form by defining the type of distribution, establishing the single value that best represents the central value of the distribution (mean), and determining the variation from the mean value (standard deviation). Summarizing data in this manner is the most meaningful form of presentation for application to design problems or for communication to others who need the results of the experiments.

The treatment of statistical methods presented in this chapter is relatively brief; therefore, only the most commonly employed techniques for representing and interpreting data are presented. A formal course in statistics, which covers these techniques in much greater detail as well as many other useful techniques, should be included in the program of study of all engineering students.

11.2 CHARACTERIZING STATISTICAL DISTRIBUTIONS

For purposes of this discussion, consider that an experiment has been conducted n times to determine the ultimate tensile strength of a fully tempered beryllium copper alloy. The data obtained represent a sample of size n from an infinite population of all possible measurements that could have been made. The simplest way to present these data is to list the strength measurements in order of increasing magnitude, as shown in Table 11.1.

Table 11.1
The ultimate tensile strength of beryllium copper, listed in order of increasing magnitude

Sample number	Strength ksi (MPa)	Sample number	Strength ksi (MPa)
1	170.5 (1175)	21	176.2 (1215)
2	171.9 (1185)	22	176.2 (1215)
3	172.6 (1190)	23	176.4 (1217)
4	173.0 (1193)	24	176.6 (1218)
5	173.4 (1196)	25	176.7 (1219)
6	173.7 (1198)	26	176.9 (1220)
7	174.2 (1201)	27	176.9 (1220)
8	174.4 (1203)	28	177.2 (1222)
9	174.5 (1203)	29	177.3 (1223)
10	174.8 (1206)	30	177.4 (1223)
11	174.9 (1206)	31	177.7 (1226)
12	175.0 (1207)	32	177.8 (1226)
13	175.4 (1210)	33	178.0 (1228)
14	175.5 (1210)	34	178.1 (1228)
15	175.6 (1211)	35	178.3 (1230)
16	175.6 (1211)	36	178.4 (1230)
17	175.8 (1212)	37	179.0 (1236)
18	175.9 (1213)	38	179.7 (1239)
19	176.0 (1214)	39	180.1 (1242)
20	176.1 (1215)	40	181.6 (1252)

These data can be arranged into seven groups to give a frequency distribution as shown in Table 11.2. The advantage of representing data in a frequency distribution is that the central tendency is more clearly illustrated.

Table 11.2
Frequency distribution of ultimate tensile strength

Group intervals ksi (MPa)	Observations in the group	Relative frequency	Cumulative frequency
169.0-170.9 (1166-1178)	1	0.025	0.025
171.0-172.9 (1179-1192)	2	0.050	0.075
173.0-174.9 (1193-1206)	8	0.200	0.275
175.0-176.9 (1207-1220)	16	0.400	0.675
177.0-178.9 (1221-1234)	9	0.225	0.900
179.0-180.9 (1235-1248)	3	0.075	0.975
181.0-182.9 (1249-1261)	1	0.025	1.000
Total	40		

11.2.1 Graphical Representations of the Distribution

The shape of the distribution function representing the ultimate tensile strength of beryllium copper is indicated by the data groupings of Table 11.2. A graphical presentation of this group data, known as a **histogram**, is shown in Fig. 11.1. The histogram method of presentation shows the central tendency and variability of the distribution much more clearly than the tabular method of presentation of Table 11.2. A curve superimposed on the histogram is showing the relative frequency of the occurrence of a group of measurements. Note that the points for the relative frequency are plotted at the midpoint of the group interval.

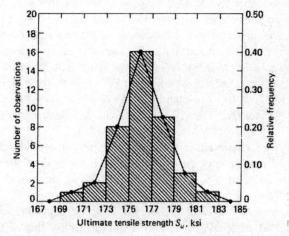

Figure 11.1 Histogram with superimposed relative-frequency diagram.

A cumulative frequency-diagram, shown in Fig. 11.2, is another way of representing the ultimate-strength data from the experiments. The cumulative frequency is the number of readings having a value less than a specified value of the quantity being measured (ultimate strength) divided by the total number of measurements. As indicated in Table 11.2, the cumulative frequency is the running sum of the relative frequencies. When the graph of cumulative frequency versus the quantity being measured is prepared, the end value for the group intervals is used to position the point along the abscissa.

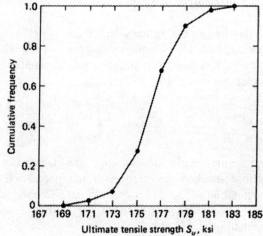

Figure 11.2 Cumulative frequency diagram.

11.2.2 Measures of Central Tendency

While histograms or frequency distributions are used to provide a visual representation of a distribution, numerical measures are used to define the characteristics of the distribution. One basic characteristic is the central tendency of the data. The most commonly employed measure of the central tendency of a distribution of data is the sample mean $\bar{x}$, which is defined as:

$$\bar{x} = \sum_{i=1}^{n} \frac{x_i}{n} \qquad (11.1)$$

where x_i is the i th value of the quantity being measured and n is the total number of measurements.

Because of time and costs involved in conducting tests, the number of measurements is usually limited; therefore, the sample mean $\bar{x}$ is only an estimate of the true arithmetic mean μ of the population. It is shown later that $\bar{x}$ approaches μ as the number of measurements increases. The mean value of the ultimate-strength data presented in Table 11.1 is $\bar{x} = 176.1$ ksi (1215 MPa).

The median and mode are also measures of central tendency. The median is the central value in a group of ordered data. For example, in an ordered set of 41 readings, the 21st reading represents the median value with 20 readings lower than the median and 20 readings higher than the median. In instances when an even number of readings are taken, the median is obtained by averaging the two middle values. For example, in an ordered set of 40 readings, the median is the average of the 20th and 21st readings. Thus, for the ultimate tensile strength data presented in Table 11.1, the median is ½ (176.1 + 176.2) = 176.15 ksi (1215 MPa).

The mode is the most frequent value of the data; therefore, it is located at the peak of the relative-frequency curve. In Fig. 11.1, the peak of the relative probability curve occurs at an ultimate tensile strength $S_u = 176.0$ ksi (1214 MPa); therefore, this value is the mode of the data set presented in Table 11.1.

It is evident that a typical set of data may give different values for the three measures of central tendency. There are two reasons for this difference. First, the population from which the samples were drawn may not be Gaussian where the three measures are expected to coincide. Second, even if the population is Gaussian, the number of measurements n is usually small and deviations due to a small sample size are to be expected.

11.2.3 Measures of Dispersion

It is possible for two different distributions of data to have the same mean but different dispersions, as shown in the relative-frequency diagrams of Fig. 11.3. Different measures of dispersion are the range, the mean deviation, the variance, and the standard deviation. The standard deviation S_x is the most popular and is defined as:

$$S_x = \left[\sum_{i=1}^{n} \frac{(x_i - \bar{x})^2}{n-1} \right]^{1/2}$$
(11.2)

Because the sample size n is small, the standard deviation S_x of the sample represents an estimate of the true standard deviation σ of the population. Computation of S_x and $\bar{x}$ from a data sample is easily performed with most scientific type calculators.

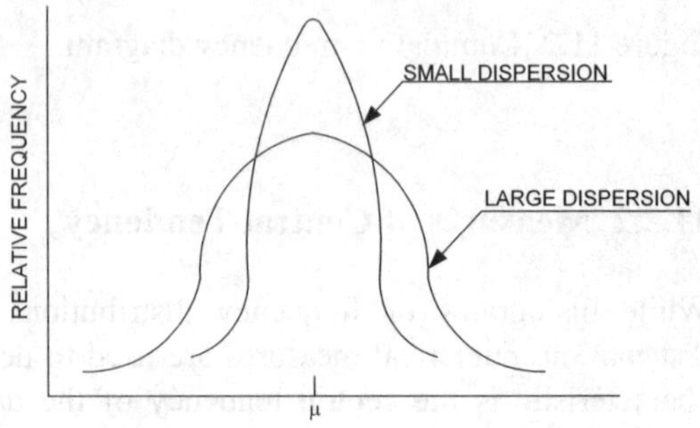

Figure 11.3 Relative frequency diagrams with large and small dispersions.

Expressions for the other measures of dispersion, namely, range R, mean deviation d_x, and variance S_x^2 are given by:

$$R = x_L - x_s$$
(11.3)

$$d_x = \sum_{i=1}^{n} \frac{|x_i - \overline{x}|}{n} \qquad (11.4)$$

$$S_x^2 = \sum_{i=1}^{n} \frac{(x_i - \overline{x})^2}{n-1} \qquad (11.5)$$

where x_L is the largest value of the quantity in the distribution and x_s is the smallest value.

Equation (11.4) indicates that the deviation of each reading from the mean is determined and summed. The average of the n deviations is the mean deviation. The absolute value of the difference $(x_i - \overline{x})$ must be used in the summing process to avoid cancellation of positive and negative deviations. The variance of the population σ^2 is estimated by S_x^2 where the denominator $(n - 1)$ in Eqs. (11.2) and (11.5) serves to reduce error introduced by approximating the true mean μ with the estimate of the mean $\overline{x}$. As the sample size n is increased, the estimates of $\overline{x}$, S_x, and S_x^2 improve as shown in the discussion of Section 11.4. Variance is an important measure of dispersion because it is used in defining the normal distribution function.

Finally, a measure known as the coefficient of variation C_v is used to express the standard deviation S_x as a percentage of the mean $\overline{x}$. Thus:

$$C_v = \frac{S_x}{\overline{x}}(100) \qquad (11.6)$$

The coefficient of variation represents a normalized parameter indicating variability of the data in relation to its mean.

11.3 STATISTICAL DISTRIBUTION FUNCTIONS

As the sample size is increased, it is possible in tabulating the data to increase the number of group intervals and to decrease their width. The corresponding relative-frequency diagram, similar to the one illustrated in Fig. 11.1, will approach a smooth curve (a theoretical distribution curve) known as a **distribution function**.

A number of different distribution functions are used in statistical analyses. The best-known and most widely used distribution in experimental mechanics is the Gaussian or normal distribution. This distribution is extremely important because it describes random errors in measurements and variations observed in strength determinations. Other useful distributions include binomial, exponential, hypergeometric, chi-square χ^2, F, Gumbel, Poisson, Student's t, and Weibull distributions. The reader is referred to references [1-5] for a complete description of these distributions. Emphasis here will be on Gaussian and Weibull distribution functions because of their wide range of application in experimental mechanics.

11.3.1 Gaussian Distribution

The Gaussian or normal distribution function, as represented by a normalized relative-frequency diagram, is shown in Fig. 11.4. The Gaussian distribution is completely defined by two parameters; the mean μ and the standard deviation σ. The equation for the relative frequency f in terms of these two parameters is given by:

$$f(z) = \frac{1}{\sqrt{2\pi}} e^{-\left(z^2/2\right)} \qquad (11.7)$$

where

$$z = \frac{\overline{x} - \mu}{\sigma} \qquad (11.8)$$

Experimental data (with finite sample sizes) can be analyzed to obtain $\overline{x}$ as an estimate of μ and S_x as an estimate of σ. This procedure permits the experimentalist to use data drawn from small samples to represent the entire population.

The method for predicting population properties from a Gaussian (normal) distribution function utilizes the normalized relative-frequency diagram shown in Fig. 11.4. The area A under the entire curve is given by Eq. (11.7) as:

$$A = \frac{1}{\sqrt{2\pi}} \int_{-\infty}^{\infty} e^{-\left(z^2/2\right)} dz = 1 \qquad (11.9)$$

Equation (11.9) implies that the population has a value z between $-\infty$ and $+\infty$ and that the probability of making a single observation from the population with a value $-\infty \le z \le +\infty$ is 100%. While the previous statement may appear trivial and obvious, it serves to illustrate the concept of using the area under the normalized relative-frequency curve to determine the probability p of observing a measurement within a specific interval. Figure 11.5 shows graphically, with the shaded area under the curve, the probability that a measurement will occur within the interval between z_1 and z_2. Thus, from Eq. (11.7) it is evident that:

$$p(z_1, z_2) = \int_{z_1}^{z_2} f(z)dz = \frac{1}{\sqrt{2\pi}} \int_{z_1}^{z_2} e^{-\left(z^2/2\right)} dz \qquad (11.10)$$

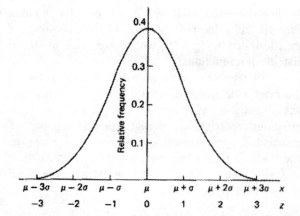

Figure 11.4 The normal or Gaussian distribution function.

Evaluation of Eq. (11.10) is most easily accomplished by using tables that list the areas under the normalized relative-frequency curve as a function of z. Table 11.3 lists one-side areas between limits of $z_1 = 0$ and z_2 for the normal distribution function.

Table 11.3
Areas under the normal distribution curve from $z_1 = 0$ to z_2 (one side)

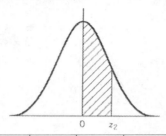

$z_2 = \dfrac{x - \bar{x}}{S_x}$	0.00	0.01	0.02	0.03	0.04	0.05	0.06	0.07	0.08	0.09
0.0	0.0000	0.0040	0.0080	0.0120	0.0160	0.0199	0.0239	0.0279	0.0319	0.0359
0.1	0.0398	0.0438	0.0478	0.0517	0.0557	0.0596	0.0636	0.0675	0.0714	0.0753
0.2	0.0793	0.0832	0.0871	0.0910	0.0948	0.0987	0.1026	0.1064	0.1103	0.1141
0.3	0.1179	0.1217	0.1255	0.1293	0.1331	0.1368	0.1406	0.1443	0.1480	0.1517
0.4	0.1554	0.1591	0.1628	0.1664	0.1700	0.1736	0.1772	0.1808	0.1844	0.1879
0.5	0.1915	0.1950	0.1985	0.2019	0.2054	0.2088	0.2123	0.2157	0.2190	0.2224
0.6	0.2257	0.2291	0.2324	0.2357	0.2389	0.2422	0.2454	0.2486	0.2517	0.2549
0.7	0.2580	0.2611	0.2642	0.2673	0.2704	0.2734	0.2764	0.2794	0.2823	0.2852
0.8	0.2881	0.2910	0.2939	0.2967	0.2995	0.3023	0.3051	0.3078	0.3106	0.3233
0.9	0.3159	0.3186	0.3212	0.3238	0.3264	0.3289	0.3315	0.3340	0.3365	0.3389
1.0	0.3413	0.3438	0.3461	0.3485	0.3508	0.3531	0.3554	0.3577	0.3599	0.3621
1.1	0.3643	0.3665	0.3686	0.3708	0.3729	0.3749	0.3770	0.3790	0.3810	0.3830
1.2	0.3849	0.3869	0.3888	0.3907	0.3925	0.3944	0.3962	0.3980	0.3997	0.4015
1.3	0.4032	0.4049	0.4066	0.4082	0.4099	0.4115	0.4131	0.4147	0.4162	0.4177
1.4	0.4192	0.4207	0.4222	0.4236	0.4251	0.4265	0.4279	0.4292	0.4306	0.4319
1.5	0.4332	0.4345	0.4357	0.4370	0.4382	0.4394	0.4406	0.4418	0.4429	0.4441
1.6	0.4452	0.4463	0.4474	0.4484	0.4495	0.4505	0.4515	0.4525	0.4535	0.4545
1.7	0.4554	0.4564	0.4573	0.4582	0.4591	0.4599	0.4608	0.4616	0.4625	0.4633
1.8	0.4641	0.4649	0.4656	0.4664	0.4671	0.4678	0.4686	0.4693	0.4699	0.4706
1.9	0.4713	0.4719	0.4726	0.4732	0.4738	0.4744	0.4750	0.4758	0.4761	0.4767
2.0	0.4772	0.4778	0.4783	0.4788	0.4793	0.4799	0.4803	0.4808	0.4812	0.4817
2.1	0.4821	0.4826	0.4830	0.4834	0.4838	0.4842	0.4846	0.4850	0.4854	0.4857
2.2	0.4861	0.4864	0.4868	0.4871	0.4875	0.4878	0.4881	0.4884	0.4887	0.4890
2.3	0.4893	0.4896	0.4898	0.4901	0.4904	0.4906	0.4909	0.4911	0.4913	0.4916
2.4	0.4918	0.4920	0.4922	0.4925	0.4927	0.4929	0.4931	0.4932	0.4934	0.4936
2.5	0.4938	0.4940	0.4941	0.4943	0.4945	0.4946	0.4948	0.4949	0.4951	0.4952
2.6	0.4953	0.4955	0.4956	0.4957	0.4959	0.4960	0.4961	0.4962	0.4963	0.4964
2.7	0.4965	0.4966	0.4967	0.4968	0.4969	0.4970	0.4971	0.4972	0.4973	0.4974
2.8	0.4974	0.4975	0.4976	0.4977	0.4977	0.4978	1.4979	0.4979	0.4980	0.4981
2.9	0.4981	0.4982	0.4982	0.4983	0.4984	0.4984	0.4985	0.4985	0.4986	0.4986
3.0	0.49865	0.4987	0.4987	0.4988	0.4988	0.4988	0.4989	0.4989	0.4989	0.4990

Because the distribution function is symmetric about $z = 0$, this one-sided table is sufficient for all evaluations of the probability. For example, $A(-1,0) = A(0,+1)$ leads to the following determinations:

$$A(-1,+1) = p(-1,+1) = 0.3413 + 0.3413 = 0.6826$$
$$A(-2,+2) = p(-2,+2) = 0.4772 + 0.4772 = 0.9544$$
$$A(-3,+3) = p(-3,+3) = 0.49865 + 0.49865 = 0.9973$$
$$A(-1,+2) = p(-1,+2) = 0.3413 + 0.4772 = 0.8185$$

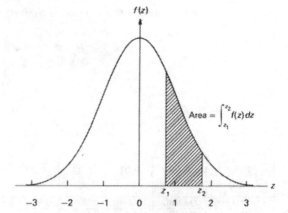

Figure 11.5 Probability of a measurement of x
between limits of z_1 and z_2 .
The total area under the curve f(z) is 1.

Because the normal distribution function has been well characterized, predictions can be made regarding the probability of a specific strength value or measurement error. For example, one may anticipate that 68.3% of the data will fall between limits of $\bar{x} \pm 1.0\ S_x$, 95.4% between limits of $\bar{x} \pm 2.0\ S_x$, and 99.7% between limits of $\bar{x} \pm 3.0\ S_x$. Also, 81.9% of the data should fall between limits of $\bar{x} - 1.0\ S_x$ and $\bar{x} + 2.0\ S_x$.

In many problems, the probability of a single sample exceeding a specified value z_2 must be determined. It is possible to determine this probability by using Table 11.3 together with the fact that the area under the entire curve is unity (A = 1); however, Table 11.4, which lists one-sided areas between limits of $z_1 = z$ and $z_2 \Rightarrow \infty$, yields the results more directly.

The use of Tables 11.3 and 11.4 can be illustrated by considering the ultimate-tensile-strength data presented in Table 11.1. By using Eqs. (11.1) and (11.2), it is easy to establish estimates for the mean $\bar{x}$ and standard deviation S_x as $\bar{x}$ = 176.1 ksi (1215 MPa) and S_x = 2.25 ksi (15.5 MPa). The values of $\bar{x}$ and S_x characterize the population from which the data of Table 11.1 were drawn. It is possible to establish the probability that the ultimate tensile strength of a single specimen drawn randomly from the population will be between specified limits (by using Table 11.3), or that the ultimate tensile strength of a single sample will not be above or below a specified value (by using Table 11.4). For example, one determines the probability that a single sample will exhibit an ultimate tensile strength between 175 and 178 ksi by computing z_1 and z_2 and using Table 11.3. Thus:

$$z_1 = \frac{175 - 176.1}{2.25} = -0.489 \qquad z_2 = \frac{178 - 176.1}{2.25} = 0.844$$

$$p(-0.489, 0.844) = A(-0.489, 0) + A(0, 0.844) = 0.1875 + 0.3006 = 0.4981$$

This simple calculation shows that the probability of obtaining an ultimate tensile strength between 175 and 178 ksi from a single specimen is 49.8%. The probability of the ultimate tensile strength of a single specimen being less than 173 ksi is determined by computing z_1 and using Table 11.4. Thus:

$$z_1 = \frac{173 - 176.1}{2.25} = -1.37$$

$$p(-\infty, -1.37) = A(-\infty, -1.37) = A(1.37, \infty) = 0.0853$$

Thus, the probability of drawing a single sample with an ultimate tensile strength less than 173 ksi is 8.5%.

Table 11.4

Areas under the normal distribution curve from z_1 to $z_2 \Rightarrow \infty$ (one side)

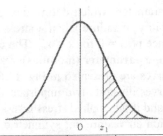

$z_1 = \dfrac{x - \bar{x}}{S_x}$	0.00	0.01	0.02	0.03	0.04	0.05	0.06	0.07	0.08	0.09
0.0	0.5000	0.4960	0.4920	0.4880	0.4840	0.4801	0.4761	0.4721	0.4681	0.4641
0.1	0.4602	0.4562	0.4522	0.4483	0.4443	0.4404	0.4364	0.4325	0.4286	0.4247
0.2	0.4207	0.4168	0.4129	0.4090	0.4052	0.4013	0.3974	0.3936	0.3897	0.3859
0.3	0.3821	0.3783	0.3745	0.3707	0.3669	0.3632	0.3594	0.3557	0.3520	0.3483
0.4	0.3446	0.3409	0.3372	0.3336	0.3300	0.3264	0.3228	0.3192	0.3156	0.3121
0.5	0.3085	0.3050	0.3015	0.2981	0.2946	0.2912	0.2877	0.2843	0.2810	0.2776
0.6	0.2743	0.2709	0.2676	0.2643	0.2611	0.2578	0.2546	0.2514	0.2483	0.2451
0.7	0.2430	0.2389	0.2358	0.2327	0.2296	0.2266	0.2236	0.2206	0.2177	0.2148
0.8	0.2119	0.2090	0.2061	0.2033	0.2005	0.1977	0.1949	0.1922	0.1894	0.1867
0.9	0.1841	0.1814	0.1788	0.1762	0.1736	0.1711	0.1685	0.1660	0.1635	0.1611
1.0	0.1587	0.1562	0.1539	0.1515	0.1492	0.1469	0.1446	0.1423	0.1401	0.1379
1.1	0.1357	0.1335	0.1314	0.1292	0.1271	0.1251	0.1230	0.1210	0.1190	0.1170
1.2	0.1151	0.1131	0.1112	0.1093	0.1075	0.1056	0.1038	0.1020	0.1003	0.0985
1.3	0.0968	0.0951	0.0934	0.0918	0.0901	0.0885	0.0869	0.0853	0.0838	0.0823
1.4	0.0808	0.0793	0.0778	0.0764	0.0749	0.0735	0.0721	0.0708	0.0694	0.0681
1.5	0.0668	0.0655	0.0643	0.0630	0.0618	0.0606	0.0594	0.0582	0.0571	0.0559
1.6	0.0548	0.0537	0.0526	0.0516	0.0505	0.0495	0.0485	0.0475	0.0465	0.0455
1.7	0.0446	0.0436	0.0427	0.0418	0.0409	0.0401	0.0392	0.0384	0.0375	0.0367
1.8	0.0359	0.0351	0.0344	0.0336	0.0329	0.0322	0.0314	0.0307	0.0301	0.0294
1.9	0.0287	0.0281	0.0274	0.0268	0.0262	0.0256	0.0250	0.0244	0.0239	0.0233
2.0	0.0228	0.0222	0.0217	0.0212	0.0207	0.0202	0.0197	0.0192	0.0188	0.0183
2.1	0.0179	0.0174	0.0170	0.0166	0.0162	0.0158	0.0154	0.0150	0.0146	0.0143
2.2	0.0139	0.0136	0.0132	0.0129	0.0125	0.0122	0.0119	0.0116	0.0113	0.0110
2.3	0.0107	0.0104	0.0102	0.00990	0.00964	0.00939	0.00914	0.00889	0.00866	0.00840
2.4	0.00820	0.00798	0.00776	0.00755	0.00734	0.00714	0.00695	0.00676	0.00657	0.00639
2.5	0.00621	0.00604	0.00587	0.00570	0.00554	0.00539	0.00523	0.00508	0.00494	0.00480
2.6	0.00466	0.00453	0.00440	0.00427	0.00415	0.00402	0.00391	0.00379	0.00368	0.00357
2.7	0.00347	0.00336	0.00326	0.00317	0.00307	0.00298	0.00288	0.00280	0.00272	0.00264
2.8	0.00256	0.00248	0.00240	0.00233	0.00226	0.00219	0.00212	0.00205	0.00199	0.00193
2.9	0.00187	0.00181	0.00175	0.00169	0.00164	0.00159	0.00154	0.00149	0.00144	0.00139

11.3.2 Weibull Distribution

In investigations of the strength of materials due to brittle fracture, of crack-initiation toughness, or of fatigue life, researchers often find that the Weibull distribution provides a more suitable approach to the statistical analysis of the available data. The Weibull distribution function p(x) is defined as:

$$p(x) = 1 - e^{-[(x-x_0)/b]^2} \qquad \text{for } x > x_0$$
$$p(x) = 0 \qquad \text{for } x < x_0 \tag{11.11}$$

where x_0, b, and m are the three parameters which define this distribution function. In studies of strength, $p(x)$ is taken as the probability of failure when a stress x is placed on the specimen. The parameter x_0 is the **zero strength** since $p(x) = 0$ for $x < x_0$. The constants b and m are known as the **scale parameter** and the **Weibull slope parameter (modulus)**, respectively.

Four Weibull distribution curves are presented in Fig. 11.6 for the case where $x_0 = 3$, $b = 10$, and $m = 2, 5, 10$, and 11. These curves illustrate two important features of the Weibull distribution. First, there is a threshold strength x_0 and if the applied stress is less than x_0, the probability of failure is zero. Second, the Weibull distribution curves are not symmetric, and the distortion in the S-shaped curves is controlled by the Weibull slope parameter m. Application of the Weibull distribution to predict failure rates of one percent or less of the population is particularly important in engineering projects where reliabilities of 99% or greater are required.

To utilize the Weibull distribution requires knowledge of the Weibull parameters. In experimental investigations, it is necessary to conduct experiments and obtain a relatively large data set to accurately determine x_0, b, and m. Consider as an illustration, Weibull's own work in statistically characterizing the fiber strength of Indian cotton. In this example, an unusually large sample (n = 3,000) was studied by measuring the load to fracture (in grams) for each fiber. The strength data obtained was placed in sequential order with the lowest value corresponding to $k = 1$ first and the largest value corresponding to $k = 3,000$ last. The probability of failure $p(x)$ at a load x is then determined from:

$$p = \frac{k}{n+1} \tag{11.12}$$

where k is the order number of the sequenced data and n is the total sample size.

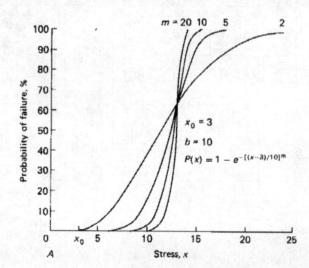

Figure 11.6 The Weibull distribution function.

At this stage it is possible to prepare a graph of probability of failure $P(x)$ as a function of strength x to obtain a curve similar to that shown in Fig. 11.6. However, to determine the Weibull parameters x_0, b, and m requires additional conditioning of the data. From Eq. 11.11, it is evident that:

$$e^{[(x-x_0)/b]^m} = \left[1 - p(x)\right]^{-1} \tag{11.13}$$

Taking the natural log of both sides of Eq. (11.13) yields:

$$\left[\frac{(x - x_0)}{b}\right]^m = \ln\left[1 - p(x)\right]^{-1} \tag{11.14}$$

Taking $\log_{10}$ of both sides of Eq. (11.14) gives a relation for the slope parameter m. Thus:

$$m = \frac{\log_{10} \ln\left[1 - p(x)\right]^{-1}}{\log_{10}(x - x_0) - \log_{10} b} \tag{11.15}$$

The numerator of Eq. (11.15) is the reduced variate $y = \log_{10} \ln[1 - p(x)]^{-1}$ used for the ordinate in preparing a graph of the conditioned data as indicated in Fig. 11.7. Note that y is a function of p alone and for this reason both the p and y scales can be displayed on the ordinates (see Fig. 11.7). The lead term in the denominator of Eq. (11.15) is the reduced variate $x = \log_{10}(x - x_0)$ used for the abscissa in Fig. (11.7).

In the Weibull example, the threshold strength x_0 was adjusted to 0.46 grams so that the data would fall on a straight line when plotted against the reduced x and y variates. The constant b is determined from the condition that:

$$\log_{10} b = \log_{10}(x - x_0) \qquad \text{when } y = 0 \tag{11.16}$$

Note from Fig. 11.7 that $y = 0$ when $\log_{10}(x - x_0) = 0.54$ which gives $b = 0.54$. Finally m is given by the slope of the straight line when the data is plotted in terms of the reduced variates x and y. In this example problem, $m = 1.48$.

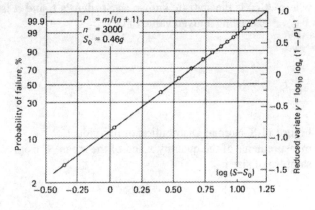

Figure 11.7 Fiber strength of Indian cotton shown in graphical format with Weibull's reduced variate (from data by Weibull).

11.4 CONFIDENCE INTERVALS FOR PREDICTIONS

When experimental data are represented with a normal distribution by using estimates of the mean $\bar{x}$ and standard deviation S_x and predictions are made about the occurrence of certain measurements, questions arise concerning the confidence that can be placed on either the estimates or the predictions. One cannot be totally confident in the predictions or estimates because of the effects of sampling error. Sampling error can be illustrated by drawing a series of samples (each containing n measurements) from the same population and determining several estimates of the mean $\bar{x}_1$, $\bar{x}_2$, $\bar{x}_3$, ... A variation in $\bar{x}$ will occur, but fortunately, this variation can also be characterized by a normal distribution function, as shown in Fig. 11.8. The mean of the x and $\bar{x}$ distributions is the same; however, the standard deviation of the $\bar{x}$ distribution $S_{\bar{x}}$ (sometimes referred to as the **standard error**) is less than S_x because:

$$S_{\bar{x}} = \frac{S_x}{\sqrt{n}} \tag{11.17}$$

When the standard deviation of the population of $\bar{x}$'s is known, it is possible to place confidence limits on the determination of the true population mean μ from a sample of size n, provided n is large (n > 25). The confidence interval within which the true population mean μ is located is given by the expression:

$$(\bar{x} - z\, S_{\bar{x}}) < \mu < [\bar{x} + z\, S_{\bar{x}}] \tag{11.18}$$

where $\bar{x} - zS_{\bar{x}}$ is the lower confidence limit and $\bar{x} + z\, S_{\bar{x}}$ is the upper confidence limit.

The width of the confidence interval depends upon the confidence level required. For instance, if z = 3 in Eq. (11.18), a relatively wide confidence interval exists; therefore, the probability that the population mean μ will be located within the confidence interval is high (99.7%). As the width of the confidence interval decreases, the probability that the population mean μ will fall within the interval decreases. Commonly used confidence levels and their associated intervals are shown in Table 11.5.
  When the sample size is very small (n < 20), the standard deviation S_x does not provide a reliable estimate of the standard deviation μ of the population and Eq. (11.18) should not be employed. The bias introduced by small sample size can be removed by modifying Eq. (11.18) to read as:

$$(\bar{x} - t(a)\, S_{\bar{x}}) < \mu < [\bar{x} + t(\alpha)\, S_{\bar{x}}] \tag{11.19}$$

where $t(\alpha)$ is the statistic known as **Student's t**, and α is the level of significance (the probability of exceeding a given value of t).

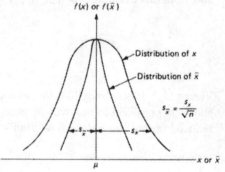

Figure 11.8 Normal Distribution of individual measurements of the quantity x and of the mean $\bar{x}$ from samples of size n.

Table 11.5
Confidence interval variation with confidence level interval = $\bar{x} + z\, S_{\bar{x}}$

Confidence level,%	z	Confidence level,%	z
99.9	3.30	90.0	1.65
99.7	3.00	80.0	1.28
99.0	2.57	68.3	1.00
95.0	1.96	60.0	0.84

The Student t distribution is defined by a relative frequency equation f(t), which can be expressed as:

$$f(t) = F_0 \left(1 + \frac{t^2}{v}\right)^{(v+1)/2}$$

(11.20)

where F_0 is the relative frequency at $t = 0$ required to make the total area under the f(t) curve equal to unity and v is the number of degrees of freedom.

The distribution function f(t) is shown in Fig. 11.9 for several different degrees of freedom v. The degrees of freedom equal the number of independent measurements employed in the determination. It is evident that as v becomes large, Student's t distribution approaches the normal distribution. One-side areas for the t distribution are listed in Table 11.6 and illustrated in Fig. 11.10.

The term $t(\alpha)S_{\bar{x}}$ in Eq. (11.19) represents the measure from the estimated mean $\bar{x}$ to one or the other of the confidence limits. This term may be used to estimate the sample size required to produce an estimate of the mean $\bar{x}$ with a specified reliability. Noting that one-half the band width of the confidence interval is $\delta = t(\alpha)S_{\bar{x}}$ and using Eq. (11.17), it is apparent that the sample size is given by:

$$n = \left[\frac{t(\alpha)S_{\bar{x}}}{\delta}\right]^2$$

(11.21)

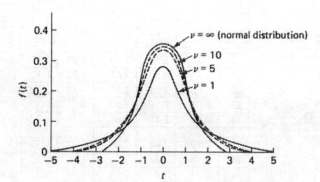

Figure 11.9 Student's t distribution for several degrees of freedom v.

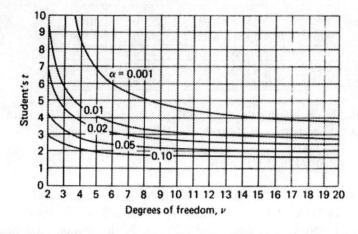

Figure 11.10 Student's t statistic as a function of the degrees of freedom v with α as the probability of exceeding t as a parameter.

Table 11.6
listribution for ν degrees of freedom showing t(α) as a function of area A (one side)

ν	\multicolumn{10}{c}{Confidence level, α}
	0.995	0.99	0.975	0.95	0.90	0.80	0.75	0.70	0.60	0.55
1	63.66	31.82	11.71	6.31	3.08	1.376	1.000	0.727	0.325	0.158
2	9.92	6.96	4.30	2.92	1.89	1.061	0.816	0.617	0.289	0.142
3	5.84	4.54	3.18	2.35	1.64	0.978	0.765	0.584	0.277	0.137
4	4.60	3.75	2.78	2.13	1.53	0.941	0.741	0.569	0.271	0.134
5	4.03	3.36	2.57	2.02	1.48	0.920	0.727	0.559	0.267	0.132
6	3.71	3.14	2.45	1.94	1.44	0.906	0.718	0.553	0.265	0.131
7	3.50	3.00	2.36	1.90	1.42	0.896	0.711	0.549	0.263	0.130
8	3.36	2.90	2.31	1.86	1.40	0.889	0.706	0.546	0.262	0.130
9	3.25	2.82	2.26	1.83	1.38	0.883	0.703	0.543	0.261	0.129
10	3.17	2.76	2.23	1.81	1.37	0.879	0.700	0.542	0.260	0.129
11	3.11	2.72	2.20	1.80	1.36	0.876	0.697	0.540	0.260	0.129
12	3.06	2.68	2.18	1.78	1.36	0.873	0.695	0.539	0.259	0.128
13	3.01	2.65	2.16	1.77	1.35	0.870	0.694	0.538	0.259	0.128
14	2.98	2.62	2.14	1.76	1.34	0.868	0.692	0.537	0.258	0.128
15	2.95	2.60	2.13	1.75	1.34	0.866	0.691	0.536	0.258	0.128
16	2.92	2.58	2.12	1.75	1.34	0.865	0.690	0.535	0.258	0.128
17	2.90	2.57	2.11	1.74	1.33	0.863	0.689	0.534	0.257	0.128
18	2.88	2.55	2.10	1.73	1.33	0.862	0.688	0.534	0.257	0.127
19	2.86	2.54	2.09	1.73	1.33	0.861	0.688	0.533	0.257	0.127
20	2.84	2.53	2.09	1.72	1.32	0.860	0.687	0.533	0.257	0.127
21	2.83	2.52	2.08	1.72	1.32	0.859	0.686	0.532	0.257	0.127
22	2.82	2.51	2.07	1.72	1.32	0.858	0.686	0.532	0.256	0.127
23	2.81	2.50	2.07	1.71	1.32	0.858	0.685	0.532	0.256	0.127
24	2.80	2.49	2.06	1.71	1.32	0.857	0.685	0.531	0.256	0.127
25	2.79	2.48	2.06	1.71	1.32	0.856	0.684	0.531	0.256	0.127
26	2.78	2.48	2.06	1.71	1.32	0.856	0.684	0.531	0.256	0.127
27	2.77	2.47	2.05	1.70	1.31	0.855	0.684	0.531	0.256	0.127
28	2.76	2.47	2.05	1.70	1.31	0.855	0.683	0.530	0.256	0.127
29	2.76	2.46	2.04	1.70	1.31	0.854	0.683	0.530	0.256	0.127
30	2.75	2.46	2.04	1.70	1.31	0.854	0.683	0.530	0.256	0.127
40	2.70	2.42	2.02	1.68	1.30	0.851	0.681	0.529	0.255	0.126
60	2.66	2.39	2.00	1.67	1.30	0.848	0.679	0.527	0.254	0.126
120	2.62	2.36	1.98	1.66	1.29	0.845	0.677	0.526	0.254	0.126
∞	2.58	2.33	1.96	1.65	1.28	0.842	0.674	0.524	0.253	0.126

The use of Eq. (11.21) can be illustrated by considering the data in Table 11.1, where $S_x = 2.25$ ksi and $\overline{x} = 176.1$ ksi. If this estimate of μ is to be accurate to ± 1% with a reliability of 99% then:

$$\delta = (0.01)(176.1) = 1.76 \text{ ksi}$$

Since t(α) depends on n, a trial-and-error solution is needed to establish the sample size n needed to satisfy the specifications. For the data of Table 11.1, n = 40: therefore ν = 39 and t(α) = t(0.995) = 2.71 from Table 11.6. The value t(α) = t(0.995) is used since 0.5% of the distribution must be excluded on each end of the curve to give a two-sided area corresponding to a reliability of 99%. Substituting into Eq. (11.21) yields:

$$n = \left[\frac{2.71(2.25)}{1.76}\right]^2 = 12.00$$

This result indicates that a much smaller sample than 40 will be sufficient. Next try n = 12, ν = 11, and t(α) = 3.11; then:

$$n = \left[\frac{3.11(2.25)}{1.76}\right]^2 = 15.80$$

Finally, with n = 15, ν = 14, and t(α) = 2.98; then:

$$n = \left[\frac{2.98(2.25)}{1.76}\right]^2 = 14.50$$

Thus, a sample size of 15 would be sufficient to ensure an accuracy of ± 1% with a confidence level of 99%. The sample size of 40 listed in Table 11.1 is too large for the degree of accuracy and confidence level specified. This simple example illustrates how sample size can be reduced and cost savings affected by using statistical methods.

11.5   COMPARISON OF MEANS

Because the Student's t distribution compensates for the effect of small sample bias and converges to the normal distribution in large samples, it is a very useful statistic in engineering applications. A second important application utilizes the t distribution as the basis for a test to determine if the difference between two means is significant or due to random variation. For example, consider the yield strength of a steel determined with a sample size of $n_1 = 20$ which gives $\bar{x}_1 = 78.4$ ksi and $S_{\bar{x}1} = 6.04$ ksi. Suppose now that a second sample from another supplier is tested to determine the yield strength and the results are $n_2 = 25$, $\bar{x}_1 = 81.6$ ksi, and $S_{\bar{x}2} = 5.56$ ksi. Is the steel from the second supplier superior in terms of yield strength? The standard deviation of the difference in means $S_{(\bar{x}2-\bar{x}1)}$ can be expressed as:

$$S_{(\bar{x}2-\bar{x}1)}^2 = S_p^2\left(\frac{1}{n_1}+\frac{1}{n_2}\right) = S_p^2\frac{n_1+n_2}{n_1 n_2} \tag{11.22}$$

where S_p^2 is the pooled variance that can be expressed as:

$$S_p^2 = \frac{(n_1-1)S_{x1}^2+(n_2-1)S_{x2}^2}{n_1+n_2-2} \tag{11.23}$$

The statistic t can be computed from the expression:

$$t = \frac{|\bar{x}_2-\bar{x}_1|}{S_{(\bar{x}2-\bar{x}1)}} \tag{11.24}$$

A comparison of the value of t determined from Eq. (11.24) with a value of t(α) obtained from Table 11.6 provides a statistical basis for deciding whether the difference in means is real or due to random variations. The value of t(α) to be used depends upon the degrees of freedom $v = n_1 + n_2 - 2$ and the level of significance required. Levels of significance commonly employed are 5% and 1%. The 5% level of significance means that the probability of a random variation being taken for a real difference is only 5%. Comparisons at the 1% level of significance are 99% certain; however, in such a strong test, real differences can often be attributed to random error.

In the example being considered, Eq. (11.23) yields $S_p^2 = 33.37$ ksi, Eq. (11.22) yields $S^2_{(\bar{x}_2 - \bar{x}_1)} = 3.00$ ksi, and Eq. (11.24) yields t = 1.848. For a 5% level of significance test with $v = 43$ and $\alpha = 0.05$ (the comparison is one-sided, since the t test is for superiority), Table 11.6 indicates that t(α) = 1.68. Because t > t(α), it can be concluded with a 95% level of confidence that the yield strength of the steel from the second supplier was higher than the yield strength of steel from the first supplier.

11.6   STATISTICAL SAFETY FACTOR

In experimental mechanics, it is often necessary to determine the stresses acting on a component and its strength in order to predict whether failure will occur or if the component is safe. The prediction can be difficult if both the stress σ_{ij}, and the strength S_y, are variables since failure will occur only in the region of overlap of the two distribution functions as shown in Fig. 11.11.

To determine the probability of failure, or conversely, the reliability, the statistic z_R is computed by using the equation:

$$z_R = \frac{\bar{x}_S - \bar{x}_\sigma}{S_{S-\sigma}} \qquad (11.25)$$

where

$$S_{S-\sigma} = \sqrt{S_S^2 - S_\sigma^2} \qquad (11.26)$$

and the subscripts S and σ refer to strength and stress, respectively.

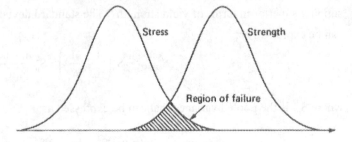

Figure 11.11 Superimposed normal distribution curves for strength and stress showing the region of failure.

The reliability associated with the value of z_R determined from Eq. (11.25) may be determined from a table showing the area $A(z_R)$ under a standard normal distribution curve by using:

$$R = 0.5 + A(z_R) \qquad (11.27)$$

Typical values of R as a function of the statistic z_R are given in Table 11.7.

Table 11.7
Reliability R as a function of the statistic z_R

R, %	z_R	R, %	z_R
50	0	99.9	3.091
90	1.288	99.99	3.719
95	1.645	99.999	4.265
99	2.326	99.9999	4.753

The reliability determined in this manner incorporates a safety factor of 1. If a safety factor of N is to be specified together with a reliability, then Eqs. (11.25) and (11.26) are rewritten to give a modified relation for z_R as:

$$z_R = \frac{\overline{x}_S - N\,\overline{x}_\sigma}{\sqrt{S_S^2 + S_\sigma^2}}$$ (11.28)

which yields the safety factor N as:

$$N = \frac{1}{\overline{x}_\sigma}\left(\overline{x}_S - z_R\sqrt{S_S^2 + S_\sigma^2}\right)$$ (11.29)

11.7 STATISTICAL CONDITIONING OF DATA

Previously it was indicated that measurement error can be characterized by a normal distribution function and that the standard deviation of the estimated mean $S_{\overline{x}}$ can be reduced by increasing the number of measurements. In most situations, sampling cost places an upper limit on the number of measurements to be made. Also, it must be remembered that systematic error is not a random variable; therefore, statistical procedures cannot serve as a substitute for precise accurately calibrated, and properly zeroed measuring instruments.

One area where statistical procedures can be used very effectively to condition experimental data is with the erroneous data point resulting from a measuring or recording mistake. Often, this data point appears questionable when compared with the other data collected, and the experimentalist must decide whether the deviation of the data point is due to a mistake (hence to be rejected) or due to some unusual but real condition (hence to be retained). A statistical procedure known as **Chauvenet's criterion** provides a consistent basis for making the decision to reject or retain such a point from a sample containing several readings.

Application of Chauvenet's criterion requires computation of a deviation ratio DR for each data point, followed by comparison with a standard deviation ratio DR_0. The standard deviation ratio DR_0 is a statistic that depends on the number of measurements, while the deviation ratio DR for a point is defined as:

$$DR = \frac{x_i - \overline{x}}{S_x}$$ (11.30)

The data point is rejected when $DR > DR_0$ and retained when $DR \leq DR_0$. Values for the standard deviation ratio DR_0 are listed in Table 11.8.

Table 11.8
Deviation ratio DR_0 used for statistical conditioning of data

Number of measurements n	Deviation ratio DR_0	Number of measurements n	Deviation ratio DR_0
4	1.54	25	2.33
5	1.65	50	2.57
7	1.80	100	2.81
10	1.96	300	3.14
15	2.13	500	3.29

If the statistical test of Eq. (11.30) indicates that a single data point in a sequence of n data points should be rejected, then the data point should be removed from the sequence and the mean $\bar{x}$ and the standard deviation S_x should be recalculated. Chauvenet's method can be applied only once to reject a data point that is questionable from a sequence of points. If several data points indicate that $DR > DR_0$, then it is likely that the instrumentation system is inadequate or that the process being investigated is extremely variable.

11.8 REGRESSION ANALYSIS

Many experiments involve the measurement of one dependent variable, say y, which may depend upon one or more independent variables, x_1, x_2, ..., x_k. Regression analysis provides a statistical approach for conditioning the data obtained from experiments where two or more related quantities are measured.

11.8.1 Linear Regression Analysis

Suppose measurements are made of two quantities that describe the behavior of a process exhibiting variation. Let y be the dependent variable and x the independent variable. Because the process exhibits variation, there is not a unique relationship between x and y and the data, when plotted, exhibit scatter, as illustrated in Fig. 11.12. Frequently, the relation between x and y that most closely represents the data, even with the scatter, is a linear function. Thus:

$$Y_i = mx_i + b \qquad (11.31)$$

where Y_i is the predicted value of the dependent variable y_i for a given value of the independent variable x_i.

A statistical procedure used to fit a straight line through scattered data points is called the least-squares method. With the least-squares method, the slope m and the intercept b in Eq. (11.31) are selected to minimize the sum of the squared deviations of the data points from the straight line shown in Fig. 11.12. In utilizing the least-squares method, it is assumed that the independent variable x is free of measurement error and the quantity

$$\Delta^2 = \sum (y_i - Y_i)^2 \qquad (11.32)$$

is minimized at fixed values of x. After substituting Eq. (11.31) into Eq. (11.32), the minimization process of Δ^2 implies that:

$$\frac{\partial \Delta^2}{\partial b} = \frac{\partial}{\partial b} \sum (y_i - mx - b)^2 = 0$$

$$\frac{\partial \Delta^2}{\partial m} = \frac{\partial}{\partial m} \sum (y_i - mx - b)^2 = 0$$

(a)

Differentiating yields:

$$2\sum (y_i - mx - b)(-x) = 0$$

$$2\sum (y_i - mx - b)(-1) = 0$$

(b)

Solving Eqs. (b) for m and b yields:

$$m = \frac{\sum x \sum y - n \sum xy}{\left(\sum x\right)^2 - n \sum x^2} \quad \text{and} \quad b = \frac{\sum y - m \sum x}{n}$$

(11.33)

where n is the number of data points. The slope m and intercept b define a straight line through the scattered data points such that Δ^2 is minimized.

In any regression analysis it is important to establish the correlation between x and y. Equation (11.31) does not predict the exact values that were measured, because of the variation in the process. To illustrate, assume that the independent quantity x is fixed at a value x_1 and that a sequence of measurements is made of the dependent quantity y. The data obtained would give a distribution of y, as illustrated in Fig. 11.13. The dispersion of the distribution of y is a measure of the correlation. When the dispersion is small, the correlation is good and the regression analysis is effective in describing the variation in y. If the dispersion is large, the correlation is poor and the regression analysis may not be adequate to describe the variation in y.

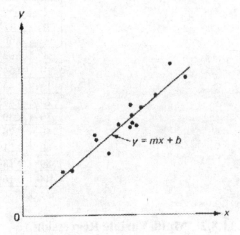

Figure 11.12 Linear regression analysis is used to fit a least squares line through scattered data points.

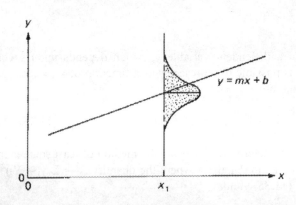

Figure 11.13 Distribution of y at a fixed value of x super-imposed on the linear-regression graph.

The adequacy of regression analysis can be evaluated by determining a correlation coefficient R^2 that is given by the following expression:

$$R^2 = 1 - \frac{n-1}{n-2} \left[\frac{\{y^2\} - m\{xy\}}{\{y^2\}} \right]$$

(11.34)

where $\{y^2\} = \Sigma y^2 - (\Sigma y)^2/n$) and $\{xy\} = \Sigma xy - (\Sigma x)(\Sigma y)/n$.

When the value of the correlation coefficient $R^2 = 1$, perfect correlation exists between y and x. If R^2 equals zero, no correlation exists and the variations observed in y are due to random fluctuations and not changes in x. Because random variations in y exist, a value of $R^2 = 1$ is not obtained even if y(x) is linear. To interpret correlation coefficients $0 < R^2 < 1$, the data in Table 11.9 is used to establish the probability of obtaining a given R^2 due to random variations in y.

As an example, consider a regression analysis with n = 15 which gives $R^2 = 0.65$ as determined by Eq. 11.34. Reference to Table 11.9 indicates that the probability of obtaining $R^2 = 0.65$ due to random variations is slightly less than one percent. Thus one can be 99% certain that the regression analysis represents a true correlation between y and x.

Table 11.9
Probability of obtaining a correlation coefficient R^2 due to random variations in y.

n	Probability			
	0.10	0.05	0.02	0.01
5	0.805	0.878	0.934	0.959
6	0.729	0.811	0.882	0.917
7	0.669	0.754	0.833	0.874
8	0.621	0.707	0.789	0.834
10	0.549	0.632	0.716	0.765
15	0.441	0.514	0.592	0.641
20	0.378	0.444	0.516	0.561
30	0.307	0.362	0.423	0.464
40	0.264	0.312	0.367	0.403
60	0.219	0.259	0.306	0.337
80	0.188	0.223	0.263	0.291
100	0.168	0.199	0.235	0.259

11.8.2 Multi-Variate Regression

Many experiments involve measurements of a dependent variable y, which depends upon several independent variables x_1, x_2, x_3, ..., etc. It is possible to represent y as a function of x_1, x_2, x_3, ..., by employing the multi-variate regression equation:

$$Y_i = a + b_1 x_1 + b_2 x_2 + ... + b_k x_k$$

(11.35)

The regression coefficients a, b_1, b_2, ..., b_k are determined by using the method of least squares in a manner similar to that employed for linear regression analysis where the quantity $\Delta^2 = \Sigma(y_i - Y_i)^2$ is minimized. Substituting Eq. (11.32) into Eq. (11.35) yields:

$$\Delta^2 = \Sigma(y_i - a - b_1 x_1 - b_2 x_2 - \ldots - b_k x_k)^2 \tag{11.36}$$

Differentiating yields:

$$\frac{\partial \Delta^2}{\partial a} = 2\left[\sum (y_i - a - b_1 x_1 - b_2 x_2 - \ldots - b_k x_k)(-1)\right] = 0$$

$$\frac{\partial \Delta^2}{\partial b_1} = 2\left[\sum (y_i - a - b_1 x_1 - b_2 x_2 - \ldots - b_k x_k)(-x_1)\right] = 0$$

$$\frac{\partial \Delta^2}{\partial b_2} = 2\left[\sum (y_i - a - b_1 x_1 - b_2 x_2 - \ldots - b_k x_k)(-x_2)\right] = 0$$

$$\text{..} \tag{11.37}$$

$$\frac{\partial \Delta^2}{\partial b_k} = 2\left[\sum (y_i - a - b_1 x_1 - b_2 x_2 - \ldots - b_k x_k)(-x_k)\right] = 0$$

Equations (11.37) lead to the following set of $k + 1$ equations, which can be solved for the unknown regression coefficients $a, b_1, b_2, \ldots, b_k$.

$$an + b_1 \sum x_1 + b_2 \sum x_2 + \ldots b_k \sum x_k = \sum y_i$$

$$a\sum x_1 + b_1 \sum x_1^2 + b_2 \sum x_1 x_2 + \ldots b_k \sum x_1 x_k = \sum y_i x_1$$

$$a\sum x_2 + b_1 \sum x_1 x_2 + b_2 \sum x_2^2 + \ldots b_k \sum x_2 x_k = \sum y_i x_2 \tag{11.38}$$

$$\text{..}$$

$$a\sum x_k + b_1 \sum x_1 x_k + b_2 \sum x_2 x_k + \ldots b_k \sum x_k^2 = \sum y_i x_k$$

The correlation coefficient R^2 is again used to determine the degree of association between the dependent and independent variables. For multiple regression equations, the correlation coefficient R^2 is given as:

$$R^2 = 1 - \frac{n-1}{n-k}\left[\frac{\{y^2\} - b_1\{yx_1\} - \{yx_2\} - \ldots - \{yx_k\}}{\{y^2\}}\right] \tag{11.39}$$

where

$$\{yx_k\} = \sum yx_k - \frac{(\sum y)(\sum x_k)}{n} \quad \text{and} \quad \{y^2\} = \sum y^2 - \frac{(\sum y)^2}{n}$$

This analysis is for linear, noninteracting, independent variables; however, the analysis can be extended to include cases where the regression equations would have higher-order and cross-product terms. The nonlinear terms can enter the regression equation in an additive manner and are treated as extra variables. With well-established computer routines for regression analysis, the set of $(k + 1)$ simultaneous equations given by Eqs. (11.38) can be solved quickly and inexpensively. No significant difficulties are encountered in adding extra terms to account for nonlinearities and interactions.

11.8.3　Field Applications of Least-Square Methods

The least-squares method is an important mathematical process used in regression analysis to obtain regression coefficients. Sanford showed that the least-squares method could be extended to field analysis of data obtained with optical techniques (photoelasticity, moiré, holography, etc.). With these optical methods, a fringe order N, related to a field quantity such as stress, strain, or displacement, can be measured at a large number of points over a field (x, y). The applications require an analytical representation of the field quantities as a function of position (x, y) over the field. Several important problems including calibration, fracture mechanics, and contact stresses have analytical solutions where coefficients in the governing equations require experimental data for complete evaluation. Two examples will be described which introduce both the linear and nonlinear least-squares method applied over a field (x, y).

Linear Least-Squares Method

Consider a calibration model in photoelasticity and write the equation for the fringe order $N(x, y)$ as:

$$N(x,y) = \frac{h}{f_\sigma} G(x,y) + E(x,y) \tag{a}$$

where $G(x,y)$ is the analytical representation of the difference of the principal stresses $(\sigma_1 - \sigma_2)$ in the calibration model, h is the model thickness, f_σ is the material fringe value and $E(x,y)$ is the residual birefringence.

Assume a linear distribution for $E(x,y)$ which can be expressed as:

$$E(x,y) = Ax + By + C \tag{b}$$

For any selected point (x_k, y_k) in the field where N_k is determined:

$$N(x,y) = \frac{h}{f_\sigma} G(x,y) + Ax_k + By_k + C \tag{11.40}$$

Note that Eq. (11.40) is linear in terms of the unknowns (h/f_σ), A, B, and C. For m selected data points, with m > 4, an overdeterministic system of linear equations results from Eq. (11.40). This system of equations can be expressed in matrix form as:

$$[N] = [a][w]$$

where

$$[N] = \begin{bmatrix} N_1 \\ N_2 \\ .... \\ .... \\ N_m \end{bmatrix} \qquad [a] = \begin{bmatrix} G_1 & x_1 & y_1 & 1 \\ G_2 & x_2 & y_2 & 1 \\ .... \\ .... \\ G_m & x_m & y_m & 1 \end{bmatrix} \qquad [w] = \begin{bmatrix} h/f_\sigma \\ A \\ B \\ C \end{bmatrix}$$

The solution of the set of m equations for the unknowns h/f_σ, A, B, and C can be achieved in a least-squares sense through the use of matrix methods. Note that:

$$[a]^T [N] = [c][w]$$

where

$$[c] = [a]^T [a]$$

and that:

$$[w] = [c]^{-1} [a]^T [N]$$

where $[c]^{-1}$ is the inverse of $[c]$. Solution of the matrix $[w]$ gives the column elements which are the unknowns. This form of solution is easy to accomplish on a small computer which can be programmed to perform the matrix manipulations.

The matrix algebra outlined above is equivalent to minimizing the cumulative error E which is:

$$\mathcal{E} = \sum_{k=1}^{m} \left[\frac{h}{f_\sigma} G(x_k, y_k) + Ax_k + By_k + C - N_k \right]^2 \tag{11.41}$$

The matrix operations apply the least-squares criteria which require that:

$$\frac{\partial \mathcal{E}}{\partial (h/f_\sigma)} = \frac{\partial \mathcal{E}}{\partial A} = \frac{\partial \mathcal{E}}{\partial B} = \frac{\partial \mathcal{E}}{\partial C} = 0 \tag{11.42}$$

The advantage of this statistical approach to calibration of model materials in optical arrangements is the use of full field data to reduce errors due to discrepancies in either the model materials or the optical systems.

Nonlinear Least-Squares Method

In the preceding section a linear least-squares method provided a direct approach to improving the accuracy of calibration with a single-step computation of an overdeterministic set of linear equations. In other experiments involving either the determination of unknowns arising in stresses near a crack tip or contact stresses near a concentrated load, the governing equations are nonlinear in terms of the unknown quantities. In these cases, the procedure to be followed involves linearizing the governing equations, applying the least-squares criteria to the linearized equations, and finally iterating to converge to an accurate solution for the unknowns.

To illustrate this statistical approach, consider a photoelastic experiment that yields an isochromatic fringe pattern near the tip of a crack in a specimen subjected to mixed-mode loading. In this example, there are three unknowns K_I, K_{II}, and σ_{0x} which are related to the experimentally determined fringe orders N_k at positions (r_k, θ_k). The governing equation for this mixed-mode fracture problem is:

$$\left(\frac{Nf_\sigma}{h} \right)^2 = \frac{1}{2\pi r} \left[(K_I \sin\theta + 2K_{II} \cos\theta)^2 + (K_{II} \sin\theta)^2 \right]$$

$$+ \frac{2\sigma_{0x}}{\sqrt{2\pi r}} \sin\frac{\theta}{2} \left[K_I \sin\theta(1 + 2\cos\theta) + K_{II}\left(1 + 2\cos^2\theta + \cos\theta\right) \right] \tag{11.43}$$

$$+ \sigma_{0x}^2$$

Equation (11.43) can be solved in an overdeterministic sense, by forming the function $f(K_I, K_{II}, \sigma_{0x})$ as:

$$f_k(K_I, K_{II}, \sigma_{0x}) = \frac{1}{2\pi r_k}\left[(K_I \sin\theta_k + 2K_{II}\cos\theta_k)^2 + (K_{II}\sin\theta_k)^2\right]$$

$$+ \frac{2\sigma_{0x}}{\sqrt{2\pi r_k}}\sin\frac{\theta_k}{2}\left[K_I \sin\theta_k(1 + 2\cos\theta_k) + K_{II}(1 + 2\cos^2\theta_k + \cos\theta_k)\right] \qquad (11.44)$$

$$+ \sigma_{0x}^2 - \left(\frac{N_k f_\sigma}{h}\right)^2 = 0$$

where $k = 1, 2, 3, \ldots$ m and (r_k, θ_k) are coordinates defining a point on an isochromatic fringe of order N_k. A Taylor series expansion of Eq. (11.44) yields:

$$(f_k)_{i+1} = (f_k)_i + \left(\frac{\partial f_k}{\partial K_I}\right)_i \Delta K_I + \left(\frac{\partial f_k}{\partial K_{II}}\right)_i \Delta K_{II} + \left(\frac{\partial f_k}{\partial \sigma_{0x}}\right)_i \Delta \sigma_{0x} \qquad (11.45)$$

where i refers to the i th iteration step and ΔK_I, ΔK_{II}, and $\Delta \sigma_{0x}$ are corrections to the previous estimate of ΔK_I, ΔK_{II}, and $\Delta \sigma_{0x}$. It is evident from Eq. (11.45) that corrections should be made to drive $f(K_I, K_{II}, \sigma_{0x})$ toward zero. This fact leads to the iterative equation:

$$\left(\frac{\partial f_k}{\partial K_I}\right)_i \Delta K_I + \left(\frac{\partial f_k}{\partial K_{II}}\right)_i \Delta K_{II} + \left(\frac{\partial f_k}{\partial \sigma_{0x}}\right)_i \Delta \sigma_{0x} = -(f_k)_i \qquad (11.46)$$

In matrix form, the set of m equations represented by Eq. (11.46) can be written as:

$$[f] = [a][\Delta K] \qquad (11.47)$$

where:

$$[f] = \begin{bmatrix} f_1 \\ f_2 \\ \ldots \\ \ldots \\ f_m \end{bmatrix} \qquad [a] = \begin{bmatrix} \partial f_1/\partial K_I & \partial f_1/\partial K_{II} & \partial f_1/\partial \sigma_{0x} \\ \partial f_2/\partial K_I & \partial f_2/\partial K_{II} & \partial f_2/\partial \sigma_{0x} \\ \ldots\ldots\ldots\ldots\ldots\ldots\ldots\ldots\ldots\ldots \\ \ldots\ldots\ldots\ldots\ldots\ldots\ldots\ldots\ldots\ldots \\ \partial f_m/\partial K_I & \partial f_m/\partial K_{II} & \partial f_m/\partial \sigma_{0x} \end{bmatrix} \qquad [\Delta K] = \begin{bmatrix} \Delta K_I \\ \Delta K_{II} \\ \Delta \sigma_{0x} \end{bmatrix}$$

The least-squares minimization process is accomplished by multiplying, from the left, both sides of Eq. (11.47) by the transpose of matrix [a], to give:

$$[a]^T [f] = [a]^T [a][\Delta K]$$

or

$$[d] = [c][\Delta K]$$

where

$$[d] = [a]^T [f]$$

$$[c] = [a]^T [a]$$

Finally, the correction terms are:

$$[\Delta K] = [c]^{-1} [d] \qquad (11.48)$$

The solution of Eq. (11.48) gives ΔK_I, ΔK_{II}, and $\Delta \sigma_{0x}$ which are used to correct initial estimates of K_I, K_{II}, and σ_{0x} and obtain a better fit of the function $f_k(K_I, K_{II}, \sigma_{0x})$ to m data points.

The procedure is executed on a small computer programmed using MATLAB. One starts by assuming initial values for K_I, K_{II}, and σ_{0x}. Then, the elements of the matrices $[f]$ and $[a]$ are computed for each of the m data points. The correction matrix $[\Delta K]$ is then computed from Eq. (11.48) and finally the estimates of the unknowns are corrected by noting that:

$$(K_I)_{i+1} = (K_I)_i + \Delta K_I$$

$$(K_{II})_{i+1} = (K_{II})_i + \Delta K_{II} \qquad (11.49)$$
(11.49)

$$(\sigma_{0x})_{i+1} = (\sigma_{0x})_i + \Delta \sigma_{0x}$$

The procedure is repeated until each element in the correction matrix $[\Delta K]$ becomes acceptably small. As convergence is quite rapid, the number of iterations required for accurate estimates of the unknowns is usually small.

11.9 CHI-SQUARE TESTING

The chi-square χ^2 test is used in statistics to verify the use of a specific distribution function to represent the population from which a set of data has been obtained. The chi-square statistic χ^2 is defined as:

$$\chi^2 = \sum_{i=1}^{k} \left[\frac{(n_o - n_e)^2}{n_e} \right] \qquad (11.50)$$

where n_o is the actual number of observations in the i th group interval and n_e is the expected number of observations in the i th group interval based on the specified distribution and k is the total number of group intervals.

The value of χ^2 is computed to determine how closely the data fits the assumed statistical distribution. If $\chi^2 = 0$, the match is perfect. Values of $\chi^2 > 0$ indicate the possibility that the data are not represented by the specified distribution. The probability p that the value of χ^2 is due to random variation is illustrated in Fig. 11.14. The degree of freedom is defined as:

$$v = n - k \qquad (11.51)$$

where n is the number of observations and k is the number of conditions imposed on the distribution.

As an example of the χ^2 test, consider the ultimate tensile strength data presented in Table 11.10 and judge the adequacy of representing the ultimate tensile strength with a normal probability distribution described with $\bar{x} = 176.1$ ksi and $S_x = 2.25$ ksi. By using the properties of a normal distribution function, the number of specimens expected to fall in any strength group can be computed. The observed number of specimens in Table 11.1 exhibiting ultimate tensile strengths within each of seven group intervals, together with the computed number of specimens in a normal distribution in the same group intervals, are listed in Table 11.10. The computation of the χ^2 value ($\chi^2 = 1.785$) is also illustrated in the table. The number of groups n = 7. Because the two distribution parameters $\bar{x}$ and S_x were determined by using these data, k = 2; therefore, the number of degrees of freedom is $v = n - k = 7 - 2 = 5$.

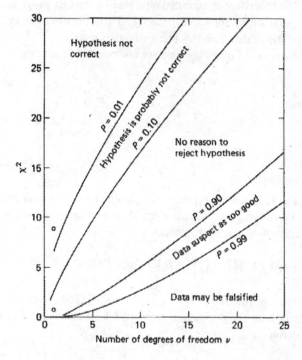

Figure 11.14 Probability of χ^2 values exceeding those shown as a function of the number of degrees of freedom.

Plotting these results ($\nu = 5$ and $\chi^2 = 1.785$) in Fig. 11.14 shows that the point falls in the region where there is no reason to expect that the hypothesis in not correct. The hypothesis is to represent the tensile strength with a normal probability function. The χ^2 test does not prove the validity of this hypothesis, but instead fails to disprove it.

The lines dividing the χ^2 - ν graph of Fig. 11.14 into 5 different regions are based on probabilities of obtaining χ^2 values greater than the values shown by the curves. For example, the line dividing the regions "no reason to reject hypothesis" and "hypothesis probably is not correct" has been selected at a probability level of 10%. Thus, there is only one chance in 10 that data drawn from a population correctly represented by the hypothesis would give a χ^2 value exceeding that specified by the p > 0.10 curve. The hypothesis rejected region is defined with the p > 0.01 curve indicating only one chance in 100 of obtaining a χ^2 value exceeding those shown by this curve.

Table 11.10

Chi-Squared χ^2 computation for grouped ultimate tensile strength data.

Group interval	Number observed	Number expected	$(n_o - n_e)^2/n_e$
0-170.9	1	0.468	0.604
171-172.9	2	2.904	0.281
173-174.9	8	9.096	0.132
175-176.9	16	13.748	0.369
177-178.9	9	9.836	0.071
179-180.9	3	3.360	0.039
180-∞	1	0.588	0.289
			$1.785 = \chi^2$

The χ^2 function can also be used to question if the data have been adjusted. Probability levels of 0.90 and 0.99 have been used to define regions where "data suspect as too good" and "data may be falsified". For the latter classification there are 99 chances out of 100 that the χ^2 value will exceed that determined by a χ^2 analysis of the data.

The χ^2 statistic can also be used in contingency testing where the sample is classified under one of two categories—pass or fail. Consider, for example, an inspection procedure with a particular type of strain gage where 10% of the gages are rejected due to etching imperfections in the grid. In an effort to reduce this rejection rate, the manufacturer has introduced new clean-room techniques that are expected to improve the quality of the grids. On the first lot of 2,000 gages, the failure rate was reduced to 8%. Is this reduced failure rate due to chance variation, or have the new clean-room techniques improve the manufacturing process? A χ^2 test can establish the probability of the improvement being the result of random variation. The computation of χ^2 for this example is illustrated in Table 11.11.

Table 11.11
Observed and expected inspection results

Group Interval	Number Observed	Number Expected	$(n_o - n_e)^2/n_e$
Passed	1840	1800	0.89
Failed	160	200	8.00
			$8.89 = \chi^2$

Plotting the results from Table 11.11 on Fig. 11.14 after noting that $v = 1$ shows that $\chi^2 = 8.89$ falls into the region "hypothesis is not correct". In this case the hypothesis was—there has been no improvement. The χ^2 test has shown that there is less than one chance in a hundred of the improvement in rejection rate (8% instead of 10%) being due to random variables. Thus, one can conclude, with confidence, that the new clean-room techniques were effective in improving yield.

11.10   ERROR PROPAGATION

Previous discussions of error have been limited to error arising in the measurement of a single quantity: however, in many engineering applications, several quantities are measured (each with its associated error) and another quantity is predicted on the basis of these measurements. For example, the volume V of a cylinder could be predicted on the basis of measurements of two quantities (diameter D and length L). Thus, errors in the measurements of diameter and length will propagate through the governing mathematical formula $V = \pi DL/4$ to the quantity (volume, in this case) being predicted. Because the propagation of error depends upon the form of the mathematical expression being used to predict the reported quantity, standard deviations for several different mathematical operations are listed below.

For addition and/or subtraction of quantities ($y = x_1 \pm x_2 \pm \ldots \pm x_n$), the standard deviation $S_{\bar{y}}$ of the mean $\bar{y}$ of the projected quantity y is given by:

$$S_{\bar{y}} = \sqrt{S_{x1}^2 + S_{x2}^2 + \ldots + S_{xn}^2}$$ (11.52)

For multiplication of quantities ($y = x_1 x_2 \ldots x_n$), the standard deviation $S_{\bar{y}}$ is given by:

$$S_{\bar{y}} = (\bar{x}_1 \bar{x}_2 \dots \bar{x}_n) \sqrt{\frac{S_{\bar{x}1}^2}{\bar{x}_1^2} + \frac{S_{\bar{x}2}^2}{\bar{x}_2^2} + \dots + \frac{S_{\bar{x}n}^2}{\bar{x}_n^2}} \qquad (11.53)$$

For division of quantities ($y = x_1/x_2$), the standard deviation $S_{\bar{y}}$ is given by:

$$S_{\bar{y}} = \frac{\bar{x}_1}{\bar{x}_2} \sqrt{\frac{S_{\bar{x}1}^2}{\bar{x}_1^2} + \frac{S_{\bar{x}2}^2}{\bar{x}_2^2}} \qquad (11.54)$$

For calculations of the form ($y = x_1^k$), the standard deviation $S_{\bar{y}}$ is given by:

$$S_{\bar{y}} = k\bar{x}_1^{k-1} S_{\bar{x}1} \qquad (11.55)$$

For calculations of the form ($y = x^{1/k}$), the standard deviation $S_{\bar{y}}$ is given by:

$$S_{\bar{y}} = \frac{\bar{x}_1^{1/k}}{k\bar{x}_1} S_{\bar{x}1} \qquad (11.56)$$

Consider, for example, a rectangular rod where independent measurements of its width, thickness, and length have yielded $\bar{x}_1 = 2.0$ with $S_{\bar{x}1} = 0.005$, $\bar{x}_2 = 0.5$ with $S_{\bar{x}2} = 0.002$, and $\bar{x}_3 = 16.5$ with $S_{\bar{x}3} = 0.040$, where all dimensions are in inches. The volume of the bar is:

$$V = \bar{x}_1 \, \bar{x}_2 \, \bar{x}_3$$

The standard error of the volume can be determined by using Eq. (11.53). Thus:

$$S_{\bar{y}} = (\bar{x}_1 \bar{x}_2 \dots \bar{x}_n) \sqrt{\frac{S_{\bar{x}1}^2}{\bar{x}_1^2} + \frac{S_{\bar{x}2}^2}{\bar{x}_2^2} + \dots + \frac{S_{\bar{x}n}^2}{\bar{x}_n^2}}$$

$$= (2.0)(0.5)(16.5) \sqrt{\frac{(0.005)^2}{(2.0)^2} + \frac{(0.002)^2}{(0.5)^2} + \frac{(0.040)^2}{(16.5)^2}}$$

$$= 0.0875 \text{ in.}$$

This determination of $S_{\bar{y}}$ for the volume of the bar can be used together with the properties of a normal probability distribution to predict the number of bars with volumes within specific limits.

The method of computing the standard error of a quantity $S_{\bar{y}}$, given by Eqs. (11.52) to (11.56) that are based on the properties of the normal probability distribution function, should be used where possible. However, in many engineering applications, the number of measurements that can be made is small; therefore, the data $\bar{x}_1$, $\bar{x}_2$, ..., $\bar{x}_n$ and $S_{\bar{x}1}$, $S_{\bar{x}2}$, ..., $S_{\bar{x}n}$ needed for statistical based estimates of the error are not available. In these instances, error estimates can still be made but the results are less reliable.

A second method of estimating error when data are limited is based on the chain rule of differential calculus. For example, consider a quantity y that is a function of several variables:

$$y = f(x_1, x_2, \dots, x_n) \qquad (11.57)$$

Differentiating yields:

$$dy = \frac{\partial y}{\partial x_1} dx_1 + \frac{\partial y}{\partial x_2} dx_2 + \ldots + \frac{\partial y}{\partial x_n} dx_n \tag{11.58}$$

In Eq. (11.58), dy is the error in y and $dx_1, dx_2, \ldots, dx_n$ are errors involved in the measurements of x_1, $x_2, \ldots x_n$. The partial derivatives $\partial y/\partial x_1, \partial y/\partial x_2, \ldots, \partial y/\partial x_n$ can be determined exactly from Eq. (11.57). Frequently, the errors $dx_1, dx_2, \ldots, dx_n$ are estimates based on the experience and judgment of the test engineer. An estimate of the maximum possible error can be obtained by summing the individual error terms in Eq. (11.58). Thus:

$$dy\big|_{max} = \left| \frac{\partial y}{\partial x_1} dx_1 \right| + \left| \frac{\partial y}{\partial x_2} dx_2 \right| + \ldots + \left| \frac{\partial y}{\partial x_n} dx_n \right| \tag{11.59}$$

Equation (11.59) gives a worst case estimate of error, because the maximum errors $dx_1, dx_2, \ldots, dx_n$ are assumed to occur simultaneously and with the same sign.

A more realistic equation for estimating error is obtained by squaring both sides of Eq. 11.58 to give:

$$(dy)^2 = \sum_{i=1}^{n} \left(\frac{\partial y}{\partial x_i} \right)^2 (dx_i)^2 + \sum_{i=1,j=1}^{n} \left(\frac{\partial y}{\partial x_i} \right) \left(\frac{\partial y}{\partial x_j} \right) dx_i dx_j \tag{11.60}$$

where $i \neq j$.

If the errors dx_i are independent and symmetrical with regard to positive and negative values then the cross product terms will tend to cancel and Eq. (11.60) reduces to:

$$dy = \sqrt{ \left(\frac{\partial y}{\partial x_1} dx_1 \right)^2 + \left(\frac{\partial y}{\partial x_2} dx_2 \right)^2 + \ldots + \left(\frac{\partial y}{\partial x_n} dx_n \right)^2 } \tag{11.61}$$

11.11 SUMMARY

Statistical methods are extremely important in engineering, because they provide a means for representing large amounts of data in a concise form, which is easily interpreted and understood. Usually, the data are represented with a statistical distribution function that can be characterized by a measure of central tendency (the mean $\bar{x}$) and a measure of dispersion (the standard deviation S_x). A normal or Gaussian probability distribution is by far the most commonly employed; however, in some cases, other distribution functions may have to be employed to adequately represent the data.

The most significant advantage resulting from use of a probability distribution function in engineering applications is the ability to predict the occurrence of an event based on a relatively small sample. The effects of sampling error are accounted for by placing confidence limits on the predictions and establishing the associated confidence levels. Sampling error can be controlled if the sample size is adequate. Use of Student's t distribution function, which characterizes sampling error, provides a basis for determining sample size consistent with specified levels of confidence. The Student t distribution also permits a comparison to be made of two means to determine whether the observed difference is significant or whether it is due to random variation.

Statistical methods can also be employed to condition data and to eliminate an erroneous data point (one) from a series of measurements. This is a useful technique that improves the data base by providing strong evidence when something unanticipated is affecting an experiment.

Regression analysis can be used effectively to interpret data when the behavior of one quantity y depends upon variations in one or more independent quantities x_1, x_2, ... , x_n. Even though the functional relationship between quantities exhibiting variation remains unknown, it can be characterized statistically. Regression analysis provides a method to fit a straight line or a curve through a series of scattered data points on a graph. The adequacy of the regression analysis can be evaluated by determining a correlation coefficient. Methods for extending regression analysis to multivariate functions exist. In principle, these methods are identical to linear regression analysis; however, the analysis becomes much more complex. The increase in complexity is not a concern, because computer subroutines are available that solve the tedious equations and provide the results in a convenient format.

Many probability functions are used in statistical analyses to represent data and predict population properties. Once a probability function has been selected to represent a population, any series of measurements can be subjected to a chi-squared (χ^2) test to check the validity of the assumed function. Accurate predictions can be made only if the proper probability function has been selected. Finally, statistical methods for accessing error propagation were discussed. These methods provide a means for determining error in a quantity of interest y based on measurements of related quantities x_1, x_2, ... , x_n and the functional relationship $y = f(x_1, x_2, ... , x_n)$.

REFERENCES

1. Bethea, R. M. and R. R. Rhinehart: Applied Engineering Statistics, Dekker, New York, 1991.
2. Bethea, R. M., B. S. Duran, and T. L. Boullion: Statistical Methods for Engineers and Scientists, 2nd Edition, Dekker, New York, 1985.
3. Blackwell, D.: Basic Statistics, McGraw-Hill, New York, 1969.
4. Bragg, G. M.: Principles of Experimentation and Measurement, Prentice-Hall, Englewood Cliffs, NJ, 1974.
5. Chou, Y.: Probability and Statistics for Decision Making, Holt, Rinehart & Winston, New York, 1972.
6. Snedecor, G. W. and W. G. Cochran: Statistical Methods, 8th Edition, Iowa State University Press, Ames, IA, 1989.
7. Davies, O. L. and P. L. Goldsmith: Statistical Methods in Research and Production, Hafner, New York, 1972.
8. McCall, C. H. Jr.: Sampling and Statistics Handbook for Research, Iowa State University Press, Ames, IA., 1982.
9. Weibull, W.: Fatigue Testing and Analysis of Results, Pergamon Press, New York, 1961.
10. Young, H. D.: Statistical Treatment of Experimental Data, McGraw-Hill, New York, 1962.
11. Zehna, P. W.: Introductory Statistics, Prindle, Weber & Schmidt, Boston, 1974.
12. Zehna, P. W.: Probability Distributions and Statistics, Allyn and Bacon, Boston, 1970.

EXERCISES

11.1   Ten measurements of the fracture strength (ksi) of an aluminum alloy are:

25.0	25.2	24.9	25.5	24.6
24.8	25.2	25.0	24.8	25.0

Determine the mean, median, and mode which represent the central tendency of this data.

11.2   Verify the mean value $\bar{x}$ of the data listed in Table 11.1.

11.3   Determine the range R, mean deviation d_x and variance S^2_x for the data given in Exercise 11.1.

11.4   Determine the range R, mean deviation d_x and variance S^2_x for the data listed in Table 11.1.

11.5   Find the coefficient of variation for the data given in Exercise 11.1.

11.6   Find the coefficient of variation for the data listed in Table 11.1.

11.7   Consider a Gaussian population with a mean $\mu = 100$ and a standard deviation $\sigma = 10$. Determine the probability of selecting a single sample with a value in the interval between:

    (a) $75 - 80$ (b) $98 - 102$ (c) $92 - 97$

    (d) $115 - 123$ (e) greater than 125

11.8   Determine the percent of data which will probably be within limits of:

    (a) $\bar{x} \pm 2.5\,S_x$ (b) $\bar{x} - 1.0\,S_x$ and $\bar{x} + 1.5\,S_x$

    (c) $\bar{x} - 1.5\,S_x$ and $\bar{x} + 1.0\,S_x$ (d) $\bar{x} \pm 0.55\,S_x$

11.9   A manufacturing process yields aluminum rods with a mean yield strength of 35,000 psi and a standard deviation of 1000 psi. A customer places a very large order for rods with a minimum yield strength of 32,000 psi. Prepare a letter for submission to the customer that describes the yield strength to be expected and outline your firm's procedures for assuring that this quality level will be achieved and maintained.

11.10 Determine the Weibull distribution function corresponding to the parameters $x_0 = 5$, $b = 5$ and $m = 10$. Plot P(x) for $0 < x < 50$.

11.11 For the Weibull distribution of Exercise 11.10, predict the probability of failure if $x = 6.5$.

11.12 A Weibull distribution function describing the strength of a brittle ceramic uses $x_0 = 3$ ksi, $b = 2$ ksi, and $n = 3$. Compute the expected values of the ten lowest strengths measured if a total of 400 specimens were tested.

11.13 Repeat 11.12 but let $b = 3$ ksi.

11.14 In calibrating a brittle coating, 12 calibration beams are tested to determine that $\bar{x} = 470$ $\mu\varepsilon$ and $S_x = 60$ $\mu\varepsilon$. Determine the standard distribution of the mean $S_{\bar{x}}$. Give the confidence level associated with the statement that the true mean μ of the calibration was between 460 and 480 $\mu\varepsilon$.

11.15 In the calibration test of the brittle coating in Exercise 11.14 the number of beams is increased from 12 to 40. The new results gives $\bar{x} = 465$ $\mu\varepsilon$ and $S_x = 70$ $\mu\varepsilon$. Determine $S_{\bar{x}}$ and give confidence limits on the statement that the true threshold strain is between 455 and 475 $\mu\varepsilon$.

11.16 Use Eq. (11.20) with two degrees of freedom and evaluate f(t) as a function of t. Plot your results on Fig. 11.9. Select F_0 so that:

$$\int_{-\infty}^{\infty} f(t)dt = 1$$

11.17 Compare the results of Exercise 11.16 with the distribution function from a normal distribution.

11.18 Determine the sample size necessary to insure that the average strength of a material exceeds 70 MPa if the sample is drawn from a population with an estimated mean of 65 MPa and an estimated standard deviation of 2 MPa. Use a confidence level of 5%.

11.19 An inspection laboratory samples two large shipments of dowel pins by measuring both length and diameter. For shipment A, the sample size was 40, the mean diameter was 6.12 mm, the mean length was 25.3 mm, the estimated standard deviation on diameter was 0.022 mm, and the estimated standard deviation on length was 0.140 mm. For shipment B, the sample size was 60, the mean diameter was 6.04 mm, the mean length was 25.05 mm, the estimated standard deviation on diameter was 0.034 mm, and the estimated standard deviation on length was 0.203 mm.

    (a) Are the two shipments of dowel pins the same?

    (b) What is the level of confidence in your prediction?

    (c) Would it be safe to mix the two shipments of pins? Explain.

11.20 Repeat Exercise 11.19 for the following two shipments of dowel pins.

	Shipment A	Shipment B
Number	20	10
Diameter	$\bar{x}$ = 6.05 mm, S_x = 0.03 mm	$\bar{x}$ = 5.98 mm, S_x = 0.04 mm
Length	$\bar{x}$ = 24.9 mm, S_x = 0.22 mm	$\bar{x}$ = 25.4 mm, S_x = 0.18 mm

11.21 Fatigue tests of a component under simulated load conditions indicated that the mean failure load for the specified life was $\bar{F}$ = 4115 N with an estimated standard deviation of 340 N. In service, this component will be subjected to an average load of 2800 N but this load may vary and the estimated standard deviation is 700 N. Determine the reliability of the component over the specified life.

11.22 For the data in Exercise 11.21, determine the safety factor for a reliability of (a) 90%, (b) 95%, and (c) 99%.

11.23 The following sequence of measurements of atmospheric pressure (millimeters of mercury) was obtained with a barometer.

764.3	764.6	764.4	765.2	764.5
764.5	765.7	765.4	764.8	765.3
765.2	764.9	764.6	765.1	764.6

Determine the mean and the standard deviation after employing Chauvenet's criterion to statistically condition the data.

11.24 Determine the slope m and the intercept b for a linear regression equation y = mx + b and the correlation coefficient R^2 for the data listed below:

x	1	2	3	4	5	6	7	8	9	10
y	2.1	3.9	6.4	8.2	9.5	11.0	13.6	16.7	17.9	19.4

11.25 The drying of a coating containing a solvent is a diffusion controlled process which can be described by the equation $C = ae^{-mt}$, where C is the concentration (% solvent), t is the time (seconds), and a and m are diffusion constants. Use linear regression methods to determine a and m for the following data which was obtained by weighing a sample of coating during drying.

t	100	200	300	400	500	700	1000
C	3.40	1.40	0.561	0.195	0.067	0.0097	0.0004

11.26 Determine the regression coefficients a, b_1, b_2, and b_3 and the correlation coefficient R^2 for the following data set.

y	x_1	x_2	x_3
6.8	1.0	2.0	1.0
7.8	1.5	2.0	1.5
7.9	2.0	2.0	2.0
8.0	2.5	3.0	1.0
8.3	3.0	3.0	1.5
8.4	3.5	3.0	2.0
8.5	4.0	4.0	1.0
8.6	4.5	4.0	1.5

8.9	5.0	4.0	2.0
9.1	5.5	5.0	1.0
9.3	6.0	5.0	1.5
9.6	6.5	5.0	2.0

11.27 Write a computer program which utilizes field data taken from a calibration disk in photoelasticity. The program should accept 20 data points N(x,y), the model thickness h, and analytic functions G(x,y) and E(x,y). The output [see Eq. (11.40)] should give f_σ, A, B, and C.

11.28 Write a computer program to implement the non-linear least squares method. Use the mixed-mode relations given in Eq. (11.43) as the example. The program input is field data N(r,θ) and calibration data f_σ/h. The output is K_I, K_{II}, and σ_{0x}.

11.29 A die-casting operation produces bearing housings with a rejection rate of 4% when the machine is operated over an 8-h shift to produce a total output of 3200 housings. The method of die cooling was changed in an attempt to reduce the rejection rate. After 2 h of operation under the new cooling conditions, 775 acceptable castings and 25 rejects had been produced.

   (a) Did the change in the process improve the output?

   (b) How certain are you of your answer?

11.30 The stress σ_x at a point on the free surface of a structure or machine component can be expressed in terms of the normal strains ε_x and ε_y measured with electrical resistance strain gages as:

$$\sigma_x = \frac{E}{1-v^2}\left(\varepsilon_x + v\varepsilon_y\right)$$

   If ε_x and ε_y are measured within ± 2% and E and v are measured within ± 5%, estimate the error in σ_x.

11.31 A gear-shaft assembly consists of a shaft with a shoulder, a bearing, a sleeve, a gear, a second sleeve, and a nut. Dimensional tolerances for each of these components are listed below:

Component	Tolerance, mm
Shoulder	0.050
Bearing	0.025
Front sleeve	0.100
Gear	0.050
Second sleeve	0.100
Nut	0.100

   (a) Determine the anticipated tolerance of the series assembly.

   (b) What will be the frequency of occurrence of the tolerance of Part (a)?

11.32 Estimate the error in determining the weight of a cylindrical rod if the dimensional measurements are accurate to 0.5% and the specific weight is accurate to 0.1%.

11.33 Estimate the error in determining strain from two displacement measurements if the displacements are measured with an accuracy of 2% and the positions x_1 and x_2 each are measured with an accuracy of 1%.

EXERCISE SOLUTIONS

EXERCISE 11.3

From Eq. (11.3) :

$$R = x_L - x_S = 25.5 - 24.6 = 0.9 \text{ ksi}$$

From Eq. (11.4) :

$$d_x = \frac{\sum\limits_{i=1}^{n} x_i - \bar{x}}{n} = \frac{1.8}{10} = 0.18 \text{ ksi}$$

From Eq. (11.5):

$$S_x^2 = \frac{\sum\limits_{i=1}^{n} (x_i - \bar{x})^2}{n - 1} = \frac{0.58}{9} = 0.0644$$

EXERCISE 11.8

(a) $p(-2.50, +2.50) = 0.4938 + 0.4938 = 0.9876 = \underline{98.8\%}$

(b) $p(-1.00, +1.50) = 0.3413 + 0.4332 = 0.7745 = \underline{77.5\%}$

(c) $p(-1.50, +1.00) = 0.4332 + 0.3413 = 0.7745 = \underline{77.5\%}$

(d) $p(-0.50, +0.50) = 0.1915 + 0.1915 = 0.3830 = \underline{38.3\%}$

EXERCISE 11.13

For the parameters $x_0 = 3$ ksi, $b = 3$ ksi, and $m = 3$:

From Eqs. (11.11): $P(x) = 0$ for $x < x_0 = 3$ ksi

$$P(x) = 1 - e^{-\left(\frac{x-3}{3}\right)^3}$$ for $x > x_0 = 3$ ksi

For the 10 weakest specimens: $P(x) = \dfrac{10}{400} = 0.025$

From Eq. 11.14 :

$$\left(\frac{x - 3}{3}\right)^3 = \ln\left[\frac{1}{1 - P(x)}\right] = \ln\left[\frac{1}{1 - 0.025}\right] = 0.0253$$

$$\frac{x - 3}{3} = (0.0253)^{1/3} = 0.2936$$

$$x = 3 + 3(0.2936) = \underline{3.88 \text{ ksi}}$$

The strength of the 10 weakest specimens would be 3.88 ksi or less.

EXERCISE 11.18

For the material, $S > 70$ MPa, $\bar{x} = 65$ MPa, and $S_x = 2$.

From Eq. (11.21) with $\delta = S - \bar{x} = 70 - 65 = 5$ MPa:

$$n = \left[\frac{t(\alpha)\, S_x}{\delta} \right]^2 = \left[\frac{2}{5}\, t(\alpha) \right]^2$$

Since $t(\alpha)$ depends on the number of samples n, the sample size must be determined by using an iteration procedure. Thus, from Table 11.6 for $\alpha = 5\%$ (one sided) and $\nu = n - 1$:

$$n = 10 \quad \nu = 9 \quad t(\alpha) = 1.83 \quad n = 0.54$$
$$n = 5 \quad \nu = 4 \quad t(\alpha) = 2.13 \quad n = 0.73$$
$$n = 3 \quad \nu = 2 \quad t(\alpha) = 2.92 \quad n = 1.36$$
$$n = 2 \quad \nu = 1 \quad t(\alpha) = 6.31 \quad n = 6.37$$

Thus, $n = \underline{3}$

EXERCISE 11.24

From Eqs. (11.31) and (11.33):

$$Y_i = mx_i + b$$

$$m = \frac{\Sigma x\, \Sigma y - n\, \Sigma xy}{(\Sigma x)^2 - n\, \Sigma x^2}$$

$$b = \frac{\Sigma y - m\, \Sigma x}{n}$$

$n = 10$
$\Sigma x = 55$
$\Sigma y = 109.7$
$\Sigma xy = 765.3$
$\Sigma x^2 = 385$
$\Sigma y^2 = 1522.69$

$$m = \frac{(55)(109.7) - 10(765.3)}{(55)^2 - 10(385)} = \frac{-1619.5}{-825} = \underline{+1.963}$$

$$b = \frac{109.7 - (1.963)(55)}{10} = \underline{0.1735}$$

From Eq. (11.34):

$$R^2 = 1 - \frac{n - 1}{n - 2} \left[\frac{\{y^2\} - m\{xy\}}{\{y^2\}} \right]$$

where

$$\{y^2\} = \Sigma y^2 - \frac{(\Sigma y)^2}{n} = 1522.69 - \frac{(109.7)^2}{10} = 319.3$$

$$\{xy\} = \Sigma xy - \frac{\Sigma x\, \Sigma y}{n} = 765.3 - \frac{(55)(109.7)}{10} = 161.95$$

$$R^2 = 1 - \frac{9}{8} \left[\frac{319.3 - (1.963)(161.95)}{319.3} \right] = \underline{0.995}$$

```
EXERCISE 11.31
                            Component        Tolerance mm
                            Shoulder            0.050
                            Bearing             0.025
                            First sleeve        0.100
                            Gear                0.050
                            Second sleeve       0.100
                            Nut                 0.100

(a)  From Eq. (11.52):
```

$$S_{\bar{y}} = \sqrt{S_{x1}^2 + S_{x2}^2 + \cdots + S_{xn}^2}$$

$$= \sqrt{2(0.05)^2 + (0.025)^2 + 3(0.100)^2} = \underline{0.1887 \text{ mm}}$$

```
(b)  Tolerance T will be within the range -0.1887 mm ≤ T ≤ +0.1887 mm for
     68.3% of the assemblies.
```

CHAPTER 12

WRITING TECHNICAL AND ENGINEERING LABORATORY REPORTS

12.1 INTRODUCTION

It is important that you enjoy writing, because engineers often have to prepare several hundred pages of reports, theoretical analyses, memos, technical briefs and letters during a typical year on the job. It is essential that you learn how to effectively communicate—by writing, speaking, listening and employing superb graphics. Communication, particularly good writing, is an extremely important skill. Advancement in your career will depend on your ability to write well. It is recognized that you will be taking several courses in the English Department and other departments in Social Sciences, Arts and the Humanities that will require many writing assignments. These courses should help you immensely with the structure of your composition and the development of good writing skills. Most of the assignments will be essays, term papers, or studies of selected works of literature. However, there are several differences between writing for an engineering company or an engineering laboratory report and writing to satisfy the requirements of courses such as English 101 or History 102.

In college, you write for a single reader—your instructor. He or she must read the paper to grade it, subsequently determining how well you are doing in class. In industry, many people within and outside the company, and with different backgrounds and experience, may read your report. In class, the teacher is the expert, but in industry the writer of the report is supposed to be the individual with the knowledge. Many of those working in industry do not want to read your report because they are busy: their phone is ringing continuously, meetings are scheduled back to back, and many important tasks must be completed before the end of the day. They read—if not skim—the report only because they must be aware of the information that it contains. They want to know the key issues, why these issues are important and who is going to take the actions necessary to resolve them. In writing reports in industry, you cut to the chase. There is no sense in writing a 200-word essay when the facts can be provided in a 40 to 50-word paragraph that is brief and cogent. An elegant writing style, so valued by instructors in the arts and humanities, is usually avoided in engineering documentation. In writing an engineering document, do not be subtle; instead be obvious, direct and factual.

In the following sections, some of the key elements of technical writing, including an overall approach, report organization, audience awareness and objective writing techniques will be described. Then a process for technical writing, which includes four phases: composing, revising, editing and proofreading is discussed.

12.2 TECHNICAL REPORT FOR INDUSTRY

12.2.1 Approach and Organization

The first step in writing a technical report is to be humble. Realize that only a very few of the many people who may receive a copy of your report will read it in its entirety. Busy managers and even your peers read selectively. To adapt to this attitude, organize your report into short, stand-alone sections that attract the selective reader. Three very important sections—the title page, summary and introduction are located at the front of the report so they are easy to find. At the front of your report, they attract attention and are more likely to be read. In college, you call the page summarizing your essay an abstract, but in industry it is often called an executive summary. If it is prepared for an executive, perhaps a manager will consider it sufficiently important to take time to read it. Follow the executive summary with an introduction and then the body of the report. A common outline to follow in organizing your technical report is provided below:

- Title page
- Executive summary
- Table of contents, list of figures and tables
- Nomenclature—only if necessary
- Introduction
- Technical issue sections
- Conclusions
- Appendices

The title page, the executive summary and the introduction are the most widely read parts of your report. Allow more time polishing these three parts, because they offer the best opportunity to convey the most important results of your investigation.

Title Page

The title page provides a concise title of the report. Keep the title short—usually less than ten words; you will have an opportunity to provide more detail in the body of the report. The authors list their names, affiliations, addresses and often their telephone and fax numbers and e-mail addresses. The reader, who may be anywhere in the world, should be provided with a means to contact the authors to ask questions. For large firms or government agencies, a report number is formally assigned and is listed with the date of release of the report on the title page. A title page of a technical report on a computer code for designing combustors is shown in Fig. 12.1. This report was prepared by several authors from different organizations and was sponsored by NASA (National Aeronautics and Space Administration) and ARL (Army Research Laboratory).

Executive Summary

The executive summary should, with rare exceptions, be less than a page in length (about 200 words). As the name implies, the executive summary provides, in a concise and cogent style, all the information that the busy executive needs to know about the content in the report. What does the big boss want to know? Three paragraphs usually satisfy the chief. First, briefly describe the objective of the study and the problems or issues that it addresses. Do not include the history leading to these issues. Although there is always history, the introduction is a much more suitable section for historical development and other background information related to the problem. In the second paragraph, describe your solution and/or the resolution of the issues. Give a very brief statement of the approach that you employed, but reserve the details for the body of the report. If actions are to be taken by others to resolve the issues, list the actions, those responsible and the dates of implementation. The final paragraph indicates the importance of the study to the business. Cost savings, improvements in the quality of the product, gains in the market share, enhanced reliability, etc. can be cited. You want to convince the executive that your work was worth its cost, valuable to the corporation and that your group performed admirably.

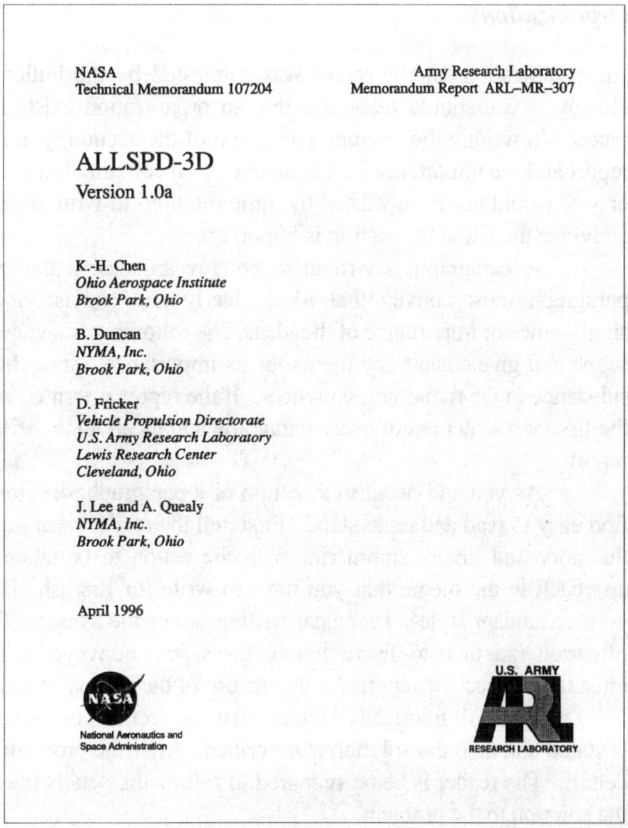

NASA
Technical Memorandum 107204

Army Research Laboratory
Memorandum Report ARL–MR–307

ALLSPD-3D

Version 1.0a

K.-H. Chen
Ohio Aerospace Institute
Brook Park, Ohio

B. Duncan
NYMA, Inc.
Brook Park, Ohio

D. Fricker
Vehicle Propulsion Directorate
U.S. Army Research Laboratory
Lewis Research Center
Cleveland, Ohio

J. Lee and A. Quealy
NYMA, Inc.
Brook Park, Ohio

April 1996

NASA
National Aeronautics and
Space Administration

U.S. ARMY
ARL
RESEARCH LABORATORY

Fig. 12.1 Illustration of a title page of a professional report.

Introduction

In the introduction, you restate the problem or issues. Although the problem was already defined in the executive summary, **redundancy is permitted in technical reports**. Recognize that you have many readers, so important information, such as a clear definition of the problem is placed in different sections of the report. In the introduction, the problem statement can be much more complete by expanding the amount of information describing the problem. A paragraph or two on the history of the problem is in order. People reading the introduction are more interested than those reading only the executive summary; therefore, more detail is appropriate.

Following the problem statement, establish the importance of the problem to both the company and the industry. Again, this is a repeat of what was included in the executive summary, but your arguments are expanded. You can cite statistics, briefly describe the analyses that lead to the alleged cost savings, give a sketch of customer comments indicating improved quality, etc. In the executive summary, you simply stated why the study was important. In the introduction, arguments are presented to convince the reader that the investigation was important and worth the time, effort and cost.

In the next segment of the introduction, you briefly describe the approach followed in addressing the problem. You begin with a literature search, followed by interviews with select customers, a study of the products that failed in service, interviews with manufacturing engineers and the design of a modification to decrease the failure rate and improve the reliability of the product. In other words, tell the reader what actions were required to solve the problem.

The final paragraph in the introduction outlines the remaining sections of the report. True, that information is already covered in the table of contents, but again, you repeat to accommodate the selective reader. Also, placing the report contents in the introduction gives you the opportunity to add a sentence or two describing the content of each section. Perhaps you can attract additional reader interest in one or more sections of the report and convince a few people to study the report more completely.

Organization

An organization for the report was suggested by the bullet list shown at the beginning of this section. However, you should recognize that an organization exists for every section and every paragraph in the report. In writing the opening paragraph of the section, you must convey the reason for including it in the report and the importance of its content. You certainly have a reason for including this section in the report, or you would not have wasted the time required to write it. By sharing this reason with your readers, you convince them that the section is important.

A paragraph is written to convey an idea, a thought or a concept. The first sentence in the paragraph must convey that idea, clearly and concisely. The second sentence should describe the significance or importance of the idea. The following sentences in the paragraph support the idea, expand its scope and give cogent arguments for its importance. State the idea in the first sentence and then add more substance in the remaining sentences. If the report is written properly, a speed-reader should be able to read the first two sentences of every paragraph and glean 80 to 90% of the important information conveyed in the report.

As you add detail to a section or a paragraph, develop a pattern of presentation that the reader will find easy to read and understand. First, tell the reader what he or she will be told, then provide the details of the story and finally summarize with the action to be taken to implement the solution. Do not try this approach in the theme that you have to write for English class, because the instructor will not appreciate your redundant style. Technical writing is not the same as theme writing. In technical writing, you will often reiterate facts to insure that the message is conveyed to the readers. Often one or more of the readers must take corrective actions for the benefit of the company and the industry.

You will frequently include analysis sections in engineering reports. In these sections, the problem is stated and then the solution is described. After the problem statement and the solution, you introduce the details. The reader is better prepared to follow the details (the difficult part of the analysis) after they know the solution to the problem.

12.3   KNOW YOUR READERS AND OBJECTIVE

Another important aspect to technical writing is to know something about the readers of your report. The language that you use in writing the technical report depends on the knowledge of the audience. When you write a report for a class assignment, you understand that the instructor is the only reader with which you need to communicate. You also know that he or she is knowledgeable. In that sense, the writing assignments in a typical college class are not realistic. For example, suppose your manager asks you to write an assembly routing (a step by step set of instructions for the assembly of a certain product) for the production of your new widget in a typical factory in the U. S. What language would you use as you write this routing? If the plant is in Florida or the Southwest for example, Spanish may be the prevalent language. You should also be aware that a significant fraction of the factory workers in the U. S. are functional illiterates and many others detest reading. In this case, it might be a good approach to use fewer words and many cartoons, photographs and drawings.

Know the audience **before** you begin to write, and adapt your language to their characteristics. Consider four different categories of readers:

- Specialists with language skills comparable to yours.
- Technical readers with mixed disciplines.
- Skilled readers, but not technically oriented.
- Poorly prepared readers who may be functional illiterates.

Category 1 is the audience that is the least difficult to address in your writings; the audience in the last category is the most difficult. Indeed, with poorly prepared readers, it is probably better to address them with visual presentations conveyed with television monitors and videotapes.

A final topic, to be considered in planning, is the classification of the technical document that you intend to write. What is the purpose of the task? Several classifications of technical writing are listed below:

- Reports: trip, progress, design, research, status, etc.
- Instructions: assembly manuals, training manuals and safety procedures.
- Proposals: new equipment, research funding, construction and development budget.
- Documents: engineering specifications, test procedures and laboratory results.

Each classification of writing has a different objective and requires a different writing style. If you are writing a proposal for development funding, you need persuasive arguments to justify the costs of the proposed program. On the other hand, if you are writing an instruction manual to assemble a product, arguments and reasons for funding are not an issue. Instead, you would prepare complete and simple descriptions with many illustrations to precisely explain how to accomplish a sequence of tasks involved in the assembly.

12.4 THE TECHNICAL WRITING PROCESS

Whether you are writing a report as part of your engineering responsibilities in industry or as a student in college, you will face a deadline. In college, the deadlines are imposed well in advance and you have a reasonable amount of time to prepare your report. In industry, you will have less time, and an allowance must be made for the delay in obtaining approvals from management before you can release the report. In both situations, you have some limited period of time to write the report. The idea is to start as soon as possible. Waiting until the day before the deadline is a recipe for disaster.

Many professionals do not like to write; consequently, they suffer from writer's block. They sit at their keyboard hoping for ideas to occur. Clearly, you do not want to join this group, and there is no need for you to do so. A technique is described in this section that should help you to avoid writer's block.

Define Your Task

Start your report by initially following the procedures described in the previous section. Understand the task at hand, and classify the type of technical document that you have to write. Define your audience; before starting to write, establish the level of detail and the language to employ. Prepare a skeletal outline of the report. Start with the outline presented previously and add the section headings for the body of the report. This outline is very brief, but it provides the structure for the report. This structure is important because it has divided the big task (writing the entire report) into several smaller tasks (writing one section of the report at a time).

Gather Information

It is impossible to write a report without information. You must generate the information to be presented in the report. You can use a variety of sources: interviews with peers, instructors or other knowledgeable persons who are willing to help; complete literature searches at the library; read the most suitable references; conduct additional Internet searches for information. Take notes as you read, gleaning the information applicable for your report. Be careful not to plagiarize. While you can use material from published works, you cannot copy the exact wording; the statements must be in your own words. If the report has an analysis, go to work and prepare a statement of the problem, execute its solution and make notes about interpreting the solution.

Organize Data

When you have collected most of the information that is to be discussed in your report, organize your notes into different topics that correspond to the section headings. Then incorporate your topics in an initial outline that will grow from a fraction of a page to several pages as you continue to incorporate notes in an organized format.

Compose Document

You are now ready to write. Writing is a tough task that requires a great deal of discipline and concentration. It is suggested that you schedule several blocks of time and reserve them exclusively for writing. The number of hours that should be scheduled will depend on the rate at which you compose, revise, edit and proofread. Some authors can compose about a page or so per hour, but most students need more time.

In scheduling a block of time for composing, you should be aware of your productive interval. Most writers take about a half an hour to come up to speed, and then they compose well for an hour or two before their attention and/or concentration begins to deteriorate. The quality of the composition begins to suffer at this time, and it is advisable to discontinue writing if you want to maintain the quality of your text. This fact alone should convince you to start your writing assignments well before the deadline date.

While you are writing, avoid distractions. Writing requires deep concentration—you must remember your message, the supporting arguments, the paragraph and sentence structure, grammar, vocabulary and spelling. Find a quiet, comfortable place and focus your entire concentration on the message and the manner in which you will present it in your report.

Naturally, some sections of a report are easier to write than others. The easiest are the appendices, because they carry factual details that are nearly effortless to report. The interior sections of the body of the report carry the technical details that are also easy to prepare, because describing detail is less concise and less cogent. Do not become careless on these sections because they are important; however, each sentence does not have to carry a knockout punch.

The most difficult sections are the introduction and the executive summary. It is advisable to write these two sections after the remainder of the first draft of the report is completed. Usually the introduction is written before the executive summary. Although the introduction contains much of the same information as the executive summary, it is more expansive. The introduction can be used as a guide in preparing the executive summary.

12.5   REVISING, EDITING AND PROOFREADING

Writing is a difficult assignment. Do not expect to be perfect in the beginning. Practice will help, but for most of us, it takes a very long time to improve our skills because writing is such a complex task. Expect to prepare several drafts of a paper or report, before it is ready to be released. In industry, several drafts are essential because you often will seek peer reviews and manager reviews are mandatory. In college, you have fewer formal requirements for multiple drafts, but preparing several drafts is a good idea if you want to improve the report and your grade.

First and Subsequent Drafts

The first draft is focused on composition, and the second is devoted to revising the initial composition. Use the first draft for expressing your ideas in reasonable form and in the correct sections of the report. In the second draft, focus on revising the composition. Defer the editing process, and concentrate on the ideas and their organization. Make sure the message is in the report and that it is clear to all of the readers. Polish the message later in the process.

Several hours should elapse between the first and second drafts of a given section of the report. If you read a section over and over again, you soon lose your ability to judge its quality. You need a fresh, rested brain for a critical review. In preparing this textbook, the author composes on one day and revises on the next day. Revising is always scheduled for an early morning block of time. When you are rested, concentration is usually at its highest level.

Let's make a clear distinction between composing, revising, editing and proofreading. Composition is writing the first draft where you formulate your ideas and organize the report into sections, subsections and paragraphs. Unless you are a super talented writer, your first draft is far from perfect. The second draft is for revisions where you focus on improving the composition. The third draft is for editing where errors in grammar, spelling, style, and usage are corrected. The fourth draft is for proofreading where typographical errors are eliminated.

Revising

When you revise your initial composition, be concerned with the ideas and the organization of the report. Is the report organized so that the reader will quickly ascertain the principle conclusions? Are the section headings descriptive? Sections and their headings are helpful to the reader because they help organize his or her thoughts. Additionally, they aid the writer in subdividing the task and keeping the subject of the section in focus. Are the sections the correct length? Sections that are too long tend to be ignored or the reader becomes tired and loses concentration before completely reading them.

Question the premise of every paragraph. Are the key ideas presented together with their importance before the details are included? Is enough detail given or have you included too many trivial items? Does the paragraph contain a single idea or have you tried to include two or even three ideas in the same paragraph? It is better to use a paragraph for every idea even if the paragraphs are short.

Have you added transition sentences or transitional phrases? The transition sentences, usually placed at the end of a paragraph, are designed to lead the reader from one idea to the next one. Transitional phrases, embedded in the paragraph, are to help the reader place the supporting facts in proper perspective. You contrast one fact with another, using words like **however** and **although**. You indicate additional facts with words such as **also** and **moreover**.

Editing

When the ideas flow smoothly and you are convinced that the reader will follow your concepts and agree with your arguments, begin to edit. Run the spell checker, and eliminate most of the typographical errors and the misspelled words in the report. Search for additional misspelled words, because the spell checker does not detect the difference between certain words like **grate** or **great**, or **like** and **lime** and between **from** and **form**.

Look for excessively long sentences. When sentences become 30 to 40 words in length, they begin to tax the reader. It is better to use shorter sentences where the subject and the verb are close together. Make sure that the sentences are actually sentences with a subject and a verb of the same tense. Have you used any comma splices (attaching two sentences together with a comma)? Examine each sentence and eliminate unnecessary words or phrases. Find the subject and the verb, and attempt to strengthen them. Look for redundant words in a sentence, and substitute different words with similar meaning to eliminate redundancy. Be certain to employ the grammar check incorporated in the word processing program. It is not perfect, but it does locate many grammatical errors.

Proofreading

The final step is proofreading the paper to eliminate errors. Start by running the spell checker for the final time. Then print out a clean, hard copy to use for proofreading. Check all the numbers and equations in the text, tables and figures for accuracy. Then read the text for correctness. Most of us have trouble reading for accuracy because we read for content. We have been trained since first grade to read for content, but we rarely read for correctness.

To proofread, read each word separately. You are not trying to glean the idea from the sentence, so do not read the sentence as a whole. Instead, read the words as individual entities. If it is possible, arrange for some help from a friend—one person reading aloud to the other with both having a copy of the manuscript. The listener concentrates on the appearance of each word and then checks the text against the spoken word to verify its correctness.

12.6 ENGINEERING LABORATORY REPORTS

12.6.1 Introduction

As an engineering student you will be required to prepare formal laboratory reports for your engineering labs. Most of the arguments made in the previous section apply also to writing formal laboratory reports with only minor changes in organization and details. The writing process, revising, editing and proofreading are essentially the same.

The object of a laboratory report is to convey information in a clear and concise manner. It should describe methods, results, conclusions, etc. in such a way that a reader will be able to duplicate the experiment. This coverage does not require specifying every electrical connection but, instead, providing **sufficient** information on equipment and potential problems.

12.6.2 Organization of a Lab Report

A formal lab report should consist of the following sections:

- Title Page
- Abstract
- Table of Contents
- Introduction
- Theory
- Experimental Procedures
- Results
- Discussion of Results
- Conclusions and Recommendations
- References
- Acknowledgements
- Appendices

The organization of these sections is discussed in the following paragraphs. Each paragraph follows the same guidelines as described previously on writing a Technical Report.

The table of contents is required in a formal lab report but may be omitted in shorter lab reports or technical notes. Nomenclatures are essential in reports with many equations and symbols, but not necessary in documents with only a few isolated symbols. References are necessary when information is used or sighted from sources other than the author's writings. Failure to reference the work of others is plagiarism, which is unethical and unacceptable.

Title Page

The title page should include:
- Experiment number and title of report
- Name of professor
- Date performed
- Name of student submitting the report

The title of the report should be brief but descriptive enough to include the purpose, what was measured, and how it was measured. The title page is not numbered.

Abstract

The abstract consists of tightly organized statements that present the salient features of the report. It begins with the objective of the study. This statement is followed by listing the assumptions made in the study, the equipment or apparatus used, and a brief description of the procedure. **The final sentence or two of the abstract should describe the major results along with errors.** As in the case of "Executive Summary of Technical Report", the abstract should be written after the rest of the lab report is completed. It should be about 100 to 150 words. No mention of figures, equations etc. should be made in the abstract. Usually, a roman numeral "i" is used for numbering this page.

Table of Contents

This second section in the report consists of a listing of all sections in the report with corresponding page numbers. The Table of Contents page is numbered "ii". If your report is very long, containing many tables and figures, it is advisable to include a separate List of Figures and a List of Tables. These listings are similar to the table of contents but display the figure or table number, caption and the page number. These usually follow the table of contents, numbered "iii", and "iv", with the nomenclature numbered "v".

Nomenclature

This page lists and defines all symbols used in a report. It also gives units used for variables. The list should be alphabetized first by capitals, then lower case, then Greek capital, Greek lower case etc. The sections following nomenclature are numbered normally 1, 2, 3, ---.

Introduction

The introduction of the lab report follows similar guidelines as discussed for the introduction section in the technical report. It is used to present an expanded version of the abstract devoted to what and why of your accomplishments. You restate the objective and then give the motivation for the study. The introduction sometimes reviews the how of what you did, particularly if your procedure is significantly different from other students. Next, it is important to present a survey of the existing literature on the field (with references) to place your work and contribution in perspective. The introduction should briefly state your salient findings. Lastly, the introduction may be used to provide a preview of the remainder of the report if its organization is unusual.

Theory

The theory section begins with a brief introduction to the problem followed by all theory relevant to the experiment. A presentation of standard equations or a derivation of special relations used in reducing the raw data is provided. Each equation is centered and numbered (right-flushed) for future reference. The equations are briefly discussed with emphasis on their limitations. Figures that assist the reader in visualizing the problem are included.

Experimental Procedure

The experimental procedure contains a detailed description of the apparatus and equipment used in the experiment. To decide relevance, the writer should include all the information necessary to permit someone to reproduce the experiment using the exact same equipment and procedure. All the equipment used in the experiment, and the name of the manufacturer and model number for each piece of equipment should be given. All this information should be provided in paragraph form and not in a list of the equipment.

All relevant dimensions of the apparatus and test specimens must be stated. One or more properly labeled figures of the experimental arrangement should be provided. It is important that the reader understand the methods and procedures used in the experiment. This information should be explained in sufficient detail to allow someone else to repeat the experiment to verify your results. Use the paragraph format to describe the procedures to demonstrate your understanding.

Results and Discussion of Results

This section normally contains a concisely written presentation of the final form of the data. The results may be in provided in tables or figures with graphs. Figures are the preferred mode with tables used only when increased accuracy is needed. The results should be discussed in detail to illustrate their significance with regards to the objective of the experiment.

Emphasis is placed on the method of reducing data on the significant results. Specific trends and values are cited. Re-emphasize the range of imposed test conditions. The experimental results are compared with theoretical results and if they are independently available. All the assumptions made while reducing the data are reiterated. Errors are discussed **only in quantitative terms**.

Conclusions and Recommendations

This section should be no more than one to three paragraphs long. Conclusions must be logical and forthright and must be derived from information contained within the report. Include a **brief** statement of the results. It is acceptable to repeat facts already made in the results and discussion sections. Some readers will only read the abstract and the conclusion sections so tailor your writing style accordingly. This section is either written in paragraph form or is sometimes structured as a list with each conclusion numbered and stated in one or two sentences. If no conclusions are available then you should state this fact and summarize the reasons for the failure of the experiment. In this case, your recommendations become important. These recommendations may be listed in this section or in a separation section. The recommendations should represent the procedures that require modification by subsequent investigators if useful data is ultimately to be generated.

References

References should be listed at the end of the report and arranged in sequence as they appear in the report or in alphabetical order according to the last name of the lead author. Each reference should include the names of all the authors followed by their initials. Citations should be made in the text by numbering them in order or by giving the last name of the lead author followed by the date of publication.

Reference to the journal articles, papers in conference proceedings, or any other collection of works by numerous authors should include:

- Year of publication
- Full title of cited article
- Full name of publication in which it appeared
- Volume number (if any)
- Inclusive page numbers if any

Reference to textbooks, monographs, theses, and technical reports should include:

- Year of publication
- The full title of the publication
- Publisher
- City of publication
- Inclusive Page numbers of the work being cited

In all cases titles of books, conference proceedings and periodicals should be underlined or in italics. In general the requirement is to be complete in the citation so that a reader wanting to find your reference should have no problems. Two examples of the protocols follow:

1. Heeder, N. J., A. Shukla, V. Chalivendra, S. Yang and K. Park, "Electrical Response of Carbon Nanotube Reinforced Nanocomposites under Static and Dynamic Loading," Experimental Mechanics, No 52, Vol. 3, (2012): 315-22.

2. Shukla, A. and J.W. Dally, Experimental Solid Mechanics, Knoxville, TN: College House Enterprises, 2010.

Acknowledgement

In the acknowledgements you list, in a paragraph form, all the individuals assisting you in performing your experiment. You also mention any financial or material help received in order to conduct the experiment.

Appendix

The appendix contains supporting documentation that is too detailed to include in the main body of the text. Examples include original data or notes taken during the experiment, computer program listings, calibration data, uncertainty analysis, sample calculations, etc. The appendix should be set apart from the body of the report by a cover page. Appendices generally should contain some text (some may be all text) to orient the reader to its contents and its relation to the body of the report. All appendices need a descriptive title. This should appear in the reports overall table of contents.

12.7 DESIGNING EFFECTIVE FIGURES

Often, the most important entities of a scientific paper or report are the figures. Figures are powerful communication tools that can convey facts, ideas and relationships more clearly and concisely than text. There are many factors to consider when effectively designing a figure.

All figures should be simple and designed with the intended audience in mind. Having knowledge of the general characteristics of the audience will assist in insuring that each figure is designed to be recognizable and clearly identifiable to the intended audience.

The actual layout of a figure should be organized in such a way to allow the viewer to easily follow and conceive the intended information in a logical and sequential order. Key features of the figure should be made prominent by using different imaging tools such as varying the size, shape, position, orientation or color. Care must be taken to not use excessive variations in these imaging tools because one can actually diminish the overall effectiveness of the figure if used improperly.

Finally, text in figures should be clear and readable at a glance. This can be accomplished by using specific fonts such as sans-serif fonts together with high contrasting colors. The use of specific fonts and high contrasting colors can significantly enhance the readability of the text used in both figures and graphs. The following guidelines can be helpful in ensuring that the reader can easily understand your graph.

12.7.1 Basic Rules for Creating Graphs

1. A graph should be designed so that the reader can easily understand and interpret the information conveyed.
2. The axes should be clearly labeled while specifying the quantities that are plotted, their units, and theirs symbols.
3. Axes should be clearly numbered and should have tick marks for significant numerical divisions. Tick marks should appear in increments of 1, 2, or 5 units of measurement multiplied or divided by factors of ten. Tick marks should be directed toward the interior of the figure and labeled such that the axes should not be cluttered.
4. Gridlines are typically used when specific quantities are being conveyed in order to help the reader comprehend the data easily. Otherwise, grid lines are not recommended.
5. Scientific notation should be used to avoid placing too many digits on the graph. When using a particular power of ten, it only needs to appear once along each axis.
6. For plotting on semi-log coordinates, real logarithmic axes should be used. Logarithmic scales should have tick marks at powers of ten and intermediate values, such as 10, 20, 50, 100, 200.
7. The axes should usually include zero. If you wish to focus on a smaller range of data, include zero and break the axis.
8. The scales and proportions of the graph should reflect the relative importance of the variations shown in the results.
9. Symbols such as ○, □, △, and ◇ should be used for data points. Open symbols should be used first, followed by filled symbols. Also, a legend should be defined on the graph (if space permits).
10. Error bars should be placed on data points in order to indicate the estimated uncertainty. Symbols, having the same size as the range of uncertainty, can also be used.
11. When several curves are plotted on one graph, different line types (solid, dashed, dash-dot, etc.) should be used for each if the curves are closely spaced. Theoretical curves should be plotted as solid lines. Also, it is not necessary for curves to pass through every data point.

12. Lettering on the graph should be held to a minimum in order to maintain clarity.
13. Labels on axes and curves should be oriented to allow the reader to read from either the bottom or from the right.
14. The title of the graph should be descriptive; yet concise. It should not be this versus that. It should appear as a caption to the figure rather than on the graph itself.

An example of a well-designed figure and graph is shown in Fig. 12.2 and Fig. 12.3, respectively. A schematic of an experimental arrangement used to measure the change in electrical resistance of a conductive material during quasi-static compressive loading is presented in Fig. 12.2. A current source is used to supply a constant current flow through the specimen via two aluminum plates, while the voltage drop of the inner section is measured using two electrometers. The difference between the two voltages is measured using the digital multimeter and recorded using a LabVIEW system.

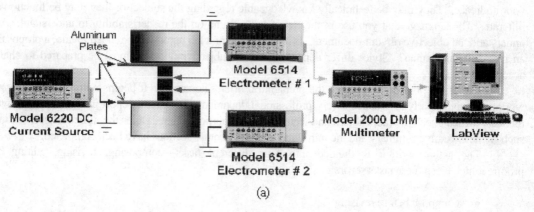

Fig. 12.2 Experimental arrangement for measuring resistance change in a nanocomposite material under quasi-static conditions.

Fig. 12.3 Typical electrical and mechanical response of a carbon nanotube/epoxy nanocomposite under quasi-static compressive loading.

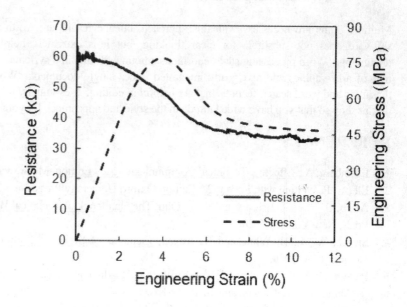

12.8   SUMMARY

Writing is a difficult skill to master; and most engineers experience significant problems when they prepare reports early in their careers. Unfortunately, the writing experiences in college do not correspond well with the writing requirements in industry. In college, you write for a knowledgeable instructor. In industry, you write for a wide range of people with different reading abilities. Moreover, the audience often varies from assignment to assignment. In both college and industry, you write to meet deadlines imposed by others. While writing is not usually an enjoyable task, there are many techniques that you can employ to make writing much easier and more pleasant.

The first technique is organization; an outline for a typical report was suggested. Gather information for the report from a wide variety of sources and generate notes that you can use to refresh your memory as you write. Sort the notes and transpose the information to expand the outline for your report.

When you organize the outline, but before you begin to write, determine as much as possible about your audience. They may be technically knowledgeable regarding the subject or they may be functionally illiterate. The language that you use in the report will depend on the reader's ability to understand. Also understand the objective of your document. Is it a technical or a lab report, an extended memo, a proposal or an instructional manual? Styles differ depending on the objective and you must be prepared to change accordingly.

There is a process to facilitate the preparation of any document. It begins with starting early and working systematically to produce a very professional document. Divide the report into sections and write the least difficult sections (appendices and technical detail portions) first. Defer the more difficult sections, such as the executive summary and the introduction until the other sections have been completed.

The actual writing is divided into four different tasks—composing, revising, editing and proofreading. Keep these tasks separate:

- Compose before revising
- Revise before editing
- Edit before proofreading
- Proofread with great care.

Multiple drafts are necessary with this approach, but the results are worth the effort. Word processing software does not substitute for clear thinking, but it is extremely helpful in preparing professional documents. Word processing saves enormous amounts of time in a systematic editing process. It enables a mix of art, graphics and text neatly integrated into a single document. Word processing software has a thesaurus and word search features that are helpful in editing. It essentially turns a computer and printer into a print shop so that you have wide latitude in the style and appearance for your professional documents.

REFERENCES

1. Eisenberg, A., Effective Technical Communication, 2nd Edition, McGraw Hill, New York, NY, 1992.
2. Elbow, P. Writing with Power, 2nd Edition Oxford University Press, New York, NY, 1998.
3. Alreb, G. T., C. T. Brusaw and W. E. Oliu, The Handbook of Technical Writing, 7th Edition, St. Martins Press, New York, NY, 2003
4. Struck, W., E. B. White and R. Angell, Elements of Style, 4th Edition, Allyn & Bacon, Needham Heights, MA, 1999.
5. Pickett, N. A. et al, Technical English: Writing, Reading and Speaking, Longman, Reading MA, 2000.
6.   Rolandi, M., K. Cheng, and S. Pérez-Kriz. "A Brief Guide to Designing Effective Figures for the Scientific Paper," Advanced Materials, 23.38 (2011): 4343-346.

Appendix A

Temperature Resistance Data for Thermistors and Thermoelectric Voltages for Thermocouples

Table A.1

Temperature Resistance Data for a Thermistor

Temp. C	Resistance ohms	Temp. C	Resistance ohms	Temp. C	Resistance ohms
-80	2,210,400	-41	107,910	-2	10,857
-79	2,022,100	-40	100,950	-1	10,311
-78	1,851,100	-39	94,470	0	9,795.0
-77	1,695,800	-38	88,440	1	9,309.0
-76	1,554,500	-37	82,860	2	8,850.0
-75	1,425,900	-36	77,640	3	8,415.0
-74	1,308,900	-35	72,810	4	8,007.0
-73	1,202,200	-34	68,280	5	7,617.0
-72	1,105,000	-33	64,080	6	7,251.0
-71	1,016,300	-32	60,150	7	6,903.0
-70	935,250	-31	56,490	8	6,576.0
-69	861,240	-30	53,100	9	6,264.0
-68	793,590	-29	49,890	10	5,970.0
-67	731,700	-28	46,920	11	5,691.0
-66	675,060	-27	44,160	12	5,427.0
-65	623,160	-26	41,550	13	5,175.0
-64	575,610	-25	39,120	14	4,938.0
-63	531,990	-24	36,840	15	4,713.0
-62	491,970	-23	34,710	16	4,500.0
-61	455,220	-22	32,730	17	4,296.0
-60	421,470	-21	30,870	18	4,104.0
-59	390,420	-20	29,121	19	3,921.0
-58	361,890	-19	27,483	20	3,747.0
-57	335,610	-18	25,947	21	3,582.0
-56	311,400	-17	24,507	22	3,426.0
-55	289,110	-16	23,154	23	3,276.0
-54	268,560	-15	21,885	24	3,135.0
-53	249,600	-14	20,694	25	3,000.0
-52	232,110	-13	19,572	26	2,871.9
-51	215,970	-12	18,519	27	2,750.1
-50	201,030	-11	17,529	28	2,633.1
-49	187,230	-10	16,599	29	2,522.1
-48	174,450	-9	15,720	30	2,417.1
-47	162,660	-8	14,895	31	2,316.9
-46	151,710	-7	14,118	32	2,220.9
-45	141,570	-6	13,386	33	2,129.1
-44	132,180	-5	12,699	34	2,042.1
-43	123,480	-4	12,048	35	1,959.0
-42	115,410	-3	11,433	36	1,880.1

Table A-1 Continued

Temp. C	Resistance ohms	Temp. C	Resistance ohms	Temp. C	Resistance ohms
37	1,805	75	444	113	141.00
38	1,733	76	429	114	137.19
39	1,664	77	415	115	133.500
40	1,598	78	402	116	129.990
41	1,535	79	389	117	126.510
42	1,475	80	377	118	123.210
43	1,418	81	365	119	120.000
44	1,363	82	353	120	116.790
45	1,311	83	342	121	113.790
46	1,260	84	331	122	110.910
47	1,212	85	321	123	108.000
48	1,167	86	311	124	105.180
49	1,123	87	301	125	102.510
50	1,081	88	292	126	99.930
51	1,040	89	283	127	97.410
52	1,002	90	275	128	94.950
53	965	91	266	129	92.580
54	930	92	258	130	90.279
55	896	93	251	131	88.041
56	863	94	243	132	85.869
57	832	95	236	133	83.751
58	803	96	229	134	81.609
59	774	97	222	135	79.710
60	746	98	216	136	77.790
61	720	99	210	137	75.900
62	695	100	203	138	74.079
63	671	101	198	139	72.309
64	647	102	192	140	70.581
65	625	103	187	141	68.910
66	603	104	181	142	67.290
67	583	105	176	143	65.700
68	563	106	171	144	64.170
69	544	107	167	145	62.661
70	526	108	162	146	61.209
71	508	109	158	147	59.799
72	491	110	153	148	58.431
73	475	111	149	149	57.099
74	459	112	145	150	55.791

Table A-2 Thermoelectric Voltages for Chromel-Alumel Thermocouples
Reference Junction at 0 °C Measurements in mV

C	0	1	2	3	4	5	6	7	8	9	10	C
-270	-6.458											-270
-260	-6.441	-6.444	-6.446	-6.448	-6.450	-6.152	-6.453	-6.455	-6.456	-6.157	-6.458	-260
-250	-6.404	-6.108	-6,413	-6.417	-6.421	-6.415	-6.429	-6.432	-6.435	-6.438	-6.441	-250
-240	-6.344	-6.351	-6.358	-6.364	-6.371	-6.377	-6.382	-6.388	-6.394	-6.399	-6.404	-240
-230	-6.262	-6.271	-6.280	-6.3S9	-6.297	-6.306	-6.314	-6.322	-6.329	-6.337	-6.344	-230
-220	-6.158	-6.170	-6.181	-6.192	-6.202	-6.213	-6,233	-6.233	-6.243	-6.253	-6.262	-220
-210	-6.035	-6.048	-6.061	-6.074	-6.087	-6.099	-6.111	-6.123	-6.135	-6.147	-6.158	-210
-200	-5.891	-5.907	-5.922	-5.936	-5.951	-5.965	-5.980	-5.994	-6.007	-6.021	-6.035	-200
-190	-5.730	-5.747	-5.763	-5.780	5.796	-5.813	-5.829	-5.815	-5.860	-5.876	-5.891	-190
-180	-5.550	-5.569	-5.587	-5.606	-5.621	-5.642	-5.660	-5.678	-5.695	-5.712	-5.730	-180
-170	-5.354	-5.374	-5.394	-5.414	-5.434	-5.451	-5.474	-5.493	-5.512	-5.531	-5.550	-170
-160	-5.141	-5.163	-5.185	-5.207	-5.228	-5.219	-5.271	-5.292	-5.313	-5.333	-5.354	-160
-150	-4.912	-4.936	-4.959	-1.983	-5.006	-5.029	-5.051	-5.074	-5.097	-5.119	-5.141	-150
-140	-4.669	-4.694	-4.719	-4.743	-4.768	-4.792	-4.617	-4.841	-1865	-4.859	-4.912	-140
-130	-4.410	-4.437	-4.463	-4.489	-4.515	-4.541	-4.567	-4.593	-4.616	-4.644	-4.669	-130
-120	-4.138	-4.166	-3.910	-4.221	-4.248	-4.276	-4.303	-4.330	-4.357	-4.384	-4.410	-120
-110	-3.852	-3.881	-3.614	-3.939	-3.968	-3.997	-1.025	-4.053	-4.082	-4.110	-4.138	-110
-100	-3.553	-3.584	-3.305	-3.614	-3.674	-3.704	-3.734	-3.164	-3.793	-3.823	-3.852	-100
-90	-3.142	-3.271	-2.985	-3.337	-3.368	-3.339	-3.430	-3.461	-3.192	-3.523	-3.553	-90
-80	-2.920	-2.953	-2.654	-3.018	-3.050	-3.082	-3.115	-3.147	-3.179	-3.211	-3.142	-80
-70	-2.586	-2.620	-2.312	-2.687	-2.721	-2.754	-2.788	-2.821	-2.654	-2.887	-2.920	-70
-60	-2.213	-2.277	-1.961	-2.347	-2.381	-2.416	-2.450	-2.484	-2.518	-2.552	-2.586	-60
-50	-1.889	-1.925	-1.600	-1.996	-2.032	-2.067	-2.102	-2.137	-2.173	-2.208	-2.213	-50
-10	-1.527	-1.563	-1.231	-1.636	-1.673	-1.709	-1.745	-1.781	-1.817	-1.853	-1.889	-10
-30	-1.156	-1.193	-0.851	-1.266	-1.305	-1.312	-1.379	-1.116	-1453	-1.490	-1.527	-30
-20	-0.777	-0.816	-0.469	-0.892	-0.930	-0.968	-1.005	-1.043	-1.081	-1.116	-1.156	-20
-10	-0.392	-0.431	-0.079	-0.508	-0.547	-0.585	-0.624	-0.662	-0.701	-0.739	-0.777	-10
0	0.000	-0.039	0.079	-0.118	-0.157	-0.197	-0.236	-0.275	-0.314	-0.353	-0.392	0
0	0.000	0.039	0.477	0.119	0.158	0.198	0.238	0.277	0.317	0.357	0.000	0
10	0.397	0.437	0.879	0.517	0.557	0.597	0.637	0.677	0.718	0.758	0.000	10
20	0.798	0.838	1.285	0.919	0.960	1.000	1.041	1.081	1.122	1.162	0.397	20
30	1.203	1.244	1.693	1.325	1.366	1.407	1.448	1.489	1.529	1.570	0.798	30
40	1.611	1.652	2.105	1.734	1.776	1.817	1.856	1.899	1.940	1.981	1.203	40
50	2.022	2.064	2.519	2.146	2.188	2.229	2.270	2.312	2.353	2.394	1.611	50
60	2.436	2.477	2.933	2.560	2.601	2.613	2.684	2.726	2.767	2.809	2.022	60
70	2.850	2.B92	3.349	2.975	3.016	3.058	3.100	3.141	3.183	3.224	2.436	70
80	3.266	3.307	3.764	3.390	3.432	3.473	3.515	3.556	3.598	3.639	2.850	80
90	3.681	3.722	4.178	3.805	3.847	3.888	3.930	3.971	4.012	4.054	3.266	90
100	4.095	4.137	4.590	4.219	4.261	4.302	4.343	4.384	4.426	4.167	3.681	100
110	4.508	4.519	5.001	4.632	4.673	4.714	4.755	4.796	4.837	4.878	4.095	110
120	4.919	4.960	5.409	5.042	5.083	5.124	5.164	5205	5.246	5.287	4.508	120
130	5.327	5.368	5.814	5.450	5.490	5.531	5.571	5.612	5.652	5.693	4.919	130
140	5.733	5.774	5.814	5.855	5.895	5.936	5.976	6.016	6.057	6.097	5.327	140
150	6.137	6.177	6.218	6.258	6.298	6.336	6.378	6.419	6.459	6.499	5.733	150
160	6.539	6.579	6.619	6.659	6.699	6.739	6.779	6.819	6.859	6.899	6.137	160
170	6.939	6.979	7.019	7.059	7.099	7.139	7.179	7.219	7.259	7.299	6.539	170
180	7.338	7.378	7.118	7.458	7.498	7.538	7.578	7.618	7.658	7.697	6.939	180
190	7.737	1.777	7.817	7.857	7.897	7.937	7.977	8.017	8.057	8.097	7.338	190
200	8.137	8.177	8.216	8.256	8.296	8.336	8.376	8.416	8.456	8.197	7.737	200
210	6.537	8.577	8.617	8.657	8.697	8.737	6.777	8.817	8.851	8.698	8.137	210
220	8.936	8.978	9.018	9.058	9.099	9.139	9.179	9.220	9.260	9.300	6.537	220
230	9.341	9.381	9.121	9.462	9.502	9.543	9.583	9.624	9.664	9.705	8.936	230
240	9.745	9.786	9.826	9.867	9.907	9.948	9.989	10.029	10.070	10.111	9.341	240
250	10.151	10.192	10.233	10.274	10.315	10.355	10.396	10.137	10.478	10.519	9.745	250
260	10.560	10.600	10.641	10.682	10.723	10.764	10.605	10.846	10.887	10.928	10.151	260
270	10.969	11.010	11.051	11.093	11.134	11.175	11.216	11.257	11.296	11.339	10.560	270
280	11.381	11.422	11.463	11.504	11.546	11.587	11.628	11.669	11.711	11.752	10.969	280
290	11.793	11.835	11.876	11.918	11.959	12.000	12.042	12.083	12.125	12.166	11.381	290

Table A-2 (Continued)

C	0	1	2	3	4	5	6	7	8	9	10	C
300	12.207	12.249	12.290	12.332	12.373	12.415	12.456	12.498	12.539	12.581	12.623	300
310	12.623	12.664	12.706	12.747	12.789	12.831	12.872	12.914	12.955	12.997	13.039	310
320	13.039	13.080	13.122	13.164	13.205	13.247	13.289	13.331	13.372	13.414	13.456	320
330	13.456	13.497	13.539	13.581	13.623	13.665	13.706	13.748	13.790	13.832	13.874	330
340	13.874	13.915	13.957	13.999	14.041	14.083	14.125	14.167	14.208	14.250	14.292	340
350	14.292	14.334	14.376	14.418	14.460	14.502	14.544	14.586	14.628	14.670	14.712	350
360	14.712	14.754	14.796	14.838	14.880	14.922	14.964	15.006	15.048	15.090	15.132	360
370	15.132	15.174	15.216	15.258	15.300	15.342	15.384	15.426	15.468	15.510	15.552	370
380	15.552	15.594	15.636	15.679	15.721	15.763	15.805	15.847	15.889	15.931	15.974	380
390	15.974	16.016	16.058	16.100	16.142	16.184	16.227	16.269	16.311	16.353	16.395	390
400	16.395	16.438	16.480	16.522	16.564	16.607	16.649	16.691	16.733	16.776	16.818	400
410	16.818	16.860	16.902	16.945	16.987	17.029	17.072	17.114	17.156	17.199	17.241	410
420	17.241	17.283	17.326	17.368	17.410	17.453	17.495	17.537	17.580	17.622	17.664	420
430	17.664	17.707	17.749	17.792	17.834	17.876	17.919	17.961	18.004	18.046	18.088	430
440	18.088	18.131	18.173	18.216	18.258	18.301	18.343	18.385	18.428	18.470	18.513	440
450	18.513	18.555	18.598	18.640	18.683	18.725	18.768	18.810	18.853	18.895	18.938	450
460	18.938	18.980	19.023	19.065	19.108	19.150	19.193	19.235	19.278	19.320	19.363	460
470	19.363	19.405	19.448	19.490	19.533	19.576	19.618	19.661	19.703	19.746	19.788	470
480	19.788	19.831	19.873	19.916	19.959	20.001	20.044	20.086	20.129	20.172	20.214	480
490	20.214	20.257	20.299	20.342	20.385	20.427	20.470	20.512	20.555	20.598	20.640	490
500	20.640	20.683	20.725	20.768	20.811	20.853	20.80%	20.938	20.981	21.024	21.066	500
510	21.066	21.109	21.152	21.194	21.237	21.280	21.322	21.365	21.407	21.450	21.493	510
520	21.493	21.535	21.578	21.621	21.663	21.706	21.749	21.791	21.834	21.876	21.919	520
530	21.919	21.962	22.004	22.047	22.090	22.132	22.175	22.218	22.260	22.303	22.346	530
540	22.346	22.388	22.431	22.473	22.516	22.559	22.601	22.644	22.687	22.729	22.772	540
550	22.772	22.815	22.857	22.90	22.942	22.985	23.028	23.070	23.113	23.156	23.198	550
560	23.198	23.241	23.284	23.326	23.369	23.411	23.454	23.497	23.539	23.582	23.624	560
570	23.624	23.667	23.710	23.752	23.795	23.837	23.880	23.923	23.965	24.008	24.050	570
580	24.050	24.093	24.136	24.178	24.221	24.263	24.306	24.348	24.391	24.434	24.476	580
590	24.476	24.519	24.561	24.604	24.646	24.689	24.731	24.774	24.817	24.859	24.902	590
600	24.902	24.944	24.987	25.029	25.072	25.114	25.157	25.199	25.242	25.284	25.327	600
610	25.327	25.369	25.412	25.454	25.497	25.539	25.582	25.624	25.666	25.709	25.751	610
620	25.751	25.794	25.836	25.879	25.921	25.964	26.006	26.048	26.091	26.133	26.176	620
630	26.176	26.218	26.260	26.303	26.345	26.387	26.430	26.472	26.515	26.557	26.599	630
640	26.599	26.642	26.684	26.726	26.769	26.811	26.853	26.896	26.938	26.980	27.022	640
650	27.022	27.065	27.107	27.149	27.192	27.234	27.276	27.318	27.361	27.403	27.445	650
660	27.445	27.487	27.529	27.572	27.614	27.656	27.698	27.740	27.783	27.825	27.867	660
670	27.867	27.909	27.951	27.993	28.035	28.078	28.120	28.162	28.204	28.246	28.288	670
680	28.288	28.330	28.372	28.414	28.456	28.498	28.540	28.583	28.625	28.667	28.709	680
690	28.709	28.751	28.793	28.835	28.877	28.919	28.961	29.002	29.044	29.086	29.128	690
700	29.128	29.170	29.212	29.254	29.296	29.338	29.380	29.422	29.464	29.505	29.547	700
710	29.547	29.589	29.631	29.673	29.715	29.756	29.798	29.840	29.882	29.924	29.965	710
720	29.965	30.007	30.049	30.091	30.132	30.174	30.216	30.257	30.299	30.341	30.383	720
730	30.383	30.424	30.466	30.508	30.549	30.591	30.632	30.674	30.716	30.757	30.799	730
740	30.799	30.840	30.882	30.924	30.965	31.007	31.048	31.090	31.131	31.173	31.214	740
750	31.214	31.256	31.297	31.339	31.380	31.422	31.463	31.504	31.546	31.587	31.629	750
760	31.629	31.670	31.712	31.753	31.794	31.836	31.877	31.918	31.960	32.001	32.042	760
770	32.042	32.084	32.125	32.166	32.207	32.249	32.290	32.331	32.372	32.414	32.455	770
780	32.455	32.496	32.537	32.578	32.619	32.661	32.702	32.743	32.784	32.825	32.866	780
790	32.866	32.907	32.948	32.990	33.031	33.072	33.113	33.154	33.195	33.236	33.277	790
800	33.277	33.318	33.359	33.400	33.441	33.482	33.523	33.564	33.604	33.645	33.686	800
810	33.686	33.727	33.768	33.809	33.850	33.891	33.931	33.972	34.013	34.054	34.095	810
820	34.095	34.136	34.176	34.217	34.258	34.299	34.339	34.380	34.421	34.461	34.502	820
830	34.502	34.543	34.583	34.624	34.665	34.705	34.746	34.787	34.827	34.868	34.909	830
840	34.909	34.949	34.990	35.030	35.071	35.111	35.152	35.192	35.233	35.273	35.314	840
850	35.314	35.354	35.395	35.435	35.476	35.516	35.557	35.597	35.637	35.678	35.718	850
860	35.718	35.758	35.799	35.839	35.880	35.920	35.960	36.000	36.041	36.081	36.121	860
870	36.121	36.162	36.202	36.242	36.282	36.323	36.363	36.403	36.443	36.483	36.524	870
880	36.524	36.564	36.604	36.644	36.684	36.724	36.764	36.804	36.844	36.885	36.925	880
890	36.925	36.965	37.005	37.045	37.085	37.125	37.165	37,205	37.245	37.285	37.325	890

Table A-2 (Continued)

C	0	1	2	3	4	5	6	7	8	9	10	C
900	37.325	37.365	37.405	37.445	37.484	37.524	37.564	37.604	37.644	37.684	37.724	900
910	37.724	37.764	37.803	37.843	37.883	37.923	37.963	38.002	38.042	38.082	38.122	910
920	38.122	38.162	38.201	38.241	38.281	38.320	38.360	38.400	38.439	38.479	38.519	920
930	38.519	38.558	38.598	38.638	38.677	38.717	38.756	38.796	38.836	38.875	38.915	930
940	38.915	38.954	38.994	39.033	39.073	39.112	39.152	39.191	39.231	39.270	39.310	940
950	39.310	39.349	39.388	39.428	39.467	39.507	39.546	39.585	39.625	39.664	39.703	950
960	39.703	39.743	39.782	39.821	39.861	39.900	39.939	39.979	40.018	40.057	40.096	960
970	40.096	40.136	40.175	40.214	40.253	40.292	40.332	40.371	40.410	40.449	40.488	970
980	40.488	40.527	40.566	40.605	40.645	40.684	40.723	40.762	40.801	40.840	40.879	980
990	40.879	40.918	40.957	40.996	41.035	41.074	41.113	41.152	41.191	41.230	41.269	990
1,000	41.269	41.308	41.347	41.385	41.424	41.463	41.502	41.541	41.580	41.619	41.657	1,000
1,010	41.657	41.696	41.735	41.774	41.813	41.851	41.890	41.929	41.968	42.006	42.045	1,010
1,020	42.045	42.084	42.123	42.161	42.200	42.239	42.277	42.316	42.355	42.393	42.432	1,020
1,030	42.432	42.470	42.509	42.548	42.586	42.625	42.663	42.702	42.740	42.779	42.817	1,030
1,040	42.817	42.856	42.894	42.933	42.971	43.010	43.048	43.087	43.125	43.164	43.202	1,040
1,050	43.202	43.240	43.279	43.317	43.356	43.394	43.432	43.471	43.509	43.547	43.585	1,050
1,060	43.585	43.624	43.662	43.700	43.739	43.777	43.815	43.853	43.891	43.930	43.968	1,060
1,070	43.968	44.006	44.044	44.082	44.121	44.159	44.197	44.235	44.273	44.311	44.349	1,070
1,080	44.349	44.387	44.425	44.463	44.501	44.539	44.577	44.615	44.653	44.691	44.729	1,080
1,090	44.729	44.767	44.805	44.843	44.881	44.919	44.957	44.995	45.033	45.070	45.108	1,090
1,100	45.108	45.146	45.184	45.222	45.260	45.297	45.335	45.373	45.411	45.448	45.486	1,100
1,110	45.486	45.524	45.561	45.599	45.637	45.675	45.712	45.750	45.787	45.825	45.863	1,110
1,120	45.863	45.900	45.938	45.975	46.013	46.051	46.088	46.126	46.163	46.201	46.238	1,120
1,130	46.238	46.275	46.313	46.350	46.388	46.425	46.463	46.500	46.537	46.575	46.612	1,130
1,140	46.612	46.649	46.687	46.724	46.761	46.799	46.836	46.873	46.910	46.948	46.985	1,140
1,150	46.985	47.022	47.059	47.096	47.134	47.171	47.208	47.245	47.282	47.319	47.356	1,150
1,160	47.356	47.393	47.430	47.468	47.505	47.542	47.579	47.616	47.653	47.689	47.726	1,160
1,170	47.726	47.763	47.800	47.837	47.874	47.911	47.948	47.985	48.021	48.058	48.095	1,170
1,180	48.095	48.132	48.169	48.205	48.242	48.279	48.316	48.352	48.389	48.426	48.462	1,180
1,190	48.462	48.499	48.536	48.572	48.609	48.645	48.682	48.718	48.755	48.792	48.828	1,190
1,200	48.828	48.865	48.901	48.937	48.974	49.010	49.047	49.083	49.120	49.156	49.192	1,200
1,210	49.192	49.229	49.265	49.301	49.338	49.374	49.410	49.446	49.483	49.519	49.555	1,210
1,220	49.555	49.591	49.627	49.663	49.700	49.736	49.772	49.808	49.844	49.880	49.916	1,220
1,230	49.916	49.952	49.988	50.024	50.060	50.096	50.132	50.168	50.204	50.240	50.276	1,230
1,240	50.276	50.311	50.347	50.383	50.419	50.455	50.491	50.526	50.562	50.598	50.633	1,240
1,250	50.633	50.669	50.705	50.741	50.776	50.812	50.847	50.883	50.919	50.954	50.990	1,250
1,260	50.990	51.025	51.061	51.096	51.132	51.167	51.203	51.238	51.274	51.309	51.344	1,260
1,270	51.344	51.380	51.415	51.450	51.486	51.521	51.556	51.592	51.627	51.662	51.697	1,270
1,280	51.697	51.733	51.768	51.803	51.838	51.873	51.908	51.943	51.979	52.014	52.049	1,280
1,290	52.049	52.084	52.119	52.154	52.189	52.224	52.259	52.294	52.329	52.364	52.398	1,290
1,300	52.398	52.433	52.468	52.503	52.538	52.573	52.608	52.642	52.677	52.712	52.747	1,300
1,310	52.747	52.781	52.816	52.851	52.886	52.920	52.955	52.989	53.024	53.059	53.093	1,310
1,320	53.093	53.128	53.162	53.197	53.232	53.266	53.301	53.335	53.370	53.404	53.439	1,320
1,330	53.439	53.473	53.507	53.542	53.576	53.611	53.645	53.679	53.714	53.748	53.782	1,330
1,340	53.782	53.817	53.851	53.885	53.920	53.954	53.988	54.022	54.057	54.091	54.125	1,340
1,350	54.125	54.159	54.193	54.228	54.262	54.296	54.330	54.364	54.398	54.432	54.466	1,350
1,360	54.466	54.501	54.535	54.569	54.603	54.637	54.671	54.705	54.739	54.773	54.807	1,360
1,370	54.807	54.841	54.875									1,370

Table A-3
Thermoelectric Voltages for Chromel-Constantan Thermocouples
Reference Junction at 0 °C   Measurements in mV

C	0	1	2	3	4	5	6	7	8	9	10	C
-270	-9.835											-270
-260	-9.797	-9.802	-9.808	-9.813	-9.817	-9.821	-9.825	-9.828	-9.831	-9.833	-9.835	-260
-250	-9.719	-9.728	-9.737	-9.746	-9.754	-9.762	-9.770	-9.777	-9.784	-9.791	-9.797	-250
-240	-9.604	-9.617	-9.630	-9.642	-9.654	-9.666	-9.677	-9.688	-9.699	-9.709	-9.719	-240
-230	-9.455	-9.472	-9.488	-9.503	-9.519	-9.534	-9.549	-9.563	-9.577	-9.591	-9.604	-230
-220	-9.274	-9.293	-9.313	-9.332	-9.350	-9.368	-9.386	-9.404	-9.421	-9.438	-9.455	-220
-210	-9.063	-9.085	-9.107	-9.129	-9.151	-9.172	-9.193	-9.214	-9.234	-9.254	-9.274	-210
-200	-8.824	-8.850	-8.874	-8.899	-8.923	-8.947	-8.971	-8.994	-9.017	-9.040	-9.063	-200
-190	-8.561	-8.588	-8.615	-8.642	-8.669	-8.696	-8.722	-8.748	-8.774	-8.799	-8.824	-190
-180	-8.273	-8.303	-8.333	-8.362	-8.391	-8.420	-8.449	-8.477	-8.505	-8.533	-8.561	-180
-170	-7.963	-7.995	-8.027	-8.058	-8.090	-8.121	-8.152	-8.183	-8.213	-8.243	-8.273	-170
-160	-7.631	-7.665	-7.699	-7.733	-7.767	-7.800	-7.833	-7.866	-7.898	-7.931	-7.963	-160
-150	-7.279	-7.315	-7.351	-7.387	-7.422	-7.458	-7.493	-7.528	-7.562	-7.597	-7.631	-150
-140	-6.907	-6.945	-6.983	-7.020	-7.058	-7.095	-7.132	-7.169	-7.206	-7.243	-7.279	-140
-130	-6.516	-6.556	-6.596	-6.635	-6.675	-6.714	-6.753	-6.792	-6.830	-6.869	-6.907	-130
-120	-6.107	-6.149	-6.190	-6.231	-6.273	-6.314	-6.354	-6.395	-6.436	-6.476	-6.516	-120
-110	-5.680	-5.724	-5.767	-5.810	-5.853	-5.896	-5.938	-5.981	-6.023	-6.065	-6.107	-110
-100	-5.237	-5.282	-5.327	-5.371	-5.416	-5.460	-5.505	-5.549	-5.593	-5.637	-5.680	-100
-90	-4.777	-4.824	-4.870	-4.916	-4.963	-5.009	-5.055	-5.100	-5.146	-5.191	-5.237	-90
-80	-4.301	-4.350	-4.398	-4.446	-4.493	-4.541	-4.588	-4.636	-4.683	-4.730	-4.777	-80
-70	-3.811	-3.860	-3.910	-3.959	-4.009	-4.058	-4.107	-4.156	-4.204	-4.253	-4.301	-70
-60	-3.306	-3.357	-3.408	-3.459	-3.509	-3.560	-3.610	-3.661	-3.711	-3.761	-3.811	-60
-50	-2.787	-2.839	-2.892	-2.944	-2.996	-3.048	-3.100	-3.152	-3.203	-3.254	-3.306	-50
-40	-2.254	-2.308	-2.362	-2.416	-2.469	-2.522	-2.575	-2.628	-2.681	-2.734	-2.787	-40
-30	-1.709	-1.764	-1.819	-1.874	-1.929	-1.983	-2.038	-2.092	-2.146	-2.200	-2.254	-30
-20	-1.151	-1.208	-1.264	-1.320	-1.376	-1.432	-1.487	-1.543	-1.599	-1.654	-1.709	-20
-10	-0.581	-0.639	-0.696	-0.754	-0.811	-0.868	-0.925	-0.982	-1.038	-1.095	-1.151	-10
0	0.000	-0.059	-0.117	-0.176	-0.234	-0.292	-0.350	-0.408	-0.466	-0.524	-0.581	0
0	0.000	0.059	0.118	0.176	0.235	0.295	0.354	0.413	0.472	0.532	0.591	0
10	0.591	0.651	0.711	0.770	0.830	0.890	0.950	1.011	1.071	1.131	1.192	10
20	1.192	1.252	1.313	1.373	1.434	1.495	1.556	1.617	1.678	1.739	1.801	20
30	1.801	1.862	1.924	1.985	2.047	2.109	2.171	2.233	2.295	2.357	2.419	30
40	2.419	2.482	2.544	2.607	2.669	2.732	2.795	2.858	2.921	2.984	3.047	40
50	3.047	3.110	3.173	3.237	3.300	3.364	3.428	3.491	3.555	3.619	3.683	50
60	3.683	3.748	3.812	3.876	3.941	4.005	4.070	4.134	4.199	4.264	4.329	60
70	4.329	4.394	4.459	4.524	4.590	4.655	4.720	4.786	4.852	4.917	4.983	70
80	4.983	5.049	5.115	5.181	5.247	5.314	5.380	5.446	5.513	5.579	5.646	80
90	5.646	5.713	5.780	5.846	5.913	5.981	6.048	6.115	6.182	6.250	6.317	90
100	6.317	6.385	6.452	6.520	6.588	6.656	6.724	6.792	6.860	6.928	0.069	100
110	6.996	7.064	7.133	7.201	7.270	7.339	7.407	7.476	7.545	7.614	7.683	110
120	7.683	7.752	7.821	7.890	7.960	8.029	8.099	8.168	8.238	8.307	8.377	120
130	8.377	8.447	8.517	8.587	8.657	8.727	8.797	8.867	8.938	9.008	9.078	130
140	9.078	9.149	9.220	9.290	9.361	9.432	9.503	9.573	9.644	9.715	9.787	140

Table A-3 Continued

C	0	1	2	3	4	5	6	7	8	9	10	C
150	9.787	9.858	9.929	10.000	10.072	10.143	10.215	10.286	10.358	10.429	10.501	150
160	10.501	10.573	10.645	10.717	10.789	10.861	10.933	11.005	11.077	11.150	11.222	160
170	11.222	11.294	11.367	11.439	11.512	11.585	11.657	11.730	11.803	11.876	11.949	170
180	11.949	12.022	12.095	12.168	12.241	12.314	12.387	12.461	12.534	12.608	12.681	180
190	12.681	12.755	12.828	12.902	12.975	13.049	13.123	13.197	13.271	13.345	13.419	190
200	13.419	13.493	13.567	13.641	13.715	13.789	13.864	13.938	14.012	14.087	14.161	200
210	14.161	14.236	14.310	14.385	14.460	14.534	14.609	14.684	14.759	14.834	14.909	210
220	14.909	14.984	15.059	15.134	15.209	15.284	15.359	15.435	15.510	15.585	15.661	220
230	15.661	15.736	15.812	15.887	15.963	16.038	16.114	16.190	16.266	16.341	16.417	230
240	16.417	16.493	16.569	16.645	16.721	16.797	16.873	16.949	17.025	17.101	17.178	240
250	17.178	17.254	17.330	17.406	17.483	17.559	17.636	17.712	17.789	17.865	17.942	250
260	17.942	18.018	18.095	18.172	18.248	18.325	18.402	18.479	18.556	18.633	18.710	260
270	18.710	18.787	18.864	18.941	19.018	19.095	19.172	19.249	19.326	19.404	19.481	270
280	19.481	19.558	19.636	19.713	19.790	19.868	19.945	20.023	20.100	20.178	20.256	280
290	20.256	20.333	20.411	20.488	20.566	20.644	20.722	20.800	20.877	20.955	21.033	290
300	21.033	21.111	21.189	21.267	21.345	21.423	21.501	21.579	21.657	21.735	21.814	300
310	21.814	21.892	21.970	22.048	22.127	22.205	22.283	22.362	22.440	22.518	22.597	310
320	22.597	22.675	22.754	22.832	22.911	22.989	23.068	23.147	23.225	23.304	23.383	320
330	23.383	23.461	23.540	23.619	23.698	23.777	23.855	23.934	24.013	24.092	24.171	330
340	24.171	24.250	24.329	24.408	24.487	24.566	24.645	24.724	24.803	24.882	24.961	340
350	24.961	25.041	25.120	25.199	25.278	25.357	25.437	25.516	25.595	25.675	25.754	350
360	25.754	25.833	25.913	25.992	26.072	26.151	26.230	26.310	26.389	26.469	26.549	360
370	26.549	26.628	26.708	26.787	26.867	26.947	27.026	27.106	27.186	27.265	27.345	370
380	27.345	27.425	27.504	27.584	27.664	27.744	27.824	27.903	27.983	28.063	28.143	380
390	28.143	28.223	28.303	28.383	28.463	28.543	28.623	28.703	28.783	28.863	28.943	390
400	28.943	29.023	29.103	29.183	29.263	29.343	29.423	29.503	29.584	29.664	29.744	400
410	29.744	29.824	29.904	29.984	30.065	30.145	30.225	30.305	30.386	30.466	30.546	410
420	30.546	30.627	30.707	30.787	30.868	30.948	31.028	31.109	31.189	31.270	31.350	420
430	31.350	31.430	31.511	31.591	31.672	31.752	31.833	31.913	31.994	32.074	32.155	430
440	32.155	32.235	32.316	32.396	32.477	32.557	32.638	32.719	32.799	32.880	32.960	440
450	32.960	33.041	33.122	33.202	33.283	33.364	33.444	33.525	33.605	33.686	33.767	450
460	33.767	33.848	33.928	34.009	34.090	34.170	34.251	34.332	34.413	34.493	34.574	460
470	34.574	34.655	34.736	34.816	34.897	34.978	35.059	35.140	35.220	35.301	35.382	470
480	35.382	35.463	35.544	35.624	35.705	35.786	35.867	35.948	36.029	36.109	36.190	480
490	36.190	36.271	36.352	36.433	36.514	36.595	36.675	36.756	36.837	36.918	36.999	490
500	36.999	37.080	37.161	37.242	37.323	37.403	37.484	37.565	37.646	37.727	37.808	500
510	37.808	37.889	37.970	38.051	38.132	38.213	38.293	38.374	38.455	38.536	38.617	510
520	38.617	38.698	38.779	38.860	38.941	39.022	39.103	39.184	39.264	39.345	39.426	520
530	39.426	39.507	39.588	39.669	39.750	39.831	39.912	39.993	40.074	40.155	40.236	530
540	40.236	40.316	40.397	40.478	40.559	40.640	40.721	40.802	40.883	40.964	41.045	540
550	41.045	41.125	41.206	41.287	41.368	41.449	41.530	41.611	41.692	41.773	41.853	550
560	41.853	41.934	42.015	0.420	42.177	42.258	42.339	42.419	42.500	42.581	42.662	560
570	42.662	42.743	42.824	42.904	42.985	43.066	43.147	43.228	43.308	43.389	43.470	570

Table A-3 Continued

C	0	1	2	3	4	5	6	7	8	9	10	C
580	43.470	43.551	43.632	43.712	43.793	43.874	43.955	44.035	44.116	44.197	44.278	580
590	44.278	44.358	44.439	44.520	44.601	44.681	44.762	44.843	44.923	45.004	45.085	590
600	45.085	45.165	45.246	45.327	45.407	45.488	45.569	45.649	45.730	45.811	45.891	600
610	45.891	45.972	46.052	46.133	46.213	46.294	46.375	46.455	46.536	46.616	46.697	610
620	46.697	46.777	46.858	46.938	47.019	47.099	47.180	47.260	47.341	47.421	47.502	620
630	47.502	47.582	47.663	47.743	47.824	47.904	47.984	48.065	48.145	48.226	48.306	630
640	48.306	48.386	48.467	48.547	48.627	48.708	48.788	48.868	48.949	49.029	49.109	640
650	49.109	49.189	49.270	49.350	49.430	49.510	49.591	49.671	49.751	49.831	49.911	650
660	49.911	49.992	50.072	50.152	50.232	50.312	50.392	50.472	50.553	50.633	50.713	660
670	50.713	50.793	50.873	50.953	51.033	51.113	51.193	51.273	51.353	51.433	51.513	670
680	51.513	51.593	51.673	51.753	51.833	51.913	51.993	52.073	52.152	52.232	52.312	680
690	52.312	52.392	52.472	52.552	52.632	52.711	52.791	52.871	52.951	53.031	53.110	690
700	53.110	53.190	53.270	53.350	53.429	53.509	53.589	53.668	53.748	53.828	53.907	700
710	53.907	53.987	54.066	54.146	54.226	54.305	54.385	54.464	54.544	54.623	54.703	710
720	54.703	54.782	54.862	54.941	55.021	55.100	55.180	55.259	55.339	55.418	55.498	720
730	55.498	55.577	55.656	55.736	55.815	55.894	55.974	56.053	56.132	56.212	56.291	730
740	56.291	56.370	56.449	56.529	56.608	56.687	56.766	56.845	56.924	57.004	57.083	740
750	57.083	57.162	57.241	57.320	57.399	57.478	57.557	57.636	57.715	57.794	57.873	750
760	57.873	57.952	58.031	58.110	58.189	58.268	58.347	58.426	58.505	58.584	58.663	760
770	58.663	58.742	58.820	58.899	58.978	59.057	59.136	59.214	59.293	59.372	59.451	770
780	59.451	59.529	59.608	59.687	59.765	59.844	59.923	60.001	60.080	60.159	60.237	780
790	60.237	60.316	60.394	60.473	60.551	60.630	60.708	60.787	60.865	60.944	61.022	790
800	61.022	61.101	61.179	61.258	61.336	61.414	61.493	61.571	61.649	61.728	61.806	800
810	61.806	61.884	61.962	62.041	62.119	62.197	62.275	62.353	62.432	62.510	62.588	810
820	62.588	62.666	62.744	62.822	62.900	62.978	63.056	63.134	63.212	63.290	63.368	820
830	63.368	63.446	63.524	63.602	63.680	63.758	63.836	63.914	63.992	64.069	64.147	830
840	64.147	64.225	64.303	64.380	64.458	64.536	64.614	64.691	64.769	64.847	64.924	840
850	64.924	65.002	65.080	65.157	65.235	65.312	65.390	65.467	65.545	65.622	65.700	850
860	65.700	65.777	65.855	65.932	66.009	66.087	66.164	66.241	66.319	66.396	66.473	860
870	66.473	66.551	66.628	66.705	66.782	66.859	66.937	67.014	67.091	67.168	67.245	870
880	67.245	67.322	67.399	67.476	67.553	67.630	67.707	67.784	67.861	67.938	68.015	880
890	68.015	68.092	68.169	68.246	68.323	68.399	68.476	68.553	68.630	68.706	68.783	890
900	68.783	68.860	68.936	69.013	69.090	69.166	69.243	69.320	69.396	69.473	69.549	900
910	69.549	69.626	69.702	69.779	69.855	69.931	70.008	70.084	70.161	70.237	70.313	910
920	70.313	70.390	70.466	70.542	70.618	70.694	70.771	70.847	70.923	70.999	71.075	920
930	71.075	71.151	71.227	71.304	71.380	71.456	71.532	71.608	71.683	71.759	71.835	930
940	71.835	71.911	71.987	72.063	72.139	72.215	72.290	72.366	72.442	72.518	72.593	940
950	72.593	72.669	72.745	72.820	72.896	72.972	73.047	73.123	73.199	73.274	73.350	950
960	73.350	73.425	73.501	73.576	73.652	73.727	73.802	73.878	73.953	74.029	74.104	960
970	74.104	74.179	74.255	74.330	74.405	74.480	74.556	74.631	74.706	74.781	74.857	970
980	74.857	74.932	75.007	75.082	75.157	75.232	75.307	75.382	75.458	75.533	75.608	980
990	75.608	75.683	75.758	75.833	75.908	75.983	76.058	76.133	76.208	76.283	76.358	990
1000	76.358											

Table A-4 Thermoelectric Voltages for Copper-Constantan Thermocouples
Reference Junction at °C   Measurements in mV

C	0	1	2	3	4	5	6	7	8	9	10	C
-270	-6.258											-270
-260	-6.232	-6.236	-6.239	-6.242	-6.245	-6.248	-6.251	-6.253	-6.255	-6.256	-6.258	-260
-250	-6.181	-6.187	-6.193	-6.198	-6.204	-6.209	-6.214	-6.219	-6.224	-6.228	-6.232	-250
-240	-6.105	-6.114	-6.122	-6.130	-6.138	-6.146	-6.153	-6.160	-6.167	-6.174	-6.181	-240
-230	-6.007	-6.018	-6.028	-6.039	-6.049	-6.059	-6.068	-6.078	-6.087	-6.096	-6.105	-230
-220	-5.889	-5.901	-5.914	-5.926	-5.938	-5.950	-5.962	-5.973	-5.985	-5.996	-6.007	-220
-210	-5.753	-5.767	-5.782	-5.795	-5.809	-5.823	-5.836	-5.850	-5.863	-5.876	-5.889	-210
-200	-5.603	-5.619	-5.634	-5.650	-5.665	-5.680	-5.695	-5.710	-5.724	-5.739	-5.753	-200
-190	-5.439	-5.456	-5.473	-5.489	-5.506	-5.522	-5.539	-5.555	-5.571	-5.587	-5.603	-190
-180	-5.261	-5.279	-5.297	-5.315	-5.333	-5.351	-5.369	-5.387	-5.404	-5.421	-5.439	-180
-170	-5.069	-5.089	-5.109	-5.128	-5.147	-5.167	-5.186	-5.205	-5.223	-5.242	-5.261	-170
-160	-4.865	-4.886	-4.907	-4.928	-4.948	-4.969	-4.989	-5.010	-5.030	-5.050	-5.069	-160
-150	-4.648	-4.670	-4.693	-4.715	-4.737	-4.758	-4.780	-4.801	-4.823	-4.844	-4.865	-150
-140	-4.419	-4.442	-4.466	-4.489	-4.512	-4.535	-4.558	-4.581	-4.603	-4.626	-4.648	-140
-130	-4.177	-4.202	-4.226	-4.251	-4.275	-4.299	-4.323	-4.347	-4.371	-4.395	-4.419	-130
-120	-3.923	-3.949	-3.974	-4.000	-4.026	-4.051	-4.077	-4.102	-4.127	-4.152	-4.177	-120
-110	-3.656	-3.684	-3.711	-3.737	-3.764	-3.791	-3.818	-3.844	-3.870	-3.897	-3.923	-110
-100	-3.378	-3.407	-3.435	-3.463	-3.491	-3.519	-3.547	-3.574	-3.602	-3.629	-3.656	-100
-90	-3.089	-3.118	-3.147	-3.177	-3.206	-3.235	-3.264	-3.293	-3.321	-3.350	-3.378	-90
-80	-2.788	-2.818	-2.849	-2.879	-2.909	-2.939	-2.970	-2.999	-3.029	-3.059	-3.089	-80
-70	-2.475	-2.507	-2.539	-2.570	-2.602	-2.633	-2.664	-2.695	-2.726	-2.757	-2.788	-70
-60	-2.152	-2.185	-2.218	-2.250	-2.283	-2.315	-2.348	-2.380	-2.412	-2.444	-2.475	-60
-50	-1.819	-1.853	-1.886	-1.920	-1.953	-1.987	-2.020	-2.053	-2.087	-2.120	-2.152	-50
-40	-1.475	-1.510	-1.544	-1.579	-1.614	-1.648	-1.682	-1.717	-1.751	-1.785	-1.819	-40
-30	-1.121	-1.157	-1.192	-1.228	-1.263	-1.299	-1.334	-1.370	-1.405	-1.440	-1.475	-30
-20	-0.757	-0.794	-0.830	-0.867	-0.903	-0.940	-0.976	-1.013	-1.049	-1.085	-1.121	-20
-10	-0.383	-0.421	-0.458	-0.496	-0.534	-0.571	-0.608	-0.646	-0.683	-0.720	-0.757	-10
0	0	-0.039	-0.077	-0.116	-0.154	-0.193	-0.231	-0.269	-0.307	-0.345	-0.383	0
0	0	0.039	0.078	0.117	0.156	0.195	0.234	0.273	0.312	0.351	0.391	0
10	0.391	0.430	0.470	0.510	0.549	0.589	0.629	0.669	0.709	0.749	0.789	10
20	0.789	0.830	0.870	0.911	0.951	0.992	1.032	1.073	1.114	1.155	1.196	20
30	1.196	1.237	1.279	1.320	1.361	1.403	1.444	1.486	1.528	1.569	1.611	30
40	1.611	1.653	1.695	1.738	1.780	1.822	1.865	1.907	1.950	1.992	2.035	40
50	2.035	2.078	2.121	2.164	2.207	2.250	2.294	2.337	2.380	2.424	2.467	50
60	2.467	2.511	2.555	2.599	2.643	2.687	2.731	2.775	2.819	2.864	2.908	60
70	2.908	2.953	2.997	3.042	3.087	3.131	3.176	3.221	3.266	3.312	3.357	70
80	3.357	3.402	3.447	3.493	3.538	3.584	3.630	3.676	3.721	3.767	3.813	80
90	3.813	3.859	3.906	3.952	3.998	4.044	4.091	4.137	4.184	4.231	4.277	90
100	4.277	4.324	4.371	4.418	4.465	4.512	4.559	4.607	4.654	4.701	4.749	100

Table A-4 Continued

C	0	1	2	3	4	5	6	7	8	9	10	C
110	4.749	4.796	4.844	4.891	4.939	4.987	5.035	5.083	5.131	5.179	5.227	110
120	5.227	5.275	5.324	5.372	5.420	5.469	5.517	5.566	5.615	5.663	5.712	120
130	5.712	5.761	5.810	5.859	5.908	5.957	6.007	6.056	6.105	6.155	6.204	130
140	6.204	6.254	6.303	6.353	6.403	6.452	6.502	6.552	6.602	6.652	6.702	140
150	6.702	6.753	6.803	6.853	6.903	6.954	7.004	7.055	7.106	7.156	7.207	150
160	7.207	7.258	7.309	7.360	7.411	7.462	7.513	7.564	7.615	7.666	7.718	160
170	7.718	7.769	7.821	7.872	7.924	7.975	8.027	8.079	8.131	8.183	8.735	170
180	8.235	8.287	8.339	8.391	8.443	8.495	8.548	8.600	8.652	8.705	8.757	180
190	8.757	8.810	8.863	8.915	8.968	9.021	9.074	9.127	9.180	9.233	9.286	190
200	9.286	9.339	9.392	9.446	9.499	9.553	9.606	9.659	9.713	9.767	9.820	200
210	9.820	9.874	9.928	9.982	10.036	10.090	10.144	10.198	10.252	10.306	10.360	210
220	10.360	10.414	10.469	10.523	10.578	10.632	10.687	10.741	10.796	10.851	10.905	220
230	10.905	10.960	11.015	11.070	11.125	11.180	11.235	11.290	11.345	11.401	11.456	230
240	11.456	11.511	11.566	11.622	11.677	11.733	11.788	11.844	11.900	11.956	12.011	240
250	12.011	12.067	12.123	12.179	12.235	12.291	12.347	12.403	12.459	12.515	12.572	250
260	12.572	12.628	12.684	12.741	12.797	12.854	12.910	12.967	13.024	13.080	13.137	260
270	13.137	13.194	13.251	13.307	13.364	13.421	13.478	13.535	13.592	13.650	13.707	270
280	13.707	13.764	13.821	13.879	13.936	13.993	14.051	14.108	14.166	14.223	14.281	280
290	14.281	14.339	14.396	14.454	14.512	14.570	14.628	14.686	14.744	14.802	14.860	290
300	14.860	14.918	14.976	15.034	15.092	15.151	15.209	15.267	15.326	15.384	15.443	300
310	15.443	15.501	15.560	15.619	15.677	15.736	15.795	15.853	15.912	15.971	16.030	310
320	16.030	16.089	16.148	16.207	16.266	16.325	16.384	16.444	16.503	16.562	16.621	320
330	16.621	16.681	16.740	16.800	16.859	16.919	16.978	17.038	17.097	17.157	17.217	330
340	17.217	17.277	17.336	17.396	17.456	17.516	17.576	17.636	17.696	17.756	17.816	340
350	17.816	17.877	17.937	17.997	18.057	18.118	18.178	18.238	18.299	18.359	18.420	350
360	18.420	18.480	18.541	18.602	18.662	18.723	18.784	18.845	18.905	18.966	19.027	360
370	19.027	19.088	19.149	19.210	19.271	19.332	19.393	19.455	19.516	19.577	19.638	370
380	19.638	19.699	19.761	19.822	19.883	19.945	20.006	20.068	20.129	20.191	20.252	380
390	20.252	20.314	20.376	20.437	20.499	20.560	20.622	20.684	20.746	20.807	20.869	390
400	20.869											400

Table A-5 Thermoelectric Voltages for Iron Constantan Thermocouples
Reference Junction at 0 °C   Measurements in mV

C	0	1	2	3	4	5	6	7	8	9	10	C
-210	-8.096											-210
-200	-7.890	-7.912	-7.934	-7.955	-7.976	-7.996	-8.017	-8.037	-8.057	-8.076	-8.096	-200
-190	-7.659	-7.683	-7.707	-7.731	-7.755	-7.778	-7.801	-7.824	-7.846	-7.868	-7.890	-190
-180	-7.402	-7.429	-7.455	-7.482	-7.508	-7.533	-7.559	-7.584	-7.609	-7.634	-7.659	-180
-170	-7.122	-7.151	-7.180	-7.209	-7.237	-7.265	-7.293	-7.321	-7.348	-7.375	-7.402	-170
-160	-6.821	-6.852	-6.883	-6.914	-6.944	-6.974	-7.004	-7.034	-7.064	-7.093	-7.122	-160
-150	-6.499	-6.532	-6.565	-6.598	-6.630	-6.663	-6.695	-6.727	-6.758	-6.790	-6.821	-150
-140	-6.159	-6.194	-6.228	-6.263	-6.297	-6.331	-6.365	-6.399	-6.433	-6.466	-6.499	-140
-130	-5.801	-5.837	-5.874	-5.910	-5.946	-5.982	-6.018	-6.053	-6.089	-6.124	-6.159	-130
-120	-5.426	-5.464	-5.502	-5.540	-5.578	-5.615	-5.653	-5.690	-5.727	-5.764	-5.801	-120
-110	-5.036	-5.076	-5.115	-5.155	-5.194	-5.233	-5.272	-5.311	-5.349	-5.388	-5.426	-110
-100	-4.632	-4.673	-4.714	-4.755	-4.795	-4.836	-4.876	-4.916	-4.956	-4.996	-5.036	-100
-90	-4.215	-4.257	-4.299	-4.341	-4.383	-4.425	-4.467	-4.508	-4.550	-4.591	-4.632	-90
-80	-3.785	-3.829	-3.872	-3.915	-3.958	-4.001	-4.044	-4.087	-4.130	-4.172	-4.215	-80
-70	-3.344	-3.389	-3.433	-3.478	-3.522	-3.566	-3.610	-3.654	-3.698	-3.742	-3.785	-70
-60	-2.892	-2.938	-2.984	-3.029	-3.074	-3.120	-3.165	-3.210	-3.255	-3.299	-3.344	-60
-50	-2.431	-2.478	-2.524	-2.570	-2.617	-2.663	-2.709	-2.755	-2.801	-2.847	-2.892	-50
-40	-1.960	-2.008	-2.055	-2.102	-2.150	-2.197	-2.244	-2.291	-2.338	-2.384	-2.431	-40
-30	-1.481	-1.530	-1.578	-1.626	-1.674	-1.722	-1.770	-1.818	-1.865	-1.913	-1.960	-30
-20	-0.995	-1.044	-1.093	-1.141	-1.190	-1.239	-1.288	-1.336	-1.385	-1.433	-1.481	-20
-10	-0.501	-0.550	-0.600	-0.650	-0.699	-0.748	-0.798	-0.847	-0.896	-0.945	-0.995	-10
0	0.000	-0.050	-0.101	-0.151	-0.201	-0.251	-0.301	-0.351	-0.401	-0.451	-0.501	0
0	0.000	0.050	0.101	0.151	0.202	0.253	0.303	0.354	0.405	0.456	0.507	0
10	0.507	0.558	0.609	0.660	0.711	0.762	0.813	0.865	0.916	0.967	1.019	10
20	1.019	1.070	1.122	1.174	1.225	1.277	1.329	1.381	1.432	1.484	1.536	20
30	1.536	1.588	1.640	1.693	1.745	1.797	1.849	1.901	1.954	2.006	2.058	30
40	2.058	2.111	2.163	2.216	2.268	2.321	2.374	2.426	2.479	2.532	2.585	40
50	2.585	2.638	2.691	2.743	2.796	2.849	2.902	2.956	3.009	3.062	3.115	50
60	3.115	3.168	3.221	3.275	3.328	3.381	3.435	3.488	3.542	3.595	3.649	60
70	3.649	3.702	3.756	3.809	3.863	3.917	3.971	4.024	4.078	4.132	4.186	70
80	4.186	4.239	4.293	4.347	4.401	4.455	4.509	4.563	4.617	4.671	4.725	80
90	4.725	4.780	4.834	4.888	4.942	4.996	5.050	5.105	5.159	5.213	5.268	90
100	5.268	5.322	5.376	5.431	5.485	5.540	5.594	5.649	5.703	5.758	5.812	100
110	5.812	5.867	5.921	5.976	6.031	6.085	6.140	6.195	6.249	6.304	6.359	110
120	6.359	6.414	6.468	6.523	6.578	6.633	6.688	6.742	6.797	6.852	6.907	120
130	6.907	6.962	7.017	7.072	7.127	7.182	7.237	7.292	7.347	7.402	7.457	130
140	7.457	7.512	7.567	7.622	7.677	7.732	7.787	7.843	7.898	7.953	8.008	140
150	8.008	8.063	8.118	8.174	8.229	8.284	8.339	8.394	8.450	8.505	8.560	150
160	8.560	8.616	8.671	8.726	8.781	8.837	8.892	8.947	9.003	9.058	9.113	160
170	9.113	9.169	9.224	9.279	9.335	9.390	9.446	9.501	9.556	9.612	9.667	170
180	9.667	9.723	9.778	9.834	9.889	9.944	10.000	10.055	10.111	10.166	10.222	180
190	10.222	10.277	10.333	10.388	10.444	10.499	10.555	10.610	10.666	10.721	10.777	190
200	10.777	10.832	10.888	10.943	10.999	11.054	11.110	11.165	11.221	11.276	11.332	200

Table A-5 Continued

C	0	1	2	3	4	5	6	7	8	9	10	C
200	10.777	10.832	10.888	10.943	10.999	11.054	11.110	11.165	11.221	11.276	11.332	200
210	11.332	11.387	11.443	11.498	11.554	11.609	11.665	11.720	11.776	11.831	11.887	210
220	11.887	11.943	11.998	12.054	12.109	12.165	12.220	12.276	12.331	12.387	12.442	220
230	12.442	12.498	12.553	12.609	12.664	12.720	12.776	12.831	12.887	12.942	12.998	230
240	12.998	13.053	13.109	13.164	13.220	13.275	13.331	13.386	13.442	13.497	13.553	240
250	13.553	13.608	13.664	13.719	13.775	13.830	13.886	13.941	13.997	14.052	14.108	250
260	14.108	14.163	14.219	14.274	14.330	14.385	14.441	14.496	14.552	14.607	14.663	260
270	14.663	14.718	14.774	14.829	14.885	14.940	14.995	15.051	15.106	15.162	15.217	270
280	15.217	15.273	15.328	15.383	15.439	15.494	15.550	15.605	15.661	15.716	15.771	280
290	15.771	15.827	15.882	15.938	15.993	16.048	16.104	16.159	16.214	16.270	16.325	290
300	16.325	16.380	16.436	16.491	16.547	16.602	16.657	16.713	16.768	16.823	16.879	300
310	16.879	16.934	16.989	17.044	17.100	17.155	17.210	17.266	17.321	17.376	17.432	310
320	17.432	17.487	17.542	17.597	17.653	17.708	17.763	17.818	17.874	17.929	17.984	320
330	17.984	18.039	18.095	18.150	18.205	18.260	18.316	18.371	18.426	18.481	18.537	330
340	18.537	18.592	18.647	18.702	18.757	18.813	18.868	18.923	18.978	19.033	19.089	340
350	19.089	19.144	19.199	19.254	19.309	19.364	19.420	19.475	19.530	19.585	19.640	350
360	19.640	19.695	19.751	19.806	19.861	19.916	19.971	20.026	20.081	20.137	20.192	360
370	20.192	20.247	20.302	20.357	20.412	20.467	20.523	20.578	20.633	20.688	20.743	370
380	20.743	20.798	20.853	20.909	20.964	21.019	21.074	21.129	21.184	21.239	21.295	380
390	21.295	21.350	21.405	21.460	21.515	21.570	21.625	21.680	21.736	21.791	21.846	390
400	21.846	21.901	21.956	22.011	22.066	22.122	22.177	22.232	22.287	22.342	22.397	400
410	22.397	22.453	22.508	22.563	22.618	22.673	22.728	22.784	22.839	22.894	22.949	410
420	22.949	23.004	23.060	23.115	23.170	23.225	23.280	23.336	23.391	23.446	23.501	420
430	23.501	23.556	23.612	23.667	23.722	23.777	23.833	23.888	23.943	23.999	24.054	430
440	24.054	24.109	24.164	24.220	24.275	24.330	24.386	24.441	24.496	24.552	24.607	440
450	24.607	24.662	24.718	24.773	24.829	24.884	24.939	24.995	25.050	25.106	25.161	450
460	25.161	25.217	25.272	25.327	25.383	25.438	25.494	25.549	25.605	25.661	25.716	460
470	25.716	25.772	25.827	25.883	25.938	25.994	26.050	26.105	26.161	26.216	26.272	470
480	26.272	26.328	26.383	26.439	26.495	26.551	26.606	26.662	26.718	26.774	26.829	480
490	26.829	26.885	26.941	26.997	27.053	27.109	27.165	27.220	27.276	27.332	27.388	490
500	27.388	27.444	27.500	27.556	27.612	27.668	27.724	27.780	27.836	27.893	27.949	500
510	27.949	28.005	28.061	28.117	28.173	28.230	28.286	28.342	28.398	28.455	28.511	510
520	28.511	28.567	28.624	28.680	28.736	28.793	28.849	28.906	28.962	29.019	29.075	520
530	29.075	29.132	29.188	29.245	29.301	29.358	29.415	29.471	29.528	29.585	29.642	530
540	29.642	29.698	29.755	29.812	29.869	29.926	29.983	30.039	30.096	30.153	30.210	540
550	30.210	30.267	30.324	30.381	30.439	30.496	30.553	30.610	30.667	30.724	30.782	550
560	30.782	30.839	30.896	30.954	31.011	31.068	31.126	31.183	31.241	31.298	31.356	560
570	31.356	31.413	31.471	31.528	31.586	31.644	31.702	31.759	31.817	31.875	31.933	570
580	31.933	31.991	32.048	32.106	32.164	32.222	32.280	32.338	32.396	32.455	32.513	580
590	32.513	32.571	32.629	32.687	32.746	32.804	32.862	32.921	32.979	33.038	33.096	590
600	33.096	33.155	33.213	33.272	33.330	33.389	33.448	33.506	33.565	33.624	33.683	600

Table A-5 Continued

C	0	1	2	3	4	5	6	7	8	9	10	C
600	33.096	33.155	33.213	33.272	33.330	33.389	33.448	33.506	33.565	33.624	33.683	600
610	33.683	33.742	33.800	33.859	33.918	33.977	34.036	34.095	34.155	34.214	34.273	610
620	34.273	34.332	34.391	34.451	34.510	34.569	34.629	34.688	34.748	34.807	34.867	620
630	34.867	34.926	34.986	35.046	35.105	35.165	35.225	35.285	35.344	35.404	35.464	630
640	35.464	35.524	35.584	35.644	35.704	35.764	35.825	35.885	35.945	36.005	36.066	640
650	36.066	36.126	36.186	36.247	36.307	36.368	36.428	36.489	36.549	36.610	36.671	650
660	36.671	36.732	36.792	36.853	36.914	36.975	37.036	37.097	37.158	37.219	37.280	660
670	37.280	37.341	37.402	37.463	37.525	37.586	37.647	37.709	37.770	37.831	37.893	670
680	37.893	37.954	38.016	38.078	38.139	38.201	38.262	38.324	38.386	38.448	38.510	680
690	38.510	38.572	38.633	38.695	38.757	38.819	38.882	38.944	39.006	39.068	39.130	690
700	39.130	39.192	39.255	39.317	39.379	39.442	39.504	39.567	39.629	39.692	39.754	700
710	39.754	39.817	39.880	39.942	40.005	40.068	40.131	40.193	40.256	40.319	40.382	710
720	40.382	40.445	40.508	40.571	40.634	40.697	40.760	40.823	40.886	40.950	41.013	720
730	41.013	41.076	41.139	41.203	41.266	41.329	41.393	41.456	41.520	41.583	41.647	730
740	41.647	41.710	41.774	41.837	41.901	41.965	42.028	42.092	42.156	42.219	42.283	740
750	42.283	42.347	42.411	42.475	42.538	42.602	42.666	42.730	42.794	42.858	42.922	750
760	42.922											760

Table A-6 Polynomial Coefficients for Six Different Types of Thermocouples

		Type of Thermocouple				
	E	J	K	R	S	T
			Temperature Range			
Coefficient	−100° to 1000°C	0° to 760°C	0° to 1370°C	0° to 1000°C	0° to 1750°C	−160° to 400°C
a_0	0.104967248	−0.048868252	0.226584602	0.263632917	0.927763167	0.100860910
a_1	171189.45282	19873.14503	24152.10900	179075.491	169526.5150	25727.94369
a_2	−282639.0850	−218614.5353	67233.4248	−48840341.37	−31568363.94	−767345.8295
a_3	12695339.5	11569199.78	2210340.682	1.90002E+10	8990730663	78025595.81
a_4	−448703084.6	−264917531.4	−860963914.9	−4.82704E+12	−1.63565E+12	−9247486589
a_5	1.10866E+10	2018441314	4.83506E+10	7.62091E+14	1.88027E+14	6.97688E+11
a_6	−1.76807E+11		−1.18452E+12	−7.20026E+16	−1.37241E+16	−2.66192E+13
a_7	1.71842E+12		1.38690E+13	3.71496E+18	6.17501E+17	3.94078E+14
a_8	−9.19278E+12		−6.33708E+13	−8.03104E+19	−1.56105E+19	
a_9	2.06132E+13				1.69535E+20	

Table A-7 Physical Properties of Several Thermocouple Alloys

Property	Thermocouple Alloy							
	Iron	Constantan	Copper	Chromel	Alumel	Platinum 13% Rhodium	Platinum 10% Rhodium	Platinum
Melting Point (°C)	1,490	1,220	108	1,427	1,399	1,860	1,850	1,769
Resistivity (μΩ-m) (at 20°C)	0.0967	0.489	0.01724	0.706	0.294	0.196	0.189	0.104
Temperature Coeff. of Resistance (10^{-4}/°C) (0 to 100°C)	65	-0,1	43	4.1	23.9	15.6	16.6	39.2
Coefficient of Thermal Expansion (10^6/°C) (20 to 100°C)	11.7	14.9	16.6	13.1	12.0	9.0	9.0	9.0
Thermal Conductivity at 100°C(W/m-°C)	67.8	21.2	377.0	19.2	29.7	36.8	37.7	71.5
Specific Heat at 20°C (J/kg-°C)	448	394	385	448	523	—	—	134
Density (kg/m³)	7,860	8,920	8,920	8,730	8,600	19,610	19,970	21,450
Tensile Strength (MPa)	345	550	245	655	585	315	315	135
Magnetic Attraction	Strong	None	None	None	Moderate	None	None	None

Appendix B

Tables of Properties of Some Common Liquids and Gases

Table B-1 Physical Properties of Water

Temperature	Specific Weight	Density	Viscosity	Kinematic Viscosity
English units °F	lb/ft³ γ	slug/ft³ ρ	lb-s/ft² $\mu \times 10^5$	ft²/s $v \times 10^5$
32	62.42	1.940	3.746	1.931
40	62.43	1.940	3.229	1.664
50	62.41	1.940	2.735	1.410
60	62.37	1.938	2.359	1.217
70	62.30	1.936	2.050	1.059
80	62.22	1.934	1.799	0.930
90	62.11	1.931	1.595	0.826
100	62.00	1.927	1.424	0.739
110	61.86	1.923	1.284	0.667
120	61.71	1.918	1.168	0.609
130	61.55	1.913	1.069	0.558
140	61.38	1.908	0.981	0.514
150	61.20	1.902	0.905	0.476
160	61.00	1.896	0.838	0.442
170	60.80	1.890	0.780	0,413
180	60.58	1.883	0.726	0.385
190	60.36	1.876	0.678	0.362
200	60.12	1.868	0.637	0.341
212	59.83	1.860	0.593	0.319
SI units: °C	kN/m³ γ	kg/m³ ρ	N - s/m² $\mu \times 10^3$	m²/s $v \times 10^6$
0	9.805	999.8	1.781	1.785
5	9.807	1,000.0	1.518	1.519
10	9.804	999.7	1.307	1.306
15	9.798	999.1	1.139	1.139
20	9.789	998.2	1.002	1.003
25	9.777	997.0	0.890	0.893
30	9.764	995.7	0.798	0.800
40	9.730	992.2	0.653	0.658
50	9.689	988.0	0.547	0.553
60	9.642	983.2	0.466	0.474
70	9.589	977.8	0.404	0.413
80	9.530	971.8	0,354	0.364
90	9.466	965.3	0.315	0.326
100	9.399	958.4	0.282	0.294

At 14.7 psia (standard atmospheric pressure).

Table B-2
Approximate Properties of Some Common Liquids at Standard Atmospheric Pressure

Liquid	Temper-ature	Specific Weight	Density	Viscosity	Kinematic Viscosity
English Units:	**°F**	**lb/ft^3** γ	**slug/ft^3** ρ	**lb-s/ft^2** $\mu \times 10^5$	**ft^2/s** $v \times 10^5$
Benzene	68	54.8	1.702	1.37	0.80
Castor oil	68	59.8	1.858	2060.0	1109.0
Crude oil	68	53.6	1.665	15.0	9.0
Ethyl alcohol	68	49.2	1.528	2.51	1.64
Gasoline	68	42.4	1.317	0.61	0.46
Glycerin	68	78.5	2.439	3120.0	1280.0
Kerosene	68	50.5	1.569	4.00	2.55
Linseed oil	68	58.6	1.820	92.0	50.0
Mercury	68	844.0	26.2	3.24	0.124
Olive oil	68	56.7	1.76	176.0	100.0
Turpentine	68	53.6	1.665	3.11	1.87
Water	68	62.32	1.936	2.10	1.085
SI units:	**°C**	**kN/m^3** γ	**kg/m^3** ρ	**N • s/m^2** $\mu \times 10^3$	**m^2/s** $v \times 10^6$
Benzene	20	8.77	895	0.65	0.73
Castor oil	20	9.39	958	979.	1025.0
Crude oil	20	8.42	858	7.13	8.32
Ethyl alcohol	20	7.73	787	1.19	1.52
Gasoline	20	6.66	679	0.29	0.43
Glycerin	20	12.33	1257	1495.0	1189.0
Kerosene	20	7.93	809	1.90	2.36
Linseed oil	20	9.21	938	43.7	46.2
Mercury	20	132.6	13500	1.54	0.12
Olive oil	20	8.91	908	83.7	92.4
Turpentine	20	8.42	858	1.48	1.73
Water	20	9.79	998	1.00	1.00

Table B-3
Approximate Properties of Air at Standard Atmospheric Pressure

Temperature	Specific Weight	Density	Viscosity	Kinematic Viscosity
English Units: °F	lb/ft^3 γ	slug/ft^3 ρ	lb-s/ft^2 $\mu \times 10^7$	ft^2/s $v \times 10^5$
0	0.0866	0.00269	3.39	1.26
10	0.0847	0.00263	3.45	1.31
20	0.0828	0.00257	3.51	1.37
30	0.0811	0.00252	3.57	1.42
40	0.0794	0.00247	3.63	1.47
50	0.0779	0.00242	3.68	1.52
60	0.0764	0.00237	3.74	1.58
70	0.0750	0.00233	3.79	1.63
80	0.0735	0.00228	3.85	1.69
90	0.0722	0.00224	3.90	1.74
100	0.0709	0.00220	3.96	1.80
150	0.0651	0.00202	4.23	2.09
200	0.0601	0.00187	4.48	2.40
300	0.0522	0.00162	4.96	3.05
400	0.0462	0.00143	5.40	3.77
SI units: °C	CN/m^3 γ	kg/m^3 ρ	N • s/m^2 $\mu \times 10^5$	m^2/s $v \times 10^5$
-20	13.7	1.40	1.61	1.16
-10	13.2	1.34	1.67	1.24
0	12.7	1.29	1.72	1.33
10	12.2	1.25	1.76	1.41
20	11.8	1.20	1.81	1.51
30	11.4	1.17	1.86	1.60
40	11.1	1.13	1.91	1.69
50	10.7	1.09	1.95	1.79
60	10.4	1.06	2,00	1.89
70	10.1	1.03	2.04	1.99
80	9.81	1.00	2.09	2.09
90	9.54	0.97	2.13	2.19
100	9.28	0.95	2.17	2.29
120	8.82	0.90	2.26	2.51
140	8.38	0.85	2.34	2.74
160	7.99	0.81	2.42	2.97
180	7.65	0.78	2.50	3.20
200	7.32	0.75	2.57	3.44

At 14.7 psia (standard atmospheric pressure).

Table B-4
Approximate Properties of Some Common Gases at Standard Atmospheric Pressure

Gas	Density	Engineering Gas Constant	Specific Heat		Adiabatic Exponent	Viscosity
English units:	slug/ft^3 ρ	ft-lb/slug°R R	ft-lb/slug° R c_p	c_v	ft^2/s k	lb = s/ft^2 $\mu \times 10^5$
Air	0.00234	1,715	6,000	4,285	1.40	0.0376
Carbon dioxide	0.00354	1,123	5,132	4,009	1.28	0.0310
Carbon monoxide	0.00225	1,778	6,218	4,440	1.40	0.0380
Helium	0.00032	12,420	31,230	18,810	1.66	0.0411
Hydrogen	0.00016	24,680	86,390	61,710	1.40	0.0189
Methane	0.00129	3,100	13,400	10300	1.30	0.0280
Nitrogen	0.00226	1,773	6,210	4,437	1.40	0.0368
Oxygen	0.00258	1,554	5,437	3,883	1.40	0.0418
Water vapor	0.00145	2,760	11,110	8,350	1.33	0.0212
SI units:	kg/m^3 ρ	N • m/kg K R	N • m/kg K c_p	c_v	k	N • s/m^2 $\mu \times 10^5$
Air	1.205	287	1,003	716	1.40	1.80
Carbon dioxide	1.84	188	858	670	1.28	1.48
Carbon monoxide	1.16	297	1,040	743	1.40	1.82
Helium	0.166	2077	5,220	3,143	1.66	1.97
Hydrogen	0.0839	4120	14,450	10,330	1.40	0.90
Methane	0.668	520	2,250	1,730	1.30	1.34
Nitrogen	1.16	297	1,040	743	1.40	1.76
Oxygen	1.33	260	909	649	1.40	2.00
Water vapor	0.747	462	1,862	1,400	1.33	1.01

At 14.7 psia (standard atmospheric pressure).

Notes:

AUTHOR INDEX

SUBJECT INDEX